ACKNOWLEDGEMENTS

Managing Editor	**Pushpish Chandra,** Educo International, Inc.
Editors	**Roxann King**, Prince George's Community College, MD **Brenda Teal**, Prince George's Community College, MD **Donna Strain**, El Centro College, Dallas TX **Ray Treadway**, Bennett College, NC **Steve Castillo**, Los Angeles Valley College, CA **Mary Bradley**, Southwestern Community College, NC
Production Services	Educo International, Inc.
Desktop Publishing	Sunita Verma and her team. Educo International, Inc.

Evaluators

The following persons have made significant contributions in this edition of the book. Several presentations throughout the book have been changed based on their contributions or recommendations.

Kalawati Iyer	Los Angeles Valley College, CA
Robert Mardirosian	Los Angeles City College, CA
Ray Treadway	Bennett College, NC

ISBN: 978-1-935168-66-9

PREFACE

This textbook is written for Primary and Secondary School Teachers taking courses in colleges to sharpen their content skills. It is written using **simple language**, **highlighted key words**, and a **step-by-step approach**. Each section of a chapter is divided into logically arranged objectives. Each objective has:

- **Discussion** leading to the statement of rules and procedures.
- **Examples** showing step-by-step procedures. Each example, in the electronic version of this book, has several randomly generated versions.
- **Multiple Options Practice Sheets** (MOPS) design to master basic computational skills.

Each **section ends** with a set of exercises covering topics from each objective of the section.

This book is supplemented with an **electronic version** that can be accessed from the **web** by faculty as lecture notes and by students as tutorials. The electronic version of the book is 100% compatible with this printed textbook and has the advantage of dynamic graphics, pedagogically sound animations, and visually appealing screen designs with attractive color combinations. As a tutorial for students, the electronic version provides an effective tool that is highly interactive and engaging. The electronic version can also be used for online teaching.

The textbook contains eleven chapters.

Highlights of Contents:

Chapter 1:	Problem Solving
Chapter 2:	Sets, Functions, and Reasoning
Chapter 3:	Whole Numbers
Chapter 4:	Number Theory
Chapter 5:	Integers and Fractions
Chapter 6:	Decimals, Rational/Irrational Numbers
Chapter 7:	Statistics
Chapter 8:	Probability
Chapter 9:	Geometric Measurement
Chapter 10:	Measurement
Chapter 11:	Motions in Geometry

TECHNOLOGY SUPPORT

One of the **most useful features** of this book is the technology support to students in the form of tutorials, practice tests, instructor-created online quizzes and tests, and instant progress reports. These features are described below in more detail. **All technology components are provided through Macromedia Flash delivered through the web and requirs no special installations**. These features are described below in more detail.

A. Multimedia Electronic Lecture Notes (ELN) for Instructors and Tutorials for Students

- Tutorials with examples are embedded with dynamic graphics, animations, and step by step solutions.
- Vivid screen designs and animations make the presentation of topics clearer, as documented by students and instructors in several pilot studies.
- The ELN for instructors are designed to enhance interactivity with students, affording instructors minimal writing and drawing and more emphasis on class discussion.
- The ELN, which can be used in class to supplement conventional teaching, are available to students as tutorials from the web for self study. Each example in the tutorial has several algorithmically generated versions. The student can see the solution for the first version, and then click the 'Next Version' to attempt similar exercises.

B. Multiple Options Practice Sheets (MOPS)

- These pre-created practice tests, for all concepts on Basic Arithmetic Skills, are available to reinforce the concepts learned in the Tutorials.
- Each MOPS can be taken in Practice Mode (with solutions), in Home work Mode (with instant feedback and option to change answer), and in Test Mode (with feedback and solutions after submitting the session).
- Each MOPS has unlimited algorithmically generated sets of questions.

C. Homework on the Internet with Embedded Tutorial

- Different types of free response questions, with several variations for each question, are used to create online homework. Instructors can create the homework using a large question bank of free response questions, provided by the system, or just assign the pre-created homework.
- Each student gets a different set of questions, with tutorial type assistance, a solution to the first variation, and feedback for other variations, with the option to change the answer. Students can complete the assignment in multiple sessions.
- Homework is instantly graded by the system and scores are transferred automatically to the grade book.

D. Quizzes/Tests on Internet (Free-Response, or Multiple-Choice or Mixed)

- Responses to test questions may be entered from the keyboard, or through a **small online keypad using the mouse**.
- The keypad contains mathematical symbols needed for the responses. After every quiz, students get instant feedback on their score. They can see step-by-step solutions, go to practice mode with an embedded tutorial, or take the quiz over again, if allowed by the instructor.
- There will be no loss of work done by the students if during a test or homework sessions the power goes off, the web connection is lost, or the student closes Test/Assignment window improperly.
- The work completed at the time of disconnect will be considered work submitted and the rest of the work can be completed in a new login session.

- A large question bank of both Multiple Choice and Free Response questions, is available for each objective of the content for web based testing and practice testing.
- A browser based math editor is available to instructors to add their own questions to the quizzes or tests.
- An easy-to-use online test generator, is available to instructors to create online quizzes/tests, to print multiple versions of class test with answer keys, or to generate and administer online tests.
- The test generator provides several options to instructors to deliver tests and homework to students in several test modes: with or without feedback, with or without solutions, single or multiple sessions, graded or just for practice, and several more.
- Instructors may conduct proctored major tests, password-protected, in local computer labs, or print the tests and transfer the scores to the online graded book

E. Activity Reports

- Instructors can view/print student activity reports at any time. These provide detailed information on time spent by students on each activity.
- There is an enhanced electronic grade book (online) with several unique features including; direct transfer of scores to the grade book, and **individualized progress reports for students**.

F. Internal E-mail, and other Communication Tools

- Instructors can compile e-mails using the system's full function e-mail editor: bolding, underlining, bulleting, and attachment. There are multiple target audiences:
  - Announcements: Faculty to his/her students, or campus coordinator to Instructors, students.
  - Chat, threaded discussion, group discussions

To the students and instructors:

We sincerely hope that the approaches followed in this book with several options of technology support will help you better prepare students for the next course in mathematics. The authors would appreciate instructors for any suggestion for improvement in any component of this package, either for the presentation of the textbook or its support materials on the web. Suggestions can be forwarded through **Contact us** link on the login page.

Man M. Sharma

Jimmy Vicente

Fundamentals of Mathematics
For Teachers
Table of Contents

PROBLEM SOLVING

1.1 PROBLEM SOLVING WITH ALGEBRA

A. IDENTIFYING AND COMBINING LIKE TERMS

Consider the algebraic expression: $3x^2 + 4x - 5$

This expression has three terms.

1st term	2nd term	3rd term
↓	↓	↓
$3x^2$ +	$4x$ +	(-5)

Each term, except the third term, has two factors or parts: a number and a variable part. The number is called the **coefficient of the term**. Terms such as the third term, having no variable part are called **constant** terms.

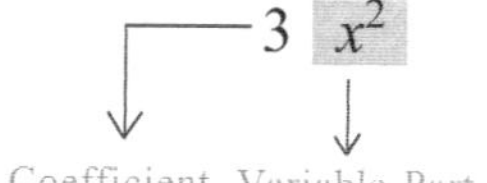

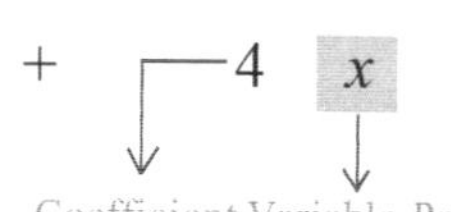

$+ \quad\quad + \quad -5$

↓ Constant

OBJECTIVES

Upon completion of this section you will be able to:

A. Identify and combine like terms;

B. Build expressions from word phrases.

EXAMPLE 1 Identify the coefficient and variable part in the following terms.

a. $3y$ **b.** $4x^2$ **c.** $\frac{2}{7}y$ **d.** $\frac{2}{y}$

Solutions:

a. $3\ y$ — 3: Coefficient, y: Variable part

b. $4\ x^2$ — 4: Coefficient, x^2: Variable part

c. $\frac{2}{7}\ y$ — $\frac{2}{7}$: Coefficient, y: Variable part

d. $\frac{2}{y}$ or $2 \cdot \frac{1}{y}$ — 2: Coefficient, $\frac{1}{y}$: Variable part

WARM-UP

1. Identify the coefficient and variable part of the following terms.

a) $13y$ **b)** $-9x^2$

c) $\frac{1}{5}y$ **d)** $\frac{9}{y}$

Answers:

1. a) 13 and y **b)** -9 and x^2

c) $\frac{1}{5}$ and y **d)** 9 and $\frac{1}{y}$

• Identifying and Combining Like Terms

Terms which differ **only in numerical coefficients** and have identical variable parts are called **like** terms. Terms which are not like terms are called **unlike terms**. All constant terms are like terms.

Warm-Up

2. Decide if the following pairs of terms are like terms.

a) $2x^6$, $7x^6$

b) $3x^3$, $3x^4$

c) $15xz^3y$, $-13xyz^3$

d) $3x^2y$, $4xy^2$

e) $3r^2$, $2s^2$

f) -12, $\frac{9}{5}$

EXAMPLE 2 Decide if the following pairs of terms are like terms.

a. $3x^2$, $-4x^2$ **b.** $4x^3$, $4x^2$ **c.** $3xy^2z$, $-5xzy^2$

d. $-5xy^2$, $5x^2y$ **e.** $3x^2$, $3y^2$ **f.** -18, $\frac{5}{8}$

Solutions:

a. $3x^2$, $-4x^2$ → Terms

↓ ↓

x^2 x^2 → Variable Parts

same

Therefore, $3x^2$ and $-4x^2$ are **like terms**.

b. $4x^3$, $4x^2$ → Terms

↓ ↓

x^3 x^2 → Variable Parts

different

Therefore, $4x^3$ and $4x^2$ are **unlike terms**.

c. $3xy^2z$, $-5xzy^2$ → Terms

↓ ↓

xy^2z xzy^2 → Variable Parts

same

Therefore, $3xy^2z$ and $-5xzy^2$ are **like terms**.

d. $-5xy^2$, $5x^2y$ → Terms

↓ ↓

xy^2 x^2y → Variable Parts

different

Therefore, $-5xy^2$ and $5x^2y$ are **unlike terms**.

e. $3x^2$, $3y^2$ → Terms

↓ ↓

x^2 y^2 → Variable Parts

different

Therefore, $3x^2$ and $3y^2$ are **unlike terms**.

f. -18, $\frac{5}{8}$ → Terms

↓ ↓

constants

Therefore, -18 and $\frac{5}{8}$ are **like terms.**

EXAMPLE 3 Combine like terms in the following algebraic expressions.

a. $4x + 7x$ b. $-7p + 5p$

c. $18t^2 - 21t^2$ d. $22y^2 + 10y - 30y^2$

e. $-11q + 17 - 4q - 3$

Solutions:

To combine like terms, we add or subtract the coefficients.

We combine constant terms by adding or subtracting constants.

a. $4x + 7x = (4 + 7)x$
$= \mathbf{11x}$

b. $-7p + 5p = (-7 + 5)p$
$= \mathbf{-2p}$

c. $18t^2 - 21t^2 = (18 - 21)t^2$
$= \mathbf{-3t^2}$

d. $22y^2 + 10y - 30y^2 = 22y^2 - 30y^2 + 10y$
$= (22 - 30)y^2 + 10y$
$= \mathbf{-8y^2 + 10y}$

e. $-11q + 17 - 4q - 3 = -11q - 4q + 17 - 3$
$= (-11 - 4)q + (17 - 3)$
$= \mathbf{-15q + 14}$

3. Combine like terms.

a) $8x + 11x$

b) $-9z + 2z$

c) $21r^2 - 32r^2$

d) $3z^2 - 12z + 4z^2$

e) $14 - 2m + 17 + 5m$

Answers:

2. a) Like b) Unlike c) Like d) Unlike e) Unlike f) Like

3. a) $19x$ b) $-7z$ c) $-11r^2$ d) $7z^2 - 12z$ e) $31 + 3m$

B. Build Expressions From Word Phrases

In order to apply mathematics to solve applications problems, the words and sentences must be translated into ***mathematical expressions.***

For this we need to be familiar with the frequently used words that translate into operations used in ***mathematical expressions.***

Words which indicate addition are:

"More than", "The sum of", "The total of", "plus" etc.,

Words which indicate subtraction are:

"Minus", "Less than", "The difference between", "Decreased by", "Subtracted from" etc.,

Words which indicate multiplication are:

"Times", "of", "The product of" etc.

Words which indicate divison are:

"Divided by", "The quotient of", "The ratio of"etc.

Some phrases may involve ***unknown quantities*** that can take, or can be assigned, any numerical value.

In such situations we use letters of alphabet ($x, y, z, a, b, c...$) to represent those ***unknown quantities***.

WARM-UP

4. Find the sum of 8, two times a number, and three times the number.

5. Jane uses 5% of her stipend on food, 3% on school materials and another 15% on transportation.

Additionally, she spends 5% on miscellaneous. If her total expenditure was 800 dollars, set up an equation which represents this information.

EXAMPLE 4 Find the sum of 5, seven times a number, and four times the number.

Solution: Assume that unknown number is x.

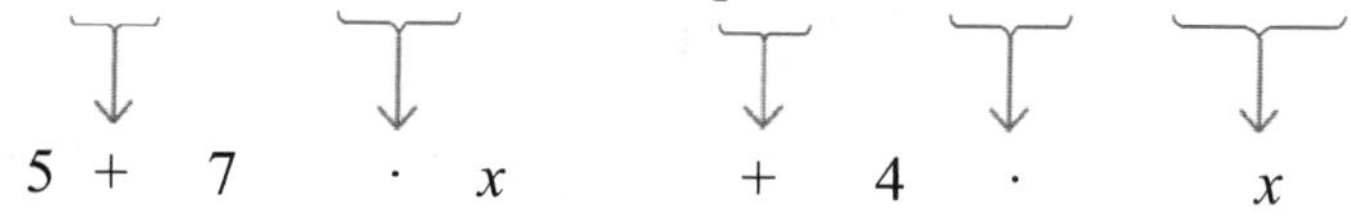

$5 + 7 \cdot x + 4 \cdot x$

Simplification:

$$\begin{aligned} 5 + 7x + 4x &= 5 + (7x + 4x) \\ &= 5 + (7 + 4)x \\ &= 5 + 11x \end{aligned}$$

EXAMPLE 5 Karen spends 10% of her paycheck on food, one fifteenth of the paycheck on clothing, 5% of the paycheck on utilities, 15% on rent, and one fourth on education. She also invests \$200. If the total expenditure is \$1,800, set up an equation that represents this information.

Solution:

Unknown: Let p represent the amount of paycheck.

Total expenses = 10% of p + $\frac{1}{15}$ of p + 5% of p + 15% of p + $\frac{1}{4}$ of p + 200

Since the total expenses **equal 1800,** we get:

$$\left(\frac{10}{100}p + \frac{1}{15}p + \frac{5}{100}p + \frac{15}{100}p + \frac{1}{4}p\right) + 200 = 1800$$

This equation is the conversion of the word problem into symbols.

We can now simplify this equation by combining like terms on the left side of the equation.

$$\left(\frac{10}{100}+\frac{1}{15}+\frac{5}{100}+\frac{15}{100}+\frac{1}{4}\right)p + 200 = 1800$$

$$\downarrow$$

$$\mathbf{\frac{37}{60} \cdot p + 200 = 1800}$$

WARM-UP

6. The sum of the following two quantities is 41.
   i. 6 multiplied by, one minus a number.
   ii. The sum of eight and the number.

   Set up an equation.

Answers:

4. $8 + 2x + 3x$
5. $\frac{5}{100}p + \frac{3}{100}p + \frac{15}{100}p + \frac{5p}{100} = 800$
6. $6 \cdot (1 - x) + (8 + x) = 41$

EXAMPLE 6 The sum of the following two quantities is 47.

i. Five multiplied by four minus a number.

ii. The sum of seven and the number.

Set up an equation that represents this information.

Solution:

Unknown: a number $= x$

First Quantity : 5 **multiplied** by four minus a number $= 5 \cdot (4 - x)$

Second Quantity: **Sum** of 7 and the number $= 7 + x$

The sum of $5(4 - x)$ and $(7 + x)$ is equal to 47.

Therefore $5(4 - x) + (7 + x) = 47$.

This equation is the conversion of the given word problem into symbols. We can now simplify this equation.

EXERCISE 1.1

In exercises 1-14, write down the numerical coefficient of each term.

1. $-15y^2z$ **2.** $2xy$ **3.** $6x$ **4.** $-3lm$ **5.** $-7mn$ **6.** $20pqr$ **7.** $4pq$

8. x^4y **9.** $-m$ **10.** $-2m^2n$ **11.** x^5 **12.** $3y^4z^2$ **13.** $-x^2yz$ **14.** $-2^2xy^2z^3$

In exercises 15-28, identify the variable part and the numerical co-efficient.

15. $2x^2$ **16.** $-p^2$ **17.** $2xy$ **18.** $-2xy^2$ **19.** x^2y^2 **20.** $5x^2y$ **21.** $-3y^2zx$

22. $10xyz$ **23.** -7 **24.** $-x^2y^2z^2$ **25.** x^2 **26.** 12 **27.** -2^2x^2y **28.** $64pq^2r$

In exercises 29-40, determine if the pair of terms are like terms.

29. $3x, 7y$ **30.** $-8p, 22p$ **31.** $-4p, 8p$ **32.** $12q, 2r$

33. $4m^2n, -m^2n$ **34.** $8x^2y, -20x^2y$ **35.** $5m^2n, 5mn^2$ **36.** $-xyz, xyz$

37. $3, -5$ **38.** $4^2x, -9x$ **39.** $4z^3, -3z^2$ **40.** $10x^2y, -10xy^2$

In exercises 41-72, simplify each expression by combining like terms.

41. $-7m + 4m$ **42.** $20x - 7x$ **43.** $5s + 6(s - 3)$ **44.** $-8(p + 3) + 9p$

45. $15t^2 + 7(4 - t^2)$ **46.** $-y^3 - 10(4 - y^3 + 10)$ **47.** $2 + x + 15 - 7x$ **48.** $2(-7 + z) + 10(2z - 3)$

49. $3y^2 + 7y + 8x - 4y + 5x - 2y^2$ **50.** $-p^2 + q + 7p - 9q^2 - 10p$ **51.** $3y - (2x + 2y) - 6x$

52. $2y - 6(y - 2) - 6x$ **53.** $5y - 2(y - 3x) + 2(7x - y)$ **54.** $3(y - 2y^2) + 4(7 - 5y) + 8(y^2 - 7)$

55. $2(z - z^2 + z^3) + 3(z - 2) + 9(-z^2 + 5)$ **56.** $6(3p - 5) - (6p + 4)$ **57.** $-6(-2pq + 3p) - 10(q + 2pq)$

58. $\frac{2}{3}x + \frac{1}{2}x - \frac{1}{3} - 2$ **59.** $\frac{1}{3}(y + 3) + \frac{1}{2}(2x + 6)$ **60.** $-6[3x + 2(7 - x)]$

61. $3[a + 3(a + 5)]$ **62.** $-6[4y - 7(y + 7)]$ **63.** $-6x - 3[2x - 5(x + 8)] - 6$

64. $\frac{3}{5}x - 3 - \frac{7}{4}x - 2$ **65.** $\frac{1}{2}(x + 3) + \frac{1}{3}(3x + 6)$ **66.** $2\left(3 - \frac{1}{3}x + 4y\right) + 6(x + 3y) - 9$

67. $\frac{12x}{5}\left(\frac{5}{12}\right) + (-6x)\left(-\frac{1}{6}\right)$ **68.** $16x\left(\frac{1}{4}\right) - (-8x)\left(-\frac{3}{4}\right)$

69. $-\frac{8}{7}\left(\frac{7x^2}{8}\right) + \frac{1}{3}\left(3x^2\right) + \left(\frac{3x^2}{4}\right)\left(\frac{4}{3}\right)$ **70.** $-\frac{3}{8}\left(24a^2\right) - \frac{1}{4}\left(-16a^2\right) + \left(\frac{3}{5}\right)\left(-5a^2\right)$

71. $0.4 + 2(x + 6) - 0.6 + 3$ **72.** $0.5 + (2x^2y + 4y + 6x^2) - 0.25(4x^2y - 8y + 12x^2)$

In exercises 73-86, convert the word phrase into a mathematical expression. Use x as the variable, and simplify the resulting expression.

73. The sum of a number and 8 times the number.

74. The sum of two consecutive integers.

75. For two consecutive integers, the sum of the smaller and twice the larger.

76. The product of two consecutive even integers.

77. Twice a number, decreased by 10.

78. The quotient of 6 and the sum of a number and 5.

79. The quotient of 6 more than two times a number, and the number.

80. The square of a number decreased by one sixth of the number.

81. The cube of a number decreased by the product of 10 and the number.

82. The ratio of four and 6 less than a number.

83. A number added to the difference of 4 and two times the number.

84. The Sum of a number and –4 added to the difference of the number and 5.

85. The product of three times a number subtracted from 8, and the sum of the number and – 4.

86. Five times a number added to twice the number and decreased by the difference of the number and 8.

Sets, Functions, and Reasoning

The discussion in this chapter is divided into three sections.

2.1 Sets: Basic Terms and Notations

Historical Background

Georg Cantor (1845-1918) is the inventor of the modern theory of sets. Amongst his many contributions to the theory of sets was his technique for counting the number of members of a set. Thereby, establishing the fact that there are more than one infinity. In fact, he established that there are an infinite number of infinities of different sizes. He was so harshly critisized by religious organizations and by fellow mathematicians that he suffered bouts of depression and spent most of his later years in a sanatorium.

Pythagoras was the first person to apply **12** mathematics to the of music, discovering the relationship between string length and musical chords. He also studied astronomy. In which celestial bodies moved in accordance to mathematical equations, creating a symphony of the heavens. His most famous accomplishment was the Pythagorean theorem. His followers kept to a strict vegetarian diet, yet did not eat legumes.

A. Sets and Set Notations

Objectives

Upon completion of this section you will study:

A. Sets and set notations;

B. Subsets and notations; and

C. Union/Intersection of Two or More Sets.

The word **set** is one of the basic terms used in the language of algebra. As we observed in Chapter 1, real numbers, rational numbers, integers, and natural numbers can be described as different sets of numbers.

***Definition*:**

A set is a well-defined collection of objects. The objects which form a set are called its **members** or **elements**.

For example,

all students in your class whose last name starts with S form a well defined collection, and is therefore a set.

On the other hand, the collection of all students in your class who are almost six feet tall is not well defined because the meaning of "**almost** six feet" is not well defined.

There are two different ways in which a set may be described.

1. ***Listing Method*:** In this method all members of the set are listed, separated by commas and enclosed in a pair of braces { }. For example, the collection of all states in the United States of America starting with M is well defined, and is therefore a set.

   In the listing method this set is written as:

   S = {Maine, Maryland, Massachusettes, Mississippi, Missouri, Montana}

Remark: The order in which elements of a set are written inside braces { } is not significant. Thus {1, 2, 3}, {1, 3, 2}, {2, 1, 3}, {2, 3, 1}, {3, 1, 2}, {3, 2, 1} all are the same set.

***Definition*:**

Two sets are said to be **equal** if they contain exactly the same elements. Thus the sets {1, 2, 3} and {2, 1, 3} are equal.

2. ***Set Builder Method*:** A set may be written by listing a property which describes the elements. For example, the set of all states in the United States whose names begin with M may be described in set builder form as

   $S = \{x \mid x$ is a state in the United States whose name begins with $M\}$

Set-Builder form has two parts.

- **i)** A variable x representing any element of the set.
- **ii)** The property which defines the elements.

The two parts are separated by a vertical bar | or a colon: which means "such that".

For example $S = \{x \mid x$ is the state in the United States whose name begins with M}

↙ ↘ ↓
variable **vertical bar** **property**

The above set S has a finite number of elements. Such a set is called a ***finite set***.

Some sets are infinite (not finite). An example is the set of all natural numbers. The set of natural numbers is usually denoted by N. We write this set by two methods as follows:

Listing Method: $N = \{1, 2, 3, \ldots\}$, here the three dots indicate that the elements continue in the same pattern.

Set-Builder Method: $N = \{n \mid n$ is a natural number}

Remark: The listing method has the advantage of actually displaying the elements of the set. But there are sets where the elements cannot be listed either finitely or infinitely by a pattern. In such situations the set-builder method has an edge over the listing method.

For example the set $\left\{0, \frac{3}{7}, \frac{8}{12}, \frac{15}{19}, \ldots\right\}$ is expected to be an infinite set, but it is difficult to find the next element of this set. But if we write the same set in a set builder notation

$\left\{x \,\middle|\, x = \frac{n^2 - 1}{n^2 + 3}, \text{ where } n \text{ is a natural number}\right\}$ then we can list any element.

Empty Set

***Definition*:**

A set containing no element is called an **empty** set or a **null set**.

***Notation*:** The empty set is written as ϕ or $\{\ \}$.

EXAMPLES:

1. There is no natural number less than 1. Therefore, the set of all natural numbers less than 1 is an empty set.
2. The set of all states of the U.S.A. whose names begin with *Z* is an empty set.

***Notation*:** If a is an element of a set S, then we write $\mathbf{a} \in \mathbf{S}$.
If a is not an element of a set S, we write $\mathbf{a} \in \mathbf{S}$.
Thus $3 \in \{0, 1, 2, 3, 4\}$, but $5 \notin \{0, 1, 2, 3, 4\}$.

EXAMPLE 1 The following sets are given in set-builder form. Write them in listing form.

a. $\{x | x$ is a natural number less than or equal to $6\}$

b. $\{n | n$ is a prime number less than $20\}$

c. $\{y | y$ is a natural number whose square is less than $25\}$

d. $\{y \mid y$ is an even natural number greater than $27\}$

Solutions:

a. 1, 2, 3, 4, 5, and 6 are the only natural numbers less than or equal to 6. Therefore, the given set in the listing form is $\{1, 2, 3, 4, 5, 6\}$.

b. The only prime numbers less than 20 are
2, 3, 5, 7, 11, 13, 17, and 19.

Therefore, the given set in the listing form is
$\{2, 3, 5, 7, 11, 13, 17, 19\}$.

c. The natural numbers with their squares less than 25 are 1, 2, 3, and 4. Therefore, the given set in the listing form is $\{1, 2, 3, 4\}$.

d. 28, 30, 32, 34, 36, ... are various even numbers greater than 27. Therefore, the given set is:
$\{28, 30, 32, 34, 36, \ldots\}$.

Notice the use of three dots in part (*d*). This set is infinite.

Warm-Up

1. The following sets are given in a set-builder form. Write them in listing form.

a) $\{x : x$ is a natural number less than or equal to $9\}$

b) $\{n : n$ is a prime number less than $30\}$

c) $\{y : y$ is a natural number whose square is less than $16\}$

d) $\{y : y$ is an odd natural number greater than $10\}$

EXAMPLE 2 Express the following sets in the set-builder form:

a. $\{3, 5, 7, 9, 11\}$ **b.** $\{8, 9, 10, 11, 12, \ldots\}$

Solutions:

2. Express the following sets in the set builder form:

a) $\{2, 4, 6, 8\}$

b) {20, 21, 22, 23, ...}

Answers:

1. **a)** {1, 2, 3, 4, 5, 6, 7, 8, 9}
   b) {2, 3, 5, 7, 11, 13, 17, 19, 23, 29}
   c) {1, 2, 3} **d)** {11, 13, 15, 17, ...}
2. **a)** {*x* : *x* is an even number between 1 and 9}
   b) {*x* : *x* is a natural number greater than or equal to 20}

a. Observe that 3, 5, 7, 9, and 11 are all the odd natural numbers between 2 and 12. Therefore, the given set in the set-builder form may be written as

$\{x \mid x$ is an odd number between 2 and $12\}$.

b. 8, 9, 10, 11, 12, ... are all the natural numbers greater than or equal to 8. Therefore, the given set in the set-builder form may be written as;

$\{x \mid x$ is a natural number greater than or equal to $8\}$.

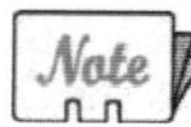

A set may be described in more than one way in the set builder method. For example the set in part (*a*) may be written as $\{x \mid x$ is an odd number between 3 and 11, both inclusive$\}$ and the set in part (*b*) may be written as $\{x \mid x$ is a natural number greater than $7\}$.

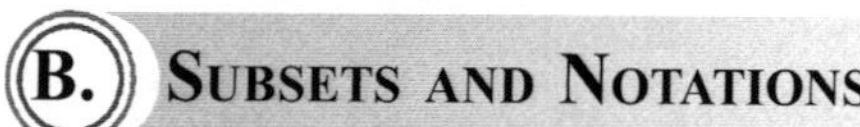

B. Subsets and Notations

***Definition*:**

A set *A* is said to be a **subset** of a set *B* if every element of *set A* is also an element of *set B*.

For Example:

1. {1, 2, 3} is a **subset** of {1, 2, 3, 4, 5}.
We write this in symbols as $\{1, 2, 3\} \subseteq \{1, 2, 3, 4, 5\}$.

2. If we can find an element of *A* which is not in *B* then A is not a subset of B. The information that *A* is **not a subset** of *B* is expressed in symbols as $A \not\subseteq B$.

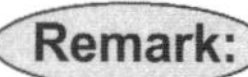

1. Note the difference between (i) and (ii) given below.

(i) $3 \in \{1, 2, 3, 4, 5\}$. The symbol $\in$ is used between an element of a set and a set.

(ii) $\{3\} \subseteq \{1, 2, 3, 4, 5\}$. The symbol $\subseteq$ is used between two sets.

2. In symbols we can express the definition of a subset as:

$$A \subseteq B \quad \text{if } x \in A \quad \Rightarrow x \in B$$

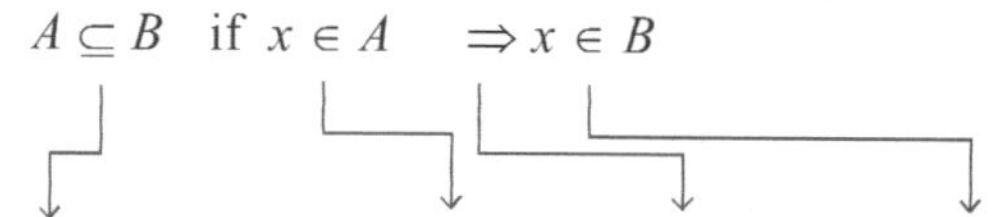

[*A* is a ***subset*** of *B* if *x* **belongs to** *A* ***implies*** *x* **belongs to** *B*]

Pictorial Representation of a Set: Venn Diagram

Pictorially, a non-empty set is represented by a circle-like closed figure inside a bigger rectangle. This is called a Venn diagram. In Figure 2.1 the set represented by a circle marked *A* is a subset of the set represented by the larger circle marked *B*. In Figure 2.2, the set *A* is not a subset of *B*.

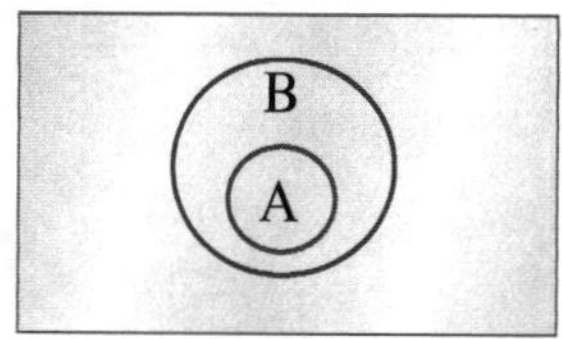

Figure 2.1

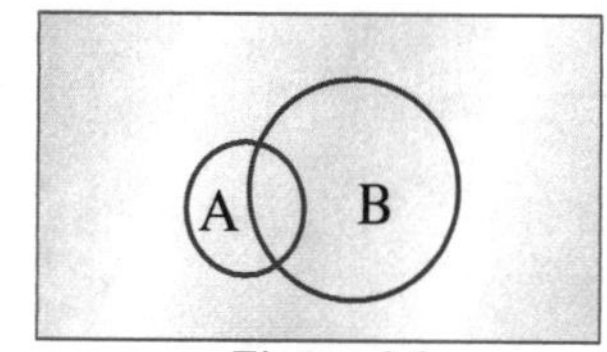

Figure 2.2

Special Properties:

1. $A \subseteq A$ for any set A. A set is always a subset of itself.
2. $\phi \subseteq A$ for any set A. The null set is a subset of every set.
3. If two sets A and B are equal, then $A \subseteq B$ and $B \subseteq A$.

EXAMPLE 3 Identify if the statement is true or false:

a. $\{2\} \subseteq \{1, 2, 3, 4\}$

b. Given $A = \{ x \mid x$ is a prime number$\}$, and $B = \{x \mid x$ is an odd natural number$\}$, then $A \subseteq B$.

c. Given $A = \{ x \mid x$ is a prime number$\}$, then $1 \in$ A.

d. $2 \subseteq \{0, 1, 2, 4\}$

Solutions:

a. The given statement is true since 2 is the only element of $\{2\}$ and it is also an element of $\{1, 2, 3, 4\}$.

b. The given statement is false because 2 is a prime number, therefore, $2 \in A$ but $2 \notin B$ since 2 is not odd.

c. The given statement, $1 \in A$, is false because 1 is not a prime number.

d. The given statement is false because 2 is an element of $\{0, 1, 2, 4\}$, not a subset as indicated by the symbol $\subseteq$.

WARM-UP

3. Identify if the statement is true or false.

a) $\{1\} \subseteq \{2, 3, 4\}$

b) Given $A = \{x : x$ is a composite number$\}$ and $B = \{x : x$ is an even natural number$\}$, then $B \subseteq A$.

c) Given $A = \{x : x$ is a prime number$\}$, then $2 \in A$.

d) $\{2\} \in \{1, 2, 3\}$

Answers:

3. a) False b) False
c) True d) False

C. Union/Intersection of Two or More Sets

Union of Two Sets

Suppose $A = \{1, 2, 3, 5\}$ and $B = \{-3, 1, 5, 9, 13\}$ are two sets. The collection containing all those elements which are either in A or B is well defined. Thus, the new collection forms a set. This new set $\{1, 2, 3, 5, -3, 9, 13\}$ is called the **union** of two sets A and B.

In general, the union of two sets is obtained by forming a set with all the elements of the two sets as its members. Symbolically we write the union of two sets A and B as $A \cup$ B. In a set builder notation, we define the union of two sets as follows:

Definition: For any two sets A and B

$$A \cup B = \{x : x \in A \text{ or } x \in B\}$$

Recall $x \in A$ means x is a member of A.

Notice "$x \in A$ or $x \in B$" includes all elements x that are either in A or in B.

Venn diagrams can be used to represent union of sets as follows.

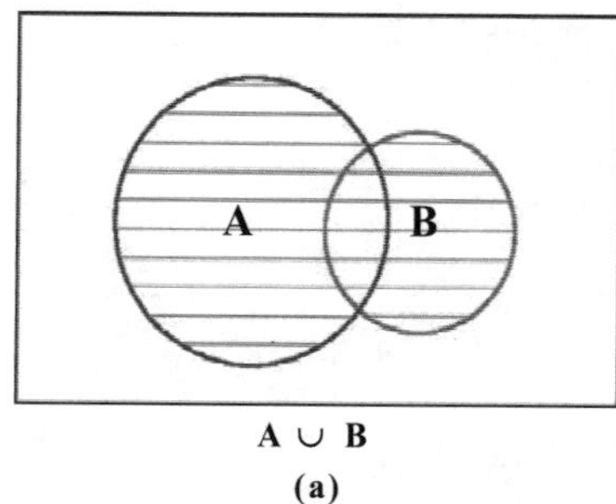

A ∪ B

(a)

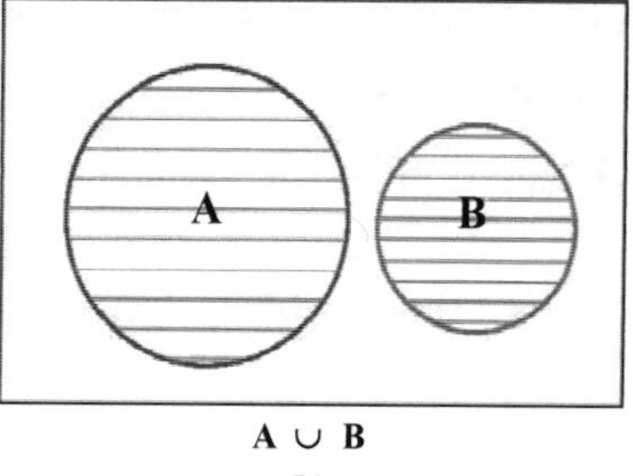

A ∪ B

(b)

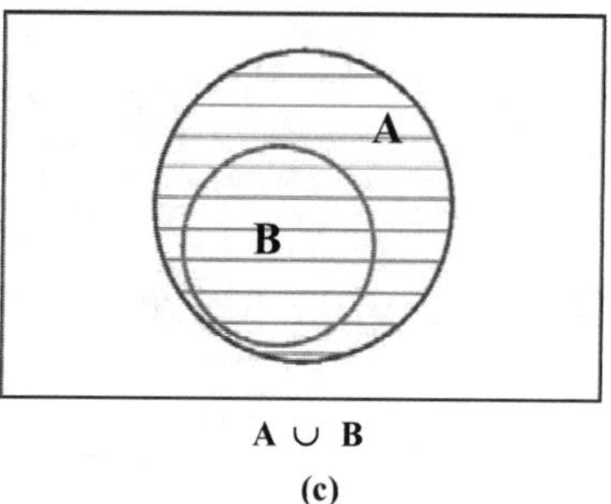

A ∪ B

(c)

Figure 2.3

WARM-UP

4. Find the union of the given two sets.

a) A = {1, 3, 5, 7, 9},
B = {3, 6, 9, 12}

b) A = set of non-negative integers,
B = set of negative integers.

c) A = closed interval [–1, 3],
B = closed interval [3, 5].

d) A = open interval (–2, 6],
B = open interval (6, 9).

Answers:

4. a) {1, 3, 5, 6, 7, 9, 12} **b)** Set of integers
c) [–1, 5] **d)** (–2, 9)

EXAMPLE 4 Find the union of the given two sets.

a. $A = \{1, 2, 4, 6, 8, 10\}$, $B = \{2, 3, 6, 12\}$

b. A = set of all prime numbers, $B = \varnothing$

c. A = closed interval $[-2, 4]$,
B = closed interval $[4, 7]$

d. A = open interval $(-3, 5)$,
B = open interval $(5, 8)$

e. A = open interval $(0, 4)$,
B = open interval $(3, 6)$

Solutions:

a. $A = \{1, 2, 4, 6, 8, 10\}$, $B = \{2, 3, 6, 12\}$
$A \cup B = \{1, 2, 3, 4, 6, 8, 10, 12\}$

b. A = set of all prime numbers, $B = \varnothing$
Since B is an empty set, it has no elements. Therefore, $A \cup$ B will consist of the elements of A only. Thus $A \cup B = A$. That is $A \cup \varnothing = A$

c. $A = [-2, 4] = \{x : -2 \le x \le 4\}$
$B = [4, 7] = \{x : 4 \le x \le 7\}$
Thus
$A \cup B = \{x : -2 \le x \le 4 \text{ or } 4 \le x \le 7\}$

Notice 4 is common to both intervals

$= \{x : -2 \le x \le 7\}$
$= [-2, 7]$

–2 7

Figure 2.4

d. $A = (-3, 5) = \{x : -3 < x < 5\}$
$B = (5, 8) = \{x : 5 < x < 8\}$

$A \cup B = \{x : -3 < x < 5 \text{ or } 5 < x < 8\}$
$= \{x : -3 < x < 8 \text{ and } x \neq 5\}$

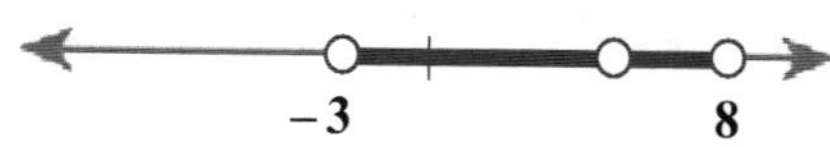

Figure 2.5

e. $A = (0, 4) = \{x : 0 < x < 4\}$
$B = (3, 6) = \{x : 3 < x < 6\}$

$A \cup B = \{x : 0 < x < 4 \text{ or } 3 < x < 6\}$

Notice that *A* and *B* have common elements.

$= \{x : 0 < x < 6\}$
$= (0, 6)$

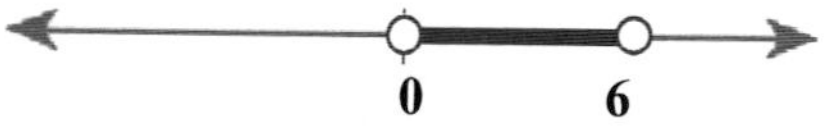

0 6

Figure 2.6

e) A = open interval (–3, 5),
B = open interval (4, 9).

EXAMPLE 5 Given three sets *A*, *B*, and *C* defined as follows:

$A = \{-2, 0, 2, 4, 6\}$.
$B = \{x : x \text{ is a prime number less than } 7\}$.
C = set consisting of the squares of the first three natural numbers.

a. compute $(A \cup B) \cup C$

b. compute $A \cup (B \cup C)$

Solutions:

Here $A = \{-2, 0, 2, 4, 6\}$

$B = \{x : x \text{ is a prime number less than } 7\}$
$= \{2, 3, 5\}$

C = set consisting the squares of the first three natural numbers.
$= \{1^2, 2^2, 3^3\} = \{1, 4, 9\}$

a. $A \cup B = \{-2, 0, 2, 4, 6\} \cup \{2, 3, 5\}$
$= \{-2, 0, 2, 3, 4, 5, 6\}$

$(A \cup B) \cup C = \{-2, 0, 2, 3, 4, 5, 6\} \cup \{1, 4, 9\}$
$= \{-2, 0, 1, 2, 3, 4, 5, 6, 9\}$

b. $B \cup C = \{2, 3, 5\} \cup \{1, 4, 9\} = \{1, 2, 3, 4, 5, 9\}$
$A \cup (B \cup C) = \{-2, 0, 2, 4, 6\} \cup \{1, 2, 3, 4, 5, 9\}$
$= \{-2, 0, 1, 2, 3, 4, 5, 6, 9\}$

Observe that: The sets of examples 5*a* and 5*b* are the same. We can generalize this observation in the following statement.

$(A \cup B) \cup C = A \cup (B \cup C)$

5. Given three sets A, B, and C defined as follows:

A = {–3, –1, 1, 3, 5, 7}
B = {x: x is an even number less than 6}
C = set consisting of squares of the first two natural numbers.

a) Compute (A ∪ B) ∪ C

b) Compute A ∪ (B ∪ C)

Answers:

4. e) (–3, 9)

5. a) {–3, –1, 1, 2, 3, 4, 5, 7}
b) {–3, –1, 1, 2, 3, 4, 5, 7}

Properties of Set Union

The operations of set union has the following important properties.

1. $(A \cup B) \cup C = A \cup (B \cup C)$ for all sets A, B, and C. Associative Property

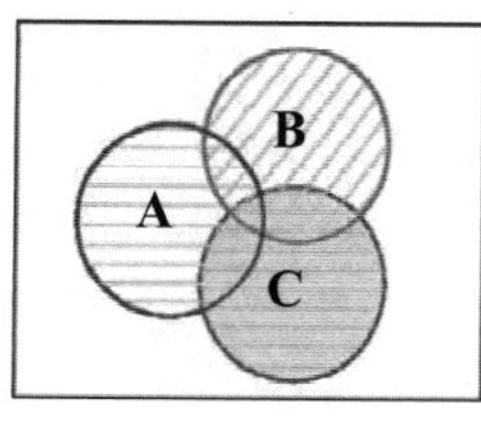

(A ∪ B) ∪ C

A ∪ (B ∪ C)

Figure 2.7

2. $A \cup B = B \cup A$ for all sets A and B. Commutative Property

3. $A \cup A = A$ 4. $A \cup \varnothing = A$

Note Property 1 was verified in Example 5, and property 4 was verified in Example 4.

Warm-Up

6. Let A = {−4, −2, 0, 2, 4, 6}
B = {1, 2, 3, 4}, C = {2, 3, 5},
and D = $\left\{\sqrt{3}, \frac{1}{2}, \frac{1}{3}, -2, 7\right\}$

Determine A ∪ B ∪ C ∪ D.

Answer:

6. $\{-4, -2, 0, 2, 4, 6, 1, 3, 5, \sqrt{3}, \frac{1}{2}, \frac{1}{3}, 7\}$

EXAMPLE 6 Let $A = \{-3, -1, 1, 3, 5\}$, $B = \{1, 2, 3, 4\}$, $C = \{1, 4, 9\}$, and $D = \left\{\sqrt{2}, \pi, 0, \frac{1}{2}, -1, 3\right\}$.

Determine $A \cup B \cup C \cup D$.

Solution: $A \cup B \cup C \cup D$ is obtained by collecting all the elements of the sets A, B, C, and D, and writing each element only once. Thus,

$$A \cup B \cup C \cup D = \left\{-3, -1, 1, 3, 5, 2, 4, 9, \sqrt{2}, \pi, 0, \frac{1}{2}\right\}$$

- ## Intersection of Sets

Intersection of Two Sets

The collection of the common elements of the two given sets is called the intersection of the given sets. Symbolically, we write the intersection of two sets A and B as $A \cap B$.

For example : The intersection of two sets

$A = \{\mathbf{1}, 2, 3, \mathbf{5}\}$ and $B = \{-3, \mathbf{1}, \mathbf{5}, 9, 13\}$

is given by $A \cap B$ = set of elements common to both A and $B = \{1, 5\}$

In a set builder notation we define the intersection of any two sets as follows.

***Definition*:**

For any two sets A and B

$A \cap B = \{x : x \in A$ **and** $x \in B\}$

Venn diagrams can be used to represent intersection of two sets as shown below.

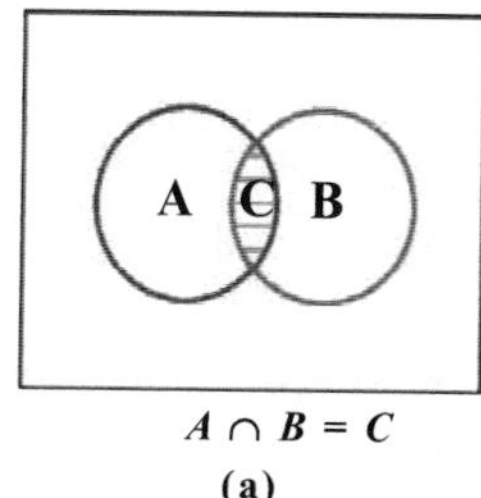

$A \cap B = C$

(a)

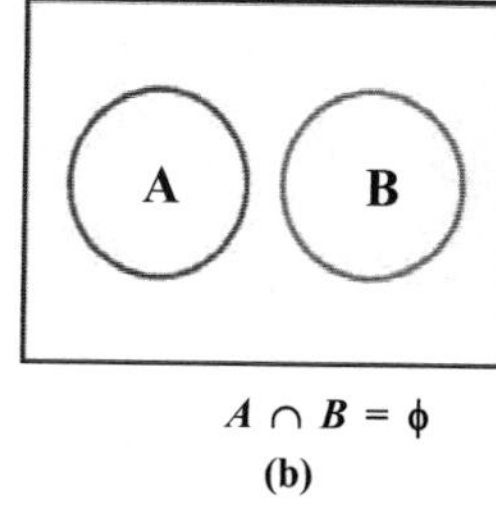

$A \cap B = \phi$

(b)

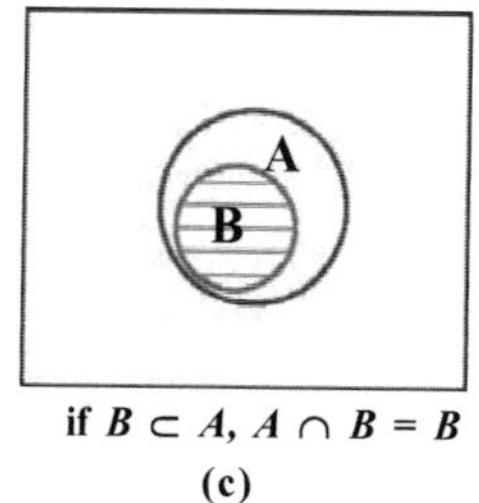

if $B \subset A$, $A \cap B = B$

(c)

Figure 2.8

Two sets A and B are said to be "disjoint(mutually disjoint)" if $A \cap B = \varnothing$ as shown in Figure 2.8 (b).

EXAMPLE 7 Find the intersection of the following pairs of sets.

a. $A = \{-2, 0, 2, 4, 6, 8\}$
$B = \{0, 4, 8, 12, 16\}$

b. A = set of all even numbers
B = set of all prime numbers

c. A = set of all integers
B = set of all real numbers

d. A = set of all even numbers
B = set of all odd numbers

e. A = set of all multiples of 4
B = set of all multiples of 6

f. $A = [3, 6]$, $B = [4, 8]$

g. $A = (-2, 5)$, $B = (0, 7)$

Solutions:

a. $A = \{-2, \mathbf{0}, 2, \mathbf{4}, 6, \mathbf{8}\}$ and $B = \{\mathbf{0}, \mathbf{4}, \mathbf{8}, 12, 16\}$
$A \cap B$ is the set of elements common to both A and B.
Thus, $A \cap B = \{0, 4, 8\}$

b. A = set of all even numbers, and
B = set of all prime numbers
We know that all prime numbers except 2 are odd.
Therefore, 2 is the only element common to A and B.
Hence $A \cap B = \{2\}$.

c. A = set of all integers, and
B = set of all real numbers
We know that every integer is a real number $A \subset B$.
Therefore, $A \cap B$ = set of all integers = A.

d. A = sets of all even numbers, and
B = set of all odd numbers
We know that no number can be both even and odd. Thus A and B do not have any element in common, or $A \cap B = \varnothing$

WARM-UP

7. Find the intersection of the following pairs of sets.

a) A = {–1, 0, 1, 3, 5, 7, 9}
B = {0, 1, 4, 9, 16}

b) A = set of all odd numbers.
B = set of all prime numbers.

c) A = set of all natural numbers.
B = set of all integers.

d) A = set of all rational numbers.
B = set of all real numbers.

Answers:

7. a) {0, 1, 9} b) Set of all odd prime numbers
c) Set of all natural numbers
d) Set of all rational numbers

e) A = set of all multiples of 6.
B = set of all multiples of 8.

e. A = set of all multiples of 4
$= \{0, \pm 4, \pm 8, \pm 12, \ldots\}$

B = set of all multiples of 6
$\{0, \pm 6, \pm 12, \pm 18, \ldots\}$

Any element which is common to both A and B must be a number which is a multiple of both 4 and 6. This means that elements common to A and B must be multiples of the LCM of 4 and 6 which is 12. Hence
$A \cap B = \{0, \pm 12, \pm 24 \ldots\}$

f) A = [–2, 4], B = [3, 7]

f. $A = [3, 6] = \{x : 3 \le x \le 6\}$

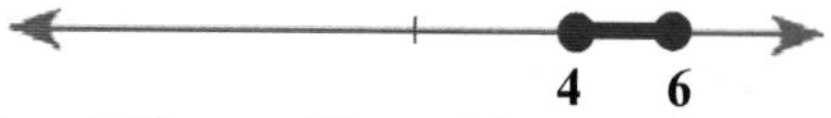

$B = [4, 8] = \{x : 4 \le x \le 8\}$

Figure 2.9

$A \cap B = \{x : 4 \le x \le 6\} = [4, 6]$

g) A = (–1, 4), B = (1, 5)

g. $A = (-2, 5) = \{x : -2 < x < 5\}$

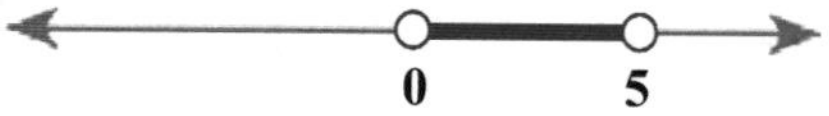

$B = (0, 7) = \{x : 0 < x < 7\}$

Figure 2.10

$A \cap B = \{x : 0 < x < 5\} = (0, 5)$

8. Suppose $A = \left\{-3, 1, 2, 3, \frac{4}{5}, \sqrt{3}\right\}$

$B = \left\{0, 2, \sqrt{3}, 6, \pi\right\}$

$C = \left\{2, 4, 6, \sqrt{2}, \sqrt{3}, \frac{7}{3}\right\}$

Determine **a)** $(A \cap B) \cap C$
b) $A \cap (B \cap C)$

Answers:

7. e) Set of all multiples of 24

Or {0, ±24, ±48, ...}

f) [3, 4] or 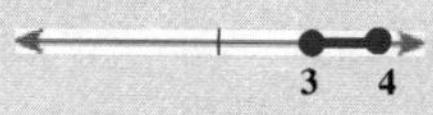

g) (1, 4) or 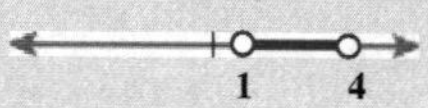

EXAMPLE 8 Suppose $A = \left\{-5, 6, 7, 8, \sqrt{2}, \pi\right\}$

$B = \left\{-3, 0, 4, \sqrt{2}, 6, \sqrt{3}\right\}$

$C = \left\{0, 2, 4, 8, \frac{5}{7}, \sqrt{2}, -\sqrt{2}\right\}$

Determine

a. $(A \cap B) \cap C$ **b.** $A \cap (B \cap C)$

Solutions:

a. $A \cap B = \{x : x \in A \text{ and } x \in B\}$
$= \left\{6, \sqrt{2}\right\}$

$(A \cap B) \cap C = \{x : x \in A \cap B \text{ and } x \in C\}$
$= \left\{\sqrt{2}\right\}$

b. $B \cap C = \left\{0, 4, \sqrt{2}\right\}$

$A \cap (B \cap C) = \left\{\sqrt{2}\right\}$

Observe that: $(A \cap B) \cap C = A \cap (B \cap C)$

EXAMPLE 9 Given three sets A, B, and C defined as follows.

$A = \{1, 2, 3, 5, 7, 9, 11, 13\}$

$B = \{1, 5, 7, 11\}$

$C = \{2, 6, 10, 14, 18\}$

Compute : **a.** $A \cap (B \cup C)$

b. $(A \cap B) \cup (A \cap C)$

Solutions:

a. $B \cup C = \{1, 2, 5, 6, 7, 10, 11, 14, 18\}$ = set of all elements in B or C.

$A \cap (B \cup C) = \{1, 2, 5, 7, 11\}$ = set of all elements common to A and $B \cup C$.

b. $A \cap B = \{1, 5, 7, 11\}$ and $A \cap C = \{2\}$

Therefore, $(A \cap B) \cup (A \cap C) = \{1, 5, 7, 11, 2\}$

Observe that: The sets of examples 9*a* and 9*b* are the same. We can generalize this observation in the following result.

$$\mathbf{A \cap (B \cup C) = (A \cap B) \cup (A \cap C)}$$

WARM-UP

9. Given three sets A, B, and C defined as follows:

A = {2, 4, 6, 8, 10, 12}

B = {2, 6, 10}

C = {1, 3, 6, 9, 12, 15}

Compute: **a)** $A \cap (B \cup C)$

b) $(A \cap B) \cup (A \cap C)$

Answers:

8. a) $\{2, \sqrt{3}\}$ b) $\{2, \sqrt{3}\}$

9. **a)** {2, 6, 10, 12} **b)** {2, 6, 10, 12}

PROPERTIES OF INTERSECTION

The operation of set intersection has the following important properties.

1. $(A \cap B) \cap C = A \cap (B \cap C)$ for all sets A, B, and C. Associative Property
2. $A \cap B = B \cap A$ for all sets A and B. Commutative Property
3. $A \cap A = A$ for all sets A.
4. $A \cap \varnothing = \varnothing$ for all sets A.
5. $A \cap (B \cup C) = (A \cap B) \cup (A \cap C)$ for all sets A, B, and C.

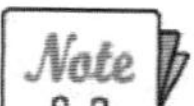

Property 1 is verified in Example 8. Properties 2, 3, and 4 can be easily verified. Property 9 is verified in Example 9.

Intersection of More than Two Sets

We observe in Example 5 that we can obtain the intersection of three sets simply by collecting the elements common to all the three sets. In general, we define the intersection of a finite number of given sets as the set of elements common to all the given sets.

EXAMPLE 10 Let $A = \{1, 2, 3, 4, 5, \mathbf{6}\}$,

$B = \{-2, 0, 2, 4, \mathbf{6}, 8\}$,

$C = \{0, 3, \mathbf{6}, 12\}$ and

$D = \{-12, -6, 0, \mathbf{6}, 12\}$.

Compute $A \cap B \cap C \cap D$.

WARM-UP

10. Let A = {2, 4, 6, 8, 10}

B = {2, 3, 5, 7, 11}

C = {1, 2, 3, 4, 5}

D = {-2, -1, 0, 1, 2}

Compute $A \cap B \cap C \cap D$.

WARM-UP

Answer:
10. {2}

Solution: $A \cap B \cap C \cap D$ is the set of all those elements which are common to the sets A, B, C, and D. We see that 6 is the only element common to the four sets.

Therefore,

$$A \cap B \cap C \cap D = \{6\}.$$

EXERCISE 2.1

In exercises 1-20, list the elements of the set.

1. The set of first five even natural numbers.

2. The set of first five odd natural numbers.

3. The set of first five consecutive whole numbers.

4. The set of five whole numbers between 3 and 9.

5. The set of all integers greater than or equal to one and less than eight.

6. The set of all integers greater than or equal to –2 and less than 5.

7. The set of all odd integers between one and eight.

8. The set of all even integers between 3 and 11.

9. $\{x \mid x$ is an even natural number less than $10\}$.

10. $\{x \mid x$ is an odd natural number less than $12\}$.

11. $\{s \mid s$ is a state in U.S.A. whose name begins with $A\}$.

12. $\{m \mid m$ is a name of the month whose name begins with A or $J\}$.

13. $\{y \mid y$ is a whole number which is a factor of $10\}$.

14. $\{y \mid y$ is a whole number which is a factor of $12\}$.

15. $\{n \mid n$ is a natural number multiple of $4\}$.

16. $\{n \mid n$ is a natural number multiple of $3\}$.

17. $\{z \mid z$ is a negative integer greater than $2\}$.

18. $\{z \mid z$ is a negative integer less than $5\}$.

19. $\{x \mid x$ is a real number whose absolute value is $1\}$.

20. $\{x \mid x$ is a real number whose absolute value is $7\}$.

In exercises 21-30, write the set in the set-builder form.

21. $\{2, 3, 5, 7\}$

22. $\{5, 7, 11, 13\}$

23. {Washington, West Virginia, Wisconsin, Wyoming}

24. {January, March, May, June, July}

25. $\{4, 9, 16, 25, 36, \ldots\}$

26. $\{1, 9, 25, 49, \ldots\}$

27. {Sunday, Tuesday, Thursday, Saturday}

28. {Monday, Wednesday, Friday, Sunday}

29. {January, March, May, July, August, October, December}.

30. {March, April, May, June, July, August, September}.

In exercises 31-36, identify whether the statement is true or false.

31. **(a)** $\{2, 3, 1\} \subseteq \{1, 3, 2\}$ **(b)** $\{2, 3, 1\} \neq \{1, 3, 2\}$

(c) $\{2, 3, 1\} \in \{1, 3, 2\}$ **(d)** $\{2, 3, 1\} \not\subseteq \{1, 3, 2\}$

32. **(a)** $\{4, 5, 3\} \subseteq \{3, 5, 4\}$ **(b)** $\{4, 5, 3\} \neq \{3, 5, 4\}$
(c) $\{4, 5, 3\} \in \{3, 5, 4\}$ **(d)** $\{4, 5, 3\} \not\subseteq \{3, 5, 4\}$

33. **(a)** $\phi \in A$ for all sets A **(b)** $A \subseteq A$ for all sets A **(c)** $2 \subseteq \{1, 2, 3\}$

34. **(a)** $\phi \subseteq A$ for all sets A **(b)** $A \subseteq \phi$ for all sets A **(c)** $\phi \in \{\phi\}$

35. **(a)** $\phi \subseteq$ set of all vowels in English alphabet.
(b) $\phi \in$ set of all states in the U.S.A.
(c) The set of all weekdays is a subset of the set of all months.

36. **(a)** $\phi \subseteq$ set of all English alphabet.
(b) $\phi \in$ set of all cities in the U.S.A.
(c) The set of weekdays starting with the letter T is a subset of the set of all weekdays.

In exercises 37-41, compute the indicated set operation using the following sets.
$A = \{1, 3, 7, 13, 21\}$, $B = \{1, 3, 5, 7, 9, 11\}$, $C = \{3, 5, 7, 11, 13\}$

37. $A \cup B$ **38.** $A \cup C$ **39.** $B \cap C$ **40.** $A \cap (B \cup C)$ **41.** $C \cap (A \cup B)$

In exercises 42-46, compute the indicated set operation using the following sets.
$A = \{2, 4, 8, 14, 22\}$, $B = \{2, 4, 6, 8, 10, 12\}$, $C = \{4, 6, 8, 11\}$

42. $A \cup B$ **43.** $A \cup C$ **44.** $B \cap C$ **45.** $A \cap (B \cup C)$ **46.** $C \cap (A \cup B)$

In exercises 47-50, compute the indicated set operation, where
***S* is the set of letters of the word "send"**
***E* is the set of letters of the word "empty"**
and *T* is the set of the letters of the word "train".

47. $S \cap (E \cup T)$ **48.** $S \cap E \cap T$ **49.** $S \cup E \cup T$ **50.** $S \cup (E \cap T)$

In exercises 51-54, compute the indicated set operation, where
***A* is the set of letters of the word "atlanta"**
***G* is the set of letters of the word "georgia"**
and *C* is the set of the letters of the word "county".

51. $A \cap (G \cup C)$ **52.** $A \cap G \cap C$ **53.** $A \cup G \cup C$ **54.** $A \cup (G \cap C)$

In exercises 55-56, compute the indicated set operation, where *A* and *B* are defined as
$A = \{x : x$ **is a multiple of 6**$\}$, $B = \{x : x$ **is a multiple of 8**$\}$. **Compute**

55. $A \cap B$ **56.** $A \cup B$

In exercises 57-58, compute the indicated set operation, where *A* and *B* are defined as
$A = \{x : x$ **is a multiple of 4**$\}$, $B = \{x : x$ **is a multiple of 6**$\}$. **Compute**

57. $A \cap B$ **58.** $A \cup B$

In exercises 59-76, compute the indicated set operation between the intervals.

59. $[-3, 7] \cup [6, 8]$ **60.** $[-1, 4] \cup [3, 5]$ **61.** $(-5, 1) \cup (0, 3)$ **62.** $(-3, 2) \cup (1, 4)$
63. $[-6, 6] \cup [6, 9]$ **64.** $[-8, 4] \cup [4, 10]$ **65.** $[0, 3] \cup (3, 5)$ **66.** $[-1, 2] \cup (2, 6)$
67. $[-3, 5] \cup [-2, 2]$ **68.** $[-4, 6] \cup [-1, 1]$ **69.** $[4, 9] \cup [6, 11]$ **70.** $[3, 5] \cup [4, 10]$
71. $(-\infty, 6) \cap (3, \infty)$ **72.** $(-\infty, 7) \cap (4, \infty)$ **73.** $[4, \infty) \cap (-\infty, 5]$ **74.** $[2, \infty) \cap (-\infty, 3]$
75. $(-\infty, 10] \cup [4, \infty)$ **76.** $(-\infty, 9] \cup [2, \infty)$

2.2 Coordinate System and Graphs

Objectives

Upon completion of this section you will study:

A. Coordinate System; and

B. Graph of Linear Equations.

Coordinate System

Cartesian Plane

Just as each point on a line can be described by a number, each point in a plane can be described by a pair of numbers. The system most commonly used is the cartesian coordinate system.

A cartesian coordinate system can be set up as follows:

Two intersecting number lines, one ***horizontal*** and another ***vertical***, are drawn in the plane, dividing it into ***four regions***. These lines are called *coordinate axes or axes of reference.*

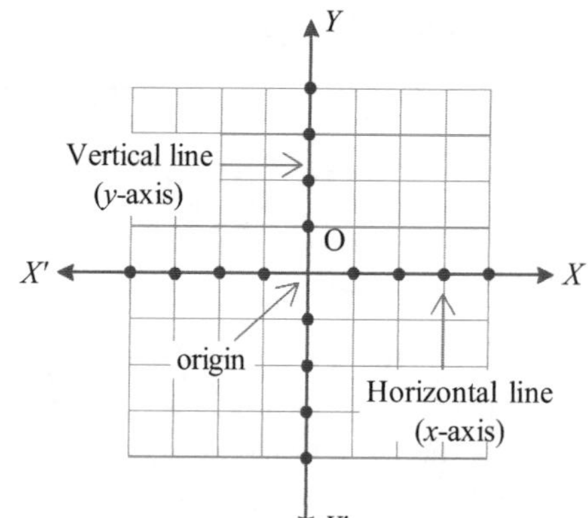

Figure 2.11

(a) The point of intersection of these lines represents **zero** on both number lines. The point O is called the origin.

(b) Numbers to the ***right of zero*** on the ***horizontal*** number line are **positive** and numbers to the ***left of zero*** are **negative.**

(c) Numbers ***above zero*** on the **vertical** line are **positive** and numbers ***below zero*** are **negative.**

- The horizontal number line *i.e.* XOX' is called the x-axis.
- The vertical line *i.e.* YOY' is called the y-axis.
- The x-axis and y-axis together constitute the rectangular coordinate system.
- The point of intersection of x-axis and y-axis denoted by O, is called origin.

Coordinates

Let P be a point in the cartesian plane and XOX' and YOY' be the coordinate axes.

Draw PL ⊥ XOX' and PM ⊥ YOY'.

OL is called the *x-coordinate* or *abscissa* of the point P.

OM is called the *y-coordinate* or *ordinate* of the point P.

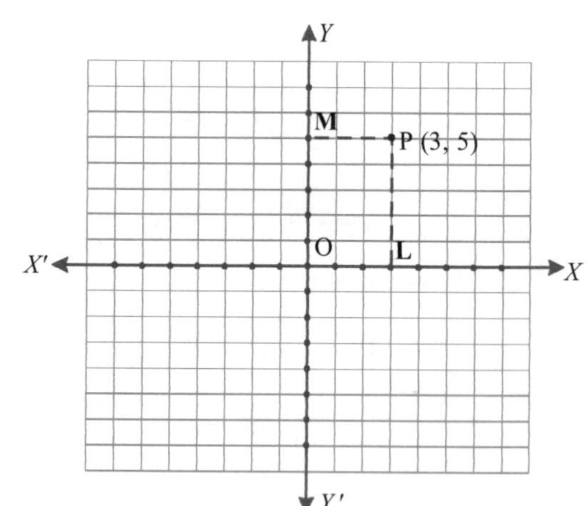

Figure 2.12

In Figure 2.12,

$$x = OL = 3, \quad y = OM = 5$$

We write it as P (3, 5). At origin $x = 0$, $y = 0$

Therefore coordinates of origin are (0, 0). The line $x = 0$ is the y-axis and line $y = 0$ is the x-axis. A point which lies on x-axis has y-coordinate as zero. Coordinates of a point on x-axis are $(x, 0)$.

A point which lies on y-axis has x-coordinate as zero. Coordinates of a point on x-axis are $(0, y)$.

Ordered Pair

The coordinate of a point P(3 , 5) are $x = 3$, $y = 5$.

We write x-coordinate first and then the y-coordinate.

As we fix the order of x and y, we say, points are represented by ordered pairs of real numbers. Corresponding to each ordered pair, there corresponds a unique point in the plane.

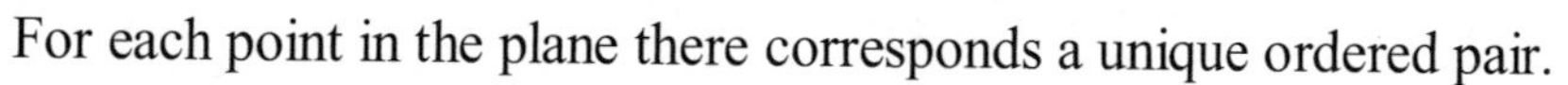

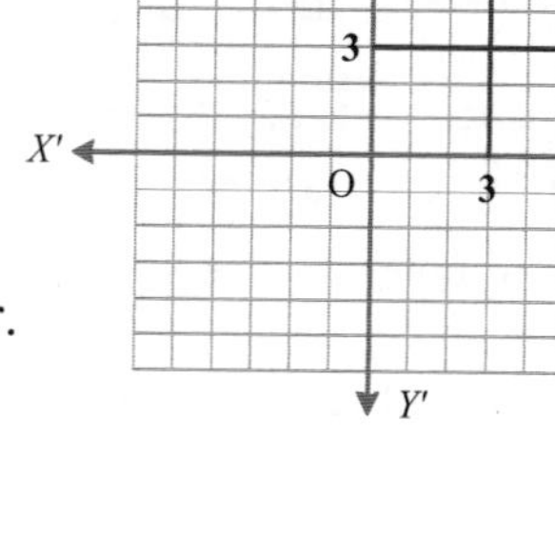

For each point in the plane there corresponds a unique ordered pair.

The pair (3 , 5) represents point P.

The pair (5 , 3) represents point Q.

i.e. $(3 , 5) \neq (5 , 3)$

Therefore ordered pair $(x , y) \neq$ ordered pair (y , x), if $x \neq y$

The order of the numbers in an ordered pair can be not interchanged.

Quadrants

The coordinate axes (plural of the word axis) XOX' and YOY' divide the plane into four regions XOY, X'OY, X'OY' and Y'OX. These four regions are called the *quadrants*. They are numbered I, II, III and IV in the counter clockwise direction beginning with XOY (as shown in Figure 2.13).

Figure 2.13

By sign convention :

On the x-axis

- Positive numbers are to the right of the origin *i.e.*, along OX. Thus, OX is called the positive direction of x-axis.
- Negative numbers are to the left of the origin *i.e.*, along OX'. Thus, OX' is called the negative direction of x-axis.

On the y-axis

- Positive numbers are above the origin *i.e.*, along OY. Thus, OY is called the positive direction of y-axis.
- Negative numbers are below the origin *i.e.*, along OY'. Thus, OY' is called the negative direction of y-axis.

The plane consisting of axes and these four quadrants is called the ***Cartesian plane*** or the ***coordinate plane*** or ***xy-plane***.

We find that :

In the I quadrant : $x > 0, y > 0$

In the II quadrant : $x < 0, y > 0$

In the III quadrant : $x < 0, y < 0$

In the IV quadrant : $x > 0, y < 0$

Plotting points in the plane

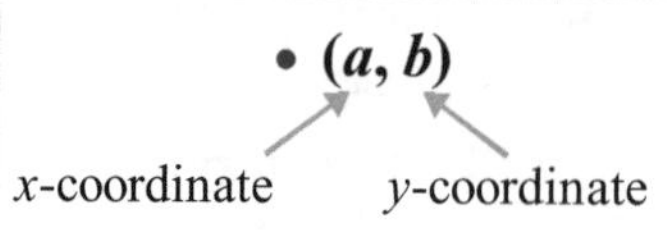

The point represented by (a, b) is said to have a as its x-coordinate and b as its y-coordinate.

In general, a and b are called the coordinates of the point (a, b).

A point with coordinates (a, b) is plotted as follows:

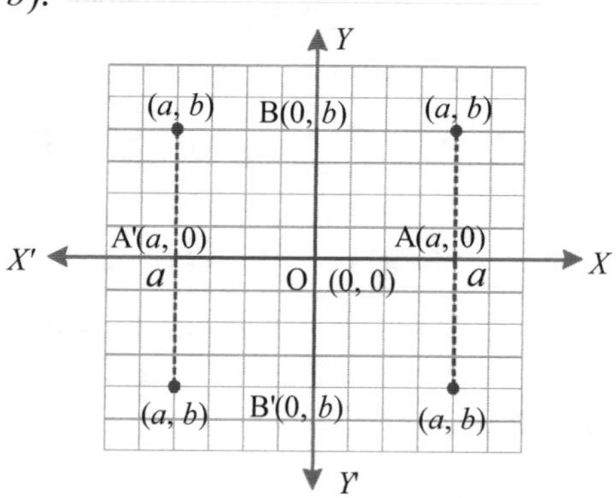

Figure 2.14

- Draw two perpendicular lines X'OX (***horizontal***) and Y'OY (***vertical***) intersecting each other at O, in a plane.
- Choose a suitable scale for a unit on x-axis and y-axis and mark the points on the both axes.
- If both $\boldsymbol{a}$ and $\boldsymbol{b}$ are zero, then the required point is the origin O.
- If $\boldsymbol{a \neq 0}$, mark $\boldsymbol{a}$ on the x-axis, starting from the origin and moving $|a|$ units along OX or OX' according as '$\boldsymbol{a}$' is ***positive*** or ***negative***.

  If $\boldsymbol{b = 0}$, then the point marked as $\boldsymbol{a}$, is the required point and its coordinates are $(\boldsymbol{a}, 0)$.

  Further if $\boldsymbol{b \neq 0}$, move $|b|$ units vertically *upwards* or *downwards* from a according as b is ***positive*** or ***negative***.

  Then we get the required point whose coordinates are (a, b).

  If $\boldsymbol{a = 0}$, $\boldsymbol{b \neq 0}$ then move $|b|$ units along OY or OY' according as b is ***positive*** or ***negative***. Then we get the required point and its coordinates are $(0, b)$.

EXAMPLE 1 Write the abscissa and ordinate of the point with coordinates (5, 7).

Solution : Let the given point be P.

The coordinates of the point P are written as P(x, y), where x is called the abscissa and y is called the ordinate.

Therefore, in the given point P (5, 7), abscissa = **5**, ordinate = **7**

EXAMPLE 2 Find the coordinates of the given point B in the figure.

Solution : Note that B is 3 units to the left of origin (along negative direction of x-axis) and 2 units above the origin (along positive direction of y-axis).

Therefore, the coordinates of B are **(–3, 2)**.

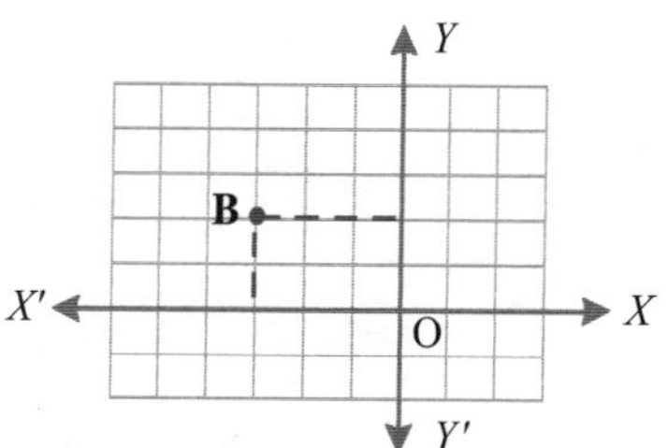

EXAMPLE 3 Find the abscissa and ordinate of the point in the figure.

Solution : The method to get abscissa and ordinate is explained below:

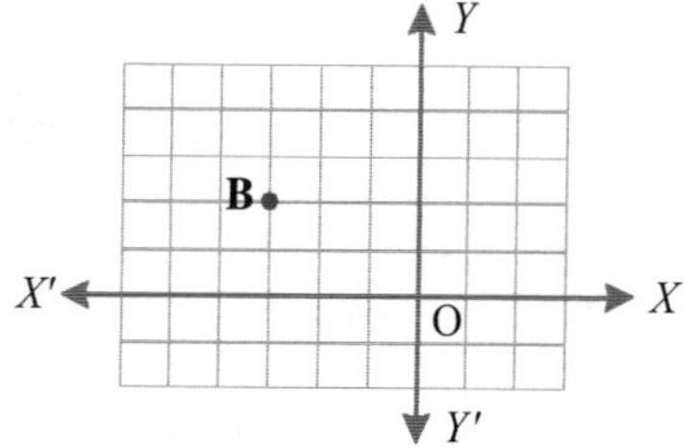

Start from the origin and go to the left exactly below the point B, so abscissa or the x-coordinate = **– 3**

Now go above till B, so ordinate or the y-coordinate = **2**

EXAMPLE 4 Write the coordinates of a point which lies on the x-axis and is at a distance of 4 units to the right of the origin.

Solution : The point lies on x-axis.

Therefore, its y-coordinate is zero.

It lies to the right of origin at a distance 4 units (See figure), therefore, x-coordinate is positive.

Hence, the coordinates of the point are (4, 0).

EXAMPLE 5 Write the coordinates of a point B whose ordinate is –3 and abscissa is 6. Also state in which quadrant does it lie.

Solution : Here, the ordinate *i.e.*, y-coordinate of the point B is –3 and abscissa of the point B *i.e.*, its x-coordinate is 6.

Hence, the coordinates of the point B are (6, –3).

Also, the ordinate is negative and the abscissa is positive. Thus, it will lie in quadrant IV.

EXAMPLE 6 Graph/Plot the point: (2, –4)

Solution :

Step 1: Draw a pair of coordinate axis, and label the x-axis, the y-axis, and the origin.

Step 2: Choose a scale. We take **1 cm = 1 unit** of length.

Step 3: To plot (2, –4)

x-coordinate = 2;
y-coordinate = –4;

Start from the origin and go to the right 2 units, Positive x-coordinate indicates "going to the right".

then go down 4 units. Negative y-coordinate indicates "go down".

The point is labeled, A, in the figure. Point A is the graph of (2, –4).

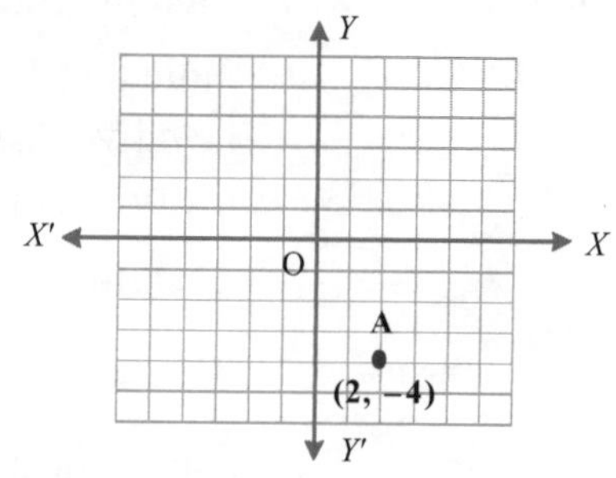

EXAMPLE 7 Plot the given point on the coordinate plane: (5, 1)

Solution :

Step 1: Move **5** units horizontally to the **right** from the origin.

Step 2: Then move **1** unit vertically **up**.

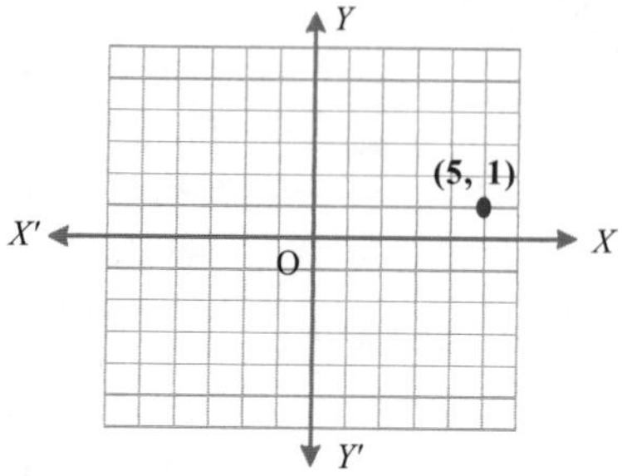

B. Graph of Linear Equations

Solution of Linear Equation

A solution of a linear equation in two variables is a pair of numbers, one for each variable, which when substituted for the respective variables makes the equation true.

e.g. $2x + 3y = 1$ is satisfied by $x = 2$ and $y = -1$.

$2(2) + 3(-1) = 1 \rightarrow 4 - 3 = 1 \rightarrow 1 = 1$ True

Thus, the pair $x = 2$ and $y = -1$ is a solution of $2x + 3y = 1$.

This is also expressed by saying that the *ordered pair*

$(x, y) = (2, -1)$ is a solution of $2x + 3y = 1$

We can get many solutions of a linear equation in two variables.

$2x + 3y = 1$

Put any value of x(say 5) in the above equation and solve the equation for y.

$$2(5) + 3y = 1$$

$$3y = 1 - 10$$

$$3y = -9$$

$$y = \frac{-9}{3} = -3$$

So, (5, –3) is another solution of equation $2x + 3y = 1$.

Remark: An ordered pair is a pair (a, b) of numbers whose sequence is important. Thus $(2, -1)$ is not the same as $(-1, 2)$. For an ordered pair (a, b), a is called the first component and b is called the second component. In general, letters representing components of an ordered pair are in alphabetical order.

A linear equation in two variables has infinitely many solutions.

Graph of Linear Equation

The graph of a *linear equation* is a line such that the ordered pairs representing points on the line are the solutions of the equation and the ordered pairs not on the line are not solutions of the equation.

A general strategy for graphing a linear equation in x and y consists of three steps.

Procedure / **Example**

***Step* 1:** Construct a table of several x and y values for the given equation, say $\mathbf{x - y = 1}$ and obtain the corresponding ordered pairs (x, y).

x	y
0	–1
1	0
–1	–2
–2	–3

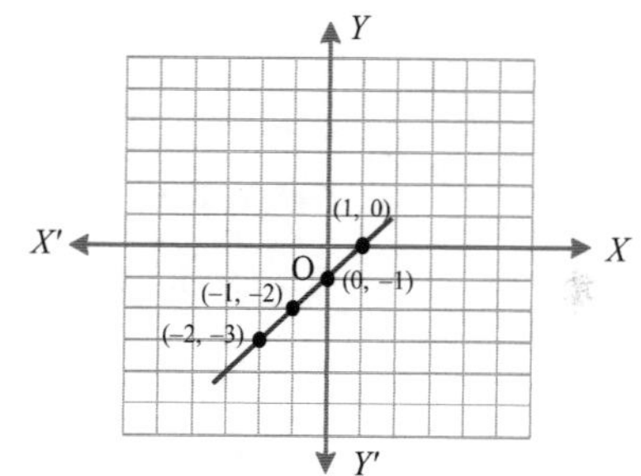

***Step* 2:** Plot the **ordered pairs**, obtained in step1, on a coordinate system.

***Step* 3:** Draw a **smooth line** passing through the points, plotted in *step* 2.

Graphical Method

Since equations are *linear*, their graphs are *straight lines*. The coordinates of any point on a line satisfy its equation. We want to find a point whose coordinates satisfy both equations. This point is the intersection of the two straight lines.

This point, if it exists, is a unique point because two intersecting lines intersect at one and only one point.

To solve a pair of simultaneous equations graphically, we draw the graphs of the two given equations on the same graph paper.

The coordinates of the point of intersection of the two straight lines representing the two equations is called the *solution of the simultaneous equations*.

Solving linear equations using graph

Consider the two linear equations: (i) $x + 3y = 6$ (ii) $x + y = 2$

Construct a table of several x and y values for both equations.

(i) $x + 3y = 6$

x	y
0	2
3	1
6	0

(ii) $x + y = 2$

x	y
0	2
1	1
2	0

We now plot the points, first from **table 1** for equation 1, then from **table 2** for equation 2.

From the figure, it is clear that the two lines (which are non-parallel) intersect at a single point *i.e.* at (0, 2). Therefore, (0, 2) is the solution of the system.

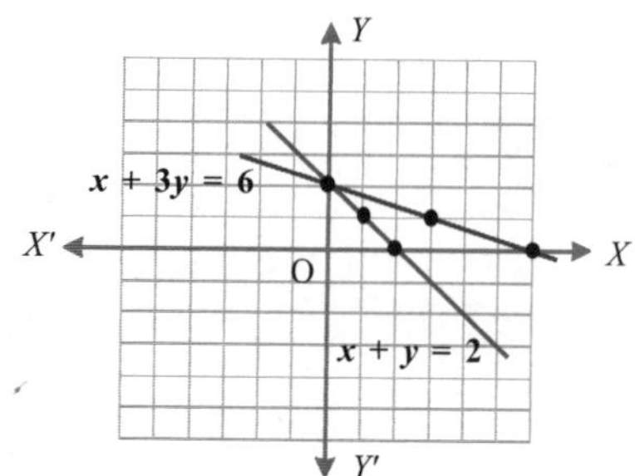

EXAMPLE 8 Solve the following system of equations by graphing and find the point of intersection:

$$x + 3y = 4 \quad \text{and} \quad 2x - y = 1$$

Solution: To draw the graph, we make a table of three ordered pairs for each equation.

Table for $x + 3y = 4$

x	y
7	–1
4	0
–5	3

Table for $2x - y = 1$

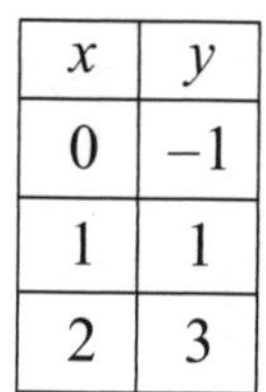

x	y
0	–1
1	1
2	3

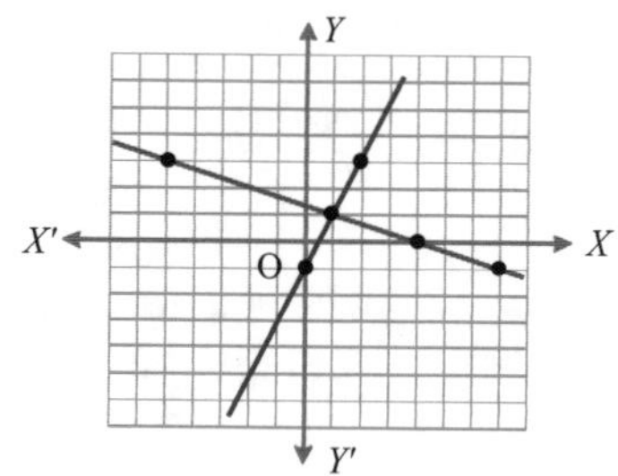

The graphs are shown in the figure. They intersect at (1, 1).

Therefore, (1, 1) is the solution of the system.

EXAMPLE 9 Identify whether the given ordered pair is a solution of the indicated equation.
(–4, 5) ; $2x - y = 10$

Solution: (–4, 5) ; $2x - y = 10$

Substitute values in

$$2x - y = 10$$
$$2(-4) - (5) = 10$$
$$-13 = 10 \quad \text{False}$$

Therefore, (–4, 5) is not a solution of $2x - y = 10$.

EXAMPLE 10 Identify whether $x = 2$, $y = 3$ and $y = -1$, $x = 4$ are both solutions of the equation $2x + y = 7$.

Solution: **Check:** $x = 2, y = 3$

Substitute values in

$$2x + y = 7$$
$$2(2) + (3) = 7$$
$$4 + 3 = 7$$
$$7 = 7 \quad \text{True}$$

Therefore, $x = 2, y = 3$ is a solution of $2x + y = 7$.

Check: $y = -1, x = 4$

Substitute values in

$$2x + y = 7$$
$$2(4) + (-1) = 7$$
$$8 - 1 = 7$$
$$7 = 7 \quad \text{True}$$

Therefore, $y = -1, x = 4$ is a solution of $2x + y = 7$.

EXAMPLE 11 Find the value of k, if $x = 2,\ y = 1$ is a solution of the equation $2x + 3y = k$.

Solution: Given, $x = 2,\ y = 1$ is a solution of the equation $2x + 3y = k$.

Substituting the values of x and y in

$$2x + 3y = k$$
$$2(2) + 3(1) = k$$
$$4 + 3 = k$$
$$7 = k \text{ or } k = 7$$

EXAMPLE 12 Graph the line $2x + 3y = 6$.

Solution: **Method 1:**

Step 1: Construct a table of three x-values and y-values for the equation $2x + 3y = 6$.

x	y
0	2
3	0
6	–2

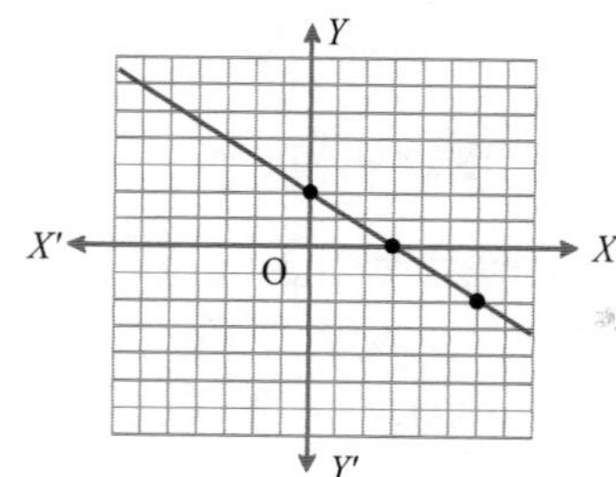

Step 2: Plot the points.

Step 3: Draw a straight line passing through these three points.

Method 2:

Step 1: Solve the equation for x or for y.

$$2x + 3y = 6$$
$$2x = 6 - 3y$$
$$x = \frac{6-3y}{2}$$

Step 2: Make a table of values as follows. Chose approximate integer values of y, so that each x-value is an integer.

x	y
0	2
3	0
6	–2

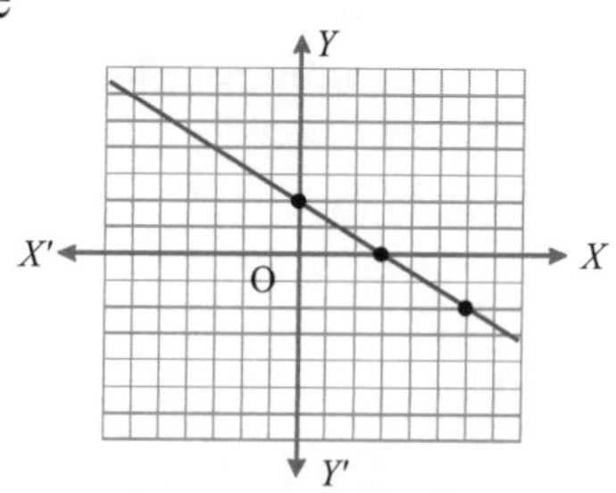

Step 3: Plot the points (0, 2), (3, 0), (6, –2), and join the points.

EXAMPLE 13 Find out whether the following pair of linear equations are consistent or inconsistent:
$3x + 2y = 5$; $2x - 3y = 7$

Solution: $3x + 2y = 5$; $2x - 3y = 7$

The given equations can be represented in the form $\boldsymbol{a_1x + b_1y + c_1 = 0; a_2x + b_2y + c_2 = 0}$

where $a_1 = 3,\ b_1 = 2,\ c_1 = -5$; $a_2 = 2,\ b_2 = -3,\ c_2 = -7$

$$\frac{a_1}{a_2} = \frac{3}{2},\ \frac{b_1}{b_2} = \frac{2}{-3} \text{ and } \frac{c_1}{c_2} = \frac{-5}{-7} \qquad \ldots \text{(i)}$$

From (i) we have, $\frac{a_1}{a_2} \neq \frac{b_1}{b_2}$ ... (ii)

From (ii) we can say that the lines will intersect in a single point.

In this case, the pair of equations has a unique solution.

Therefore, the pair of linear equations are consistent.

EXAMPLE 14 Determine the vertices of the triangle formed by the lines representing the equations:

$x + y = 5$; $x - y = 5$ and $x = 0$

Solution: In order to determine the vertices of the triangle formed by the lines representing the equations, we have to draw the graph of each linear equation.

To draw the graph, we draw the table of three ordered pairs which satisfy each linear equation.

Tables for given equations are:

$x + y = 5$

x	5	0	2
y	0	5	3

$x - y = 5$

x	5	0	3
y	0	–5	–2

$x = 0$

x	0	0	0
y	1	2	3

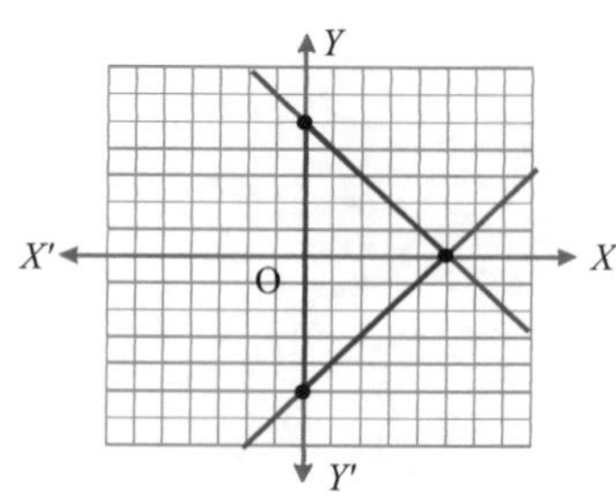

The graph of the equation $x = 0$ is the y-axis itself.

The vertices of ΔABC formed by the lines representing the equations are A(0, 5), B(5, 0) and C(0, –5).

EXAMPLE 15 Check whether the following pair of linear equations are consistent/inconsistent? If consistent, obtain the solution graphically.

$x + y = 5$ and

$2x + 2y = 10$

Solution: The given linear equations are: $x + y = 5$ ...(i)

$2x + 2y = 10$ ...(ii)

On comparing equation (i) and (ii) with $a_1x + b_1x + c_1 = 0$ and $a_2x + b_2x + c_2 = 0$ respectively, we get $\frac{a_1}{a_2} = \frac{b_1}{b_2} = \frac{c_1}{c_2} = \frac{1}{2}$.

Therefore, the given pair of linear equations is consistent and has a unique solution.

The solution can be obtained graphically.

Let us draw the graphs of the equation (i) and (ii). For this, we find two solutions of each of the equations, which are given in Table 1 and Table 2.

Table 1

x	0	1
$y = 2x - 2$	-2	0

Table 2

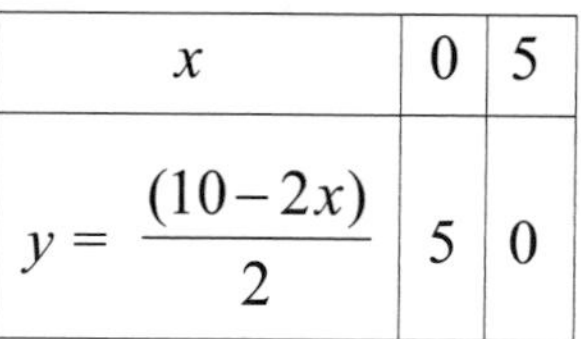

x	0	5
$y = \frac{(10-2x)}{2}$	5	0

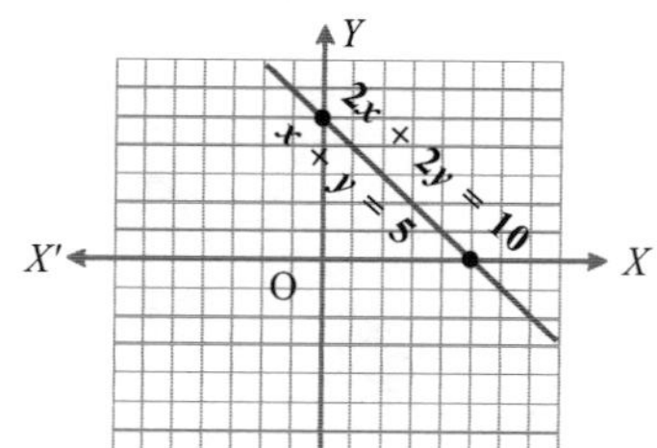

On plotting the points graphically, we find that, both lines are coincident. Therefore, the given pair of linear equations are consistent.

EXERCISE 2.2

1. Write the abscissa and ordinate of the point whose coordinates are

   (a) (0, 2) **(b)** (–3, 0) **(c)** (–8, 5) **(d)** (4, –4) **(e)** (–7, –1)

   (f) (9, –2) **(g)** (1, –1) **(h)** (–8, –4) **(i)** (–4, 3)

2. Find the coordinates of the given point.

(a)

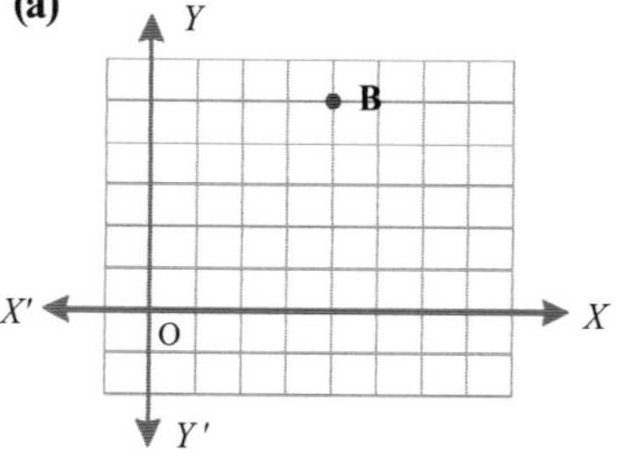

(b)

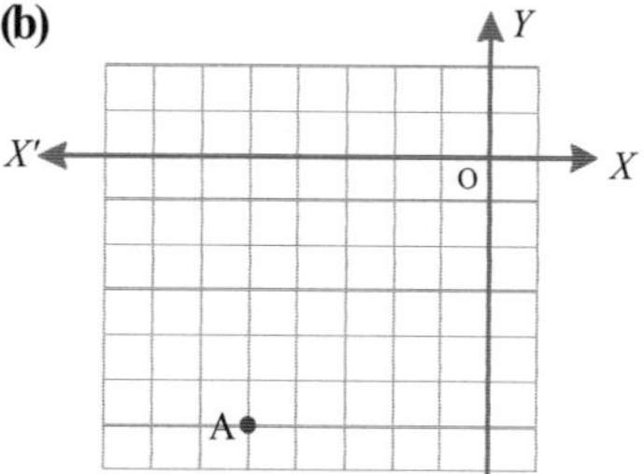

(c)

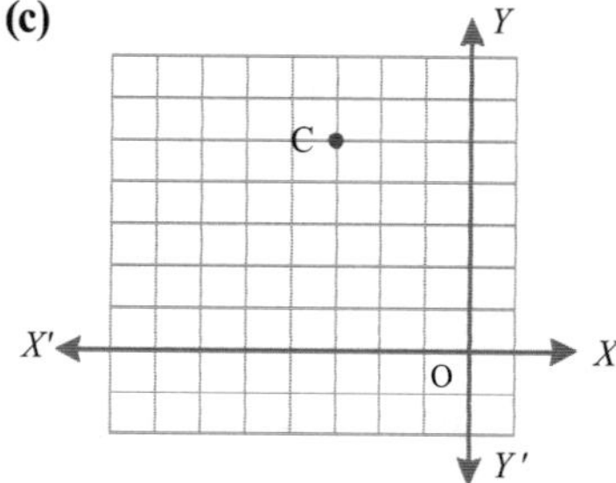

(d)

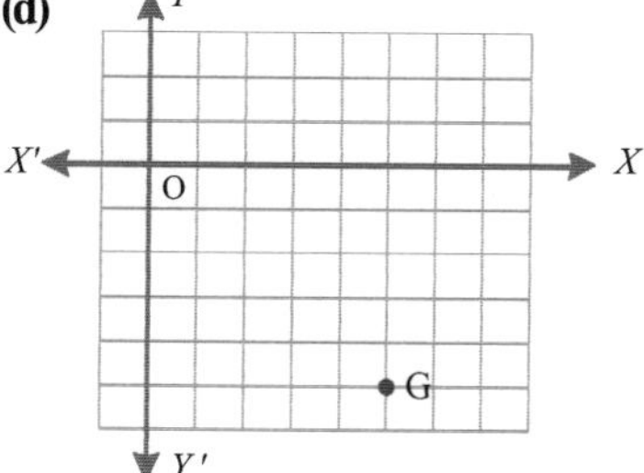

(e)

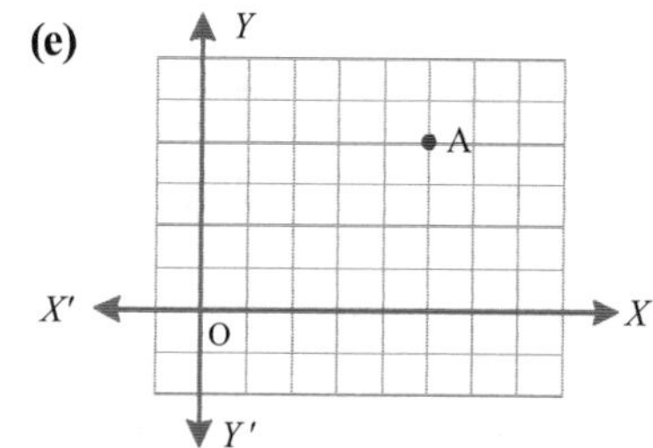

(f)

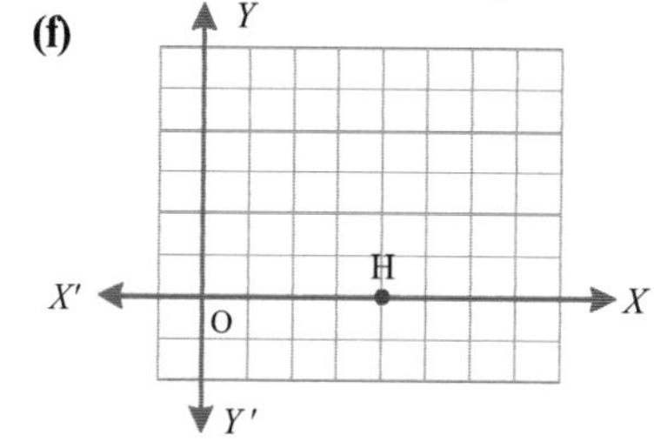

3. Determine the coordinates of the point shown in each of the following figures :

(a)

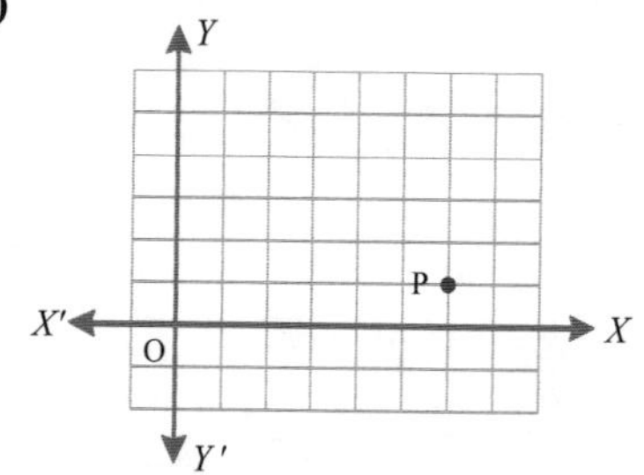

(b)

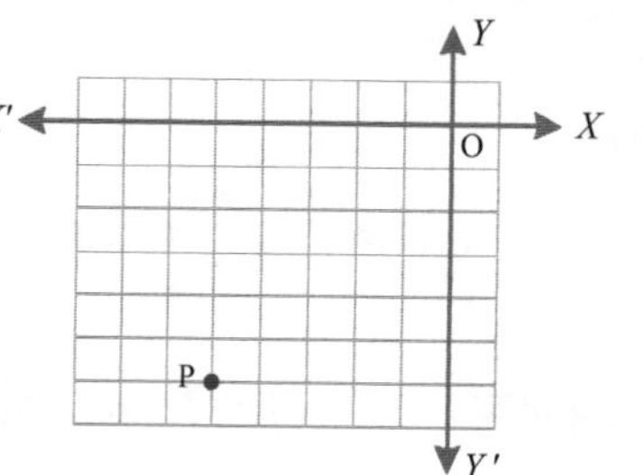

(c)

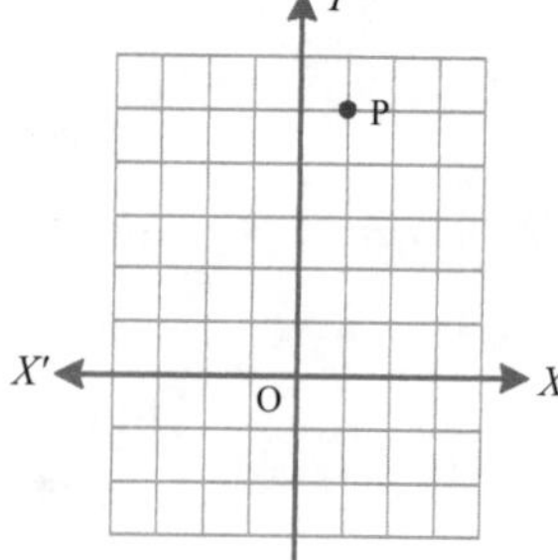

(d)

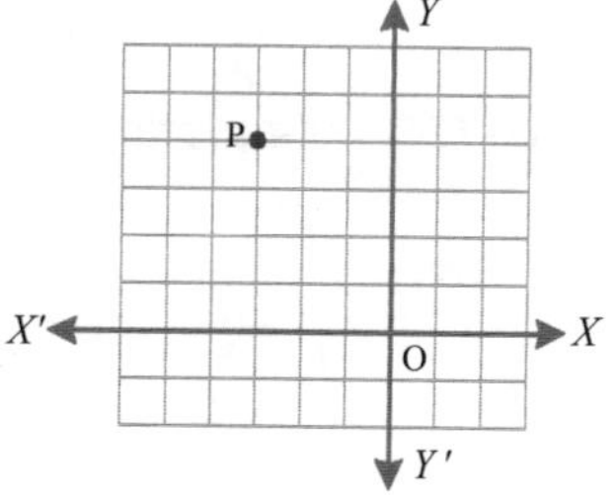

(e)

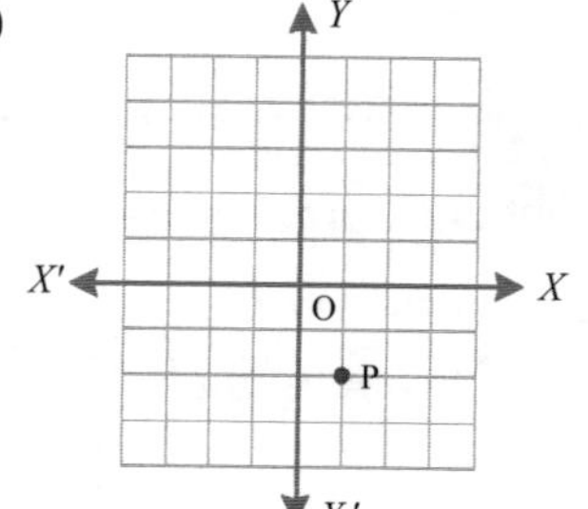

(f)

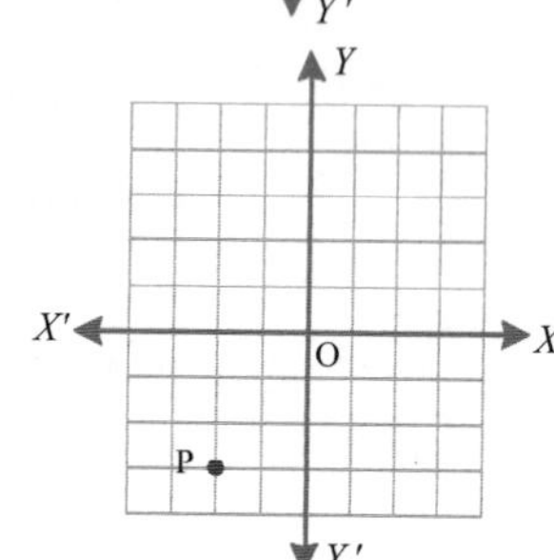

(g)

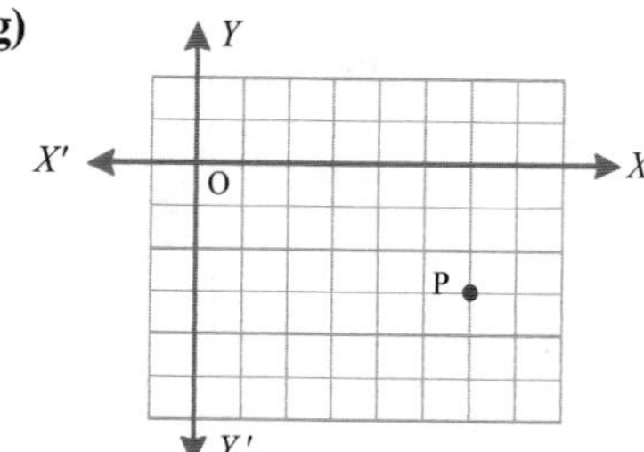

(h)

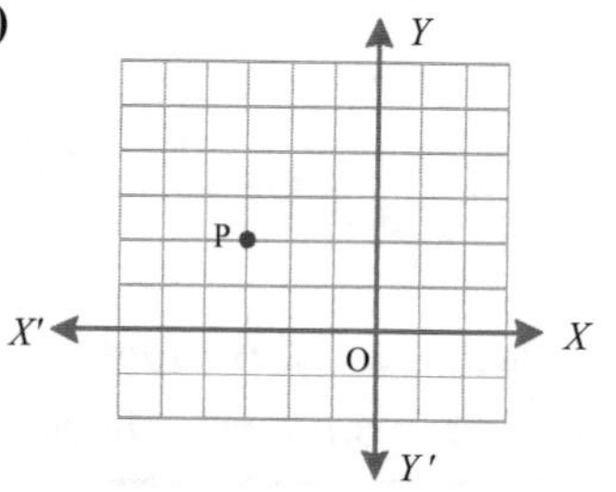

(i)

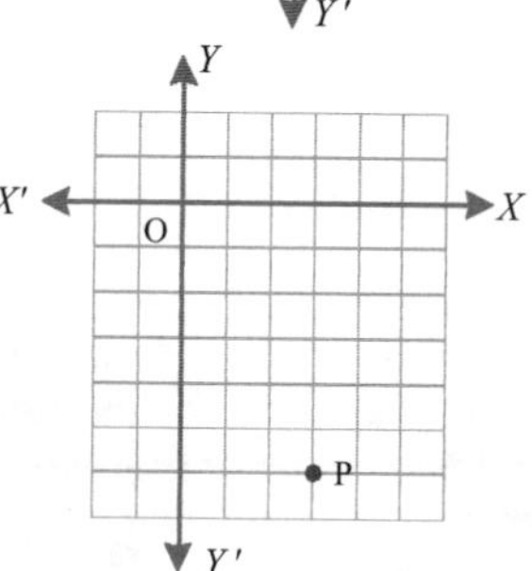

4. Find the abscissa and ordinate of the point in the figure :

(a)

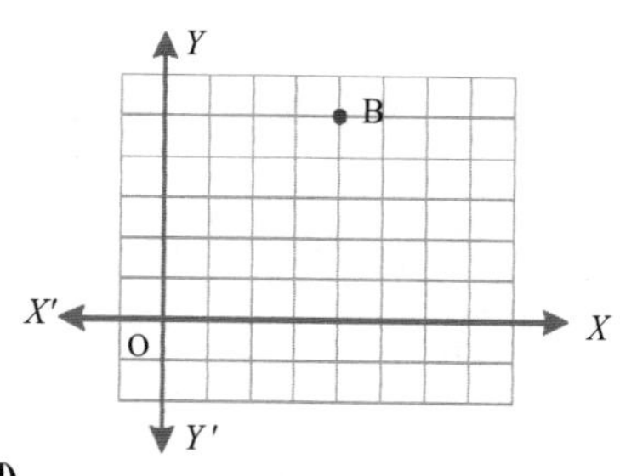

(b)

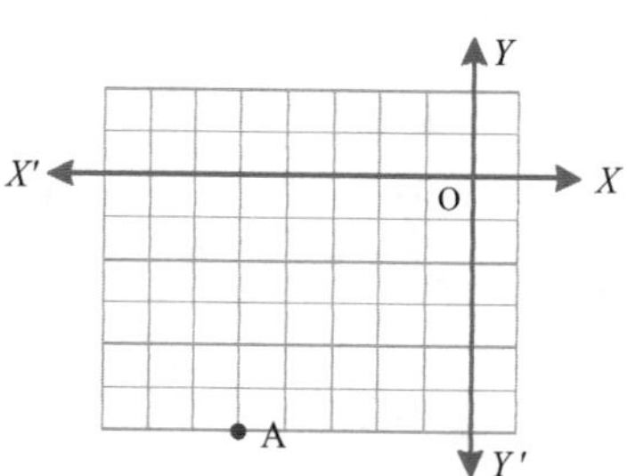

(c)

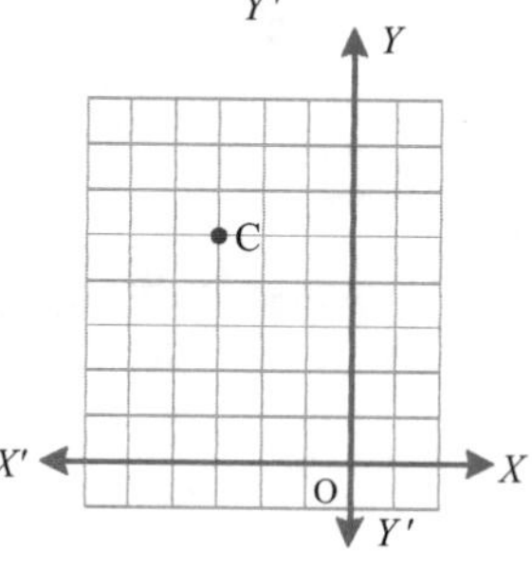

(d)

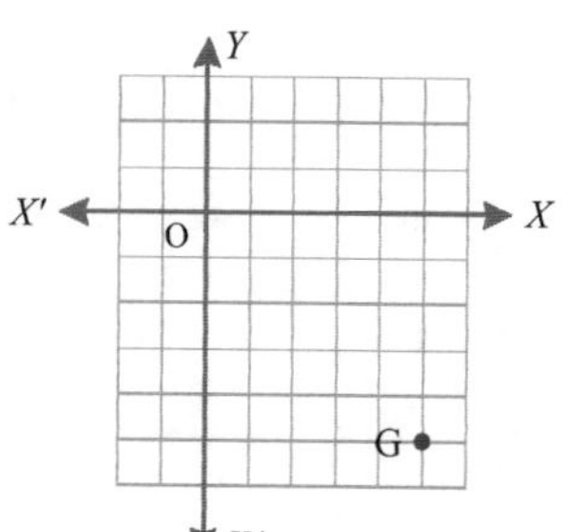

(e)

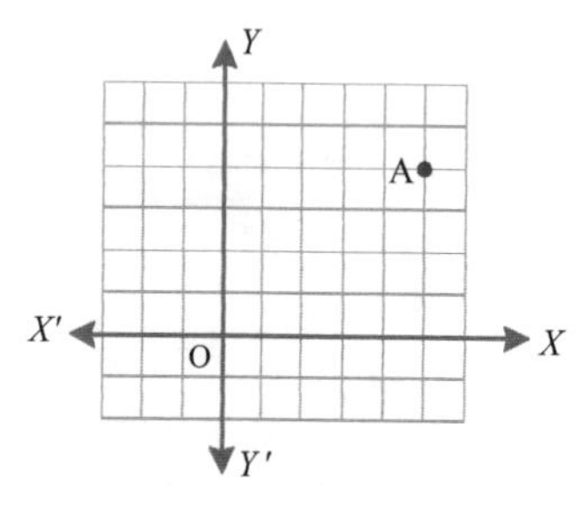

(f)

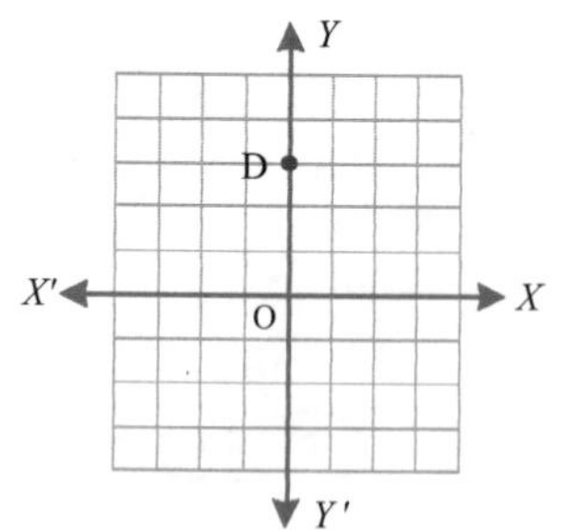

5. State the quadrant in which the following points lie :

(a) (4, –4) **(b)** (–3, –3) **(c)** (–5, 8) **(d)** (3, 4) **(e)** (–3, 7) **(f)** (5, –6) **(g)** (–4, –8)

In exercises 6-9, write the coordinates of a point which lies on the

6. y-axis and is at a distance of 5 units above x-axis.

7. x-axis and is at a distance of 3 units to the left of the origin.

8. y-axis and is at a distance of 2 units below x-axis.

9. y-axis and the x-axis.

10. What will be the ordinate of a point if it lies on the x-axis?

11. What will be the abscissa of a point if it lies on y-axis ?

12. Find the coordinates of the points A, B and C in each of the given figures.

(a)

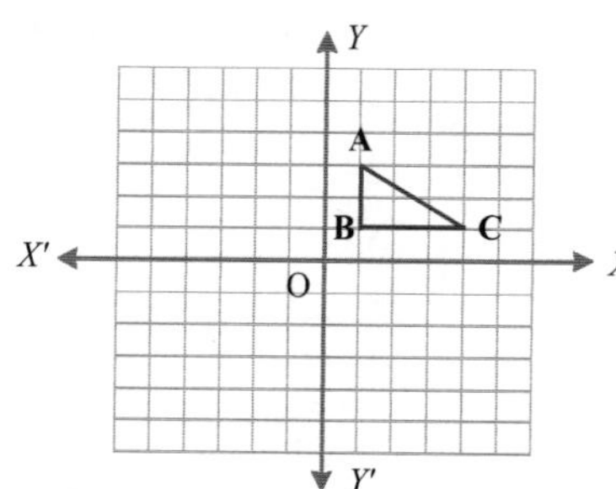

(b)

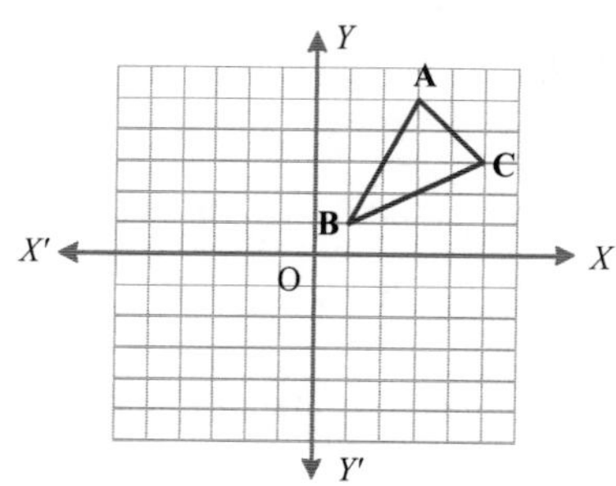

(c)

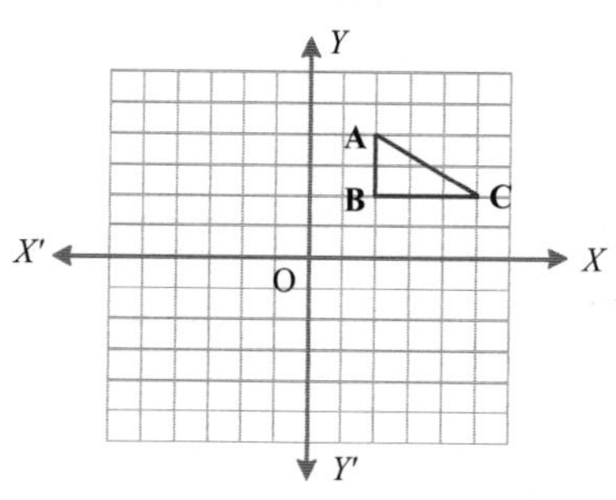

(d)

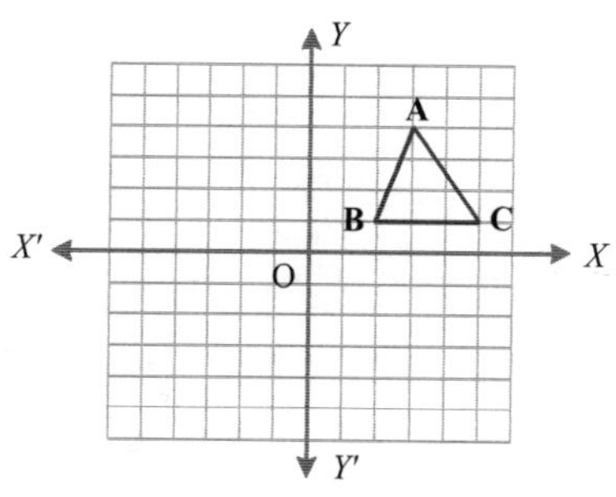

In exercises 13-16, write the coordinates of a point B whose ordinate is

13. 7 and abscissa is 5. Also state in which quadrant does it lie.

14. -2 and abscissa is -3. Also state in which quadrant does it lie.

15. 4 and abscissa is -3. Also state in which quadrant does it lie.

16. -3 and abscissa is 4. Also state in which quadrant does it lie.

In exercises 17-20, determine, how far is the point P from the

17. x-axis, if its ordinate is 5 and abscissa is -3.

18. y-axis, if its ordinate is -3 and abscissa is -5.

19. y-axis, if its ordinate is 6 and abscissa is 4.

20. y-axis, if its ordinate is 3 and abscissa is -2.

21. In the following figure, write the ordinate and abscissa of the point L. Also write its coordinates.

(a)

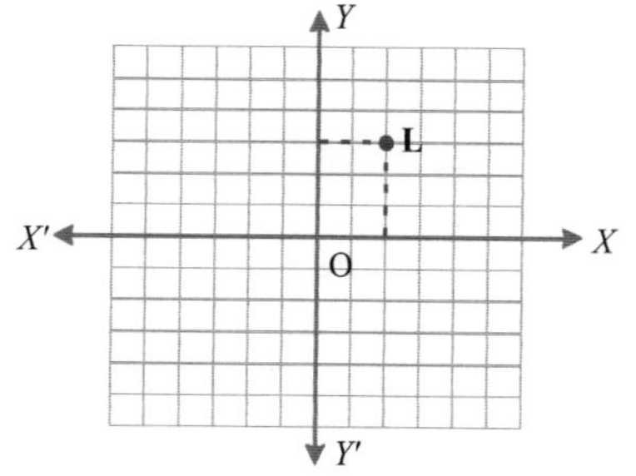

(b)

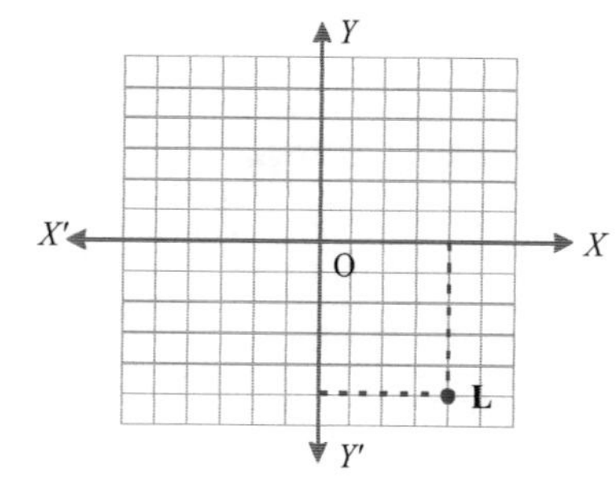

(c)

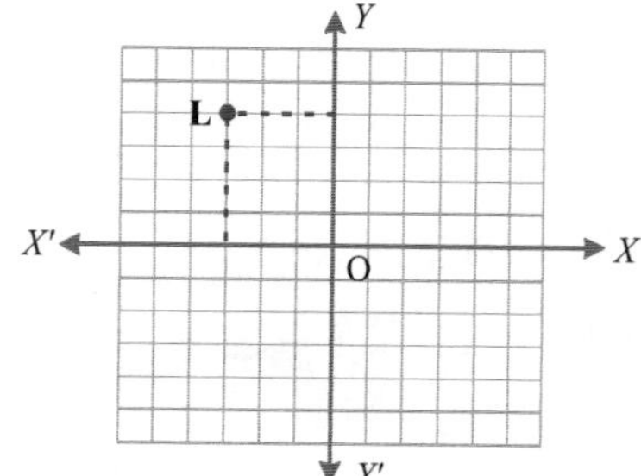

(d)

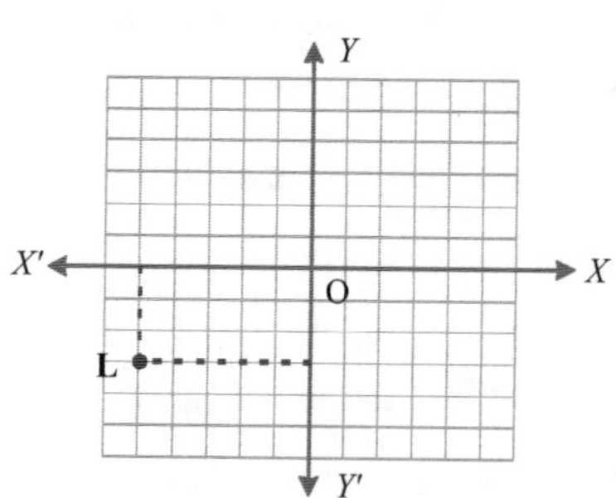

In exercises 22-31, Identify whether the given ordered pair is a solution of the indicated equation.

22. $(2, -1)$; $x - 2y = -2$

23. $(1, 1)$; $x - y = 0$

24. $(1, 3)$; $2y - x = 5$

25. $(-2, 4)$; $x - 2y = -8$

26. $(-3, -2)$; $2x + 3y = 0$

27. $(5, -6)$; $5y + 6x = -30$

28. $(-3, -3)$; $3x + 4y = 3$

29. $(-5, 2)$; $2x + 5y = 0$

30. $(4, -5)$; $4x + 5y = -9$

31. $(-4, 5)$; $2x - y = 10$

In exercises 32-39, Identify whether values of *x* and *y* are solutions of given equation.

32. $x = 1, y = 1$ and $y = 4, x = 2$; $6x - 2y = 4$

33. $x = 6, y = -5$ and $y = 1, x = 2$; $5x - 6y = 2$

34. $x = 4, y = 2$ and $y = 5, x = 9$; $3x - 5y = 2$

35. $x = -2, y = -2$ and $y = 4, x = 5$; $4x - 5y = 2$

36. $x = -3, y = -2$ and $y = 1, x = 3$; $3x - 5y = 4$

37. $x = 6, y = 7$ and $y = -5, x = -4$; $6x - 5y = 1$

38. $x = -1, y = -3$ and $y = 1, x = -1$; $5x - 3y = 1$

39. $x = -3, y = -3$ and $y = 2, x = 3$; $5x - 6y = 3$

In exercises 40-45, Find the value of *k*, if

40. $x = -1, \; y = -2$ is a solution of the equation $3x - 4y = k$.

41. $x = 3, \; y = -3$ is a solution of the equation $kx + 4y = 12$.

42. $x = -2, \; y = 4$ is a solution of the equation $3x + y = k$.

43. $x = 4, \; y = 5$ is a solution of the equation $x - ky = 14$.

44. $x = 3, \; y = -2$ is a solution of the equation $kx + 2y = 5$.

45. $x = 5, \; y = 3$ is a solution of the equation $3x - ky = 3$.

In exercises 46-50, Graph the line for the given equations.

46. $2x + y = 0$

47. $y = 4$

48. $7x + 2y = 0$

49. $2x - 3y = 0$

50. $5x + 2y = 4$

In exercises 51-54, Find out whether the following pair of linear equations are consistent or inconsistent:

51. $5x - 3y = 11; -10x + 6y = -22$

52. $4x + 2y = 8; 6x + 3y = 12$

53. $2x - 3y = 8; 4x - 6y = 9$

54. $3x + 5y = 7; 9x - 10y = 14$

In exercises 55-58, Determine the vertices of the triangle formed by the lines representing the equations:

55. $y = x; x + 2y = 6 ; y = 0$

56. $y = x; 2x - 3y = 6 ; x = 0$

57. $x + y = 6; y = x + 2 ; y = 0$

58. $x - y = 2; x + y = 6 ; x = 0$

In exercises 59-62, Check whether the following pair of linear equations are consistent/inconsistent? If consistent, obtain the solution graphically.

59. $x - y = 8$ and $x - y = \dfrac{16}{3}$

60. $2x + y - 6 = 0$ and $4x - 2y - 4 = 0$

61. $2x - 2y - 2 = 0$ and $4x - 4y - 5 = 0$

62. $2x - y - 2 = 0$ and $4x - y - 4 = 0$

2.3 FUNCTIONS

The concept of a function is central to all of mathematics. It allows us to translate real life situations into mathematical language and create mathematical models. In this section, we will introduce the idea of a function, give its precise mathematical definition, and study some elementary functions.

Objectives

Upon completion of this section you will study:

A. The definition of a Function.

B. Elementary Functions.

C. Finding the Value of a Function

In our everyday life, we often observe that one quantity depends on another. Suppose that an electronic store makes a profit of $50 when it sells a DVD player of a particular brand. How much profit does the storekeeper make when 2 or 8 or 15 DVD players are sold? We know that the profit (denote it by P) depends upon the number (say, x) of DVD players sold and can be calculated by multiplying 50 by x. We can symbolize it mathematically by writing $P = 50x$. We may then say, "If the store sells x DVD players then the profit will be $50x$ dollars". This is a simple example of a relation between the number of DVD players sold and the profit made, where the last quantity (profit $50x$) depends on the former (DVD players sold (x)). To describe this dependence between two quantities, we use the term **function.**

In general, we can consider relations (or associations) between any sets X and Y (consisting of objects which may or may not be numbers), and speak of functions from X to Y, under certain conditions.

A. THE DEFINITION OF A FUNCTION

Loosely speaking, a function is a rule which describes how to associate elements of a set X with elements of a set Y in an unambiguous manner, or, in other words, a rule that describes how one quantity (element of Y) depends on another (element in X). Now, we give a precise mathematical definition of a function.

Function

A function f from a set X to a set Y is a relation (a rule) that assigns to each element of X a unique element of Y.

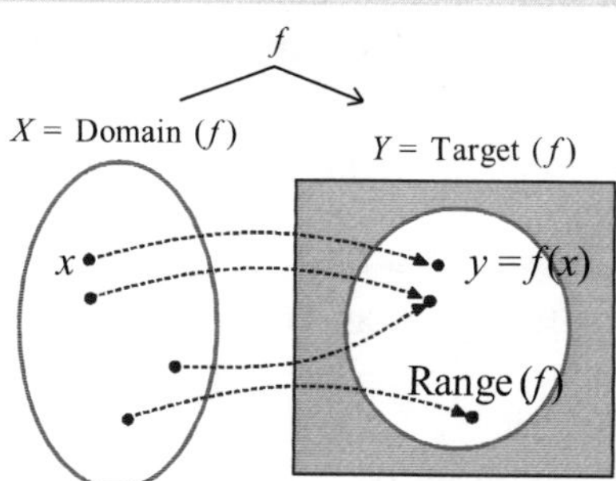

In the Figure above we can visualize all the components that go in the definition of a function f. Here, X is the **domain** of f (the set of all possible inputs (x) for the function f), Y is the **target set** of f (the set whose elements we want to associate with the elements of X). We write $y = f(x)$, where y is the element of the set Y which is associated to the element x of the set X via the function f. We say y is the **value** of the function f at x, or the **image** of f at x. The set of all images $f(x)$ of the function f in the set Y is called the **range** of the function f. The range of the function f is a subset of Y. Range $(f) = \{f(x) \mid x \in \text{Domain } (f)\}$.

EXAMPLE:

The example below illustrates that Range (*f*) does not have to equal the target set, Target (*f*), as shown in the Figure above.

Consider the **function** $f : \mathbf{R} \to \mathbf{R}$ given by the rule $f(x) = x^2$.

It's clear how the rule works - f accepts any real number as an input and squares it to produce an output : $f(0) = 0, f(2) = 4, f(-2) = 4$.

Here, **Domain** $(f) = \mathbf{R}$ – set of all acceptable inputs;

Target $(f) = \mathbf{R}$ – set that we want to associate with the domain (f).

What about Range (f) or Image (f)? Is it the whole set of real numbers **R**? We observe that the collection of actual outputs (the set of all images of the elements in the domain) consists necessarily of non-negative numbers because square of any real number cannot be negative.

Thus, **Range** $(f) = [0, \infty) \subset \mathbf{R}$.

Three Important things to Remember

1. Every element of X is associated with an element of Y.
2. Every element of X is associated with **exactly one element of** Y. This is required for the association to be unambiguous.
3. More than one element of X may be associated to the same element of Y and there may be elements of Y which are not associated to any element of X.

Explanation of the components in the Notation of a Function

f: $X \to Y$ *(indicates elements of X are associated with elements of Y via the function f).*

a. f is the **name** of the function (note that different letter can be used)

b. X is called the **domain** of the function f.

c. $\to$ indicates the direction of association.

d. $f(x)$ = The unique associate in Y that is associated to the generic element x in X by the function f- it is usually written as an algebraic **expression** (if possible) and defines a rule that associates a generic element x of X with an element of Y.

e. Y is the target set of f (set that we want to associate with X). Remember that the **Range** of f can be a subset of Y (see the Figure and example above).

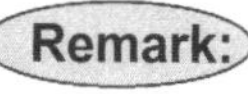

It is worth noticing that functions may be represented in different ways, not necessarily by an expression. You will see these different representations further in the book.

If $f: X \to Y$ is a function then

1. $f(\boldsymbol{a})$ is called the image of $\boldsymbol{a}$ under f or the f-image of a, and
2. $\boldsymbol{a}$ is called a pre-image of $f(\boldsymbol{a})$ under f.

Remark: By the definition of a function every element of its domain has exactly one image. **An element of the set Y** may have none, one, or more pre-images.

Function as an Input-Output Machine

Very often it is convenient to think of a function as an input-output machine. The function $f: R \rightarrow R_+$ described by $f(x) = x^2 + 1$ takes any real number x (element of R) and produces a positive number (element of R_+), by adding 1 to the square of x. Thus, under f

the associate of 2 is $2^2 + 1 = 5$,

the associate of -1 is $(-1)^2 + 1 = 2$,

the associate of 0 is $0^2 + 1 = 1$,

and so on.

Thus the function f acts like an input-output machine which takes the input x and produces the output $f(x) = x^2 + 1$.

Pictorially, $f: x^2 + 1$

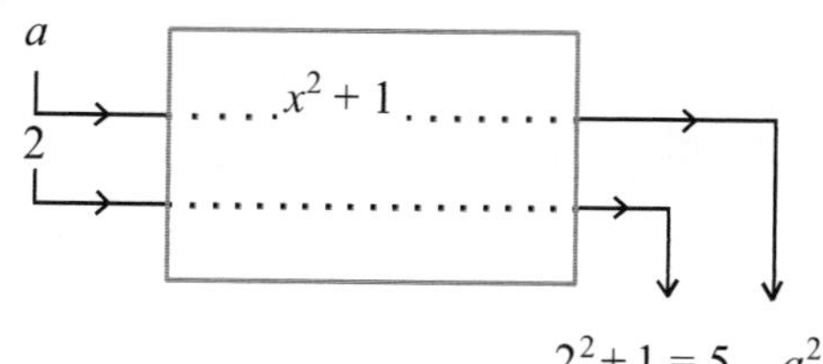

EXAMPLES:

a. f is not a function. Although all elements of X are associated with elements of Y, the element b is associated with two elements 7 and 8 and thus does not have a unique associate in Y. Therefore f is a not a function.

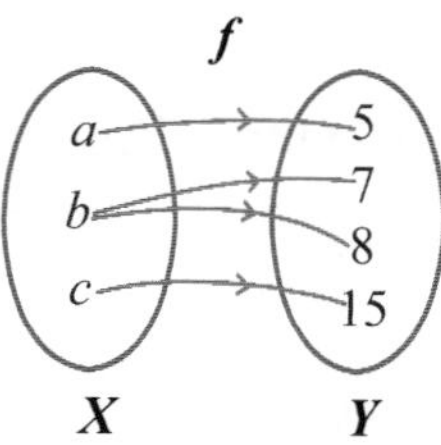

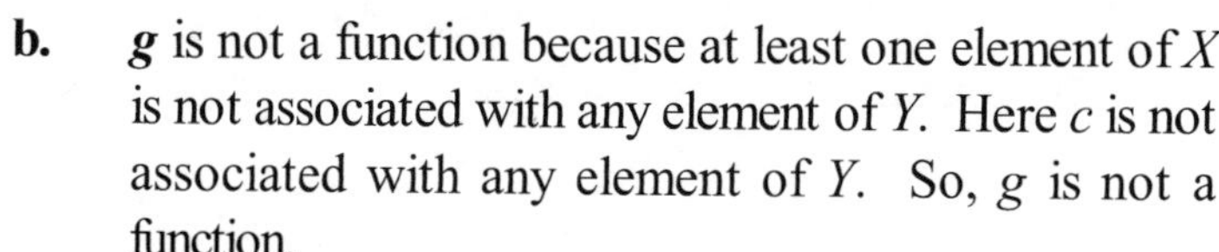

b. g is not a function because at least one element of X is not associated with any element of Y. Here c is not associated with any element of Y. So, g is not a function.

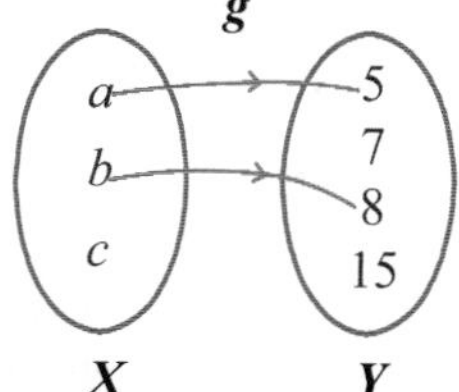

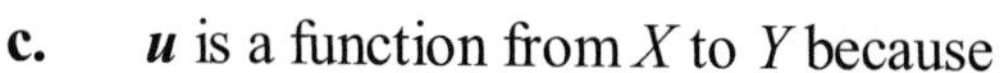

c. u is a function from X to Y because

i. All elements of X are associated with exactly one element of Y.

ii. No element of X is associated with more than one element of Y.

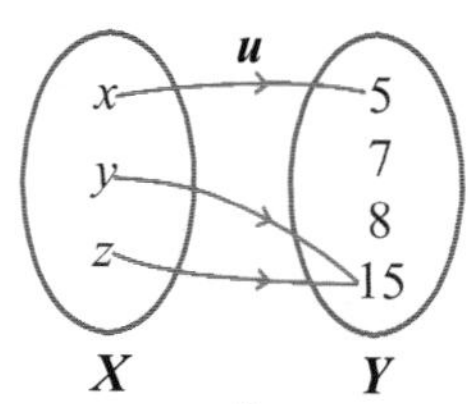

d. v is a function from X to Y because

i. All elements of X are associated with exactly one element of Y.

ii. No element of X is associated with more than one element of Y.

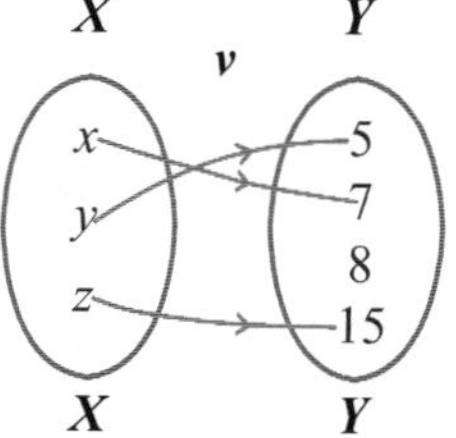

e. w is a function from X to Y because

i. All elements of X are associated with exactly one element of Y.

ii. No element of X is associated with more than one element of Y.

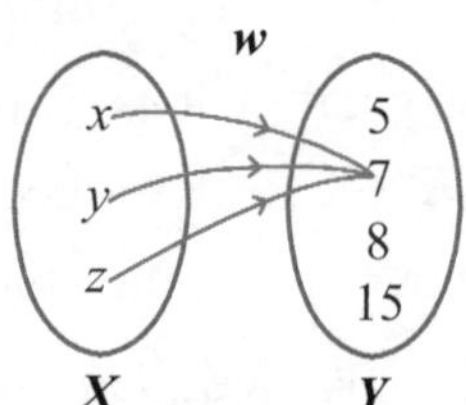

When the domain X of a function is a finite set and no pattern is visible in the association or correspondence between the elements of the domain X and the set Y, it is best to describe the function with diagrams or by listing the output of each input.

EXAMPLE 1 $X = \{a, b, c, d\}$, $Y = \{0, -1, 1\}$

$f: X \to Y$ is defined by the following association:

$f(a) = -1$, $f(b) = 1$, $f(c) = -1$, $f(d) = 1$

Observe here that Domain (f) = X, Target (f) = Y, but Range (f) = Image (f) = $\{-1, 1\}$, which is proper subset of Y.

The function may be described alternatively by using the diagram:

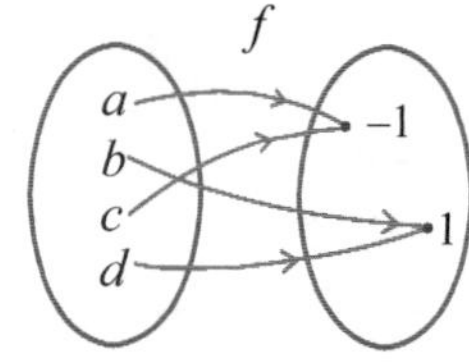

EXAMPLE 2 Find the rule of correspondence that describes the function f between X and Y, where: $X = \{1, 2, 3, 4, 5, 6\}$

Y = the set of integers.

and $f: X \to Y$ is defined by

$f(1) = 1$, $f(2) = 4$, $f(3) = 9$, $f(4) = 16$, $f(5) = 25$, and $f(6) = 36$.

Notice that f squares the input. Thus this function $f: X \to Y$ may be described by the rule $f(x) = x^2$.

Remark: We may describe the rule in example 1 by simply listing the images. Thus we will say that for the function in example 1, the rule is:

$a \to -1$

$b \to 1$

$c \to -1$

$d \to 1$

An alternative definition of a function

Definition 1 *Let X and Y be given sets. A subset R of the Cartesian product $X \times Y$ is said to define a "relation" between the sets X and Y.*

Definition 2 *Let $X = \{a, b, c\}$ and $Y = \{5, 7, 8, 15\}$ and let $R = \{(a, 5), (b, 7), (b, 8), (c, 15)\}$ be a subset of $X \times Y$. Then R defines a relation between X and Y. Now, we* *see that the subset R of X × Y establishes a correspondence between the elements of X and Y as follows:*

$a \to 5$

$b \to 7$

$b \to 8$

$c \to 15.$

However, this correspondence does not define a function from X into Y because it associates to the element b of X two elements 7, 8 of Y. On the other hand, let us consider the subset $S = \{(a, 5), (b, 7), (c, 15)\}$ of $X \times Y$. *Now S defines a relation between X and Y and also establishes a correspondence between the elements of X and Y* as follows:

$a \to 5$

$b \to 7$

$c \to 15.$

This correspondence defined by the subset $S = \{(a, 5), (b, 7), (c, 15)\}$ of $X \times Y$ *clearly defines a function, since it associates to each element of X a unique element of Y.*

The above example shows that while every subset of the Cartesian product $X \times Y$ of two given sets X and Y define a relation between X and Y and establishes a correspondence between elements of the set X and the set Y, but that correspondence may or may not define a function.

Next, a function $f : X \to Y$ defines a subset G of $X \times Y$ given by $G = \{(x; f(x)) \mid x \in X\}$ and hence defines a relation between X and Y. Observe that the subset G of $X \times Y$ is such that (i) each element of X is the first component of some element in G and (ii) no two second components of elements in G share the same first component.

This leads us to give the following "alternate definition" of a function from X into Y.

Definition 3 *Let X and Y be given sets. A subset G of the Cartesian product X × Y is said to define a "function" from X into Y if the following two conditions hold:*

A. Each element of the set X is the first component of some element in G.

B. If $(x, y_1) \in G$ *and* $(x, y_2) \in G$, *then we must have* $y_1 = y_2$.

In other words, no two elements of G can have the same first component.

Thus a function $f : X \to \mathrm{Y}$ may be defined as a relation from X into Y (equivalently as a subset of $X \times Y$) which satisfies the two conditions given in the above definition.

Now let us look at more examples of functional relationships.

EXAMPLE 3 Express area A of a circle as a function of its radius.

Solution: This simply means that we write A as an expression in x (the radius) and then write A in the function form.

We know that area of a circle is $\pi(\text{radius})^2$. Thus, if the radius of a circle is x, then its area, A, in the function form is:

$$A(x) = \pi x^2$$

EXAMPLE 4 To encourage bulk buying a company reduces the list price of $ 1000 per unit by four cents, times the number of units bought. Express the company's revenue R as a function of units x bought by a particular customer.

Solution: Notice that the company's revenue R is linked to the number of units, x, bought. Thus, if x units are bought, then the price per unit is reduced by $.04x$ (4 cents or .04 dollar per unit bought). So the discounted price per unit would become $\$(1000 - .04x)$.

Since x units are bought, the revenue from x units equals $x(1000 - .04x)$.

Hence, the revenue can be written as a function of the number of units, x, bought as follows:

$$R(x) = x(1000 - .04x)$$

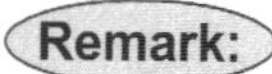

Here R: N → R is a function from the set of counting numbers to the set of real numbers, and the function is given by the rule

$$R(x) = x(1000 - .04x)$$

Observe that Range here consists of non negative real numbers, not all of R.

EXAMPLE 5 The following table gives the price per unit of different volume purchases.

Number bought	2	3	4	5	6
Price per unit	3	2	5/3	3/2	7/5

a. Find a suitable function which gives the price per unit when certain number of units is bought.

b. Determine the price per unit when 21 units are purchased.

Solutions: **a.** If we observe the table carefully, we can find a pattern (relationship) in the price per unit for the number of units bought.

Number of Units Bought x	Price per unit p	Pattern
6	7/5	$\frac{6+1}{6-1}$
5	3/2 = 6/4	$\frac{5+1}{5-1}$
4	5/3	$\frac{4+1}{4-1}$
Lets us try this pattern for 2 and 3 units		
3	$2 = \frac{4}{2}$	$\frac{3+1}{3-1}$
2	$3 = \frac{3}{1}$	$\frac{2+1}{2-1}$

So, the pattern shows that if x units were bought, then the price per unit will be $\frac{x+1}{x-1}$. Hence price p can be expressed as a function of the number of units, x, bought by the following function

$$p(x) = \frac{x+1}{x-1}.$$

b. The price per unit when the number of units brought is 21 is given by:

$$p(21) = \frac{21+1}{21-1} = \frac{22}{20} = \frac{11}{10} = 1.10$$

Remark: Notice that the rule of association in the above example is not applicable for the purchase of a single unit ($x = 1$) since $p(1) = \frac{1+1}{1-1} = \frac{2}{0}$ (undefined). Hence the domain of p is the set of natural numbers greater than or equal to 2.

EXAMPLE 6 Express the distance d of a point x on the number line from the point O, the origin, as a function of x.

Solution: We know that distance of a point on the number line from the origin (the point zero) is expressed in terms of the absolute value of the number.

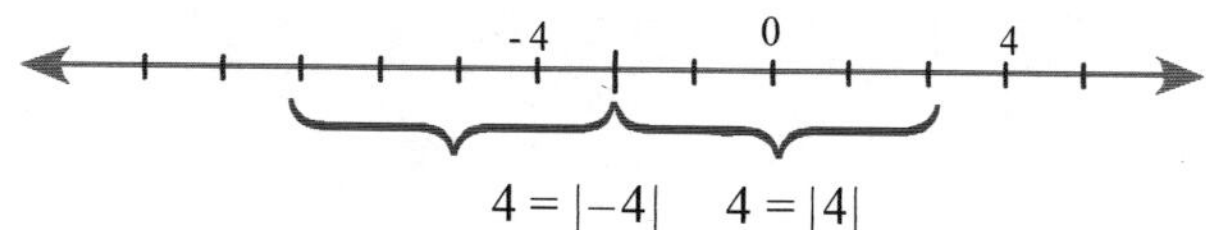

In other words, the distance d of a point x on a number line from the origin is $|x|$. This can be written in the function form as $d(x) = |x|$.

EXAMPLE 7 A shipping company charges \$5 per pound for packages weighing five pounds or less. The charge is \$ 3.50 per pound if a package weighs more than five pounds. Determine a function r that gives rate per pound if a package weighs x pounds.

Solution: It is clear that the rates are different for two different weight categories. This is the case of a function that has different rule for a different value of the input. If r denotes the rate per pound then

$r(x) = 5$ when the weight, x, is up to five pounds.

$r(x) = 3.5$ when the weight, x, is more than five pounds.

Thus, we write the two pieces of the rule as follows to describe the function $r: \boldsymbol{N} \to \boldsymbol{R}$:

$$r(x) = \begin{cases} 5 & \text{if } x \leq 5 \\ 3.5 & \text{if } x > 5 \end{cases}$$

Remark: A function that is described by more than one rule depending upon the value of the input is called a piecewise-defined function. A piecewise-defined function is written in the following format:

$$f(x) = \begin{cases} \textit{rule } 1, & \textit{condition } 1 \\ \textit{rule } 2, & \textit{condition } 2 \\ \ldots, & \ldots \\ \ldots, & \ldots \end{cases}$$

B. Some Elementary Functions

A function can have different forms (depending on the form of its 'expression' part). Most of these forms can be classified as:

(1) Power Functions	**(2) Polynomial Functions**	**(3) Rational Functions**
(4) Absolute Value Functions	**(5) Root or Radical Functions**	**(6) Piecewise Functions**

Later, we will add logarithmic, exponential, and circular (trigonometric) functions to the list.

1. Power Function

A power function is a function whose algebraic expression consists of the independent variable raised to a constant integral power. In general, a **power function** is in the form

$f(x) = cx^n$, where c is a constant and n is a non-negative integer.

EXAMPLES :

a. The area A of a circle of radius r is given by $\boldsymbol{A(r) = \pi r^2}$.

b. The volume V of a cube of side x is given by $\boldsymbol{V(x) = x^3}$.

2. Polynomial Function

A polynomial function is obtained by applying any combination of the operations like addition, subtraction, on constant multiples of power functions. In general, a polynomial function $f(x)$ is

$f(x) = a_n x^n + a_{n-1}x^{n-1} + \ldots + a_1 x + a_0$, where $a_n, a_{n-1}, \ldots, a_1, a_0$ are real numbers $\left(a_n \neq 0\right)$ and n is a non-negative integer.

In a special case when $n = 0$, $f(x)$ is a constant function.

EXAMPLES :

a. Since in the function $f(x) = 5x - 7$, the polynomial $5x - 7$ is of degree one, we call this a **linear function**.

b. The polynomial in $f(x) = 2x^2 - 7x + 10$ is of degree two, so we call this a **quadratic function**.

c. $f(x) = 7$ is an example of a constant function.

3. Rational Function

A **rational function** is a ratio of two polynomial functions. In general, a rational function looks like

$f(x) = \dfrac{\text{Polynomial 1}}{\text{Polynomial 2}}$, where Polynomial 2 $\neq 0$.

EXAMPLES :

a. The reciprocal function $f(x) = \dfrac{1}{x}$ b. $g(x) = \dfrac{3x-2}{x^2-16}$

- A rational function can be reduced to its lowest terms by dividing the Polynomial 1 and Polynomial 2 by the GCF of the numerator and the denominator.

EXAMPLE 8 Reduce the following to lowest terms.

a. $\dfrac{t^2-9}{t-3}$ b. $\dfrac{x^2-3x+2}{x^2+x-6}$

Solutions:

a. $\dfrac{t^2-9}{t-3}$:

- $t^2 - 9 = (t - 3)(t + 3)$ Factor the numerator.

  $t - 3 = 1(t - 3)$ Factor the denominator.

So, the greatest common factor is $t - 3$.

- $\dfrac{t^2-9}{t-3} = \dfrac{(t-3)(t+3)}{1\cdot(t-3)} = t+3$ Divide the numerator and the denominator by the GCF. Division by $t - 3$ is possible if $t \neq 3$, since division by 0 is not permitted.

b. $\dfrac{x^2-3x+2}{x^2+x-6}$

$= \dfrac{(x-2)(x-1)}{(x+3)(x-2)}$ Factor the numerator and denominator.

$= \dfrac{x-1}{x+3}$ Divide the numerator and denominator by $x - 2$. Division by $x - 2$ is possible if $x \neq 2$.

WARM-UP

8. Reduce the following in lowest terms.

a) $\dfrac{t^2-4}{t+2}$

b) $\dfrac{x^2+5x+6}{x^2+2x-3}$

Answers:

8. a) $t - 2$ for $t ^1 -2$

b) $\dfrac{x+2}{x-1}$ for $x ^1 -3$

4. Absolute Value Function

A function whose expression part contains an absolute value is called an **absolute value function**.

EXAMPLES

a. $f(x) = |x-2|$ b. $g(x) = 3-|x+1|$ c. $h(x) = x+|x^2+1|$

EXAMPLE 9 Write each of the absolute value functions as a piecewise function without the absolute value bar.

a. $f(x) = |x - 3|$ b. $k(x) = |(x + 2)(x - 6)|$

c. $k(x) = |x - 1| - |x - 5|$

Solutions:

a. The quantity $x - 3$ has different signs for different values of x.

If $x < 3$, $x - 3$ is negative.

WARM-UP

9. Write each of the absolute value functions as a piecewise function without the absolute value bar.

a) $f(x) = |x + 2|$

b) $g(x) = |(x + 1)(x - 2)|$

c) $|5 - 2x| + |x - 4|$

Answers:

9. a) $f(x) = \begin{cases} -x-2 & \text{for } x<-2 \\ x+2 & \text{for } x\geq -2 \end{cases}$

b) $g(x) = \begin{cases} (x+1)(x-2) & \text{for } x \leq -1 \text{ or } x \geq 2 \\ -(x+1)(x-2) & \text{for } -1<x<2 \end{cases}$

c) $h(x) = \begin{cases} 9-3x & \text{for } x\leq\frac{5}{2} \\ x-1 & \text{for } \frac{5}{2}<x<4 \\ 3x-9 & \text{for } x\geq 4 \end{cases}$

Therefore, $|x - 3| = -(x - 3)$ for $x < 3$.

Similarly, if $x \geq 3$, $x - 3$ is non-negative.

Therefore, $|x - 3| = x - 3$ for $x \geq 3$.

Hence, $|x - 3| = \begin{cases} -(x - 3) & \text{for } x<3 \\ x - 3 & \text{for } x\geq 3 \end{cases}$

b. $(x + 2)(x - 6)$ becomes zero for $x = -2$ for $x = 6$.

For $x \leq -2$: $x + 2 \leq 0$ and $x - 6 \leq 0$, so $(x + 2)(x - 6) \geq 0$

For $-2 < x < 6$: $x + 2 > 0$ and $x - 6 < 0$, so $(x + 2)(x - 6) \leq 0$

For $x \geq 6$: $x + 2 > 0$ and $x - 6 > 0$, so $(x + 2)(x - 6) \geq 0$

Therefore, $|(x+2)(x-6)| = \begin{cases} -(x+2)(x-6) & \text{for } -2<x<6 \\ (x+2)(x-6) & \text{for } x\leq -2 \text{ or } x\geq 6 \end{cases}$

c. Since $x - 1$ and $x - 5$ become zero at $x = 1$ and $x = 5$, respectively, we examine the sign of these quantities on both sides of 1 and 5.

For $-\infty < x \leq 1$: $x - 1$ and $x - 5$ are negative,

so $|x - 1| - |x - 5| = -(x - 1) - \{-(x - 5)\}$

$= -x + 1 + x - 5$

$= -4$

For $1 < x < 5$: $(x - 1)$ is positive and $x - 5$ is negative,

so $|x - 1| - |x - 5| = x - 1 - \{-(x - 5)\}$

$= x - 1 + x - 5$

$= 2x - 6$

For $5 \leq x$: $(x - 1)$ is non-negative and $x - 5$ is positive,

so $|x - 1| - |x - 5| = x - 1 - (x - 5)$

$= x - 1 - x + 5 = 4$

Therefore, $|x-1|-|x-5| = \begin{cases} -4 & \text{for } x\leq 1 \\ 2x-6 & \text{for } 1<x<5 \\ 4 & \text{for } x\geq 5 \end{cases}$

5. Root or Radical Function

A function whose expression part contains a root of the variable is called a root function.

EXAMPLES :

a. $f(x) = \sqrt{x}$, a square root function

b. $g(x) = \sqrt[3]{x}$, a cube root function

6. Piecewise Function

Sometimes we need more than one expression to describe the function completely. As in Example 6, the cost function was expressed in two parts (pieces). Such a function is called a piecewise function.

EXAMPLES :

a. **First-class mailing cost function** $f(x)$, where x is weight in ounces.

$$f(x) = \begin{cases} \$0.32 & if \;\; 0 < x \le 1 \\ \$0.55 & if \;\; 1 < x \le 2 \\ \$0.78 & if \;\; 2 < x \le 3 \end{cases}$$

b. $$f(x) = \begin{cases} x^2 & if \;\; -2 \le x < 2 \\ 4 & if \;\; x \ge 2 \end{cases}$$

c. $$g(x) = \begin{cases} x^2 & if \;\; -2 \le x < 2 \\ 6 & if \;\; x = 2 \\ x & if \;\; x > 2 \end{cases}$$

C. Evaluating a Function

Recall that a function f assigns to each element x of a non-empty set A **exactly one** element $f(x)$ of a set B. The element x of the set A is called an **input** and the corresponding element $f(x)$ of the set B is called the **output**.

This terminology makes more sense if we regard the **"function f "** as a **'machine f'** that changes x into $f(x)$.

x → INPUT → $f(x)$ → $f(x)$ ↓ OUTPUT

For example, the amount $A(x)$ of John's pledge is described in terms of the amount x of Don's pledge as

x → INPUT → $A(x)$ → $x + 5$ ↓ OUTPUT

If Don pledges \$2, then the amount of John's pledge is given as

2 → INPUT → $A(2)$ → $2 + 5 = 7$

Technically speaking, the output 7 is the value of the function $A(x)$ when $x = 2$. In short, we write it as $A(2)$.

We generalize the notation as follows:

> **Evaluating a Function**
>
> For a function f that assigns to each x in set A exactly one element in set B, the value of the function $f(x)$ when $x = k$, written as $f(k)$, is given by the element of set B that corresponds to $x = k$.
> Or $f(k)$ = value of the expression when $x = k$.

WARM-UP

10. (Function in numerical form).

Use the following table and find the values, if possible.

Time (t)	8	10	12	14	16	18
Temp(T)	65	67	70	69	67	63

a) $T(10)$ **b)** $T(15)$

c) $T(18)$

11. (Polynomial Function).

For $f(t) = 3t^2 + 2t + 7$, find

a) $f(0)$

b) $f(-1)$

c) $f(3)$

Answers:

10. a) 67 **b)** not possible **c)** 63

11. a) 7 **b)** 8 **c)** 40

EXAMPLE 10 (Function in numerical form)

Use the following table and find the values, if possible.

Time(t)	Noon	1	2	3	4	5
Temp(T)	70	73	74	74	76	78

a. $T(1)$ **b.** $T(3)$ **c.** $T(6)$

Solutions:

a. When $t = 1$, $T = 73$, so $T(1) = \mathbf{73}$

b. Similarly, $T(3) = \mathbf{74}$

c. Usually a numerical form of a function does not describe a function as completely as an algebraic (formula) form. Therefore, in the present form we cannot answer the question. However, if we can find the corresponding algebraic form, then we will be able to answer the question. For this, we have to wait until we learn how to change a numerical representation into a formula representation of a function.

EXAMPLE 11 (Polynomial Function)

For $f(x) = 5x^2 - 2x + 8$, find

a. $f(0)$ **b.** $f(1)$ **c.** $f(-2)$

d. $f(a + 1)$ **e.** $f(x + h)$

Solutions:

a. $\mathbf{f(0)}$ = the value of the expression for $x = 0$

Substitute the 'input' $x = 0$ in the expression

$= 5(0)^2 - 2(0) + 8 = 5(0) - 0 + 8 = 0 - 0 + 8 = \mathbf{8}$

Thus, the value of the function 'f' when $x = 0$ is 8.

b. $\mathbf{f(1)}$ = the value of the expression for $x = 1$

Substitute the 'input' $x = 1$ in the expression

$= 5(1)^2 - 2(1) + 8 = 5(1) - 2 + 8 = 5 - 2 + 8 = \mathbf{11}$

c. $\mathbf{f(-2)} = 5(-2)^2 - 2(-2) + 8$ The 'input' is -2

$= 5(4) + 4 + 8$

$= 20 + 4 + 8 = \mathbf{32}$

d. $\mathbf{f(a + 1)}$ = value of the expression for $x = a + 1$

Substitute the 'input' $x = a + 1$ in the expression

$= 5(a + 1)^2 - 2(a + 1) + 8$ The 'input' is $a + 1$

$= 5\left(a^2 + 2a + 1\right) - 2a - 2 + 8$

$= 5a^2 + 10a + 5 - 2a + 6$

$= \mathbf{5a^2 + 8a + 11}$

e. $f(x + h)$ = value of the expression for $x + h$

Substitute the input $x + h$ for x

$= 5(x+h)^2 - 2(x+h) + 8$

$= 5\left(x^2 + 2xh + h^2\right) - 2x - 2h + 8$

$= \mathbf{5x^2 + 10xh + 5h^2 - 2x - 2h + 8}$

EXAMPLE 12 (Polynomial Function)

If $f(x) = -3x^2 + 4x$, find

a. $f(-2)$ **b.** $f(x+h) - f(x)$

Solutions:

a. $f(-2)$: We replace x with -2 in the expression $f(x) = -3x^2 + 4x$.

$f(-2) = -3(-2)^2 + 4(-2) = -3(4) - 8 = -12 - 8 = \mathbf{-20}$

b. $f(x + h) - f(x)$

$= -3(x+h)^2 + 4(x+h) - \left(-3x^2 + 4x\right)$

$= -3\left(x^2 + 2xh + h^2\right) + 4x + 4h + 3x^2 - 4x$

$= \mathbf{-3x^2} - 6xh - 3h^2 + \mathbf{4x} + 4h + \mathbf{3x^2 - 4x}$

$= \mathbf{-6xh - 3h^2 + 4h}$

EXAMPLE 13 (Rational Function)

If $f(x) = \dfrac{x^2 - 5x + 6}{x + 4}$, find

a. $f(1)$ **b.** $f(3)$

Solutions:

a. $f(1)$: We replace x with 1,

$$f(1) = \frac{(1)^2 - 5(1) + 6}{1 + 4} = \frac{1 - 5 + 6}{5} = \mathbf{\frac{2}{5}}$$

b. $f(3)$: We replace x with 3,

$$f(3) = \frac{(3)^2 - 5(3) + 6}{3 + 4} = \frac{9 - 15 + 6}{7} = \frac{0}{7} = \mathbf{0}$$

d) $f(c - 1)$

e) $f(x - a)$

12. (Polynomial Function).

If $f(x) = 2x^2 - x$, find

a) $f(3)$ **b)** $f(x) - f(x - h)$

13. (Rational Function).

If $f(x) = \dfrac{x^2 + 3x - 1}{x + 1}$, find

a) $f(0)$ **b)** $f(2)$

Answers:

11. d) $3c^2 - 4c + 8$

e) $3x^2 + 2(1 - 3a)x + 3a^2 - 2a + 7$

12. a) 15 **b)** $4xh - 2h^2 - h$

13. a) -1 **b)** 3

WARM-UP

14. (Absolute Value Function)
If $f(x) = |3x - 1|$, find

a) $f(-2)$ **b)** $f(a - h)$

15. (Absolute Value Function)

If $f(x) = \frac{x-3}{|x-3|}$, find

a) $f(h + 3), h > 0$

b) $f(h + 3), h < 0$

16. (Piecewise Function)

If $f(x) = \begin{cases} \frac{x^2-1}{x-1} & \text{if } x \neq 1, \\ 2 & \text{if } x = 1 \end{cases}$, find

a) $f(1)$

b) $f(0)$

c) $f(2)$

Answers:

14. a) 7 **b)** $|3a - 3h - 1|$

15. a) 1 **b)** -1

16. a) 2 **b)** 1 **c)** 3

EXAMPLE 14 (Absolute Value Function)

If $f(x) = |2x - 3|$, find

a. $f(1)$ **b.** $f(a + h)$

Solutions:

a. $f(1)$: We replace x with 1 in the expression.

$$f(1) = |2(1) - 3| = |2 - 3| = |-1| = \mathbf{1}$$

b. $f(a + h)$: We replace x with $a + h$ in the expression.

$$f(a+h) = |2(a+h) - 3| = |\mathbf{2a} + \mathbf{2h} - 3|$$

EXAMPLE 15 (Absolute Value Function)

If $f(x) = \frac{|x-2|}{x-2}$, find

a. $f(2 + h), h > 0$ **b.** $f(2 + h), h < 0$

Solutions:

a. $f(2 + h)$: We replace x with $2 + h$ in the expression.

$$f(2+h) = \frac{|2+h-2|}{2+h-2} = \frac{|h|}{h} = \frac{\mathbf{h}}{\mathbf{h}}$$ $|h| = h$ when $h > 0$

$$= \mathbf{1}$$

b. $$f(2+h) = \frac{|h|}{h} = \frac{-\mathbf{h}}{\mathbf{h}}$$ $|h| = -h$ when $h < 0$

$$= \mathbf{-1}$$

EXAMPLE 16 (Piecewise Function)

If $f(x) = \begin{cases} \frac{x^2-4}{x-2} & \text{if} \quad x \neq 2 \\ 5 & \text{if} \quad x = 2 \end{cases}$,

find **a.** $f(2)$ **b.** $f(0)$ **c.** $f(-3)$

Solutions:

a. $f(2)$: 5 (given)

b. $f(0)$: We replace x with 0 in the expression $\frac{x^2-4}{x-2}$.

$$f(0) = \frac{\mathbf{0}^2 - 4}{\mathbf{0} - 2} = \frac{-4}{-2} = \mathbf{2}$$

To evaluate a piecewise function, first select the appropriate piece and then substitute the **input**.

c. $f(-3)$: We replace x with -3 in $\frac{x^2-4}{x-2}$.

$$f(-3) = \frac{(\mathbf{-3})^2 - 4}{(\mathbf{-3}) - 2} = \frac{9-4}{-5} = \frac{5}{-5} = -\mathbf{1}$$

EXAMPLE 17 (Rational Function)

If $f(x) = \dfrac{x^2 + x - 2}{x^2 + 2x - 3}$, find

a. $f(-3)$ **b.** $f(1)$

Solutions:

a. $f(-3)$**:** We replace x with -3.

$$f(-3) = \frac{(-3)^2 + (-3) - 2}{(-3)^2 + 2(-3) - 3} = \frac{9 - 3 - 2}{9 - 6 - 3} = \frac{\mathbf{4}}{\mathbf{0}} \quad \textbf{(undefined)}$$

b. $f(1)$**:** We replace x with 1

$$f(1) = \frac{(1)^2 + (1) - 2}{(1)^2 + 2(1) - 3} = \frac{1 + 1 - 2}{1 + 2 - 3} = \frac{\mathbf{0}}{\mathbf{0}} \quad \textbf{(indeterminate)}$$

EXAMPLE 18 (Root Function)

If $f(x) = \sqrt{x - 13}$, find **a.** $f(21)$ **b.** $f(5)$

Solutions:

a. $f(21)$**:** We replace x with 21 in the expression.

$$f(21) = \sqrt{21 - 13} = \sqrt{8} = \sqrt{2^2 \cdot 2} = \mathbf{2\sqrt{2}}$$

b. $f(5)$**:** We replace x with 5 in the expression.

$f(5) = \sqrt{5 - 13} = \sqrt{-8}$ does not exist in the set of real numbers because there is no real number whose square is –8.

WARM-UP

17. (Rational Function)

If $f(x) = \dfrac{x^3 + 1}{x^2 - 1}$, find

a) $f(1)$

b) $f(-1)$

178. (Root Function)

of $f(x) = \sqrt{2x - 7}$, find

a) $3f(5)$ **b)** $f(2)$

Answers:

176. a) Undefined **b)** indeterminate

18. a) $3\sqrt{3}$ **b)** does not exist in the set of real numbers.

EXERCISE 2.3

In exercises (1-12), write an expression that describes one of the variables in terms of the other.

1. The surface area (S) of a sphere in terms of its radius r.
2. The total cost (C) of purchasing printers at the rate of \$450 per unit in terms of the number (x) of printers bought.
3. The volume (V) of a sphere in terms of its radius r.
4. The revenue (R) of a company that sells an item for \$5.00 in terms of the items (x) sold by the company.
5. The area (A) of a square in terms of its side (a).
6. The surface area (S) of a cube in terms of its edge (x).
7. The volume (V) of a cube in terms of its edge (x).
8. The perimeter (p) of a square in terms of its side (a).
9. The perimeter (p) of an equilateral triangle in terms of its base (x).
10. The length (L) of a part of the number line segment between 2 and 5 in terms of n, the number of equal parts into which it is divided.
11. The temperature (C) in Celsius in terms of temperature (F) in Fahrenheit.
12. The cost (C) of x units if each unit is marked \$1.5, given the sales tax is 7.25%.

Which picture in exercises (13-20) represents a function? Explain.

13.

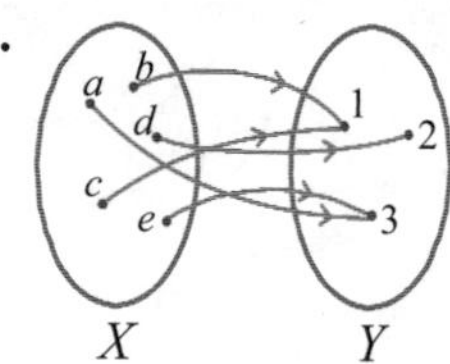

14.

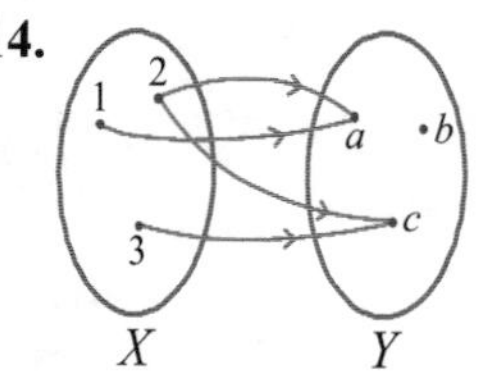

15.

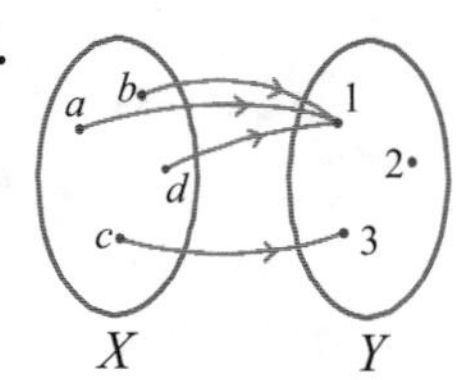

16.

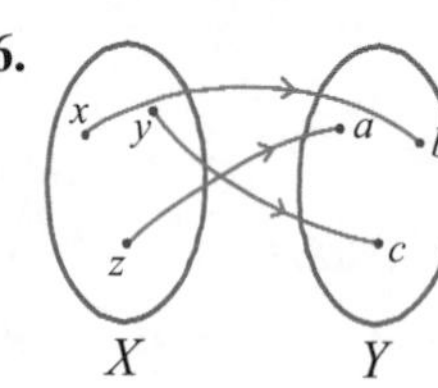

17.

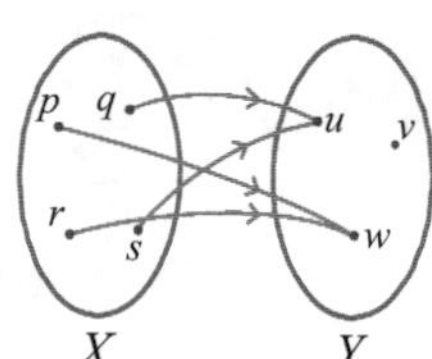

18.

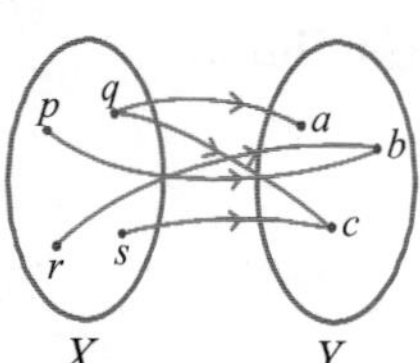

19.

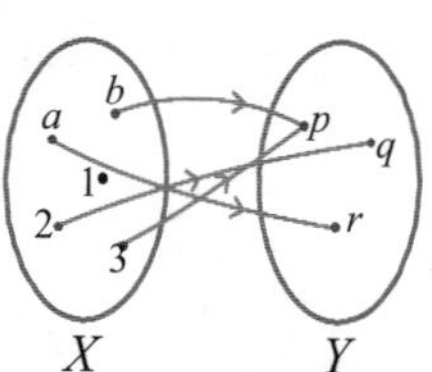

20.

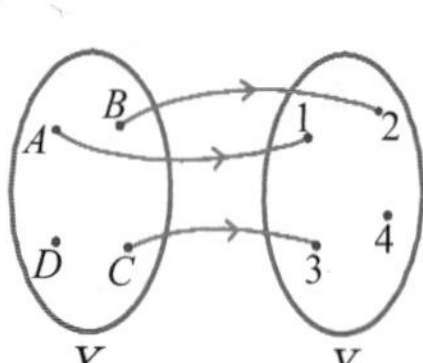

Which rule in exercises (21-30) defines a function?

21. From a set S to a set A, where S = set of all states of USA ;
A = the set of all letters in the English alphabet.

Rule: To each state associate the first letter in the name of the state.

22. From set A to set P, where
A = set of all letters in the English alphabet;
P = the set of the last names of letters in all the presidents of USA.

Rule: To each letter in the English alphabet associate the last name (of the president) that starts with the letter.

23. From the set N of counting numbers to the set N of counting numbers.

Rule: To every counting number associate the square of the number.

24. From the set S of squares of whole numbers to the set Z of all integers.

Rule: To each whole number s in S associate an integer whose square is s.

25. Let $X = \{a, b\}$, $Y = \{\phi, \{a\}, \{b\}, \{a, b\}\}$

Rule: To each element of X associate an element of Y that contains the chosen element of X.

26. Let $X = \{a\}$, $Y = \{\phi, \{a\}\}$

Rule: To each element of X associate an element of Y that contains the chosen element of X.

27. From the set N of natural numbers to the set N of natural numbers.

Rule: To every natural number associate its successor.

28. From the set N of natural numbers to the set N of natural numbers.

Rule: To every natural number associate its predecessor.

29. X = set of all students in your class.
Y = set of all real numbers between 0 and 1

Rule: To each student associate the number obtained by dividing his/her social security number by 10^9.

30. From N to the set $\{0, 1\}$, where N is the set of counting numbers.

Rule: If n is odd, associate 0.
If n is even, associate 1.

In exercise (31-40) determine if the given rule defines a function.

31. Input: x, output $= 1 - x^2$

32. Input x, output $= 2 - \sqrt{x}$

33. Input: x, output $= 1 \pm \sqrt{x}$

34. Input t, output $= \pm\sqrt{t-1}$

35. Input: x, output $= \left|\pm(x+2)\right|$

36. Input x, output $= \pm\left|x+2\right|$

37. Input: x, output $= \dfrac{3x-1}{x+2}$

38. Input t, output $= 2t^2 - 1$

39. Input s, output $= \dfrac{-3\pm\sqrt{s^2+4}}{2}$

40. Input x, output $= \dfrac{2-3x}{x^2+1}$

In exercises (41-48), determine if the table defines a function or not.

41.

x	0	1	2	3	4	5
$f(x)$	3	2	1	3	5	2

42.

x	1	2	3	2	5	6
$g(x)$	5	1	2	3	0	7

43.

x	3	10	5	8	7	2
$h(x)$	100	90	80	90	70	50

44.

x	2	4	6	8	6	10
$f(x)$	5	3	2	7	2	9

45.

x	-3	2	0	1	4	5
$s(x)$	-1	1	0	0	3	4

46.

t	1	2	3	3	4	5	6
$h(t)$	6	5	4	0	3	2	1

47.

x	2	3	4	5	6	7	8
$p(x)$	2	3	3	5	5	7	7

48.

x	1	2	1	3	4	5
$f(x)$	3	4	3	9	8	15

In exercises (49-67), classify the function as a power, polynomial, rational, absolute value, radical, or a piecewise function.

49. $f(x) = -\left|3x+2\right|$

50. $g(x) = 3 - 5x + x^3$

51. $h(x) = 5x^{-2}$

52. $f(x) = x(100 - 0.02\,x)$

53. $C(x) = \sqrt{(100-3x)}$

54. $R(x) = \sqrt[3]{100+2x-x^2}$

55. $C(x) = \sqrt{(100-3x)^2}$

56. $f(x) = \left|x-5\right|$

57. $f(x) = \begin{cases} x^2 & \text{if } x > 2 \\ -2x+1 & \text{if } x \le 2 \end{cases}$

58. $f(x) = 3x^{2/3}$

59. $g(x) = (x^3 - 3x)(x+1)^2$

60. $P(x)$ = postage charged by united States Postal Services on the regular shipping of a package that weighs x pounds.

61. $I(x)$ = Income tax that one pays to IRS (Internal Revenue Service) for a taxable income of x dollars.

62. $f(x) = \left|3x+1\right| - 4\left|2x+5\right|$.

63. The cost function $C(x)$ for a purchase of x items when a wholeseller sells an item for \$5 each for a purchase of less than 10 items, and \$4 each for a purchase of ten or more items.

64. $h(x) = \dfrac{\left|2x+7\right|}{x^2+1}$

65. $p(x) = \left|3x^2-7\right| + x^2 - 2x$

66. $f(x) = \dfrac{4x^2-1}{2-3x}$

67. $g(x) = \dfrac{2x-3}{5x+9}$

In exercises (68-74), write the polynomial function in factored form. Review factoring techniques before you start.

68. $f(x) = 9 - 18x$

69. $g(x) = 12x - 4$

70. $g(x) = 25x^2 - 9$

71. $f(x) = 5x^2 - 20$

72. $f(x) = -5x^2 + 7x - 2$

73. $h(x) = 3x^2 - 5x + 2$

74. $H(x) = 54x^3 - 2$

In exercises (75-82), write the absolute value function as a piecewise function without absolute value bars.

75. $f(x) = |2+x^2|$ **76.** $g(x) = |(x+1)^4|$ **77.** $h(x) = |x-5|$

78. $f(x) = |2x-7|$ **79.** $H(x) = |x-3| + |x-4|$ **80.** $f(x) = |2x-1| - |x+2|$

81. $f(x) = |\sqrt{x+9}|$ **82.** $p(x) = |\sqrt{2x-5}|$

In exercises (83-87), write the rational function in reduced form.

83. $f(x) = \dfrac{x^2-4}{x^2-x-2}$ **84.** $s(x) = \dfrac{x^3-1}{x^2+x+1}$ **85.** $h(x) = \dfrac{x^2-5x}{x^3+5x^2+6x}$

86. $g(x) = \dfrac{x^2-2x+1}{x^2-1}$ **87.** $f(x) = \dfrac{x^2-1}{x^3-1}$

In exercises (88-92), write the radical function without the radical form.

88. $f(x) = \sqrt[3]{(x+1)^4}$ **89.** $g(x) = \dfrac{3x}{\sqrt{x^2(x+1)}}$ **90.** $h(x) = \sqrt{x^2(x+2)^2}$

91. $b(x) = \left(\sqrt[5]{(x+3)}\right)^2$ **92.** $p(x) = \sqrt[4]{(2x-3)^2}$

In exercises 93-102, find **a.** $f(0)$ **b.** $f(3)$ **c.** $f(-2)$ **d.** $f(a+1)$

93. $f(x) = 7x + 8$ **94.** $f(x) = 3x - 5$ **95.** $f(x) = 10$ **96.** $f(x) = -3$

97. $f(x) = 7 - 2x^2$ **98.** $f(x) = -3x^2 + 1$ **99.** $f(x) = 7x^2 + 3x$ **100.** $f(x) = 5x^2 - 3x + 1$

101. $f(x) = \sqrt{15-x}$ **102.** $f(x) = \sqrt{2x+9}$

In exercises 103-112, find **a.** $f(0)$ **b.** $f(1)$ **c.** $f(3)$ **d.** $f(2)$

103. $f(x) = \dfrac{5}{x-2}$ **104.** $f(x) = \dfrac{4}{x+3}$ **105.** $f(x) = \dfrac{x}{x+1}$ **106.** $f(x) = \dfrac{x+2}{x-2}$

107. $f(x) = \dfrac{2x-1}{x-5}$ **108.** $f(x) = \dfrac{2x+1}{4x+5}$ **109.** $f(x) = \dfrac{x-3}{x^2-25}$ **110.** $f(x) = \dfrac{x-1}{x^2+1}$

111. $f(x) = \dfrac{x-2}{x^2-4}$ **112.** $f(x) = \dfrac{x^2}{2x^2+3}$

In exercises 113-120, find **a.** $f(3)$ **b.** $f(5)$ **c.** $f(2)$ **d.** $f(3+h);\ h > 0$

113. $f(x) = |x| + 2$ **114.** $f(x) = |x| - 4$ **115.** $f(x) = |x-1|$ **116.** $f(x) = |3x-2|$

117. $f(x) = \dfrac{|x|}{x}$ **118.** $f(x) = \dfrac{|x-2|}{x-2}$ **119.** $f(x) = \dfrac{x-3}{|x-3|}$ **120.** $f(x) = \dfrac{3x-2}{|x+1|-1}$

In exercises 121-128, find **a.** $f(-1)$ **b.** $f(0)$ **c.** $f(5)$ **d.** $f(2+h)\ ;\ h > 0$

121. $f(x) = \begin{cases} x+2, & x < 1 \\ 2-x, & x \geq 1 \end{cases}$ **122.** $f(x) = \begin{cases} \dfrac{2x-1}{x+2}, & x > 3 \\ 3, & x \leq 3 \end{cases}$ **123.** $f(x) = \begin{cases} 2x-1, & x < 0 \\ 5, & x = 0 \\ x^2, & x > 0 \end{cases}$

124. $f(x)=\begin{cases} x^2, & x<1 \\ 3x-2, & x\ge 1 \end{cases}$

125. $f(x)=\begin{cases} \dfrac{1}{x}, & x<0 \\ x^2, & x\ge 0 \end{cases}$

126. $f(x)=\begin{cases} -5, & x\le 0 \\ 6, & 0<x<4 \\ 1/2, & x\ge 4 \end{cases}$

127. $f(x)=\begin{cases} -2, & x<2 \\ 3, & x=2 \\ 2, & x>2 \end{cases}$

128. $f(x)=\begin{cases} |3x-5|+2, & x\le 0 \\ \dfrac{2}{x+1}, & x>0 \end{cases}$

129. The following is the 1994 United State income tax rate schedule for a single taxpayer. It is a 5-part piecewise function:
If taxable income (x) is

Over	But not over	Tax owed is	Of the amount over
\$0	\$22,750	15%	\$0
22,750	55,100	\$3,412.50 + 28%	22,750
55,100	115,000	12,470.50 + 31%	55,100
115,000	250,000	31,039.50 + 36%	115,000
250,000	...	79,639.50 + 39.6%	250,000

Find the federal income tax for a single taxpayer whose taxable income is
(a) \$15,000 **(b)** \$50,000 **(c)** \$115,000 **(d)** \$300,000

130. The cost (C), Revenue (R), and Profit (P) on x items are as follows:
$C(x) = 4000 + 1.5x$, $R(x) = 5x$, and $P(x) = R(x) - C(x) = 3.5x - 4000$
What will be the cost, revenue, and profit if the company produces 20,000 items?

131. The cost (C), Revenue (R), and Profit (P) on x items are as follows:
$C(x) = 2500 + 2.5x$, $R(x) = 8x$, and $P(x) = R(x) - C(x) = 5.5x - 2500$
What will be the cost, revenue, and profit if the company produces 15,000 items?

132. A wholesaler can sell each VCR for $150-\dfrac{x}{50}$, if x units are sold. Write an expression for the company's revenue function. Evaluate the revenue and price per VCR if the wholesaler sells 500 such VCR's.

133. A wholesaler can sell each DVD for $300-\dfrac{x}{40}$, if x units are sold. Write an expression for the company's revenue function. Evaluate the revenue and sale price per DVD if the wholesaler sells 400 such DVD's.

134. The time T taken to harvest x tons of apples is given by $T(x)=\dfrac{x+1}{50-x}$ days ($x < 50$). Show that the time taken to harvest 10 tons of apples in the beginning of the job is less than the time taken in harvesting 10 tons near the end of the job. (Economists refer to this as the Law of Diminishing Returns.)

135. If we plant "x more than 24" trees per acre, then the yield per tree is $600 - 12x$. Write the total yield (Y) function. Find the total yield (Y) if we plant 29 trees per acre.

136. If we plant "x more than 30" trees per acre, then the yield per tree is $800 - 15x$. Write the total yield (Y) function. Find the total yield (Y) if we plant 35 trees per acre.

137. The price (P) per bushel of corn after x number of weeks of the harvest is given by
$$P(x) = 2 + 0.01x - 0.02x^2$$
Should the farmer sell this crop after 2 weeks or 3 weeks?

138. The price (P) per bushel of corn after x number of weeks of the harvest is given by
$$P(x) = 4 + 0.02x - 0.01x^2$$
Should the farmer sell the crop after 3 weeks or 4 weeks.

A. LOGICAL REASONING: A FOUNDATION FOR GEOMETRIC PROOFS

Objectives

Upon completion of this section you will study:

A. Logical Reasoning: A foundation for geometric proofs;

B. Logical Statements; and

C. Valid Vs. Invalid Arguments.

DISCUSSION:

Suppose one day, in a park, someone notices a baby bird on the ground next to a tree. How did the bird get there? One might conclude that it must have fallen from its nest. On what basis is this conclusion formed: on past similar observations or from an established law of nature? Was it just a guess? If it were, then we would be using our intution, which is based on feeling and uses no formal reasoning.

We routinely make judgements and draw conclusions from facts and events that we encounter daily.

- **Conjecture:**

  A conclusion reached by casual observation or incomplete analysis is called a **conjecture**. Conjectures provide the **starting point** for a more thorough, rigorous investigation.

- **Counterexample:**

  While it may sometimes be difficult to prove that a conjecture is true, it is sufficient to find just one example that fails to work in order to prove that a conjecture is false. This is called a **counterexample**. For instance, look at the following observations:

  3 is an odd number and is prime,
  5 is an odd number and is prime,
  7 is an odd number and is prime.

  It could be conjectured that "*All* odd numbers are prime".

  But, the number 9 is an odd number and is *not* prime. The reasoning (observations) leading to the conjecture that "all odd numbers are prime" does not form a valid conclusion. The number 9 is a *counterexample* to this conjecture.

➔ Inductive and Deductive Reasoning

DISCUSSION:

We have just seen that one counter-example is sufficient to prove that a conjecture is false. To prove that a conjecture is *true* we need a proof. A proof is a *demonstration* that the conjecture is true. We normally communicate an *informal* proof with 'reasoning' or 'argument' that combines everyday English with symbols and terms/words that appear in the statement to be proved. On the other hand, a *formal* proof in Geometry requires the reasoning to be put forward in a specific format which we will learn in this book.

We now introduce the **two types of reasoning** that are used to form **valid** conclusions.

1. **Inductive Reasoning: Inductive reasoning is the process that involves examining several examples, observing a pattern, and then assuming that the pattern will always hold.**

The reasoning involved in making the conjecture that "all odd numbers are prime" is an example of *inductive reasoning*. *Inductive reasoning moves from the specific to the general.*

Although inductive reasoning does not produce a valid proof, it often suggests statements (conjectures) that *can* be proved (or contradicted by a counter-example).

2. **Deductive Reasoning: Deductive reasoning is the process of drawing a conclusion from a sequence of accepted facts.**

Deductive reasoning may be considered to be *opposite* of inductive reasoning. Following is an example of deductive reasoning:

> The sum of any two odd numbers is an even number.
>
> 17 and 11 are both odd numbers.
>
> The sum of 17 and 11 is 28 (17 + 11 = 28.)

We may conclude that '28 is an even number'.

Deductive reasoning moves from general to specific.

We will continue our discussion with the development of Deductive Reasoning.

Before we demonstrate just how Deductive Reasoning is used we need to define a few more terms and develop some basic ideas. We will do this in Section 1.2.

B. Logical Statements

➔ **To understand the meaning of the term Statement (Proposition) in logic**

DISCUSSION:

The four basic types of sentences that occur in ordinary language may be categorized as: assertions, commands, questions, and exclamations. **Logic** is based upon the first type of sentence. An assertion that can be meaningfully classified as true or false, is called a *statement* or *proposition*. The words 'statement' and 'proposition' are used as synonyms in Logic.

We can now give formal definition of these terms.

- **Statement:** A **statement** or **proposition** is a assertion that is either true or false.

Example 1 Tiger Woods won the 1997 Masters by 12 strokes.

This is a *statement* or *proposition* that is true. It is an historical fact.

Example 2 The month of June has 31 days.

This is a *statement* or *proposition* that is false.

Example 3 5 + 2 = 7.

This is a mathematical *statement* or *proposition* that is true.

Remark: For some statements, it may not be known whether they are true or false. For instance consider the statement. 'There are infinitely many twin primes.'

This **is** a **statement** or **proposition**. It makes an assertion that is either true or false. However, mathematicians do not know at the present time, whether it is true or false.

- **Opinion:**

Sometimes, because of unclear meaning or imprecise language, it is not always possible to classify an assertion as either true or false. As a result, this assertion is not considered to be a *statement* or *proposition*, but is rather interpreted to be an "opinion". As an illustration, take the following example:

Example Mozart composed wonderful music.

This is **not** a **statement** or **proposition.** Even though many people consider this assertion to be true, it is an **opinion** since there is no definitive agreement on what makes music wonderful.

➜ Logical Connectives and their symbols; Compound statements.

- **Logical Connectives:**

Words such as "**and**", "**or**", "**not**", "**if ... then**" which can be used to combine statements are called **Logical Connectives**.

Connectives	*Symbol*
and	$\wedge$
or	$\vee$
not	$\sim$
if ... then	$\rightarrow$

- **Negation:**

Let P be a statement. The ***negation*** of the statement is "**not P**" and is stated symbolically as $\sim$ **P**.

Example : The school is open.

The **negation** $\sim$ P is: The school is **not** open.

Note that a statement and its negation cannot both be true at the same time. Neither can they both be false at the same time. If the statement "The school is open" is true, then the statement "The school is not open" must be false (and vice versa). This is known as **"The Law of the Excluded Middle"**.

- **Compound Statement:** A ***compound statement*** is formed by combining two or more statements with **logical connectives**.

In order to continue our discussion we will denote 'Statements' by the symbols P and Q. Following are general forms of some important compound statements:

(i) **Conjunction:** Let P, Q be statements. The compound statement "P **and** Q" is called a **conjunction**, stated symbolically as **P** $\wedge$ **Q**.

Example : P: The algebra class is closed.

Q: Parking fees have increased this semester.

The **conjunction** $P \wedge Q$ is: The algebra class is closed ***and*** the parking fees have increased this semester.

(ii) Disjunction: Let P, Q be statements. The compound statement "P **or** Q" is called a **disjunction**, stated symbolically as $\mathbf{P \vee Q}$.

Example : P : The triangle is a right triangle.

Q: The triangle is an obtuse triangle.

The **disjunction** $P \vee Q$ is: The triangle is a right triangle **or** it is obtuse.

It is acceptable to use common rules of grammar to simplify a statement.

➜ Implications (Conditional Statements) and their Symbolic Forms.

- **Implications, Hypothesis, and conclusion:**

  Let P, Q be statements. The compound attement. **If** "P **then** Q" is called an ***implication*** or ***conditional statement***. Stated symbolically $P \to Q$, it is also read "P implies Q.

  In the implication $P \to Q$, P is called the ***hypothesis*** while Q is called the ***conclusion***. For instance, consider the following conditional statement

  "**If** Wilber has a 3.78 GPA, **then** he is on the dean's list".

  In this statement,

  Hypothesis: Wilber has a 3.78 GPA.

  Conclusion: He is on the dean's list.

  If we let

  P represent : Wilber has a 3.78 GPA

  and Q represent : He is an the dean's list.

  then the given statement, can be restated as $\mathbf{P \to Q}$.

- **Rewriting Statements as implication:** A statement can contain a hypothesis and conclusion even though it is not stated in standard form. We simply identify the hypothesis and conclusion from the given statement and rewrite it in the standard "**if** P **then** Q" form. For clarity, study the following two examples carefully:

Example 1 *Statement:* Joe will sell his stock immediately **if** the stock price falls.

P → **Q**

↓ ↓ ↓

Implication: **If** the stock price falls, **then** Joe will sell his stock immediately.

Hypothesis: The stock price falls.

Conclusion: Joe will sell his stock immediately.

Remember, each part of an implication is itself a complete statement.

Example 2   *Statement:*   A psychiatrist is a physician.

P → Q
↓ ↓ ↓

Implication: **If** a person is a psychiatrist **then** that person is a physician.
Hypothesis: A person is a psychiatrist
Conclusion: The person is a physician.

➡ Converse, Inverse, Contrapositive, and Bi-conditional

The implication, "If a baby is hungry then it will cry", states that a hungry baby will cry. But, what about the reverse implication, "if a baby is crying then is it hungry"? Not necessarily. Neither is "If a baby is not hungry, then it will not cry." necessary true.

- **Converse:** When the **hypothesis** and **conclusion** of an implication are switched, the result is called the ***converse***. For the implication $P \rightarrow Q$, the ***converse*** is $Q \rightarrow P$.

Example *Implication:* **If** there are seats available, **then** I may purchase tickets.
Converse: **If** I purchase tickets, **then** there are seats available.

- **Inverse:** When both the hypothesis and conclusion are negated, the result is called the ***inverse***. For the implication $P \rightarrow Q$, the ***inverse*** is $\sim P \rightarrow \sim Q$.

Example *Implication:* **If** an animal is a dolphin, **then** it is a mammal.
Inverse: **If** an animal is *not* a dolphin, **then** it is *not* a mammal.

- **Contrapositive:** If we consider "the converse of the inverse" or "the inverse of the converse" for the implication $P \rightarrow Q$ then the result is called the ***contrapositive***, which is $\sim Q \rightarrow \sim P$.

Example *Implication:* **If** a number is an even number **then** it is divisible by two.
Contrapositive: **If** a number is not divisible by two, **then** it is not an even number.

- **Bi – Conditional:**

A statement and its contrapositive are **logically equivalent.** That is, they have the same truth value. Its converse and inverse are also **logically equivalent.**

When the statement and its converse are both true, then it is possible to include them both as one compound statement. This statement is said to be bi-conditional.

Let P, Q be statements. The compound statement "P if and only if Q" is said to be **bi-conditional**. It is abbreviated by "**P iff Q**" and is denoted symbolically $P \leftrightarrow Q$. It should be noted that the bi-conditional $P \leftrightarrow Q$ is equivalent to the conjunction $(P \rightarrow Q) \wedge (Q \rightarrow P)$.

For example, consider the bi-conditional

"Lisa is happy **iff and only if** she is studying geometry."

That is:

P : Lisa is happy.

and Q : She is studying geometry.

Then the above bi-conditional, in symbols, is $P \leftrightarrow Q$, and the two implications are :

" If Lisa is happy, then she is studying geometry" $(P \rightarrow Q)$

" If she is studying geometry, then Lisa is happy," $(Q \rightarrow P)$.

We conclude the discussion by the following paragraph:

The implication "If Lisa is happy then she is studying geometry" $(P \rightarrow Q)$ means that a ***necessary condition*** for Lisa to be happy is that she is studying geometry. Further, "if she is studying geometry then Lisa is happy" $(Q \rightarrow P)$ means that a ***sufficient condition*** for Lisa to be happy is that she is studying geometry. Therefore the bi-conditional $P \leftrightarrow Q$ means that a **necessary and sufficient** condition for Lisa to be happy is that she is studying geometry.

C. VALID VS. INVALID ARGUMENTS

➔ Valid Arguments

Recall that a **conjecture** is a conclusion arrived at without formal proof. The steps involved in the reasoning process, used to establish the truth (or falsehood) of a conjecture, must be in correct order for any conclusion to be accepted. These steps constitute a **valid** argument.

- A ***valid argument*** is a sequence of statements called ***premises*** followed by a statement called a ***conclusion*** in which the truths of the premises guarantee the truth of the conclusion.

Four **valid** arguments, commonly used by mathematicians to demonstrate that a conclusion is valid, are given below. Each argument is first illustrated by means of an example, and then stated in symbols.

Argument 1: The **Law of detachment:**

Premise: If today is Monday then I will go to work.

Premise : Today is Monday.

Conclusion: I will go to work.

This specifies the original implication and is therefore true.

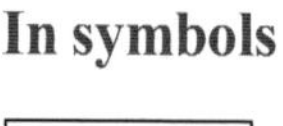

In symbols

$P \rightarrow Q$ P
Q

Argument 2: The **Law of Syllogism:**

Premise: If Masami lives in Tokyo then Masami lives in Japan.

Premise: If Masami lives in Japan then Masami lives in Asia.

Conclusion: If Masami lives in Tokyo then Masami lives in Asia.

In symbols

$P \rightarrow Q$ $Q \rightarrow R$
$P \rightarrow R$

Note: The law of Syllogism is an extension of the transitive property that you know from Algebra.

Argument 3: The **Law of Negative Inference:**

Premise:	If x is even then x is divisible by 2.
Premise:	x in not divisible by 2.
Conclusion:	x is not even.

In symbols

$P \to Q$
$\sim Q$
$\therefore \sim P$

Remember: This is known as the contrapositive and is true whenever the original implication is true.

Argument 4: The **Law of Disjunctive Syllogism:**

Premise:	The figure is a square or the figure is a circle.
Premise:	The figure is not a circle.
Conclusion:	The figure is a square.

In symbols

$P \vee Q$
$\sim Q$
$\therefore P$

The validity of each of these arguments can be shown using truth tables. It is important to note that **Deductive Reasoning**, mentioned earlier and used in the proofs in the upcoming chapters, contain these arguments.

➜ Invalid Arguments (Fallacies)

- An invalid argument is called a **fallacy**.

A **fallacy** results from errors in reasoning. Two common fallacies are illustrated below with their general symbolic form.

1. The fallacy of the Converse

Premises :	If today is Monday then I will go to work today.
Premises :	I will go to work today.
Conclusion:	Today is Monday.

In symbols

$P \to Q$
Q
P

2. The fallacy of the Inverse

Premises :	If x is a multiple of 6 then x is divisible by 2.
Premises :	x is not multiple of 6.
Conclusion:	x is not divisible by 2.

In symbols

$P \to Q$
$\sim P$
$\sim Q$

Remember: Neither the inverse nor the converse are logically equivalent to the original implication.

Exercise 2.4

A. **Fill in the Blank**

1. A conclusion reached by casual observation or incomplete analysis is called a ___________ .
2. Any conjecture may be ______ or ______ .
3. The two types of reasoning that are used to form valid conclusions are ___________ and ___________ .
4. The process in which a general principle is reached from a limited number of observations or examples is ___________ .
5. The process in which a specific example is determined to be a special case of a general rule or principle is ________________ .

Determine if the type of reasoning is (A) inductive, (B) deductive, or (C) neither.

6. Every fish has gills. An eel is a fish. *Therefore an eel has gills.*
7. Aspirin relieves headache pain. You have a painful headache. *Taking aspirin will relieve your headache pain.*
8. On the first day of class you notice that your instructor is very tall. *You conclude that it will be a strictly run class.*
9. Two years ago it rained on your birthday and last year it did not rain on your birthday. Since it rained on your birthday this year, *you conclude that next year it will not rain on your birthday.*
10. Curtis and Sally's first three children were girls. They are expecting a new baby. *Curtis thinks it will be a girl.*
11. $x < y$ and $y < z$. *Therefore* $x < z$.
12. Terry is late for the first 4 rehearsals. *You expect Terry to be late for the next rehearsal.*
13. Joey tells you that he is a liberal. *Therefore Joey must not eat chicken.*
14. The Shepherds are a very religious couple. *Therefore they are not educated.*
15. A sequence of numbers begins: 1, 3, 6, 10, 15, 21, 28,... *You conclude that the next number is* 36.
16. Halley's comet orbits the solar system once every 75 years. The last time it passed by the earth was in 1986. *It will be seen passing by the earth again in* 2061.
17. The Queen Mary II is a passenger ship that weight 150,000 tons. A ton is 2000 pounds. *Therefore the Queen Mary II weights* 300,000,000 pounds.
18. John's dog is a pretty dog. *Therefore it will not bite you.*
19. Whenever Sam works on his car, his hands get dirty. This morning Sam was working on his car. *You conclude that his hands became dirty.*

Multiple Choice: Choose the best answer

20. A conclusion reached by casual observation or incomplete analysis is called
    (a) a conjecture **(b)** inductive reasoning **(c)** deductive reasoning **(d)** none
21. Any conjecture may be... **1.** True **2.** False
    (a) 1 **(b)** 2 **(c)** 1 & 2 **(d)** 1 or 2
22. The type(s) of reasoning that are used to form valid conclusions are...
    1. inductive reasoning **2.** deductive reasoning **3.** intuition
    (a) 1 and 2 **(b)** 1 **(c)** 2 **(d)** 1 and 3 **(e)** 1, 2 and 3
23. The process in which a general principle is reached from a limited number of observations or examples is.
    (a) Inductive reasoning **(b)** Deductive reasoning **(c)** neither

24. The process in which a specific example is determined to be a special case of a general rule or principle is
 (a) Inductive reasoning (b) Deductive reasoning (c) neither

B. Fill in the blanks:

25. Of the four types of sentences used in ordinary languages logic is based upon the _________ .

26. An assertion that is either true or false is called a(an) ____________________ .

27. Sometimes, because of unclear meaning or imprecise language, an assertion is interpreted to be an _________ .

28. Words such as "and", "or", "not", "if...then" which can be used to combine statements are called __________ .

29. A __________ is formed by combining two or more statements with logical connectives.

30. The compound statement "P and Q" is called a __________ .

31. The compound statement "P or Q" is called a __________ .

32. The *negation* of a statement "P", is _________ .

33. A statement and its negation cannot both be true (or false) at the same time. This is known as ____________________ .

34. The compound statement "If P then Q" is called an ____________________ .

35. In the implication P → Q, P is called the _________ while Q is called the __________ .

36. When the hypothesis and conclusion of an implication are switched, the result is called the _________ .

37. When both the hypothesis and conclusion are negated, the result is called the _________ .

38. When we consider "the converse of the inverse" or "the inverse of the converse" the result is called the _________ .

39. When an impleation and its converse have the same truth values, they can be represented as a __________ statement.

Classify each of the following as a (an):

(a) statement (b) impl ication (c) conjunction (d) disjunction (e) not a statement

40. Vicky is at the convention and Jimmy is practicing the violin.

41. $x < 3$ or $x > 3$.

42. Is geometry a difficult subject?

43. Tiger will play golf if it does not rain.

44. A real number is rational or it is irrational.

45. The empty set.

46. Two is a prime number.

47. Today I will go to school and later I will go shopping.

48. If x and y are both positive, then the solution is in the first quadrant.

49. This triangle is acute or it is obtuse.

50. Positive integers greater.

51. No suspect is innocent.

52. We are wasting energy if all the lights are on.

53. $y > -2$ and $y < 4$.

54. Is trigonometry more difficult than geometry?

55. Each successive term in the Fibonacci sequence is obtained by summing the previous two terms.

56. If pigs fly then the sun rises in the west.

57. Today is Monday and today is Wednesday.

58. Absolute value of negative 5.

59. Truth or consequences.

True or False:

60. A sentence is called an *assertion.*

61. An assertion that is either true or false is called a *statement or proposition.*

62. Sometimes, because of unclear meaning or imprecise language, an assertion is interpreted to be an "*opinion*".

63. Words such as "and", "or", "not", "if...then" which can be used to combine statements are called *logical connectives.*

64. A *conjunction* is formed by combining two or more statements with logical connectives or by negating a statement.

65. The compound statement "P **and** Q" is called a *conjunction.*

66. The compound statement "P **or** Q" is called a *conjunction.*

Multiple Choice : Choose the best answer

67. When a statement "P" is given, "not P" is the

 (a) logical connective **(b)** compound statement **(c)** conjunction **(d)** disjunction **(e)** negation

68. A statement and its negation cannot both be true (or false) at the same time. This is known as

 (a) a conditional statement **(b)** "The Law of the Excluded Middle" **(c)** a bi-conditional statement **(d)** none

69. The compound statement "If P then Q" is called

 (a) a conditional statement **(b)** "The Law of the Excluded Middle" **(c)** a bi-conditional statement **(d)** none

70. In the implication $P \to Q$, P is called the

 (a) hypothesis **(b)** conclusion **(c)** converse **(d)** inverse **(e)** contrapositive

71. In the implication $P \to Q$, Q is called the

 (a) hypothesis **(b)** conclusion **(c)** converse **(d)** inverse **(e)** contrapositive

72. When a hypothesis and conclusion of an implication are switched, the result is called the

 (a) hypothesis **(b)** conclusion **(c)** converse **(d)** inverse **(e)** contrapositive

73. When both the hypothesis and conclusion are negated, the result is called the

 (a) hypothesis **(b)** conclusion **(c)** converse **(d)** inverse **(e)** contrapositive

74. When we consider "the converse of the inverse" or "the inverse of the converse" the result is called the

 (a) hypothesis **(b)** conclusion **(c)** converse **(d)** inverse **(e)** contrapositive

75. When a conditional statement and its converse have the same truth value they can be replaced with

 (a) a conditional statement **(b)** "The Law of the Excluded Middle" **(c)** a bi-conditional statement **(d)** none

Give the hypothesis and conclusion.

76. If the song is a hit then I will buy it.

77. Dogs wag their tails if they are happy.

78. If Helan is motivated then she will study.

79. If Charles is a vegan then he does not eat sushi

80. A triangle is a convex figure.

81. All students take geometry.

82. Danny says, "Bless you" if he hears anyone sneeze.

83. The set of prime numbers is an infinite set.

In each exercise, an implication is given. Determine for each statement that follows whether it is:

(a) the converse **(b)** the inverse **(c)** the contrapositive **(d)** none of the above

84. If two lines are perpendicular, then they intersect
If 2 lines intersect, then they are perpendicular.
If 2 lines are parallel, then they do not intersect.
If 2 lines are not perpendicular, then they do not intersect.

85. If the discriminant is negative then the solutions are complex
If the solutions are not complex, then the discriminant is not negative
If the discriminant is positive, then the solutions are not complex
If the discriminant is not negative, then the solutions are not complex

86. If Brandon lied, then he is guilty
If he is not guilty, then Brandon did not lie.
If he is guilty, then Brandon lied.
If Brandon did not lie, then he is guilty.

C. Fill in the blank:

87. A sequence of statements called *premises* followed by a statement called a *conclusion* in which the truth of the premises guarantees the truth of the conclusion is a ____________ .

88. Every Saturday I work in the yard. Today is Saturday. Therefore, I work in the yard. This is an example of The ____________ .

89. If Remi lives in Toledo then Remi lives in Ohio. If Remi lives in Ohio then Remi lives in the U.S.A. Remi lives in Toledo, then Remi lives in the U.S.A. This is an example of the ____________ .

90. If x is a multiple of 4, then x is divisible by 4. x is not divisible by 4, therefore, x is not a multiple of 4. This is an example of ____________ .

91. Jan is a man or Jan is a woman. Jan is not a woman. Therefore Jan is a men. This is an example of The ____________ .

92. An invalid argument is called a _______ .

93. If today is Friday then i will meet with you. I am meeting with you. Therefore today is Friday. This is an example of The ____________ .

94. If it is raining, then it is cloudy. It is not raining. Therefore it is not cloudy. This is an example of The ____________ .

True or False:

95. A sequence of statements called **premises** followed by a statement called a **conclusion** is a valid argument.

96. Every Saturday I work in the yard. Today is Saturday. Therefore, I work in the yard. This is an example of the Law of Detachment.

97. If Remi lives in Toledo then Remi lives in Ohio. If Remi lives in Ohio then Remi lives in the U.S.A. Remi lives in Toledo, then Remi lives in the U.S.A. This is an example of the Law of Symmetry.

98. If x is a multiple of 4, then x is divisible by 4. <u>x is not divisible by 4</u>. Therefore, x is not a multiple of 4. This is an example of The Law of Negative Inference.

99. Jan is a man or Jan is a woman. Jan is not a woman. Therefore Jan is a man. This is a example of The Law of Injunctive Syllogism.

100. An invalid statement is called a fallacy.

101. If today is Friday then I will meet with you. I am meeting with you. Therefore today is Friday. This is an example of The Fallacy of the Converse.

102. If it is raining, then it is cloudy. It is not raining. Therefore it is not cloudy. This is an example of The Fallacy of the Converse.

Multiple Choice: Pick the best answer

103. A sequence of statements called **premises** followed by a statement called a ***conclusion*** in which the truth of the premises guarantees the truth of the conclusion is a (the)

(a) Valid argument **(b)** Law of Detachment **(c)** Law of Syllogism
(d) Law of Negative Inference **(e)** Law of Disjunctive Syllogism.

104. Every Saturday I work in the yard. Today is Saturday. Therefore, I work in the yard. This is an example of a (the)

(a) Valid argument **(b)** Law of Detachment **(c)** Law of Syllogism
(d) Law of Negative Inference **(e)** Law of Disjunctive Syllogism.

105. If Remi lives in Toledo then Remi lives in Ohio. If Remi lives in Ohio then Remi lives in the U.S.A. Remi lives in Toledo, then Remi lives in the U.S.A. This is an example of a (the)

(a) Valid argument **(b)** Law of Detachment **(c)** Law of Syllogism
(d) Law of Negative Inference **(e)** Law of Disjunctive Syllogism.

106. If x is a multiple of 4, then x is divisible by 4. x is not divisible by 4. Therefore, x is not a multiple of 4. This is an exmaple of a (the)

(a) Valid argument **(b)** Law of Detachment **(c)** Law of Syllogism
(d) Law of Negative Inference **(e)** Law of Disjunctive Syllogism.

107. Jan is a man or Jan is a woman. Jan is not a woman. Therefore Jan is a man. This is a example of a (the)

(a) Valid argument **(b)** Law of Detachment **(c)** Law of Syllogism
(d) Law of Negative Inference **(e)** Law of Disjunctive Syllogism.

108. An invalid argument is called a

(a) Fallacy **(b)** Fallacy of the Converse **(c)** Fallacy of the Inverse **(d)** none

109. If today is Friday then I will meet with you. I am meeting with you. Therefore today is Friday. This is an example of (the)

(a) Fallacy **(b)** Fallacy of the Converse **(c)** Fallacy of the Inverse **(d)** none

110. If it is raining, then it is cloudy. It is not raining. Therefore it is not cloudy. This is an exmaple of a (the)

(a) Fallacy **(b)** Fallacy of the Converse **(c)** Fallacy of the Inverse **(d)** none

WHOLE NUMBERS

3

INTRODUCTION

In this chapter, we will discuss how to read and write whole numbers, and perform basic operations (addition, subtraction, multiplication, and division) on whole numbers.

This chapter is divided into the following sections.

3.1 *Numeration Systems ;*

3.2 *Addition and Subtraction of Whole Numbers ;*

3.3 *Multiplication of Whole Numbers ; and*

3.4 *Division and Exponents.*

3.1 NUMERATION SYSTEMS

VOCABULARY

1. The **natural numbers** or **counting numbers** are 1, 2, 3, 4, ….

   The set of natural numbers is infinite. There is no *largest* natural number. The smallest natural number is 1.

2. The **whole numbers** include all the natural numbers as well as the number *zero*. Thus, 0, 1, 2, 3, 4, … are whole numbers. The number 0 is the smallest whole number.

   The only whole number which is not a natural number is 0.

3. The symbols used to express numbers, such as 0, 1, 2, 45, and 117, are called **numerals**.

OBJECTIVES

After completing this section you will be able to:

A. Determine the place value of a digit, and identify a digit with a given place value ; and

B. Write a whole number in words, and write the word name of a number as a numeral.

C. Write numbers in both expanded form and standard form.

D. Round a whole number to a given place.

4. The ten numerals 0, 1, 2, 3, 4, 5, 6, 7, 8, and 9 are called **digits**. The digits of the number 63 are 6 and 3.

5. A number is in **standard form** when numerals are used to represent the number. 345 is in standard form.

6. A number is in **written form** or **oral form** when we use words to represent the number instead of numerals. The word name for 45 is forty-five and for 345 is three hundred forty-five.

7. The **digit value** or the value of a digit is the product of the digit and its place value. In 75,291, the value of the digit 5 is 5×1000 or 5000.

8. The **expanded form** of a whole number is the sum of the digit values.

9. The symbols < (read **less than**), and > (read **greater than**) are used to express a relationship between two numbers that are not equal.

10. To **round** a whole number means to give an approximate value to a given rounding place. The number 457,249 rounded to the tens place is 457,250 and we write

    $457{,}249 \approx 457{,}250$ to the nearest ten.

    The symbol $\approx$ is used to mean *approximately equal to*.

Verify Skill

Objective 3.1A

(a) Determine the place value of 3 in 3,518.

(b) Identify the digit in 153,927 whose place value is ten thousand.

If your answers to these questions are the same as given below then you may skip this objective.

Answers: (a) Thousand (1000) ; **(b)** 5

A. Place Values in Whole Numbers

➜ **(a)** Determine the place value of a digit.

(b) Identify the digit that has a given place value.

Illustrations

(a) The place value of **7** in 2,754 is hundred (100).

(b) The digit in 2,754 whose place value is thousand (1,000) is **2**.

Discussion

- Throughout history, there have been a variety of *systems of numeration* used in different parts of the world.

  The commonly accepted system of 'positional numeration' enables us to express any counting number using any of the ten basic symbols or digits. This is called the *Hindu Arabic System* or *Decimal System*.

- Numbers greater than 9 are written using more than one digit in positions which have **place values.** For example,

  in 15:

  5 has a place value of **one**,
  and **1** has a place value of **ten**.

  in 347:

  7 has a place value of **one**,
  4 has a place value of **ten**,
  and **3** has a place value of **one hundred**.

- Numbers written using digits with place values are called "numerals". If a number is written using three digits, it is a 3-digit number. For example,

Group 5			Group 4			Group 3			Group 2			Group 1		
HUNDREDS	TENS	ONES	HUNDREDS	TENS	ONES	HUNDREDS	TENS	ONES	HUNDREDS	TENS	ONES	HUNDREDS	TENS	ONES
Trillions			Billions			Millions			Thousands			Ones		

Figure 3.1

347 is a 3-digit number,

and **4,321** is a 4-digit number.

To facilitate reading and writing large numbers, digits are ordinarily grouped (from right to left) into groups of three, which are separated by commas. For example, the number 725931680 is written as 725,931,680. In 725,931,680 the three digit groups are

680 from the *right most* group,

931 from the *second* group,

and 725 from the *third* group.

- From right to left, the first five groups are respectively called **units (or ones)**, **thousands**, **millions**, **billions**, and **trillions**. Each digit within a group has a place value which, taken from right to left, is one, ten, and hundred respectively (*see*, Figure 3.1). Although the groups continue beyond the trillions, we eventually stop naming them.

The left most group may have one, two, or three digits, but all the other groups *must* have three digits. For example,

in	**7**,251,394	the left most group has *one* digit;
in	**54**,389	the left most group has *two* digits;
in	**131**,702	the left most group has *three* digits.

The place value of a position in the *units group* is one, ten or one hundred. For example, in 435,

the digit **5** has a place value of one (1),

the digit **3** has a place value of ten (10), and

the digit **4** has a place value of one hundred (100).

So, **435** = **4** hundreds + **3** tens + **5** ones.

The place value of a position in any group, other than the units group, is one, ten or one hundred, followed by the group name.

For example, 39,625,173,480 = | 3 | 9 |, | 6 | 2 | 5 |, | 1 | 7 | 3 |, | 4 | 8 | 0 |

Billions Millions Thousands Units

The group name and place value of some of the digits are as follows.

Digit	Place	Group	Place value
0	ones	units	one (1)
4	hundred	units	hundred (100)
5	one	millions	one million (1,000,000)
2	ten	millions	ten million (10,000,000)
1	hundred	thousands	hundred thousand (100,000)
9	one	billions	one billion (1,000,000,000)

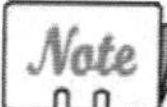

Our system of numeration is often called the **Decimal System** or base-10 system.

Observe that:

- every whole number can be written using only ten symbols - the digits.
- each place value is based on 10.

One hundred	=	10 tens
One thousand	=	10 hundreds
Ten thousand	=	10 thousands
One hundred thousand	=	10 ten thousands
One million	=	10 hundred thousands
Ten million	=	10 millions
One hundred million	=	10 ten millions

Figure 3.2

Procedure to determine the place value of a digit.

***Step* 1** Identify the digit's group using Figure 3.2.

***Step* 2** Identify the position of the digit within the group.

***Step* 3** Write the place value.

WARM-UP

1. Determine the place value of the indicated digits in 18,705,243.

(a) **3** in 18,705,24**3**

EXAMPLE 1 Determine the place value of the following digits in 57,932.

(a) 5 **(b)** 9 **(c)** 3

Solutions

(a) 57,932

Step 1 5 is in the **thousands** group.

Step 2 5 is in the **tens** position within the group.

Step 3 The place value of the digit 5 is **ten thousand**.

(b) 57,**9**32

Step 1 9 is in the **units** group.

Step 2 9 is in the **hundreds** position within the group.

Step 3 The place value of digit 9 is **one hundred**.

Caution:	Do not write the group name "unit".

(c) 57,9**3**2

Step 1 3 is in the **units** group.

Step 2 3 is in the **tens** position within the group.

Step 3 The place value of digit 3 is **ten**.

Caution:	If the group name is "units", it is not mentioned.

Procedure to identify the digit in a given position.

***Step* 1** Identify the group separated by commas which contains the digit.

***Step* 2** Identify the digit's position within the group.

***Step* 3** Write the digit.

EXAMPLE 2 Identify the digit in the

(a) thousands place in 378,925

(b) ten millions place in 92,456,821

(c) hundred thousands place in 34,587,446

Solutions

(a) thousands place in 378,925

Step 1 The thousands group is the second group from the right, so 378 is in the thousands group.

Step 2 The ones place is the right most place in the group.

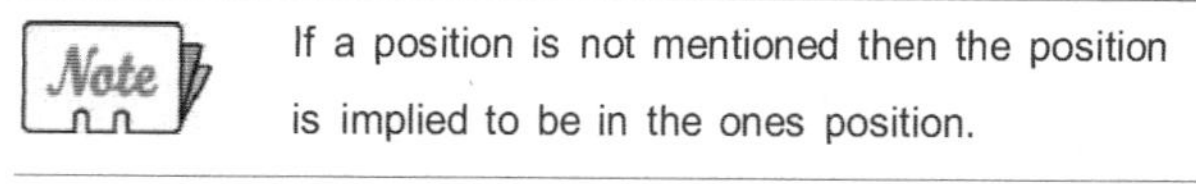

If a position is not mentioned then the position is implied to be in the ones position.

Step 3 The digit in the thousands place is **8**.

(b) ten millions place in 92,456,821

(b) **7** in 18,**7**05,243

(c) **1** in **1**8,705,243

2. Identify the digit in the

(a) Hundred thousands place in 3,468,923

(b) Ten millions place in 1,567,892,000

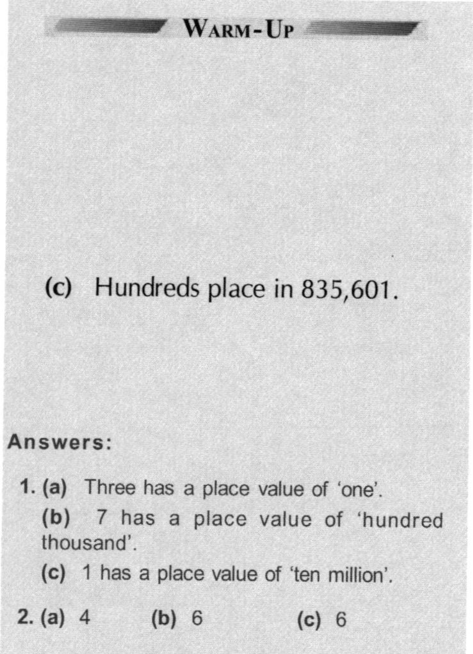

WARM-UP

(c) Hundreds place in 835,601.

Answers:

1. (a) Three has a place value of 'one'.
   (b) 7 has a place value of 'hundred thousand'.
   (c) 1 has a place value of 'ten million'.
2. (a) 4 (b) 6 (c) 6

Step 1 The millions group is the third group, so 92 is in the millions group.

Step 2 The tens place is the second place in the group.

Step 3 The digit in the ten millions place is **9**.

(c) hundred thousands place in 34,587,446

Step 1 The thousands group is the second group, so 587 is in the thousands group.

Step 2 The hundreds place is the left most place in the group.

Step 3 The digit in the hundred thousands place is **5**.

Verify Skills

Objective 3.1B

(a) Write 25,309 in words.

(b) Write the following number in numerals.
Twenty million, seven thousand, twenty-three.

If your answers to these questions are the same as given below then you may skip this objective.

Answers: **(a)** Twenty-five thousand, three hundred nine.
(b) 20,007,023

B. EXPRESSING WHOLE NUMBERS IN WORDS

➜ **(a)** Write a whole number in words.

(b) Write a whole number in standard form from its word name.

Bill Rogers 0953
479-294-2975
295 PIEDMONT AVE 493
ATLANTA, GA 30308
64-1/610
02/09/2004
PAY TO THE ORDER OF *John Hart* **$78,650.00**
DOLLARS
Wachovia Bank of Georgia, N.A.
Atlanta, GA 30383
For five automobiles
Bill Rogers
1:061000010: 01 669 034 ''' 0953

Application

An automobile dealer, Bill Rogers, purchases five automobiles from John for $78,650.00. What word name (for the amount) will he write on the check?

Illustrations

Number	Word Name
34,901	Thirty-four thousand, nine hundred one.
603,630,063	Six hundred three million, six hundred thirty thousand, sixty-three.

Discussion

(a) • Written form (or the word name) is the spoken or written form of a number. For example, the written form of 7 is **seven**.

The word names of some 2-digit and 3-digit numbers are written below:

The Number	Word Name	The Number	Word Name
27	Twenty-seven	275	Two hundred seventy-five
85	Eighty-five	308	Three hundred eight
40	Forty	999	Nine hundred ninety-nine
19	Nineteen	560	Five hundred sixty
43	Forty-three	100	One hundred

• It is **not** correct to read 275 as two hundred **and** seventy-five.

Caution: Do not use "**and**" when reading or writing a whole number. The word **and** is reserved for decimal numbers. We shall discuss this more in chapter 4.

• Let us see how to write the word names of large numbers from their place-value names. To write the word name of a number with more than three digits, begin with the *left most* group and write the word name for the group followed by its group name. Repeat the same step for all groups one by one (from left to right), separating them by commas. Do not write the group name "unit".

Grouped digits (from left to right)	27	502	375
Word name for group	Twenty seven	Five hundred two	Three hundred seventy-five
Group name	↓ million	↓ thousand	↓ units (not to be written)

So, the word name of 27,502,375 is:

Twenty-seven million, five hundred two thousand, **three hundred seventy-five**.

(b) • To write a number or numeral from its word name, write the numeral for each group, from left to right, inserting commas between groups.

The numeral for:

Four million (4), five hundred eighty-nine thousand, (589) twenty-four (24) is 4,589,024.

Note Each group after the first or left most group must have three digits. Thus, it may be necessary to insert zeros.

Procedure to write the word name of a number.

Step **1** Start with the left most group. Write the word name for the group followed by the group name.

Step **2** Repeat step 1 for the remaining groups until all groups are named.

WARM-UP

3. Write the word name for

(a) 67,799

(b) 351,006,042

4. Write the numeral for the word name.

(a) One million, forty-five thousand, eighty-two.

EXAMPLE 3 Write the word names for

(a) 73,458,695 **(b)** 230,429

Solutions **(a)** 73,458,695

Step 1	**73**	Left most group
	Seventy-three	Word name for group
	million	Group name
Step 2	**458**	Next group
	Four hundred fifty-eight	Word name for group
	thousand	Group name
Step 3	**695**	Last group
	Six hundred ninety-five	"units" is not written.

The word name for 73,458,695 is :

Seventy-three million, four hundred fifty-eight thousand,
six hundred ninety-five.

(b) Following the steps explained in (a), the word name for 230,429 is:

Two hundred thirty thousand, four hundred twenty-nine.

Procedure to write a number in standard form from its word name.

Write the numerals for the groups from left to right placing commas in between the groups. Each group after the first group must have three digits. Insert zeros when needed.

EXAMPLE 4 Write the numeral for the word name.

(a) Three million, sixty-seven thousand, nine hundred thirty-two.

(b) Seven hundred fifty-six million, three hundred forty-two.

Solutions

(a) Three million, sixty-seven thousand, nine hundred thirty-two.

Millions group **3**

Thousands group **067**

Units group **932**

Note that a zero is added on the left to fill out the three digits in the group.

The numeral is 3,067,932.

(b) Seven hundred fifty six million, three hundred forty two

Millions group **756**

Thousands group **000**

Units group **342**

Note that three zeros are added to fill out the thousands group.

The numeral is 756,000,342.

Warm-Up

(b) Five billion, fourteen thousand, eight hundred forty.

Answers:

3. **(a)** Sixty-seven thousand, seven hundred ninety-nine
   (b) Three hundred fifty-one million, six thousand, forty-two

4. **(a)** 1,045,082 **(b)** 5,000,014,840

Solution to the Application:

An automobile dealer, Bill Rogers, purchases five automobiles from John for \$78,650. What word name will he write on the check?

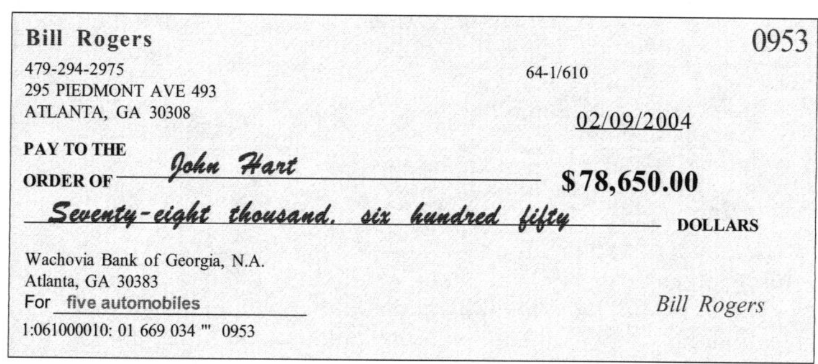
Bill Rogers 0953
479-294-2975 64-1/610
295 PIEDMONT AVE 493
ATLANTA, GA 30308
02/09/2004
PAY TO THE ORDER OF John Hart \$78,650.00
Seventy-eight thousand, six hundred fifty DOLLARS
Wachovia Bank of Georgia, N.A.
Atlanta, GA 30383
For five automobiles
Bill Rogers
1:061000010: 01 669 034 "' 0953

To write the word name for \$78,650, he will write: Seventy-eight thousand, six hundred fifty.
(The group name "units" is not written.)

C. Expanded Form and Comparison

➜ **Write numbers in both expanded form and standard form.**

Application

A grade school teacher has some blocks. Some are single cubes, some are sticks made up of 10 single cubes and some are flats made up of 100 single cubes. Write the expanded form used to represent 8 flats, 7 sticks and 4 cubes. (874 cubes).

Verify Skill

Objective 3.1C

(a) Write the expanded form of 408,735.

(b) Write 40,000 + 5000 + 20 + 5 in standard form.

If your answers to these questions are the same as given below then you may skip this objective.

Answers: (a) 400,000 + 8000 + 700 + 30 + 5
(b) 45,025

Illustrations

(a) The expanded form of the whole number 75,298 is 70,000 + 5000 + 200 + 90 + 8.

(b) 30,000 + 2000 + 50 + 1 is the expanded form of the numeral 32,051.

Discussion

- The expanded form is quite useful in gaining an understanding of our numeration system, computation with whole numbers, and comparing numbers.

  To write a whole number in expanded form, we need the value of each digit in the number. The value of a digit, called the **digit value**, is found by multiplying the digit by its place value.

  So in 576, the digit value of 5 = 5 × 100 = 500,
  the digit value of 7 = 7 × 10 = 70,
  the digit value of 6 = 6 × 1 = 6.

  The expanded form of 576 is the sum of the digit values.

  Thus, the expanded form of 576 is 500 + 70 + 6

  Sometimes, instead of the digit values, we use the digits and the word names for their place values. Thus, the expanded form of 576 can also be written as

  5 hundreds + **7** tens + **6** ones.

Note: The digit value of zero is always 0, irrespective of its place value and is usually not written in expanded form.

Procedure to write the digit value of a given digit in a number.

Multiply the digit by its place value.

WARM-UP

5. Write the digit values of 3, 7 and 1 in 18,705,243.

EXAMPLE 5 Write the digit values of 5, 3, and 9 in 57,932.

Solution

The place value of 5 is 10,000. (Refer to Example 1/ Obj. 1.1A.)
So, the digit value of 5 is 5 × 10,000 = 50,000.

The place value of 3 is 10.
So, the digit value of 3 is 3 × 10 = 30.

The place value of 9 is 100.
So, the digit value of 9 is 9 × 100 = 900.

Procedure to write a whole number in expanded form.

***Step* 1** Obtain the digit value of each digit in the number in order from left to right.

***Step* 2** Write the sum of the digit values. (You may or may not choose to include 0's.)

EXAMPLE 6 Write the expanded form of the numbers.

(a) 54,934 **(b)** 2,034,654

Solutions

(a) 54,934

Step 1 The digit value of 5 is $5 \times 10{,}000 = 50{,}000$

The digit value of 4 is $4 \times 1{,}000 = 4{,}000$

The digit value of 9 is $9 \times 100 = 900$

The digit value of 3 is $3 \times 10 = 30$

The digit value of 4 is $4 \times 1 = 4$

Step 2 The expanded form is

$50{,}000 + 4000 + 900 + 30 + 4$

or 5 ten thousands + 4 thousands + 9 hundreds + 3 tens + 4 ones.

(b) 2,034,654

The digit value of 2 is $2 \times 1{,}000{,}000 = 2{,}000{,}000$

The digit value of 0 is $0 \times 100{,}000 = 0$

(***Note:*** The digit value of 0 is always 0)

The digit value of 3 is $3 \times 10{,}000 = 30{,}000$

The digit value of 4 is $4 \times 1{,}000 = 4{,}000$

The digit value of 6 is $6 \times 100 = 600$

The digit value of 5 is $5 \times 10 = 50$

The digit value of 4 is $4 \times 1 = 4$

Thus, the expanded form of 2,034,654 is

$2{,}000{,}000 + 30{,}000 + 4000 + 600 + 50 + 4.$

Note It is not necessary to write the 0.

WARM-UP

6. Write the expanded form of the numbers:

(a) 54,365

(b) 170,307

Procedure to write a whole number in standard form from its expanded form.

Find the sum of the digit values or use the place value chart given in **Figure 3.3.**

Trillions			Billions			Millions			Thousands			Units (Ones)		
HUNDRED TRILLION 100,000,000,000,000	TEN TRILLION 10,000,000,000,000	TRILLION 1,000,000,000,000	HUNDRED BILLION 100,000,000,000	TEN BILLION 10,000,000,000	BILLION 1,000,000,000	HUNDRED MILLION 100,000,000	TEN MILLION 10,000,000	MILLION 1,000,000	HUNDRED THOUSAND 100,000	TEN THOUSAND 10,000	THOUSAND 1,000	HUNDRED 100	TEN 10	ONE 1

Figure 3.3

WARM-UP

7. Write the whole number from its expanded form.

   (a) 80,000 + 5,000 + 4

7. Write the numeral for:

   (b) 9 thousands + 3 tens + 5 ones.

EXAMPLE 7 Write the whole number from its expanded form.

(a) 5,000,000 + 300,000 + 40,000 + 2,000 + 500 + 20 + 8

(b) 7 millions + 5 ten thousands + 4 tens.

Solutions

(a) 5,000,000 + 300,000 + 40,000 + 2,000 + 500 + 20 + 8

Enter each digit value in the appropriate part of the place-value chart of **Figure 3.3.**

	Millions			Thousands			Units (Ones)		
	100,000,000	10,000,000	1,000,000	100,000	10,000	1,000	100	10	1
NUMBER →			5	3	4	2	5	2	8

The corresponding number is **5,342,528**. We can also find this number by adding the digit values.

(b) 7 millions + 5 ten thousands + 4 tens.

Enter each digit value in the appropriate column of the place-value chart of **Figure 3.3.**

Millions			Thousands			Units (Ones)		
		MILLION	HUNDRED THOUSAND	TEN THOUSAND	THOUSAND	HUNDRED	TEN	ONE
		7	0	5	0	0	4	0

NUMBER →

Write 0 in the vacant places. The numeral is **7,050,040**.

Note In practice, you should try to visualize the place-value chart rather than actually making it.

WARM-UP

Answers:

5. 3 ; 700,000 ; 10,000,000.

6. (a) 50,000 + 4,000 + 300 + 60 + 5
(b) 100,000 + 70,000 + 300 + 7

7. (a) 85,004 **(b)** 9,035

Solution to the Application:

A grade school teacher has some blocks. Some are single cubes, some are sticks made up of 10 single cubes and some are flats made up of 100 single cubes. Write the expanded form used to represent 8 flats, 7 sticks and 4 cubes. (874 cubes).

8 flats represents $8 \times 100 = 800$ cubes,

7 sticks represents $7 \times 10 = 70$ cubes

and 4 cubes represents $4 \times 1 = 4$ cubes

Thus, the expanded form is $800 + 70 + 4$

D. ROUNDING WHOLE NUMBERS

Application

The annual budget of a community college is $23,567,850, but the newspaper report rounded this figure to the nearest million dollars. What amount was reported?

Illustrations

(a) The number 2,754 rounded to the nearest ten is 2,750.

(b) The number 2,754 rounded to the nearest hundred is 2,800.

Verify Skill

Objective 3.1D

(a) Round the number 236,888 to the nearest ten.

(b) Round 457,249 to the nearest ten thousand.

(c) Round 6,949 to the nearest hundred.

If your answers to these questions are the same as given below then you may skip this objective.

Answers: **(a)** 236,890 **(b)** 460,000 **(c)** 6,900

Discussion

We deal with two kinds of numbers, some state exact values and others give approximate values. For example, if the monthly income of a person is \$4,752, he may say that his monthly income is approximately \$4,750, or he may even say that his monthly income is about \$4,800, or \$5,000.

In this case, the income has been rounded respectively to the nearest ten (\$4,750), hundred (\$4,800),
or thousand (\$5,000).

A number can be rounded to any desired place value.

- We can use the number line to see how whole numbers are rounded. Suppose we want to round 46 to the nearest ten. Looking at the number line,

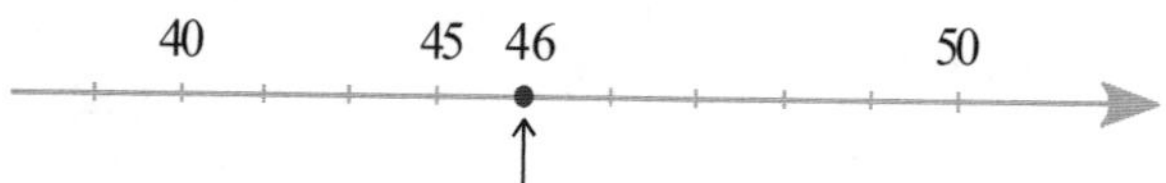

we observe that 46 is closer to 50 than to 40. We say that 46 rounds to 50, and write $46 \approx 50$. The symbol $\approx$ means "approximately equal to".

To ensure that the rounded number is as close as possible to the original number, use the following rules:

***Rule* 1** If the digit to the right of the rounding place is five or greater, **round up** by adding one to the *digit* at the rounding place, and change the remaining digits to the right of it to zeros.

***Rule* 2** If the digit to the right of the rounding place is less than five, **round down** by changing the digits to the right of the rounding place to zeros.

Round 579,623 to the nearest thousand.

57**9**,623
↑

Since the digit to the right of the arrow is 6, *round up* by Rule 1. That is, add one to the digit in the rounding place, which is 9 in this case, and replace each digit to the right of it with a zero. If one is added to the 9 then 579 thousand becomes 580 thousand.

$$579{,}623 \approx 580{,}000.$$

Procedure to round a whole number to a given place.

***Step* 1** Identify the digit in the rounding place by drawing an arrow under it.

***Step* 2** Round up or round down according to Rule 1 or Rule 2, whichever is applicable.

EXAMPLE 8 Round the following numbers to the given place value.

(a) 27,389; thousand

(b) 36,419,850; ten thousand

(c) 4,392; ten

(d) 1,985,027; hundred thousand

Solutions

(a) 27,389 ; thousand

Step 1 27,389 The rounding place is the thousands place.

↑ (Thousand)

Step 2 Since the digit to the right is 3, *round down* by Rule 2. That is, change each digit to the right of the arrow to zero.

27,389 ≈ 27,000 to the nearest thousand.

(b) 36,419,850 ; ten thousand

Step 1 36,419,850 The rounding place is the ten thousands place.

↑ (ten thousand)

Step 2 Since the digit to the right is 9 *round up* by Rule 1. That is, add one to the digit at the rounding place, and change the remaining digits to its right to zeros.

36,419,850 ≈ 36,420,000 to the nearest ten thousand.

(c) 4,392 ; ten

Step 1 4392 The rounding place is the tens place

↑ (ten)

Step 2 Since the digit to the right of the rounding place is 2, *round down* by Rule 2.

4,392 ≈ 4,390

(d) 1,985,027; hundred thousand

1,985,027 The rounding place is the hundred thousands place

↑ (hundred thousand)

Since the digit to the right of the rounding place is 8, add 1 to 19 and change the digits to the right to zeros.

1,985,027 ≈ 2,000,000

WARM-UP

8. **(a)** Round 367,231 to the nearest thousand.

(b) Round 450,780,000 to the nearest million.

(c) Round 2,945 to the nearest hundred.

(d) Round 95,702 to the nearest ten thousand.

Answers:

8. (a) 367,000 (b) 451,000,000
(c) 2900 (d) 100,000

Solution to the Application:

The annual budget of a local community college is $23,567,850. The newspaper report rounded this figure to the nearest million dollars. What amount was reported?

Step 1	23,567,850 ↑	Identify the digit in the millions place.
Step 2	24,000,000	The digit to the right is 5, so round up.

To the nearest million, the reported budget was $24,000,000.

EXERCISE 3.1

A. **In exercises 1-5, determine the place value of 7.**

1. 3,670 **2.** 70,936 **3.** 400,700 **4.** 5,982,763,210 **5.** 87,052,100,455

In exercises 6-10, identify the digit in the hundreds place.

6. 4,792 **7.** 60,039 **8.** 27,531 **9.** 111,220 **10.** 763,210

In exercises 11-13, identify the digit in the ten millions place.

11. 680,234,000 **12.** 14,668,394,250 **13.** 705,394,627

B. **In exercises 14-25, write the word name.**

14. 538 **15.** 530 **16.** 5,622 **17.** 13,084

18. 703,109 **19.** 6,597 **20.** 1,235,956 **21.** 4,580,000,250

22. 32,302,002 **23.** 3,030,300 **24.** 51,510,501 **25.** 300,030,003,300

In exercises 26-33, write the number for the word name.

26. Seventy thousand, five hundred ninety-nine.

27. Two hundred fifteen thousand.

28. Nine hundred twenty-five.

29. Seven billion, two hundred fifty-five million, thirty-two thousand, seventy.

30. One hundred fifty million, forty thousand, thirty-one

31. Eight hundred seven thousand, two hundred thirty

32. Thirty-four thousand, nine hundred ten.

33. Six million, two

34. Fill in the box with the correct digit

(a) 38,206 = 3 ten thousands + ☐ thousands + ☐ hundreds + 0 tens + ☐ ones.

(b) 230,504 = 2 hundred thousands + 3 ten thousands + ☐ thousands + ☐ hundreds + 0 tens + ☐ ones.

35. Write a number by interchanging the digits in the thousands and the ones places of 27,531.

36. Write a number by interchanging the digits in the tens and the hundred thousands places of 8,956,200.

37. Write the numeral for:
Thirty-two million, twenty-seven thousand, nine hundred ten.

38. Write the numeral for:
One hundred fifteen billion, three hundred million, four hundred thousand, sixty-five.

Applications

39. Elena buys a new dress for $575 and writes a check to pay for it. What word name should she write on the check?

40. The author of a book on mathematics received $12,750 as royalty from the publishers in 2002. Write the word name for the amount received.

41. Red Lion Inns earned ten million, six hundred fifty-eight thousand, five hundred dollars during the first quarter of 2003. Write the numeral indicating the earnings of Red Lion Inns.

42. The officials for Power Ball, an interstate lottery game, estimate the prize money for the next drawing to be thirty-one million, six hundred fifty thousand dollars. Write the numeral for the prize.

43. The total land area of the earth is approximately 52,425,000 square miles. Write the word name for the area.

In exercises 44-49, write the digit value of the bold faced digit.

44. 3**2**5 **45.** 5**6**,978 **46.** 7,6**5**4,321 **47.** 53,**4**39 **48.** 684,**0**94 **49.** 6,43**5**

C. **In exercises 50-55, write the whole number in expanded form.**

50. 978 **51.** 433 **52.** 45,389 **53.** 50,327 **54.** 70,053 **55.** 96,007

In exercises 56-61, write the whole number from the expanded form.

56. 7,000 + 200 + 50 + 6 **57.** 70,000 + 500 + 20 + 9 **58.** 2,000,000 + 30,000 + 200 + 70 + 6

59. 8,000 + 50 + 2 **60.** 6 millions + 8 ten thousands + 3 tens

61. 2 ten thousands + 5 thousands + 6 hundreds + 2 tens + 4 ones.

D. **In exercises 62-75, round the number to the given place.**

62. 78; ten **63.** 743; hundred **64.** 4,175; ten **65.** 1,751,100; thousand

66. 1,751,900; thousand **67.** 5,83 7; ten **68.** 5,837; hundred **69.** 52,425,000; ten thousand

70. 456,172,978; million **71.** 82,579,090; hundred thousand **72.** 2,951; hundred

73. 1,619; ten **74.** 935,700; hundred thousand **75.** 72,238; thousand

Applications

76. A publishing company sold 258,630 books on basic mathematics during the first six months of 2002. Write the number of volumes sold to the nearest thousand.

77. Tom Peterson's Appliances buys 5 television sets for a total of $1,375 each. What is the total price to the nearest hundred?

78. An office space in downtown San Francisco is listed for $4,689,250. Give the list price of the space to the nearest ten thousand dollars.

79. Linda, Kevin and Jesse went on vacation. They spent $1,250, $890 and $1,275 respectively. Who spent the most? Who spent the least?

80. A community college receives two bids for the construction of its new library: bid A for $6,874,500 and bid B for $6,456,950. It wants to award the contract to the lower bidder. To which bidder should the contract be awarded?

81. To teach his students the place value system, Mr. Martinez uses blocks consisting of single cubes, sticks composed of 10 cubes each and flats consisting of 100 cubes each. If Ricardo has 7 flats, 9 sticks and 3 cubes, how many cubes does he have altogether? Represent this number in expanded form.

3.2 ADDITION AND SUBTRACTION OF WHOLE NUMBERS

OBJECTIVES

After completing this section you will be able to:

A. Add whole numbers and estimate the sum of whole numbers;

B. Subtract whole numbers and estimate the difference; and

VOCABULARY

1. • The symbol to indicate addition is "+" and is read as "plus".

   • The result of an addition is called the **sum**.

   • A number being added is called an **addend** or **term**.

   In 8 + 3 = 11 ; 8 and 3 are the *addends* or *terms*, 11 is the *sum*.

2. • The symbol for subtraction is "–" and is read as "minus".

   • When one number is subtracted from another the result is called the **difference**.

   • 9 is the difference between 12 and 3 because 12 – 3 = 9.

Verify Skill

Objective 3.2A

(a) Find the sum of the numbers 378; 4,091 and 46.

(b) Estimate the sum of the numbers 1,456; 834; 375 and 5,980 by rounding to the nearest thousand.

If your answers to these questions are the same as given below then you may skip this objective.

Answers: (a) 4,515 (b) 8,000

A. ADDING WHOLE NUMBERS AND ESTIMATING

➜ **Add whole numbers and estimate the sum of a group of whole numbers.**

Illustrations

(a) Find the sum of the numbers : 725 ; 473 ; 1,289

$$\begin{array}{r} 725 \\ 473 \\ +\ 1289 \\ \hline 2,487 \end{array}$$

(b) Estimate the sum of the numbers 725; 473; and 1,289 by rounding to the nearest hundred.

$725 \approx 700$; $473 \approx 500$; $1289 \approx 1300$

$725 + 473 + 1,289 \approx 700 + 500 + 1300 \approx \mathbf{2500}$

Discussion

• The addition of whole numbers is a simple extension of the counting process. A method of adding whole numbers can be demonstrated using the number line shown in Figure 3.4.

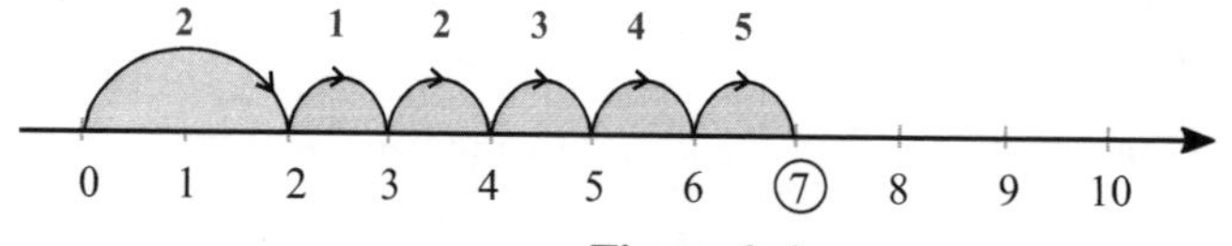

Figure 3.4

"2 + 5 = 7" is an **addition fact**.

Here, 7 is the **sum** of 2 and 5.

• Consider the two addition facts.

$4 + 8 = \mathbf{12}$ and $8 + 4 = \mathbf{12}$

The two addends are added in a different order but the **sum** is the same. This addition property is known as the **commutative property of addition.**

Changing the order of the terms does not change the product.

- Consider the sum

$$45 + 34$$

The sum can be obtained by writing the numbers (addends) in expanded form, putting the digit of the same place value in columns, and then finding the sum of each column.

45	=	4 tens	+	5 ones
+ 34	=	3 tens	+	4 ones
SUM	=	7 tens	+	9 ones = 79

Addition without regrouping

The sum of 45 and 34 is 79. **or** 45 + 34 = 79

- Since each place can contain only a single digit, it sometimes becomes necessary to rewrite the sum of a column as in the following addition.

57	=	5 tens	+	7 ones
+ 28	=	2 tens	+	8 ones
SUM	=	7 tens	+	15 ones

Since 15 ones is a two digit number, it must be renamed:

7 tens + 15 ones = 7 tens + 1 ten + 5 ones
= 8 tens + 5 ones
= 85

Addition with regrouping

The sum of 57 and 28 is 85 **or** 57 + 28 = 85

The above addition in short form is demonstrated below.

T (tens)	O (ones)
1	
5	7
+ 2	8
8	1 5

⟵ *Columns have been named for clarity.*

7 + 8 = 15 = 1 ten 5 ones

The "5" is placed under the ones column, and the 10 ones are regrouped as 1 ten and placed above the other tens to be added in the tens column.

Hence, the sum is 85.

In practice, the digit that is regrouped is kept in memory, and the addition is written in a more compact
form such as:

```
       1
       5 7
     + 2 8
Sum =  8 5
```

- At certain times, we may wish to **estimate the sum** rather than finding the *actual* sum. The sum can be estimated by first rounding each member of the group to a particular *place value* and then adding these rounded numbers.

  If you choose to round to a large place value, the addition will be quicker and easier but the answer will be less accurate. If you choose to round to a smaller place value, the answer will be more accurate but the addition will take longer. Thus, deciding where to round depends on the need for accuracy and the desire for speed. This, you will need to decide by the context of the problem. For now, we will tell you where to round in any given exercise.

  For example, there is more than one way in which we can estimate the sum of 725, 1,973 and 1,189.

Rounding to the thousands	Rounding to the hundreds	Rounding to the tens
$725 \approx 1000$	$725 \approx 700$	$725 \approx 730$
$1973 \approx 2000$	$1973 \approx 2000$	$1973 \approx 1970$
$1189 \approx 1000$	$1189 \approx 1200$	$1189 \approx 1190$
The estimate sum is :	The estimate sum is :	The estimate sum is :
1000	700	730
2000	2000	1970
+ 1000	+ 1200	+ 1190
4000	3900	3890

Symbolically, we write $725 + 1973 + 1189 \approx 4000$ (or either of the two estimates).

> The estimated sum is a good check on addition. If the actual sum is not close to the estimated sum, it indicates a possible error.

In this case, the actual sum is 3,887, which is close to the estimates.

> **Procedure** to add two or more whole numbers.
>
> ***Step* 1** Write the numbers in columns so that the places are lined up.
>
> ***Step* 2** Add the right most column (ones place). If the sum is more than 9, write the ones digit of the sum below the column and regroup each set of 10 ones to one set of tens and place above the next column to the left.
>
> ***Step* 3** Repeat step 2 for each column moving from right to left.

WARM-UP

1. Add

(a) 521 and 656

EXAMPLE 1 Add using expanded form

(a) 365 and 204 **(b)** 256 and 379

Also, write the sum in compact form in each case.

Solutions

(a)

365	=	3 hundreds + 6 tens + 5 ones
+ 204	=	2 hundreds + 0 tens + 4 ones
Sum	=	5 hundreds + 6 tens + 9 ones = 569

or $365 + 204 = 569$

Compact (Short) form:

Write the numbers in columns, lining up the places, and add the digits in each column.

	H	T	O
	3	6	5
+	2	0	4
Sum =	5	6	9

Here, **O** stands for Ones, **T** for Tens and **H** for Hundreds. Naming columns is not necessary. It is shown here only for clarity.

(b) 256 = 2 hundreds + 5 tens + 6 ones

+ 379 = 3 hundreds + 7 tens + 9 ones

Sum = 5 hundreds + 12 tens + 15 ones

Addition with regrouping

Now, 12 tens + 15 ones

= 12 tens + 1 ten + 5 ones (after expanding 15 ones)

= 13 tens + 5 ones

= 1 hundred + 3 tens + 5 ones (after expanding 13 tens)

Thus, **Sum** = 5 hundreds + 1 hundred + 3 tens + 5 ones

= 6 hundreds + 3 tens + 5 ones

= 635

or $256 + 379 = 635$

Short form:

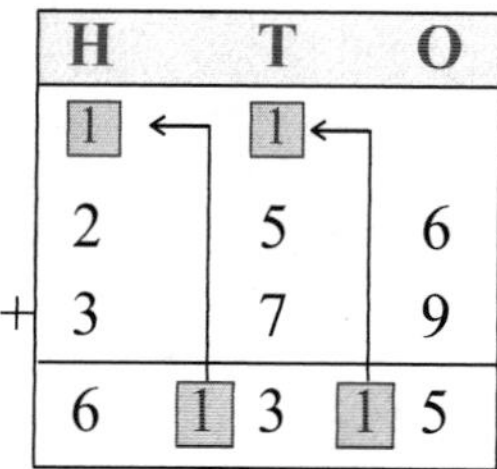

So, 256 + 379 = 635.

Alternatively,

Write the numbers in columns, lining up the places, and then add the numbers in each column.

		1	1
	2	5	6
+	3	7	9
	6	3	5

Regrouping is done mentally.

WARM-UP

Add

(b) 437 and 286

2. Find the sum of 7,629; 1,682 and 4,491.

EXAMPLE 2 Add 1,691; 9,441 and 6,785.

Solution In compact form, the addition is performed as:

		1	2			⟶ digits arrived at by regrouping
		1	6	9	1	
		9	4	4	1	
	+	6	7	8	5	
Sum	= 1	7,	9	1	7	

The sum is 17,917.

3. Find the sum of 973 + 32 + 156 + 4678.

EXAMPLE 3 Add the following numbers.

4,678; 345; 76,458 and 69

Solution Write the numbers in columns, lining up the places. Then add the numbers in each column.

(Regroup when necessary)

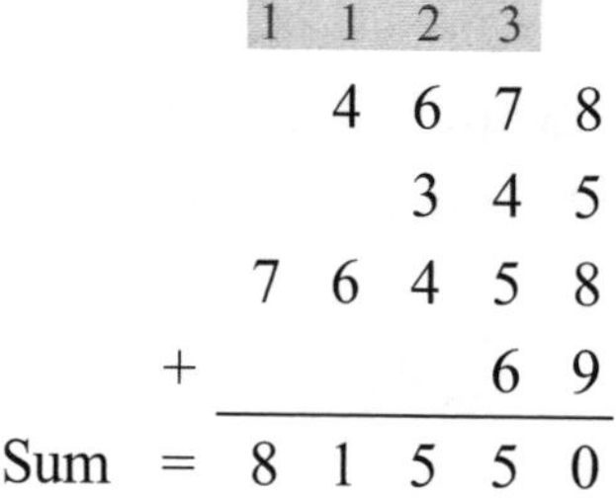

> ***Caution:*** The digit which is arrived at by regrouping should always be written at the top of the entire column of numbers, in the next group.

The sum is 81,550.

4. Find the sum of the numbers in "warm up" 3 above using a calculator, and verify the answer you get in "warm up" 3.

EXAMPLE 4 Add the numbers 207; 64; and 3,759 on a calculator.

Solution Use the [+] key on your calculator to get the sum.

On most calculators you can enter:

207 [+] 64 [+] 3759 [=] or [Enter]

Upon completion, the calculator should display 4030

The sum is 4,030.

Procedure to estimate the sum of a group of whole numbers.

***Step* 1** Round each number in the group to the indicated place value.

***Step* 2** Add the rounded numbers.

EXAMPLE 5 Estimate the sum by rounding to the hundreds.

973 + 32 + 156 + 4,678

Solution Round each number to the hundreds place.

973	≈	1000	
32	≈	0	
156	≈	200	
4678	≈	4700	
		5900	Add

The estimated sum is 5900.

WARM-UP

5. Estimate the sum of 27,805; 7,390 and 857 by rounding to the hundreds.

Answers:

1. (a) 1,177 (b) 723 2. 13,802
3. 5839 4. 5839 5. 36,100

B. SUBTRACTING WHOLE NUMBERS AND ESTIMATING

➜ **Subtract whole numbers and estimate the difference.**

Illustrations

(a) 325 – 218 = 107

(b) An estimated difference of 475 and 237 is 300.

475 – 237 ≈ 500 – 200 = 300

Verify Skill

Objective 3.2 B

(a) Find the difference of 8934 and 963.

(b) Estimate the difference of 8934 and 963 by rounding to the thousands.

If your answers to these questions are the same as given below then you may skip this objective.

Answers: (a) 7,971 **(b)** 8000

Discussion

- The concept of subtraction is as elementary as the concept of addition. To subtract means to take away. Subtract 4 from 9, symbolically written as 9 – 4 (read: "9 minus 4"), means take away 4 from 9.

  "9 – 4 = 5" is a **subtraction fact** which can be easily understood with the help of the number line given in Figure 3.5.

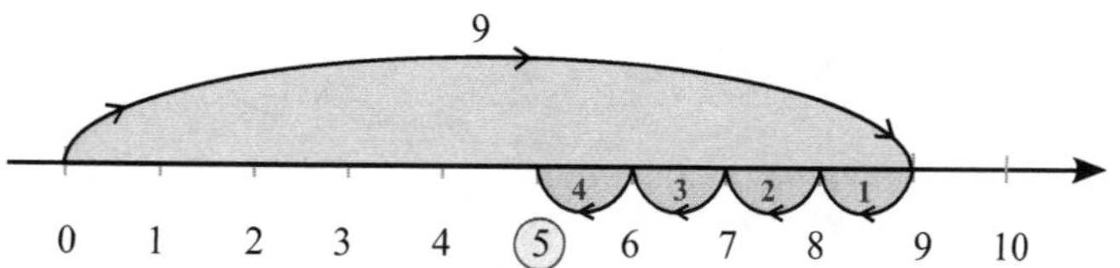

Figure 3.5

First mark 9, then count back 4 units to the left to arrive at the point corresponding to the answer, 5.

Here, 5 is the **difference** of 9 and 4.

- Addition and subtraction are *inverse processes*. In addition we find the sum; in subtraction we find an addend. For each addition fact, we can write two related subtraction facts. For instance, $5 + 4 = 9$ gives two subtraction facts:

$$9 - 4 = 5 \quad \text{and} \quad 9 - 5 = 4.$$

- The subtraction facts and place value are used to find the difference between whole numbers containing more than one digit. We can show the process of subtraction using the column format or using expanded notation.

  Consider the difference 987 – 234.

987	=	9 hundreds + 8 tens + 7 ones
– 234	=	–(2 hundreds + 3 tens + 4 ones)
difference	=	7 hundreds + 5 tens + 3 ones

***Step* 1** Subtract the ones, 7 – 4 = 3. Write 3 in the ones column.

***Step* 2** Subtract the tens, 8 – 3 = 5. Write 5 in the tens column.

***Step* 3** Subtract the hundreds, 9 – 2 = 7. Write 7 in the hundreds column.

So, 987 – 234 = 753

The above solution in short form is shown below:

	H	T	O
	9	8	7
–	2	3	4
	7	5	3

← *Columns have been named for clarity.*

Subtraction without regrouping

Check by adding:

	2	3	4
+	7	5	3
	9	8	7

- When using the column format, it is possible that subtraction in a given column cannot be done. For example, let us subtract 365 from 892.

892	=	8 hundreds + 9 tens + 2 ones
– 365	=	– (3 hundreds + 6 tens + 5 ones)

5 ones cannot be subtracted from 2 ones. More than 2 ones are needed so we regroup. Rewrite the subtraction

892	=	8 hundreds + 8 tens + 12 ones
– 365	=	–(3 hundreds + 6 tens + 5 ones)
difference		5 hundreds + 2 tens + 7 ones

That is, regroup **9 tens** + 2 ones as:

8 tens + **1 ten** + 2 ones

or 8 tens + 10 ones + 2 ones

or 8 tens + 12 ones.

So, 892 – 365 = 527

The above subtraction in short form is shown below.

	H	T	O
		8	12
	8	~~9~~	~~2~~
−	3	6	5
difference	5	2	7

Subtraction with regrouping

- At times, we may wish to *estimate* the difference of two whole numbers rather than finding their actual difference. The difference can be estimated by rounding each number to a particular *place value* and then subtracting these rounded numbers. For example, to estimate the difference between 7,593 and 521, first round each number to the hundreds and then subtract.

$$\begin{array}{rcr} 7\,5\,9\,3 & \approx & 7600 \\ -\,5\,2\,1 & \approx & -\,500 \\ \hline & & 7,100 \end{array}$$

Thus, the estimated difference is 7,100. Symbolically, we write

$$7,593 - 521 \approx \mathbf{7,100}$$

The estimated difference provides a good check on subtraction. If the actual difference is not close to the estimated difference, it indicates the need to check the subtraction again.

In this case, the actual difference is 7072, which is close to the estimate.

Procedure to find the difference of two whole numbers.

***Step* 1** Write the numbers in columns so that the places are lined up.

***Step* 2** Find the difference of the digits in the right most column (ones place). If subtraction in this column cannot be done, regroup the next column and rename the upper digits in both columns.

***Step* 3** Repeat step 2 for each column moving from right to left.

EXAMPLE 6 Subtract

(a) 255 from 687

(b) 306 from 725

Solutions

In expanded form :

(a)

687	=	6 hundreds + 8 tens + 7 ones
− 255	=	− (2 hundreds + 5 tens + 5 ones)
difference		4 hundreds + 3 tens + 2 ones

or 687 − 255 = 432

WARM-UP

6. Subtract using expanded form

(a) 351 from 974

Warm-Up

In short form:

	H	T	O
	6	8	7
−	2	5	5
	4	3	2

***Step* 1** Write the numbers in columns, and line up the places.

***Step* 2** Subtract the ones column : 7 − 5 = 2
Subtract the tens column : 8 − 5 = 3
Subtract the hundreds column : 6 − 2 = 4

Check: Add the subtrahend and the difference

	2	5	5	(the subtrahend)
+	4	3	2	(the difference)
	6	8	7	(the minuend)

So, 687 − 255 = 432 is correct.

(b) Subtract 457 from 838

(b) *In short form:*

	H	T	O
		1	15
	7	~~2~~	~~5~~
−	3	0	6
	4	1	9

***Step* 1** Write the numbers in columns, and line up the places.

***Step* 2** Since 6 ones cannot be subtracted from 5 ones, we regroup. 2 tens and 5 ones are equivalent to 1 ten and 15 ones.

Check: Add the numbers in the second and third rows:

		1	
	3	0	6
+	4	1	9
	7	2	5

= the number in the first row

With practice, you should be able to perform subtraction in the short form, showing the process of regrouping and then subtracting mentally.

7. Subtract

(a) 267 from 569.

EXAMPLE 7 Subtract

(a) 365 from 734 **(b)** 395 from 2604

(c) 327 from 6000

Solutions

(a)

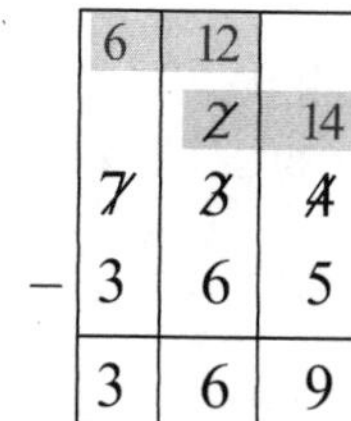

	6	12	
		~~2~~	14
	~~7~~	~~3~~	~~4~~
−	3	6	5
	3	6	9

- Write the numbers in columns, and line up places.
- Name the columns mentally.
- To subtract in the ones column regroup:
  3 tens + 4 ones = 2 tens + 14 ones
- To subtract in the tens column, regroup.
  7 hundreds + 2 tens = 6 hundreds + 12 tens

(b) Subtract 395 from 2604.

		9	14
	5	10	
2	6	0	4
–	3	9	5
2	2	0	9

2604 – 395 = 2209

- Write the numbers in columns, and line up the places.
- Name the columns mentally.
- Subtraction cannot be done in the ones column.
- Regroup : 6 hundreds and 4 ones
  = 5 hundreds, 10 tens and 4 ones
  = 5 hundreds, 9 tens and 14 ones
- Now subtract.

(b) 449 from 2,364.

(c) Subtract 327 from 6000.

	9	9	
5	10	10	10
6	0	0	0
–	3	2	7
5	6	7	3

6000 – 327 = 5673

- Write the numbers in columns, and line up the places.
- Name the columns mentally.
- Subtraction cannot be done in the ones column.
- Regroup : 6 thousands
  = 5 thousands and 10 hundreds
  = 5 thousands, 9 hundreds and 10 tens
  = 5 thousands, 9 hundreds, 9 tens and 10 ones
- Now subtract.

(c) 519 from 7000.

EXAMPLE 8 Subtract 15,397 from 21,310 on a calculator.

Solution Use the [–] key on your calculator to get the difference.

For most calculators, enter:

21310 [–] 15397 [=] or [Enter]

Upon completion, the calculator should display 5913

The difference is 5,913.

8. Do warm up 7 given above on a calculator and verify the answer.

Procedure to estimate the difference of two whole numbers.

***Step* 1** Round each number to the indicated place value.

***Step* 2** Subtract the rounded numbers.

EXAMPLE 9 Estimate the difference by rounding to the indicated place.

(a) 48696 – 31976
ten - thousands

(b) 8349 – 657
hundreds

9. Estimate the difference of 53,904 and 37,723 by rounding to the ten thousands place.

Solutions

(a) Estimate the difference: 48696 – 31976.

Given number		Rounded to the ten thousands place
48696	≈	50,000
– 31976	≈	– 30,000
16720	≈	20,000

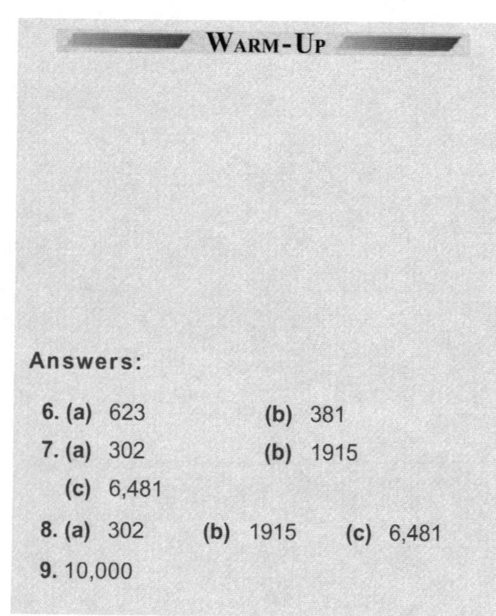

The estimated difference is 20,000.

(b) Estimate the difference: 8349 – 657

Given number		Rounded to the hundreds place	
12			
7 2 14			
8 3 4 9	≈	8 3 0 0	
– 6 5 7	≈	– 7 0 0	
7 6 9 2	≈	7 6 0 0	Difference

The estimated difference is 7,300.

or 8,349 – 657 ≈ 7,300.

EXERCISE 3.2

In exercises 1-5, add the pair of numbers using expanded form.

1. 172 and 417 **2.** 334 and 215 **3.** 45 and 27 **4.** 473 and 284 **5.** 387 and 86

In exercises 6-10, add the given numbers.

6. 1,123 ; 224 and 412 **7.** 425 ; 503 and 926 **8.** 5,461 and 3,587

9. 1,592 ; 2,601 and 5,543 **10.** 3,436 and 0 (State your observation)

In exercises 11-15, find the sum.

11.	**12.**	**13.**	**14.**	**15.**
5,437	3,693	1,592	34,675	17
209	209	2,601	3,201	1,859
88	3,147	55	57,832	5,937
+ 1,879	+ 33	+ 592	+ 72	+ 32,164

16. Add the numbers in Exercises 11-15 on a *calculator* and verify your answers.

In exercises 17-20, estimate the sum by rounding to the indicated place.

17. 34 + 549 + 1,008 + 1,456; tens **18.** 4,083 + 16,756 + 8,270 + 12; thousands

19. 4,392 + 945 + 6,110 + 7,515 + 5,785; hundreds **20.** 546 + 39 + 52 + 185; tens

21. **(a)** Estimate the sum of 56 and 77. **(b)** Find the sum of 56 and 77. Round the answer to the tens.

22. **(a)** Estimate the sum of 349 and 538. **(b)** Find the sum of 349 and 538. Round the answer to the hundreds.

In exercises 23-25, subtract using expanded form.

23. 162 from 274 **24.** 238 from 453 **25.** 785 from 1,947

In exercises 26-30, subtract and check using addition.

26. 3,969 from 5,636 **27.** 897 from 1,265 **28.** 2,543 from 9,802 **29.** 470 from 6,789 **30.** 6,893 from 9,863

In exercises 31-35, find the difference.

31. 4,002 – 1,271 **32.** 8,000 – 4,444 **33.** 10,000 – 1,872 **34.** 1,375 – 0 **35.** 6,785 – 6,785

36. Compute the difference in exercises 26-35 on a *calculator*, and verify your answers.

In exercises 37-40, estimate the difference by rounding to the indicated place.

37. $\begin{array}{r} 76532 \\ -\ 20496 \\ \hline \end{array}$ thousands **38.** $\begin{array}{r} 73913 \\ -\ 31397 \\ \hline \end{array}$ ten thousands **39.** $\begin{array}{r} 19039 \\ -\ 7450 \\ \hline \end{array}$ thousands **40.** $\begin{array}{r} 3783 \\ -\ 569 \\ \hline \end{array}$ hundreds

41. Subtract the sum of 4,805 and 2,967 from the sum of 3,835 and 4,990.

42. Subtract the difference of 5,305 and 4,839 from the sum of 3,525 and 4,839.

43. **(a)** Estimate the difference between 762 and 344.

(b) Find the difference between 762 and 344. Round the answer to the hundreds.

44. Find the sums of 578 + 1,693 and 1,693 + 578. Observe that the sum of two numbers does not change even when we change the order of the numbers.

45. Find the difference 342 – 150. Can we find 150 – 342 when we are dealing with whole numbers only? Observe that **we cannot change the order of numbers when finding a difference.**

46. Find the sum of each of the following groups of numbers.

$\begin{array}{r} 4,752 \\ 390 \\ +\ 7,818 \\ \hline \end{array}$ $\begin{array}{r} 7,818 \\ 4,752 \\ +\ 390 \\ \hline \end{array}$ $\begin{array}{r} 390 \\ 4,752 \\ +\ 7,818 \\ \hline \end{array}$

Observe that **three numbers added in any order have the same sum.**

3.3 Multiplication of Whole Numbers

Objectives

After completing this section you will be able to:

A. Multiply whole numbers and estimate the product.

Vocabulary

1. • The common symbol which indicates multiplication is "×", and is read "multiplied by" or "times".

 • The numbers being multiplied are called the **factors** and the result obtained is called the **product**.

 3 × 5 (read: "3 multiplied by 5" or "3 times 5") is 15

 3 and 5 are ***factors***, and 15 is the ***product***.

 • The product 2 × 4 may be written as

 $2 \cdot 4$ **or** 2(4) **or** (2)4 **or** (2)(4).

Verify Skill

Objective 3.3A

(a) Find the product 375 × 47.

(b) Estimate the product 2,517 × 684.

If your answers to these questions are the same as given below then you may skip this objective.

Answers: (a) 17,625 **(b)** 2,100,000

A. Multiplying Whole Numbers and Estimating

➜ **Multiply two or more whole numbers and estimate the product.**

Illustrations

(a) Find the product 58 × 32

$$\begin{array}{r} 58 \\ \times\ 32 \\ \hline 116 \\ 1740 \\ \hline 1856 \end{array}$$

Product: 1856

(b) Estimate the product 445 × 472.

$445 \times 472 \approx 400 \times 500 = 200{,}000$

Discussion

- Multiplication is basically a shorter form of repeated addition when all the addends are the same.

 $\underbrace{4 + 4}_{\text{2 fours}} = 2 \times 4$ (read: 2 multiplied by 4 or 2 times 4)

 $\underbrace{4 + 4 + 4}_{\text{3 fours}} = 3 \times 4$ (read: 3 multiplied by 4 or 3 times 4)

 $\underbrace{4 + 4 + 4 + \ldots + 4}_{\text{52 fours}} = 52 \times 4$ (read: 52 multiplied by 4 or 52 times 4)

 In 2 × 4, the sign × is called the "multiplication" sign.

- $2 \times 4 = 8$ is a **multiplication fact**. Some more multiplication facts are:

  $7 \times 8 = 56$; $5 \times 9 = 45$; $4 \times 1 = 4$; $6 \times 1 = 6$; $1 \times 3 = 3$

If you do not already know or do not remember the basic multiplication facts, you should learn them as soon as possible.

In the multiplication fact $7 \times 8 = 56$, the number 56 is called the **product** of 7 and 8. The numbers 7 and 8 are called **factors** of 56.

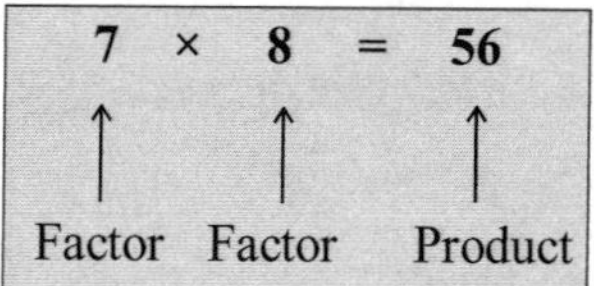

- Consider the two multiplication facts

  $4 \times 8 = \mathbf{32}$ and $8 \times 4 = \mathbf{32}$.

  The two factors are multiplied in a different order but the product is the same. This multiplication property is known as the **commutative property of multiplication**.

  Changing the order of the factors does not change the product.

- To multiply a number by 10, 20, 30, …, 90, multiply the given number by 1, 2, 3 …, 9 respectively, and write one zero to the right of the product. Similarly, to multiply a number by 100, 200, 300 …, 900, multiply the given number by 1, 2, 3, …, 9 respectively and write two zeros to the right of the product.

  For example,

  $$52 \times \mathbf{30} = 52 \times 3 \text{ tens} = 156 \text{ tens} = 156\mathbf{0}$$

  • Compute 52×3, which is 156, and then write one zero to the right of it.

  $$214 \times 200 = 214 \times 2 \text{ hundreds} = 428 \text{ hundreds} = 42{,}8\mathbf{00}$$

  • Multiply 214 by 2 to get 428, and then write two zeros to the right of it to get $214 \times 200 = 42{,}800$.

- The expanded form of a number is used to multiply a number with several digits by a single digit number:

  To multiply 312 by 3 we write

312	=	3 hundreds + 1 tens + 2 ones	
× 3	=	× 3	
Product	=	9 hundreds + 3 tens + 6 ones	= 936

  Multiply the digit at each place by 3

  So, $312 \times 3 = 936$

  The above multiplication is usually written as;

H	T	O
3	1	2
×		3
9	3	6

Product = 936

- 2 ones × 3 = 6 ones. Write 6 in the ones column.
- 1 ten × 3 = 3 tens. Write 3 in the tens column.
- 3 hundreds × 3 = 9 hundreds. Write 9 in the hundreds column.

- The next example illustrates the algorithm we use to multiply large numbers.
  - To compute the product 184 × 42 arrange the number as follows:

```
    H T O      (Columns should be named mentally)
    1 8 4
×     4 2 ,    42 = 4 tens + 2 ones
```

***Step* 1** Multiply 184 by 2 ones

184 × 2 ones = 184 × 2 = 368 ⟶

```
  H T O
  1 8 4
×   4 2
  3 6 8
```

```
1
  1 8 4
×     2
  3 6 8
```

***Step* 2** Multiply 184 by 4 tens

184 × 4 tens = 184 × 40 = 7,360 ⟶

```
    H T O
    1 8 4
×     4 2
    3 6 8
  7 3 6 0
```

```
3 1
  1 8 4
×     4 tens
  7 3 6 tens
```

***Step* 3** Add 368 to 7,360

368 + 7360 = 7,728 ⟶

184 × 42 = 7,728

```
    H T O
    1 8 4
×     4 2
    3 6 8
+ 7 3 6 0
  7 7 2 8
```

```
   1
   3 6 8
 7 3 6 0
 7 7 2 8
```

The steps of the procedure explained above and the whole computation can be performed in a more compact form as follows:

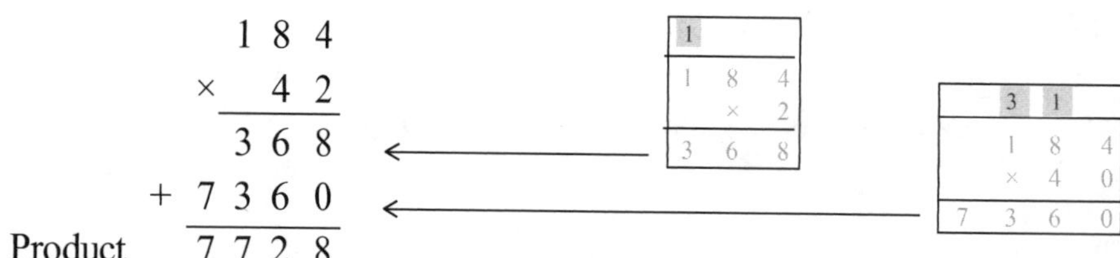

```
          1 8 4
    ×       4 2
          3 6 8
    +   7 3 6 0
Product 7 7 2 8
```

- Estimate the product of two (or more) whole numbers by rounding each number to the largest place value in that number, and then multiplying the rounded numbers. For example, to estimate the product 5,875 × 495, proceed as follows:

$$\begin{array}{lcrl} 5875 & \approx & 6000 & \text{Round to the nearest thousand} \\ 495 & \approx & \times\ 500 & \text{Round the nearest hundred} \\ & & 3{,}000{,}000 & \text{Multiply} \end{array}$$

$5875 \times 495 \approx 3{,}000{,}000$ is an estimate of the product.

The estimate of the product is a good check on multiplication. If the actual product is not close to the estimated product, it indicates the need for rechecking calculations. We should mentally estimate the product in order to detect errors, especially when computing the product on calculator.

$5{,}875 \times 495 = 2{,}908{,}125$. This is close to the estimate previously calculated.

Procedure to multiply

***Step* 1** Write the numbers in columns, lining up the places.

***Step* 2** Start multiplying with the ones digit. If the product is ten or more, regroup.

***Step* 3** When the multiplication is complete, add all the results to find the product.

EXAMPLE 1 Multiply

(a) 371(58) **(b)** 1872 × 405

Solutions

(a)

$$\begin{array}{r} 371 \\ \times\ 58 \\ \hline 2968 \\ +18550 \\ \hline 21{,}518 \end{array}$$

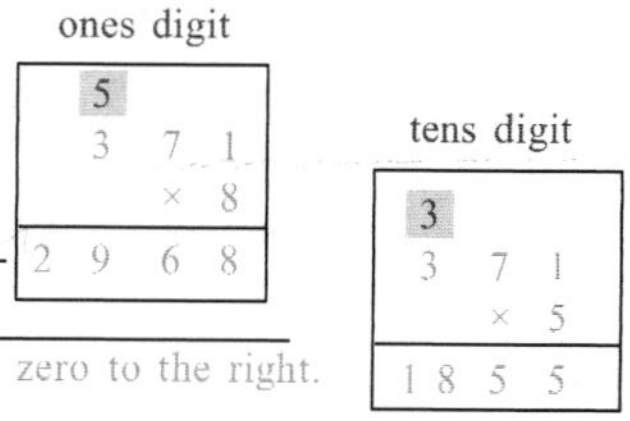

ones digit: 5 / 3 7 1 / × 8 / 2 9 6 8

tens digit: 3 / 3 7 1 / × 5 / 1 8 5 5

Insert one zero to the right.

(on adding)

$371 \times (58) = 21{,}518$

(b)

$$\begin{array}{r} 1872 \\ \times\ 405 \\ \hline 9360 \\ +00000 \\ +\ 748800 \\ \hline 758{,}160 \end{array}$$

Product = 758,160

Multiply by ones digit, 4 3 1 / 1 8 7 2 / × 5 / 9 3 6 0

tens digit, 1 8 7 2 / × 0 / 0 0 0 0

Insert one zero to the right

hundreds digit, 3 2 / 1 8 7 2 / × 4 / 7 4 8 8

Insert two zeros to the right

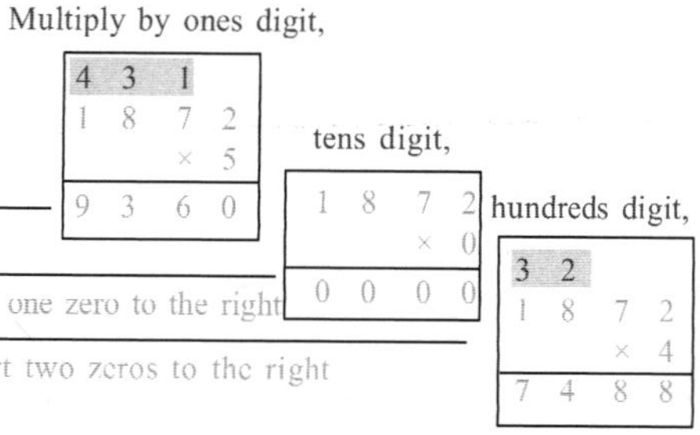

Showing a row of zeros can be omitted since the product of any number and zero is zero, and adding zero does not change the number.

EXAMPLE 2 Multiply 523 by 85 on a calculator.

Solution Use the ☒ key on your calculator to get the product.

On most calculators, you can enter

WARM-UP

1. Multiply

(a) 847 (75)

(b) 9321 × 807

2. Obtain the products in example 1 (a) and (b) on a calculator.

523 [×] 85 [=] or [ENTER]

Upon completion, the calculator should display 44455.

The product is 44,455.

Procedure to estimate the product of two whole numbers.

***Step* 1** Round each number to its largest place.

***Step* 2** Multiply the rounded numbers.

EXAMPLE 3 Estimate the product

472 × 8593

Solution Product estimate

$$\begin{array}{rcr} 8593 & \approx & 9000 \\ 472 & \approx & \times\ 500 \\ \hline & & 4{,}500{,}000 \end{array}$$

Multiply 9 by 5 and append five zeros to the right of the product.

The estimate of the product is 4,500,000.

WARM-UP

Answers:

1 and 2. (a) 63,525 **(b)** 7,522,047

3. 1,200,000

EXERCISE 3.3

In exercises 1-20, find the indicated product.

1. 41 × 5 **2.** 232 × 3 **3.** 879 × 0 **4.** 0 × 37 **5.** 706(6)

6. 30(40) **7.** 251 × 1 **8.** 700 × 50 **9.** (400)(19) **10.** (0) 999

11. 414 × 23 **12.** 235 × 31 **13.** 82 × 98 **14.** 253 × 4,052 **15.** 313 × 214

16. 305(209) **17.** (75) (25) (154) **18.** 2,972 × 569 **19.** 1,372 × 208 **20.** 1,790 × 230

In exercises 21-30, estimate the product and compute its exact value using calculator.

21. 687 and 34 **22.** 346 and 276 **23.** 633 and 2361 **24.** (32) (71) (82) **25.** 412 and 593

26. 89 and 19 **27.** 3,941 and 587 **28.** 3,947 and 594 **29.** 4,977 and 5,124 **30.** 45,974 and 3,452

3.4 Division and Exponents

Vocabulary

Objectives

After completing this section you will be able to:

A. Divide whole numbers and Estimating;

B. Expressions Involving Exponents; and

C. Simplifying Numerical Expressions

1. • One symbol used to indicate division is "÷" and is read as "divided by".

• The number divided by another is called the **dividend**.

The number dividing the dividend is called the **divisor**, and the answer obtained is called the **quotient**.

36 ÷ 4 (read: "36 divided by 4") is 9,

36 is the *dividend*, 4 is the *divisor*, and 9 is the *quotient*.

• The expression 47 ÷ 5 does not have a whole number quotient.

It can be written as 47 ÷ 5 = 9 R 2.

In this case, 9 is called the quotient, and 2 is called the **remainder**.

• The division 758 ÷ 15 can also be written as

$$\frac{758}{15} \quad \text{or} \quad 758/15 \quad \text{or} \quad 15\overline{)758}$$

• The expression $4x$ is the common way to write "4 times x" or "4 multiplied by x".

• The expression $\frac{x}{3}$ is read as "x divided to 3".

2. The symbol 3^5 (read the fifth power of 3, or 3 to the fifth power) represents the repeated product $3 \times 3 \times 3 \times 3 \times 3$ and is called the **exponential form** of the product.

3. In 3^5, 3 is called the **base**, and 5 is called the **exponent** or the **power**.

4. Exponents 2 and 3 are often read as **"squared"** and **"cubed"**.

4^2 is read as **"4 squared"**;

7^3 is read as **"7 cubed"**.

5. A **numerical expression** is an expression involving numbers, operations (+, –, ×, ÷), and exponents.

6. To **evaluate** or **simplify** means to perform all possible calculations.

A. Dividing Whole Numbers and Estimating

➜ **Divide whole numbers.**

Verify Skill

Objective 3.4A

(a) Find the product 375 × 47.

Illustrations

(a) Divide 235 by 21.

(b) Divide 2461 by 23.

If your answers to these questions are the same as given below then you may skip this objective.

Answers: (a) Quotient 1373 R 31 (b) 107

```
                11   <— Quotient
Divisor —> 21) 235   <— Dividend
               21
               25
               21
                4    <— Remainder
```

(b) Divide 3502 by 17.

```
                206   <— Quotient
Divisor —> 17) 3502   <— Dividend
               34
               10
                0
               102
               102
                 0    <— Remainder
```

Discussion

Division is the *inverse* process of multiplication. Dividing 75 by 25 is the same as finding a number whose product with 25 is 75. In other words, to find the quotient $75 \div 25$ means to find the missing factor in the product $25 \times \_\_\_ = 75$. The missing factor can be found by repeatedly subtracting 25 from 75.

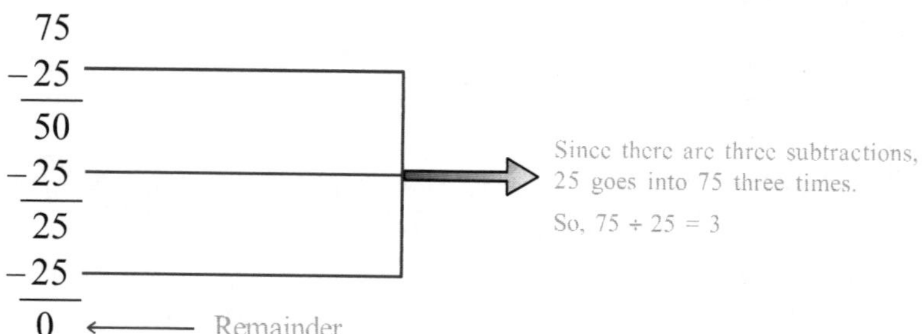

Division is a short form of repeated subtraction.

Recall multiplication is the same as repeated addition.

- $75 \div 25 = 3$ is a **division fact**;

75	÷	25	=	3
↓		↓		↓
Dividend		Divisor		Quotient

The division $75 \div 25$ can also be written as:

$\frac{75}{25}$,   75/25   or $25\overline{)75}$

Corresponding to each multiplication fact for two non-zero numbers there are two division facts. For example,

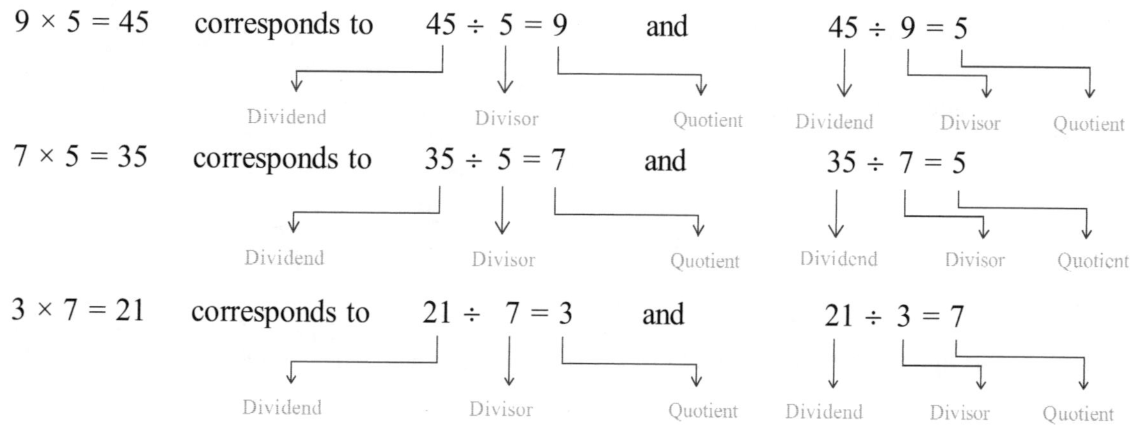

- Observe that **Divisor × Quotient = Dividend**

- It is important to note that a non zero whole number cannot be divided by zero. For example, try to divide 7 by 0. Dividing 7 by 0 is the same as finding the missing factor in the product $0 \times ? = 7$, but $0 \times$ any number $= 0$. No whole number can be found to meet this requirement.

  It is not possible to divide any whole number by 0.

  We say $\frac{x}{0}$ is undefined for any number x. So $\frac{8}{0}$ is undefined.

- However, we can divide zero by any non-zero whole number.

  Since,

  $11 \times 0 = 0$, we can say $0 \div 11 = 0$

  $0 \times 9 = 0$, we can say $0 \div 9 = 0$

  $1 \times 0 = 0$, we can say $0 \div 1 = 0$

  Observe that the quotient in each case is zero.

  When zero is divided by any non-zero number, the quotient is always zero.

  It is interesting to note that the multiplication fact $0 \times 0 = 0$ does not give rise to any division fact.

- The most common form of division is called "long division".

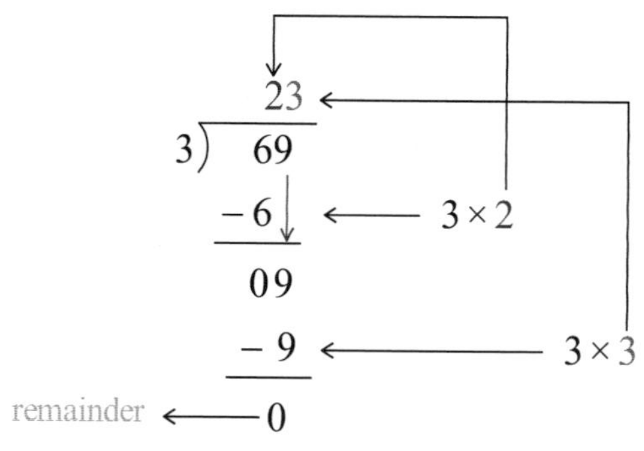

- Divide the left most place (tens place in this case) by 3: 6 tens ÷ 3 = 2 tens.

  Write the quotient (2) on the top of 6, and the product (divisor × quotient) below the dividend, lining up the places. Do subtraction in the tens places, and bring the *next* **digit** down from the dividend. Make sure to bring down just **one** digit.

- Divide in the next place, which is the ones place in this case: 9 ones ÷ 3 = 3 ones.

  Write the quotient (3) on the top of 9 and the product (divisor × quotient) below the digit, which was brought down, lining up the places.

- Continue the process until all the digits in the dividend have been used.

- Not all division problems do "come out even". There may be a remainder.

  Consider for example 37 ÷ 5.

```
                      7 ———→ partial quotient (or quotient)
divisor ———→  5) 37
                −35
                 ——
                  2 ———→ remainder
```

5 goes into 37 only 7 times; in other words 37 contains 7 fives with 2 left over.

7 is called the **quotient** and 2 is called the **remainder**.

Symbolically, we write

$$37 \div 5 = 7 \text{ R } 2$$

Quotient (7) remainder (2)

R is the abbreviation for Remainder. We write the quotient (partial) to the left of R and the remainder to the right of R.

- The remainder is always smaller than the divisor (2 < 5), and
- Divisor × Quotient + Remainder = Dividend

Divisor	×	Quotient	+	Remainder	=	Dividend
↓	↓	↓	↓	↓	↓	↓
5	×	7	+	2	=	37

Consider one more division. Divide 2,718 by 5

```
     543
 5) 2718
   −25↓
     21
    −20↓
      18
     −15
       3
```

- 5 cannot divide 2 (the left most digit in the dividend). So, consider the first two digits from the left, 27.
- 5 can go into 27 five times. Write 5 above 7 (the right most digit in the group) and the product 5 × 5 = 25 below 27 lining up the places. Subtract to get the remainder 2.
- Bring down the next digit in the dividend, and write it next to the remainder 2 to get the new number 21.
- Now, divide 21 by 5 in a similar manner, and continue the process until all the digits in the dividend have been used.

So, $2718 \div 5 = 543 \text{ R } 3$

Quotient (543) remainder (3)

- The process explained above works regardless of the size of the numbers. Study the following example carefully.

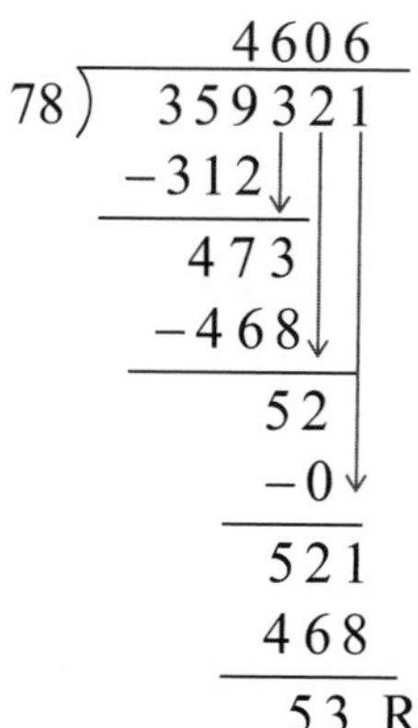

- Since the divisor consists of two digits, consider the group of the first two digits (from left) as the dividend. It is 35, which is smaller than 78, so enlarge the group to include the next **digit**, which is 9 in this case. Thus, the first group to be considered is 359.
- By either subtracting 78 from 359 repeatedly or by making a guess, we find that 78 goes into 359 four times. Write 4 above the 9 (the right most digit in the group), and the product of 78 × 4 (= 312) below the 359 lining up the places. Subtract to get the remainder 47.
- Bring down the next digit in the dividend, and write it to the right of the remainder 47, to get the number 473. Repeat the above step for this group.
- 78 goes into 473 six times. Write the quotient 6 above the digit that was brought down, which is 3. Write the product of 6 and 78 (= 468) below the 473 and subtract. Bring down the next **digit**, 2, in the dividend and write it to the right of the remainder 5 to get the number 52.
- Now, 78 cannot divide 52 or we say that 78 goes into 52 zero times. So write 0 above the 2, (the digit which was brought down in this step). Subtract the product 78 × 0 = 0 from 52, to get the remainder (difference) 52.
- Bring down the next digit in the dividend (1) and append it to the right of 52. Continue the process until all the digits in the dividend have been brought down and division is performed in each group.

Thus, $359321 \div 78 =$ **4,606 R 53**

Many students miss the zero in this process. To avoid this common error, be sure to write a digit above the division bar **each** time you bring a digit down.

Procedure to divide a number by a single digit divisor.

***Step* 1** Divide the left most digit of the dividend by the divisor if it is greater or equal to the divisor. Otherwise divide the two left most digits of the dividend by the divisor. Write the answer above that portion of the dividend.

***Step* 2** Find the product of your answer from *step* 1 and the divisor. Write the answer under the left most digit(s) of the dividend.

***Step* 3** Find the difference between the number just written and the left most digit(s) in the dividend.

***Step* 4** Bring down the next digit in the dividend and divide by the divisor.

***Step* 5** Repeat steps 1 through 4 until all the digits in the dividend have been used.

EXAMPLE 1 Divide

(a) $5609 \div 8$ **(b)** $2924 \div 7$

Solutions:

(a)
```
     701 R 1
8 ) 5609
   -56↓
    00
    -0
    09
    -8
     1
```

- The left most digit in the dividend is 5, which is less than the divisor, 8. So divide the two left most digits, 56, by 8. Write the 7 above the 6 in 56.
- Find the product of 7 and 8. Write the answer under 56.
- Subtract 56 from 56
- Bring down the 0.
- Divide 8 into 0. Put the answer, 0 above the 0.
- Find the product of 0 and 8. Write the answer under 0.
- Bring down the 9.
- Divide 8 into 9. Put the answer above the 9.
- Find the product of 1 and 8. Write the answer below 9.
- Subtract. Since there are no more digits to bring down, we are done and 1 is the remainder.

WARM-UP

1. Find the quotient and the remainder, if any.

(a) $4{,}891 \div 4$

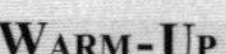

WARM-UP

(b) $5224 \div 6$

Check:

divisor × quotient + R = dividend, or

quotient × divisor + R = dividend

$701 \times 8 + 1$

$= 5608 + 1$

$= 5609$

(b)

```
      417  R 5
  7 ) 2924
     -28
     ---
       12
      -7
     ---
       54
      -49
      ---
        5
```

29 ÷ 7 = 4
4 × 7 = 28
29 − 28 = 1
Bring down the 2
12 ÷ 7 = 1
1 × 7 = 7
12 − 7 = 5
Bring down the 4
54 ÷ 7 = 7
7 × 7 = 49
54 − 49 = 5
There is nothing to bring down so the remainder is 5.

Check:

Quotient × divisor + R = dividend

417 × 7 + 5 = 2919 + 5 = 2924

Procedure to divide a number by a non-single digit divisor.

***Step* 1** Divide the left most digits of the dividend by the divisor. The number of digits taken on the left side of the divisor should be the fewest digits necessary so that this group of digits is larger or equal to the divisor.

***Step* 2** Find the product of your answer from *step* 1 and the divisor. Write the answer under the left most digits of the dividend.

***Step* 3** Find the difference between the number just written and the left most digits in the dividend.

***Step* 4** Bring down the next digit in the dividend and divide by the divisor.

***Step* 5** Repeat steps 1 through 4 until all the digits in the dividend have been used.

WARM-UP

2. Find the quotient and the remainder, if any.

5,395 ÷ 26

EXAMPLE 2 Divide 4293 ÷ 14

Solution

```
        306
  14 ) 4293
      -42
      ---
        09
        -0
       ---
         93
        -84
        ---
          9
```

42 ÷ 14 = 3
3 × 14 = 42
42 − 42 = 0
Bring down the 9
9 ÷ 14 = 0
0 × 14 = 0
9 − 0 = 9
Bring down the 3
93 ÷ 14 = 6
6 × 14 = 84
93 − 84 = 9
There is nothing to bring down so 9 is the remainder.

Check:

Quotient × divisor + R = dividend

306 × 14 + 9 = 4,284 + 9 = 4,293

EXAMPLE 3 Divide using a calculator. Find the remainder, if any.

(a) 70,577 ÷ 89 **(b)** 59,602 ÷ 103

Solutions

(a) Use the ÷ key on your calculator to get the quotient.

For most calculators , enter

ENTER 70577 [÷] 89 [=] or [ENTER]

Upon completion, the calculator should display 793.

The quotient is 793, and the remainder is 0

(b) ENTER 59602 [÷] 103 [=] or [ENTER]

Upon completion, the calculator should display **578**.66019.

The quotient is 578. Now find the remainder,

$$103\overline{)\,59{,}602}\quad 578 \text{ R ?}$$

To find the remainder, first find the product of 103 and 578

ENTER 103 [×] 578 [=] or [ENTER]

Upon completion, the calculator should display 59534.

Now, subtract this product from the dividend to get the remainder.

ENTER 59602 [−] 59534 [=] or [ENTER]

Upon completion, the calculator should display 68.

$$\begin{array}{r} 578 \text{ R } 68 \\ 103\overline{)\,59{,}602} \\ -\ 59\,534 \\ \hline 68 \end{array}$$

So, 59602 ÷ 103 = 578 R 68

Note Some calculators will calculate the quotient and the remainder.

WARM-UP

3. Divide using a calculator and find the remainder, if any.

(a) 57,704 ÷ 73

(b) 123,474 ÷ 124

Answers:

1. (a) 1222 R 3 (b) 870 R 4
2. 207 R 13
3. (a) 790 R 34 (b) 995 R 94

B. EXPRESSIONS INVOLVING EXPONENTS

➜ Find the value of an expression involving exponents.

Application

The volume of a cube can be found by cubing the length of a side of the cube. Find the volume of a cube having sides of length 6 inches.

Verify Skill

Objective 3.4B

Evaluate the following expressions:

(a) $7^2 - 5$ **(b)** $3^4 + 5^3$

If your answers to these questions are the same as given below then you may skip this objective.

Answers: **(a)** 44, **(b)** 206

Illustration

Find the value of the expression $4^3 + 7$:

$$\begin{aligned} 4^3+7 &= 4 \cdot 4 \cdot 4+7 \\ &= 64+7 \\ &= 71 \end{aligned}$$

Discussion

Repeated multiplications of a number by itself can be written in a symbolic form, called the **exponential form**. The product $4 \times 4 \times 4 \times 4 \times 4$ is written as 4^5, and is read *the fifth power* of 4 or 4 *to the fifth power.*

4^5 is the exponential form of the product $4 \times 4 \times 4 \times 4 \times 4$ (= 1024),

and the number 1024 is called the **value** of 4^5.

In 4^5, 4 is called the **base**, and 5 is called the **exponent** or **power**.

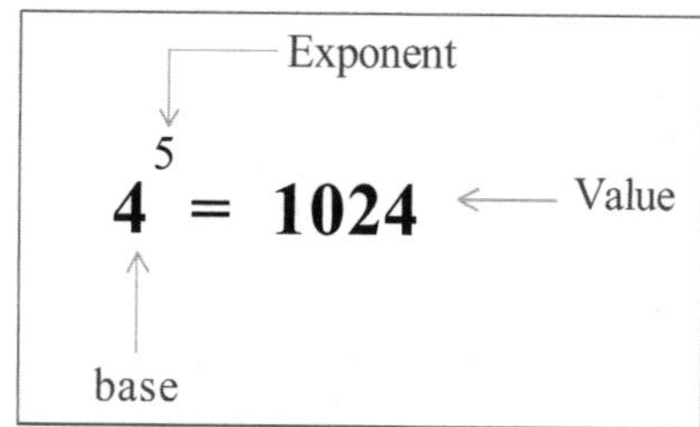

The exponent is a whole number that is used to represent the number of times the base is represented in the product. The whole numbers 0 and 1 may also be used as exponents.

- If 1 is used as the exponent, the value is equal to the base.

  That is, $3^1 = 3$ $5^1 = 5$ $9^1 = 9$.

  If *zero* is used as the exponent of any non-zero base the value is always equal to 1.

  That is, $4^0 = 1$ $7^0 = 1$ $2^0 = 1$.

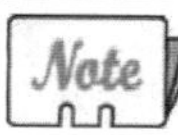

0^0 is not defined.

- Consider a few more examples for illustration.

$3^0 = 1$

$3^1 = 3$

$3 \times 3 = 3^2$ (read as *the square of* 3 or 3 *squared*)

$3 \times 3 \times 3 = 3^3$ (read as *the cube of* 3 or 3 *cubed*)

$3 \times 3 \times 3 \times 3 = 3^4$ (read as *the fourth power of* 3 or 3 *to the fourth power*)

$3 \times 3 \times 3 \times 3 \times 3 = 3^5$ (read as *the fifth power of* 3 or 3 *to the fifth power*)

$3 \times 3 \times 3 \times 3 \times 3 \times 3 = 3^6$ (read as *the sixth power of* 3 or 3 *to the sixth power*)

- To evaluate a number written in exponential form, use the base as a factor as many times as the exponent. Thus,

$$4^3 = 4 \times 4 \times 4 = 64 \; ; \qquad 5^4 = 5 \times 5 \times 5 \times 5 = 625$$

- Writing the repeated product of a number in exponential form is very useful in mathematics because it is less cumbersome than writing the repeated product or the value of the exponent when the value is very large.

Procedure to find the value of a number written in exponential form.

***Step* 1** Identify the base and the exponent

***Step* 2**
- If the exponent is zero, and the base is not zero, then the value is one;
- If the exponent is one, then the value is the base;
- If the exponent is larger than one, use the base as a factor as many times as the exponent and compute the product;

EXAMPLE 4 Evaluate the following

(a) 7^4 **(b)** 8^3 **(c)** 9^0 **(d)** 1^6

Solutions

(a) 7^4: The base is 7, and the exponent is 4.

Use 7 as a factor 4 times:

$$\begin{aligned} 7^4 &= 7 \cdot 7 \cdot 7 \cdot 7 \\ &= 49 \cdot 7 \cdot 7 \\ &= 343 \cdot 7 \\ &= 2401. \end{aligned}$$

Thus, the value of 7^4 is 2401.

(b) 8^3: The base is 8, and the exponent 3.

Use 8 as a factor three times: $8^3 = 8 \cdot 8 \cdot 8$
$= 64 \cdot 8 = 512$

Thus the value of 8^3 is 512.

(c) 9^0: The base is 9 and the exponent is *zero.*

Therefore, the value is 1.

That is $9^0 = 1$

(d) 1^6: The base is 1, therefore the value is *one* for any exponent.

That is $1^6 = 1$

WARM-UP

4. Find the value.

(a) 3^4

(b) 6^3

(c) 2^0

(d) 1^9

5. Evaluate 13^5 using a calculator.

6. Evaluate the following expressions

(a) $103 + 7^3$

(b) $5^4 - 125$

(c) $8^3 \cdot 4$

(d) $848 \div 2^4$

EXAMPLE 5 Evaluate $(15)^4$ using a calculator

Solution The power button on a scientific calculator may be x^y, y^x or ^ .

On most calculators, enter

15 x^y 4 = or ENTER

Upon completion, the calculator should display 50625.

Therefore, $15^4 = 50{,}625$.

> **Procedure** to find the value of an expression involving exponents
>
> ***Step* 1** Evaluate all the numbers written in exponential form.
>
> ***Step* 2** Perform the other operations.

EXAMPLE 6 Evaluate the following expression

(a) $4^3 + 15$ **(b)** $248 - 3^5$

(c) $5 \cdot 7^3$ **(d)** $6^4 \div 4$

Solutions

(a) $4^3 + 15 = 4 \cdot 4 \cdot 4 + 15$ • Evaluate 4^3.

$= 64 + 15$ • Simplify (add).

$= 79$

(b) $248 - 3^5 = 248 - 3 \cdot 3 \cdot 3 \cdot 3 \cdot 3$ • Evaluate 3^5.

$= 248 - 243$ • Simplify (subtract).

$= 5$

(c) $5 \cdot 7^3 = 5 \cdot 7 \cdot 7 \cdot 7$ • Evaluate 7^3.

$= 5 \cdot 343$ • Simplify (multiply).

$= 1{,}715$

(d) $\frac{6^4}{4} = \frac{6 \cdot 6 \cdot 6 \cdot 6}{4}$ • Evaluate 6^4.

$= (6 \cdot 6 \cdot 6 \cdot 6) \div 4$ • Simplify (divide).

$= (1296) \div 4$

$= 324$

Solution to the Application

The volume of a cube can be found by cubing the length of a side of the cube. Find the volume of a cube having sides of length 6 inches.

Solution: Volume $= 6$ in cubed

$= (6 \text{ in})^3$

$= 6 \text{ in} \times 6 \text{ in} \times 6 \text{ in} = 216 \text{ in}^3$

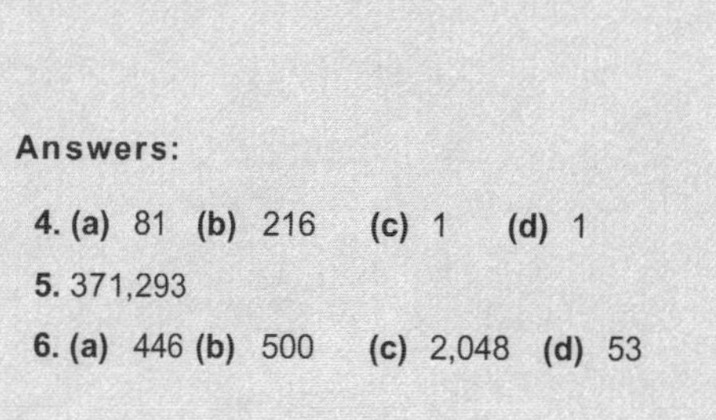

Answers:

4. (a) 81 (b) 216 (c) 1 (d) 1

5. 371,293

6. (a) 446 (b) 500 (c) 2,048 (d) 53

C. Simplifying Numerical Expressions

➜ **Simplify numerical expressions involving different operations.**

Illustration

Evaluate $(2^4 - 2 \cdot 5)^2 \div 4 \cdot 3^2 + 15 - 4 \cdot 7.$

$\mathbf{(2^4 - 2 \cdot 5)^2} \div 4 \cdot 3^2 + 15 - 4 \cdot 7.$

$= \mathbf{(16 - 10)^2} \div 4 \cdot 9 + 15 - 4 \cdot 7$

$= 6^2 \div 4 \cdot 9 + 15 - 4 \cdot 7$

$= \mathbf{36 \div 4} \cdot 9 + 15 - 4 \cdot 7$

$= \mathbf{9 \cdot 9} + 15 - \mathbf{4 \cdot 7}$

$= \mathbf{81 + 15} - 28 = 96 - 28 = 68.$

Verify Skill

Objective 3.4 C

Evaluate the following expressions.

(a) $17 - 2(4^2 - 3 \times 4) + 3$

(b) $(4^2 \div 8 \cdot 5)(7 - 4 \div 2) \div 5 + 2(52 + 6 \div 3)$

If your answer to this question is the same as given below then you may skip this objective.

Answer: (a) 12 (b) 118

Discussion

A numerical expression is a combination of numbers, exponents and operations (+, –, ×, and ÷). In previous sections, the expressions involved only one of these operations. The next step is to evaluate numerical expressions which may involve any combination of operations on whole numbers.

To do this, it is necessary to have some laws or rules of order in which the various operations should be performed, so that people, calculators, and computers get the same results. For example, in the absence of such rules, it is possible to interpret $4 \cdot 5 + 7$ in two ways:

		or		
$\mathbf{4 \cdot 5} + 7$			$4 \cdot \mathbf{5 + 7}$	
20 + 7	First multiply		$4 \cdot \mathbf{12}$	First add,
27	then add.		**48**	then multiply.

This gives two different results from the same numerical expression. In order to avoid such a situation, there are universally accepted rules called the *order of operations*.

Rules for Order of Operations:

1. First, evaluate exponents.
2. Next, perform Multiplications and Divisions in the order in which they appear from left to right.
3. Then, perform Additions and Subtractions in the order in which they appear from left to right.
4. If the expression involves *parentheses* ( ), then the operations within parentheses should be carried out first, following the above order of operations.

For example,

$25 - \mathbf{6 \div 3} + \mathbf{8 \cdot 4} = \mathbf{25 - 2} + 32$ • Divide ($6 \div 3 = 2$) and multiply ($8 \cdot 4 = 32$).

$= 23 + 32$ • Subtract and then add in order of appearance from left to right.

$= 55$

Procedure to simplify (or evaluate) a numerical expression.

***Step* 1** PARENTHESES - Perform the operation within the parentheses, in the order given in steps 2, 3 and 4.

***Step* 2** EXPONENTS - Evaluate exponents.

***Step* 3** MULTIPLY and DIVIDE - Perform multiplications and divisions in the order in which they appear from the left to right.

***Step* 4** ADD and SUBTRACT - Perform additions and subtractions in the order in which they appear from left to right.

WARM-UP

7. Simplify the following numerical expressions:

(a) $3 \times 5 + 4$

(b) 21 – 15 ¸ 3

(c) 15 + 24 ¸ 2

EXAMPLE 7 Simplify the following numerical expressions.

(a) $3 \times 2 + 4$ **(b)** $5 + 2 \times 3$ **(c)** $7 - 3 \times 2$

Solutions

(a) $\mathbf{3 \times 2} + 4$ Multiply first

$= 6 + 4$

$= 10$

(b) $5 + \mathbf{2 \times 3}$ Multiply first

$= 5 + \mathbf{6}$

$= 11$

(c) $7 - \mathbf{3 \times 2}$ Multiply first

$= 7 - \mathbf{6}$

$= 1$

EXAMPLE 8 Simplify the following expressions.

(a) $2(5 + 3) - 10$ **(b)** $5 + 2(4 + 3)$

(c) $17 + 3\ (5 - 10 \div 2)$

Solutions

(a) $2(\mathbf{5 + 3}) - 10$

$= \mathbf{2(8)} - 10$

$= 16 - 10$

$= 6$

(b) $5 + 2(\mathbf{4 + 3})$

$= 5 + \mathbf{2(7)}$

$= 5 + 14$

$= 19$

(c) $17 + 3\ (5 - \mathbf{10 \div 2})$

$= 17 + 3(\mathbf{5 - 5})$

$= 17 + \mathbf{3(0)}$

$= 17 + 0$

$= 17$

EXAMPLE 9 Evaluate the following numerical expression.

$$15 - 21 \div 7 + 25$$

Solution

$15 - \mathbf{21 \div 7} + 25$ • Divide $21 \div 7$

$= \mathbf{15 - 3} + 25$ • Subtract $15 - 3$

$= \mathbf{12} + 25$ • Add

$= 37$

EXAMPLE 10 Perform the indicated operations and simplify.

$$5 \cdot 2^3 - 2 \cdot 4^2 + 25 - 7 \cdot 3$$

Solution

$5 \cdot \mathbf{2^3} - 2 \cdot \mathbf{4^2} + 25 - 7 \cdot 3$ • Exponents $2^3 = 8$, $4^2 = 16$

$= \mathbf{5 \cdot 8 - 2 \cdot 16} + 25 - \mathbf{7 \cdot 3}$ • Multiply

$= \mathbf{40 - 32} + 25 - 21$

$= \mathbf{8 + 25} - 21 = 33 - 21$ • Add and subtract in the order of appearance from left to right.

$= 12$

WARM-UP

8. Simplify the following expressions:

(a) $2(3 + 7) - 15$

(b) $9 + 2(4 + 3)$

(c) $21 - 5(12 - 4 \times 2)$

9. Evaluate

$12 \times 2 \div 6 + 16$

10. Perform the indicated operations

$3 \cdot 4^3 - 8 \cdot 3^2 + 11$

WARM-UP

11. Evaluate

$75 \div 15 \cdot 2^4 - 3 \cdot 8 - 4.$

EXAMPLE 11 Evaluate $49 \div 7 \cdot 3^3 + 7 \cdot 4 - 17.$

Solution

$49 \div 7 \cdot \mathbf{3^3} + 7 \cdot 4 - 17$ • Exponent $3^3 = 27$.

$= \mathbf{49 \div 7} \cdot 27 + 7 \cdot 4 - 17$ • Multiply and divide in the order of appearance from left to right.

$= \mathbf{7 \cdot 27} + \mathbf{7 \cdot 4} - 17$

$= \mathbf{189 + 28} - 17$ • Add and subtract in the order of appearance from left to right.

$= 217 - 17$

$= 200$

12. Calculate the value using a calculator.

$3 \cdot 4^3 - 8 \cdot 3^2 + 11$

EXAMPLE 12 Evaluate the expression in example 8 on a calculator.

Solution The expression is: $5 \cdot 2^3 - 2 \cdot 4^2 + 25 - 7 \cdot 3$

Recall the power button on a scientific calculator may be $\boxed{x^y}$, $\boxed{y^x}$, or $\boxed{\wedge}$

On most calculators, enter

5 $\boxed{\times}$ 2 $\boxed{x^y}$ 3 $\boxed{-}$ 2 $\boxed{\times}$ 4 $\boxed{x^y}$ 2.

$\boxed{+}$ 25 $\boxed{-}$ 7 $\boxed{\times}$ 3 $\boxed{=}$ or $\boxed{\text{ENTER}}$

Upon completion, the calculator should display 12.

The value is 12, which is the same value obtained earlier in Example 8.

Answers:

7. (a) 19	(b) 16	(c) 27
8. (a) 5	(b) 23	(c) 1
9. 20	10. 131	11. 52
12. 131		

EXERCISE 3.4

In exercises 1-10, divide. Check your answer by multiplying.

1. $2{,}947 \div 7$ **2.** $\dfrac{3{,}012}{4}$ **3.** $\dfrac{6{,}304}{8}$ **4.** $711 \div 9$ **5.** $7{,}364 \div 7$

6. $\dfrac{235}{4}$ **7.** $\dfrac{2{,}512}{7}$ **8.** $\dfrac{5{,}313}{5}$ **9.** $538 \div 3$ **10.** $43{,}210 \div 6$

In exercises 11-20, divide and check the answer using multiplication. Also, round the quotient to its largest place.

11. $729 \div 21$ **12.** $1{,}397 \div 18$ **13.** $7{,}380 \div 47$ **14.** $1{,}248 \div 12$ **15.** $11{,}376 \div 237$

16. $\dfrac{1{,}245{,}648}{613}$ **17.** $\dfrac{153{,}874}{215}$ **18.** $\dfrac{10{,}172{,}486}{206}$ **19.** $\dfrac{10{,}616}{975}$ **20.** $\dfrac{46{,}087}{356}$

In exercises 21-28, find the quotient and remainder if any, without long division.

21. $2{,}356 \div 10$ **22.** $2{,}356 \div 100$ **23.** $9{,}073 \div 10$ **24.** $9{,}073 \div 1000$

25. $8{,}923{,}104 \div 1000$ **26.** $573 \div 573$ **27.** $0 \div 47$ **28.** $0 \div 1$

29. Can we divide 24 by 0 ? Explain : ______________________

____

30. Can we divide by 0 by 0 ? Explain : ______________________

____

31. Can we divide by 0 by 4 ? Explain : ______________________

____

B. In exercises 32-46, find the value of the expression.

32. 3^5 **33.** 4^3 **34.** 2^5 **35.** 12^0 **36.** 1^{48}

37. $2^3 - 5$ **38.** $3^2 + 7$ **39.** $5^2 - 11$ **40.** $6^2 + 10$ **41.** $7^2 - 15$

42. $2^3 - 4$ **43.** $12 + 3^3$ **44.** $4^2 \cdot 3$ **45.** $25 \div 5^2$ **46.** $2^3 \times 3^2$

C. In exercises 47-70, perform the indicated operations.

47. $48 + 72 \div 9$ **48.** $30 - (13 + 2)$ **49.** $12 \div 2 - 3$ **50.** $4 \times 3 + 9$

51. $5 \times 2 + 8$ **52.** $7 \times 3 - 10$ **53.** $10 \div 5 - 2$ **54.** $20 \div 4 + 7$

55. $7 + 3 \times 2$ **56.** $19 + 6 \times 2$ **57.** $19 - 6 \times 2$ **58.** $40 \div 10 + 25 \div 5$

59. $10 \div 5 + 20 \div 10$ **60.** $4 + 6 \div 3 - 14 \div 7$ **61.** $10 - 4 \div 4 - 9$ **62.** $21 \div 7 - 2$

63. $25 \div 5 - 5$ **64.** $25 - 5 \div 5$ **65.** $10 - 2(10 \div 5 - 2)$ **66.** $5 + 2(10 - 7)$

67. $15 + 3(2 + 7 \times 2)$ **68.** $60 - 5(7 + 6 \div 2)$ **69.** $9 + 3(7 + 20 \div 4)$ **70.** $3(4 + 2 \times 3) - 3(10 \div 2 + 3)$

In exercises 71-78, simplify the numerical expression.

71. $2^5 - 6 \cdot 2 + 4 \div 4$ **72.** $(5+2\cdot 2-3)^2 \div (4^2-3\cdot 2+2)$ **73.** $(2^2 + 2\cdot 3)^2 + 3^2$ **74.** $(3^2 - 4\cdot 2)^2 + 5^2$

75. $5^2 - 2(4 + 12 \div 2)$ **76.** $9 + 2^2(15 - 6 \div 3)$ **77.** $7(3^2 \cdot 2 - 8) \div 5 + 4 + (80 - 24 \div 4) + 4(8 - 3)^3 - 4^3$

78. $6(2^2 + 3^3) - 5 \cdot 7 + 12 \div 2 \times 6$

Evaluate the numerical expression in exercises 71 to 78 with a *calculator* and verify your answers for these exercises.

NUMBER THEORY

The discussion in this chapter is divided into two sections.

4.1 *Factors; and*

4.2 *Multiples, GCF and LCM.*

4.1 FACTORS

VOCABULARY

OBJECTIVES

Upon completion of this section you will study about:

A. Factors of Whole Numbers and Prime Factorization.

1. When two or more numbers are multiplied together, each number is a **factor** of the product. Also, the product is *divisible* by each of the factors. Thus, if a number is a *factor* of a second number, then the first number is also a **divisor** of the second number.

   4 is a factor (divisor) of 12 because $12 = 4 \cdot 3$

   9 is *not* a factor of 28, so 28 is *not divisible* by 9.

2. A **prime number** is a whole number greater than 1 with **exactly two** different factors or divisors, 1 and the number itself.

   2, 3, 5, 7 are examples of prime numbers.

   2 is the smallest prime number.

3. A **composite number** is a whole number greater than 1 with **more than two** different factors.

   6 is a composite number because it has factors 1, 2, 3 and 6.

   Every *even* number other than 2 is a composite number because 2 is a factor of every even number.

4. When a number is expressed as a product of prime numbers, the product is said to be the **prime factorization** of the number.

   $15 = 3 \cdot 5$ and $18 = 2 \cdot 3 \cdot 3$ are prime factorizations.

   $16 = 2 \cdot 8$ is *not* a prime factorization.

5. The **Greatest Common Factor** (abbreviated: GCF) of a group of natural numbers is:

   The largest natural number that is a factor of each number in the group.

(A.) FACTORS OF WHOLE NUMBERS AND PRIME FACTORIZATION

Application

A radio station has 122 minutes of programming to fill. In what ways can the time be scheduled if each program must last a whole number of minutes and if all programs must be of the same length.

Verify Skill

Objective 4.1A

(a) Write 36 as a product of two factors in all possible ways.

(b) List all the factors of 48.

If your answers to these questions are the same as given below then you may skip this objective.

Answers:

(a) $1 \cdot 36$, $2 \cdot 18$, $3 \cdot 12$, $4 \cdot 9$, $6 \cdot 6$

(b) 1, 2, 3, 4, 6, 8, 12, 16, 24, 48

Illustrations

- Write 28 as a product of two factors in all possible ways. Use the square method described in this objective.

  Since $5^2 = 25$ which is less than 28, and $6^2 = 36$ which is greater than 28, the first number whose square is larger than 28 is 6. Search for factors of 28 starting with 1 and ending with **5**, which is one less than 6.

  $1 \cdot 28$

  $2 \cdot 14$

  ~~3~~

  $4 \cdot 7$

  ~~5~~

  Hence, 28 written as a product of two factors in all possible ways is

  $1 \cdot 28$

  $2 \cdot 14$

  $4 \cdot 7$

- List all the factors of 68.

  $8^2 = 64$, which is < 68,

  $9^2 = 81$, which is > 68.

  Therefore, the first number whose square is greater than 68 is 9. Search for factor pairs up to the number 8.

$1 \cdot 68$	~~5~~
$2 \cdot 34$	~~6~~
~~3~~	~~7~~
$4 \cdot 17$	~~8~~

  The factors are 1, 2, 4, 17, 34, and 68.

Discussion

- Recall that when two or more numbers are multiplied together, the result obtained is the **product** of the numbers, and each of the numbers multiplied is a **factor** of the product.

  6 and 5 are factors of 30, since $6 \times 5 = 30$

  4 and 6 are factors of 24, since $4 \times 6 = 24$.

  Here, the numbers 30 and 24 are written as products of two numbers. There may be more than one way to write a number as a product of two numbers.

  For instance,

  $30 = 1 \times 30$; $30 = 2 \times 15$; $30 = 3 \times 10$; $30 = 5 \times 6$.

  are the four different ways to write 30 as a factor pair.

A factor of a natural number is always less than or equal to the number.

To write a number as a product of two factors in all possible ways, we can use trial and error method. However, in the case of a large number, say 136, trying all the smaller numbers would take too long. We use a short cut method, commonly known as the 'square method'. According to this method, it is sufficient to test only those numbers whose squares are less than or equal to the given number.

- To write 136 as a product of two factors in all possible ways, use the following two steps:

***Step* 1** List all the natural numbers from 1 up to but not including the first number whose *square* is larger than 136. Since $11^2 = 121$, and $12^2 = 144$, stop at 11.

1	5	9
2	6	10
3	7	11
4	8	

Stop at 11 since the square of 12 is larger than 136.

***Step* 2** Divide each of the listed natural number into 136. If it divides evenly, write the second factor. If not, cross out the number.

$1 \cdot 136$	~~5~~	~~9~~
$2 \cdot 68$	~~6~~	~~10~~
~~3~~	~~7~~	~~11~~
$4 \cdot 34$	$8 \cdot 17$	

These steps give a list of all the factor pair products.

Hence, all possible factor pair products of 136 are:

$1 \cdot 136$, $2 \cdot 68$, $4 \cdot 34$, $8 \cdot 17$

- It is important to note that if a first number is a factor of a second number, it is also a **divisor** of the second number.

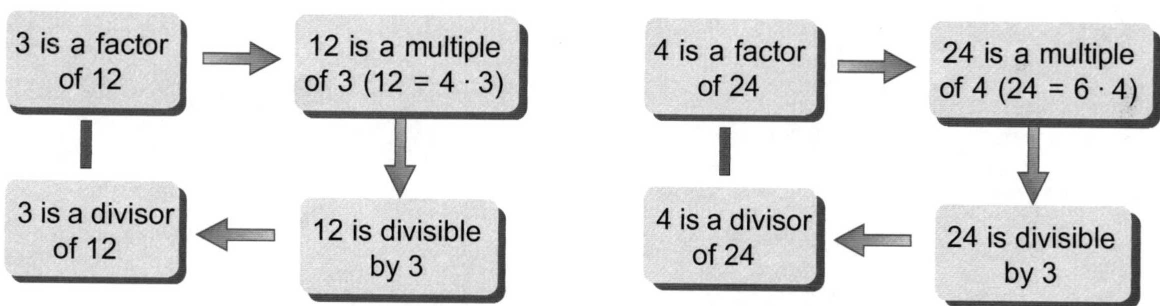

Writing a number as a product of factor pairs in all possible ways enables us to write all the possible factors or divisors of the number. All possible factor pairs of 136 are:

$1 \cdot 136$, $2 \cdot 68$, $4 \cdot 34$, and $8 \cdot 17$.

Thus, all possible factors of 136: 1, 136, 2, 68, 4, 34, 8, and 17.

The 'square method' used to find factors of a number can also be used to list all the factors in increasing order. List the factor pairs of 136 vertically, then read the factors as indicated by arrows.

$$\begin{array}{l} \downarrow \\ 1 \cdot 136 \\ 2 \cdot 68 \\ 4 \cdot 34 \\ 8 \cdot 17 \\ \llcorner\!\!\rightarrow\!\uparrow \end{array}$$

Read down the left column of the factors and then up the right column of factors.

By reading the factors in the direction of the arrows, the ordered list of all the factors of 136 is:

1, 2, 4, 8, 17, 34, 68, and 136.

> **Procedure** to write a whole number as a product of two factors in all possible ways.
>
> Use the 'square method'.
>
> ***Step* 1** List all the counting numbers whose squares are less than or equal to the given number.
>
> ***Step* 2** For each listed number, test whether the number is a divisor of the given number.
>
> ***Step* 3** (a) If the number is not a divisor, cross it off the list.
>
> (b) If the number is a divisor, write the factor pair.

WARM-UP

1. Write the numbers as products of two factors in all possible ways.

(a) 42

(b) 220

EXAMPLE 1 Write the following whole numbers as a product of two factors in all possible ways.

(a) 50 **(b)** 31

Solutions

(a) **50:** $1 \cdot 50$ $5 \cdot 10$

$2 \cdot 25$ ~~6~~

~~3~~ ~~7~~ Stop at 7, since $8^2 > 50$.

~~4~~

Thus, all possible pairs of factors of 50 are :

$1 \cdot 50$, $2 \cdot 25$, $5 \cdot 10$.

(b) **31:** $1 \cdot 31$ ~~5~~ Stop at 5, since $6^2 > 31$.

~~2~~

~~3~~

~~4~~

Thus, there is only one pair of factors of 31: $\mathbf{1 \cdot 31}$

Recall that 31 is a prime number by definition.

> **Procedure** to list in increasing order, all the factors or divisors of a whole number.
>
> ***Step* 1** Find all possible **factor pairs** of the number by the 'square method'.
>
> ***Step* 2** List all pairs of factors of the number in vertical form.
>
> ***Step* 3** Read down the left column of factors and up the right column.

EXAMPLE 2 List in increasing order all the factors of the number 68.

Solution First, find all possible factor pairs of 68 using the 'square method'.

$1 \cdot 68$ ~~7~~

$2 \cdot 34$ ~~8~~ Stop at 8, since $9^2 > 68$.

~~3~~

$4 \cdot 17$

~~5~~ ·

~~6~~

Now, list the pairs vertically:

$1 \cdot 68$

$2 \cdot 34$

$4 \cdot 17$ Read down the left column and then up the right column

All the factors (divisors) of 68 in increasing order are:

1, 2, 4, 17, 34, 68.

2. List in increasing order all factors of the number 112.

Answers:

1. **(a)** $1 \cdot 42$; $2 \cdot 21$; $3 \cdot 14$; $6 \cdot 7$

(b) 1×220; 2×110; 4×55; 5×44; 10×22; 11×20

2. 1, 2, 4, 7, 8, 14, 16, 28, 56, 112

Solution to the Application:

A radio station has 122 minutes of programming to fill. In what ways can the time be scheduled if each program must last a whole number of minutes and if all programs must be of the same length?

Solution: There are two ways to write 122 as a product of two whole numbers.

1 · 122, and **2 · 61**

1 · 122: 1 program that is 122 minutes long ;
or 122 programs that are 1 minute long each ;

2 · 61: 2 programs that are 61 minutes long each;
or 61 programs that are 2 minutes long each.

EXERCISE 4.1

A. In exercises 1-15, use the "square method" to write the whole number as a product of two factors in all possible ways.

1. 10	**2.** 12	**3.** 14	**4.** 20	**5.** 22
6. 28	**7.** 41	**8.** 65	**9.** 68	**10.** 100
11. 105	**12.** 116	**13.** 142	**14.** 250	**15.** 1,230

In exercises 16-30, list in ascending order all the factors of the given whole number.

16. 18	**17.** 6	**18.** 8	**19.** 12	**20.** 15
21. 22	**22.** 30	**23.** 56	**24.** 75	**25.** 116
26. 288	**27.** 105	**28.** 239	**29.** 231	**30.** 213

4.2 Multiples, GCF and LCM

Objectives

Upon completion of this section you will study about:

A. Finding Multiples and LCM;

B. Finding the Greatest Common Factor.

Vocabulary

1. A **multiple** of a natural number is the product of that number and another natural number.

   120 is a multiple of 8: $120 = 8 \times 15$.

   45 is a multiple of 9: $45 = 5 \times 9$.

2. The **Least Common Multiple** (abbreviated: LCM) of a group of natural numbers is:

   a. The smallest natural number that is a multiple of each of the numbers in the group.

   b. The smallest number that is divisible by each of the given numbers.

   c. The smallest number that has each of the given numbers as a factor.

   These three statements are equivalent.

A. Finding Multiples and LCM

Verify Skill

Objective 4.2A

(a) Find the fifth and eighteenth multiples of 11.

(b) Is the number 4,321,098 a multiple of 6 ?

If your answers to these questions are the same as given below then you may skip this objective.

Answers:

(a) 55,198 (b) Yes

➜ **List multiples of a natural number, and determine whether one natural number is a multiple of another natural number.**

Illustrations

- List the first four multiples of 7. $1 \cdot 7 = 7$, $2 \cdot 7 = 14$, $3 \cdot 7 = 21$, $4 \cdot 7 = 28$.

- Determine whether 729 is a multiple of 9

  Sum of the digits is $7 + 2 + 9 = 18$,

  which is divisible by 9, therefore 729 is a multiple of 9.

Discussion

- A **multiple** of a natural number is the product of that natural number with another natural number. For example, 35 is a multiple of 5 and 7, since $35 = 5 \times 7$. When two or more natural numbers are multiplied together, the product obtained is a multiple of each of the numbers multiplied.

  To list the multiples of 5, multiply 5 by 1, 2, 3, *etc...*

  Multiples of 5: 5 10 15 20 25 65 105…

  Notice that there are an infinite number of multiples of five. The list goes on forever.

  In the above list, 5, 10, 15,… are respectively called the first multiple of 5, the second multiple of 5, the third multiple of 5, and so on.

To find any particular multiple, say the 21st multiple of a number, multiply the number by 21. Thus, the 21st multiple of 7 is: 21×7 or 147.

- It is interesting to note the following facts:
  - **(a)** Every natural number is a multiple of itself.
  - **(b)** Every natural number is a multiple of 1.
  - **(c)** A multiple of a natural number is always greater than or equal to the number.
  - **(d)** Every even natural number is a multiple of 2.

- If a natural number is a **multiple** of another natural number, then the first number is necessarily **divisible** by the second number. 48 is a *multiple* of 6 since $48 = 6 \times 8$

  and $48 = 6 \times 8 \longrightarrow 48 \div 6 = 8 \longrightarrow$ 48 is *divisible* by 6.

  Conversely, if a natural number is divisible by another natural number, then the first number must be a **multiple** of the second number.

  579 is *divisible* by 3 since $579 \div 3 = 193$, and

  $579 \div 3 = 193 \longrightarrow 579 = 3 \times 193 \longrightarrow$ 579 is a *multiple* of 3.

  To determine whether a number, such as 252 is a multiple of another number, such as 21, it is sufficient to check whether 252 is divisible by 21. To check the divisibility, we divide 252 by 21, since there is no divisibility test available for 21.

$$\begin{array}{r} 12 \\ 21\overline{)252} \\ \underline{21} \\ 42 \\ \underline{42} \\ 0 \end{array}$$

The remainder is 0, which means that 252 is divisible by 21. Therefore, 252 is a multiple of 21.

> **Procedure** to find multiples of a natural number.
>
> Multiply the natural number by the numbers specified.

EXAMPLE 1

(a) Find the first five multiples of 4.

(b) Find the 11th multiple of 45.

Solutions

WARM-UP

1. (a) List the first three odd multiples of 4.

WARM-UP

(a)

$1 \times 4 = 4$
$2 \times 4 = 8$
$3 \times 4 = 12$
$4 \times 4 = 16$
$5 \times 4 = 20$

Multiply 4 by 1, 2, 3, 4, and 5.

(b) Find the 12th multiple of 25.

(b) The 11th multiple of 45 is

$11 \times 45 = 495$

$$\begin{array}{r} 45 \\ \times\ 11 \\ \hline 45 \\ +450 \\ \hline 495 \end{array}$$

Procedure to determine whether a natural number is a multiple of another natural number.

Check if the first natural number is divisible by the second natural number.

2. Determine whether 1089 is a multiple of 9.

EXAMPLE 2 Determine whether 2,130 is a multiple of 6.

Solution It is sufficient to check if 2,130 is divisible by 6. Use the divisibility tests for 6.

2,130 is **divisible by 2.** The last digit is 0.

2,130 is **divisible by 3.** The sum of the digits is divisible by 3.

Since 2,130 is divisible by both 2 and 3, it is divisible by 6. Hence **2,130 is a multiple of 6.**

3. Determine if 1,432 is a multiple of 15.

EXAMPLE 3 Determine if 4,531 is a multiple of 13.

Solution It is sufficient to check whether the number is divisible by 13.

Since no divisibility criteria is available for 13, use long division or a calculator to check divisibility.

Verify that **4,531 ÷ 13 = 348 R 7**

Since the remainder is not zero, 4531 is not divisible by 13.

Therefore, 4,531 is not a multiple of 13.

Answers:

1. (a) 4,12,20 (b) 300
2. Yes
3. No

- **Finding the Greatest Common Factor**

➡ **Find the least common multiple of two or more natural numbers.**

Application

Two gongs strike at intervals of 16 and 20 minutes respectively. At what time will they strike together again if they start simultaneously at 12 noon?

Illustration

Find the least common multiple (LCM) of 12 and 18.

Method 1: **Listing of Multiples Method.**

Multiples of 12 : 12, 24, **36**, 48, 60, **72,** ...

Multiples of 18 : 18, **36,** 54, **72,** 90, ...

Common multiples : 36, 72, ...

Least common multiple : 36.

Method 2: **Individual Prime Factoring Method.**

Since $12 = 2^2 \cdot 3$,

and $18 = 2 \cdot 3^2$

The least common multiple of 12 and 18 is $2^2 \cdot 3^2 = \mathbf{36}$.

> **Verify Skill**
>
> **Objective 4.2B**
>
> Find the LCM of 12, 15, and 20.
>
> **If your answer to this question is the same as given below then you may skip this objective.**
>
> **Answer:** $2^2 \cdot 3 \cdot 5$ or 60

Discussion

The concept of **Least Common Multiple (LCM)** is important in arithmetic when dealing with fractions. The *least common multiple of the denominators* of fractions is needed for adding, subtracting or comparing fractions with different denominators. This discussion covers two different methods for finding the LCM of numbers.

- **Listing of Multiples Method**

The most important word in "least common multiple" is MULTIPLE. To find the LCM, first list the multiples of each number.

We list several of their multiples first.

Multiples of 12 : 12 24 36 48 **60** 72 84 96 108 **120 ...**

Multiples of 15 : 15 30 45 **60** 75 90 105 **120** ...

Next, we try to find common multiples. If there are no common multiples, you will need to list more multiples.

Two of the common multiples are 60 and 120. The smallest amongst them is 60. Therefore, the least common multiple of 12 and 15 is 60.

Finding the LCM by this method has a drawback: there are times when many multiples must be listed before a common multiple is arrived at. In such cases the LCM can be found more conveniently by using the prime factorization method.

- **Prime Factoring Method**

To find the least common multiple of 36 and 126, write the prime factorization of each.

$$\left.\begin{array}{l} 36 \;= 2 \cdot 2 \cdot 3 \cdot 3 = 2^2 \cdot 3^2 \\ 126 = 2 \cdot 3 \cdot 3 \cdot 7 = 2^1 \cdot 3^2 \cdot 7^1 \end{array}\right\}$$

The primes with the *largest exponents* are:

2^2, 3^2 and 7^1

Since the LCM must be divisible by 36, the LCM has $2 \cdot 2 \cdot 3 \cdot 3$ among its factors. Similarly, the LCM must be divisible by 126, so it has $2 \cdot 3 \cdot 3 \cdot 7$ among its factors.

The LCM is $2 \cdot 2 \cdot 3 \cdot 3 \cdot 7 = 2^2 \cdot 3^2 \cdot 7$

Note that the LCM is in fact the product of all the prime factors of both the numbers where each prime factor has an exponent which is the largest of its exponents appearing in the prime factorization of each number.

> **Procedure** to find the LCM of two or more natural numbers using the Listing of Multiples Method.
>
> ***Step* 1** List several multiples of each given number.
>
> ***Step* 2** Find the smallest multiple common to all the lists.

WARM-UP

4. Find the LCM of 5 and 7 by listing their multiples.

EXAMPLE 4 Find the LCM of 6 and 8.

Solution

The multiples of 6 are : 6, 12, 18, **24**, 30, 36, 42, **48** …

The multiples of 8 are : 8, 16, **24**, 32, 40, **48**, 56 …

The smallest number common to both lists is 24.

Hence, the LCM of 6 and 8 is 24.

> **Procedure** to find the LCM of two or more natural numbers using the Prime Factoring Method.
>
> ***Step* 1** Find the prime factorization of each of the given numbers, and write it using exponents.
>
> ***Step* 2** Write the product of each prime factor with the highest exponent.

5. Find the LCM of 112 and 140.

EXAMPLE 5 Find the LCM of 108 and 180 using the Individual Prime Factoring Method.

WARM-UP

Answers:

4. 35 **5.** 560

Solution

2	108
2	54
3	27
3	9
3	3
	1

2	180
2	90
3	45
3	15
5	5
	1

So,

$108 = 2 \cdot 2 \cdot 3 \cdot 3 \cdot 3 = 2^2 \cdot 3^3$

$180 = 2 \cdot 2 \cdot 3 \cdot 3 \cdot 5 = 2^2 \cdot 3^2 \cdot 5^1$

Thus, the LCM of 108 and 180 is $2^2 \cdot 3^3 \cdot 5^1$ or 540.

- Write the numbers as products of primes in exponent form.
- The different primes are 2, 3, and 5.
- The largest exponent of 2 is 2; the largest exponent of 3 is 3; the largest exponent of 5 is 1.
- Multiply.

Solution to the Application:

Two gongs strike at intervals of 16 and 20 minutes respectively. At what time will they strike together again if they start simultaneously at 12 noon?

We find the LCM of 16 and 20.

2	16
2	8
2	4
2	2
	1

2	20
2	10
5	5
	1

So,

$16 = 2 \cdot 2 \cdot 2 \cdot 2 = 2^4$

$20 = 2 \cdot 2 \cdot 5 = 2^2 \cdot 5^1$

The least common multiple of 16 and 20 is $2^4 \cdot 5^1 = 80$. The gongs will strike again together after 80 minutes = 1 hour 20 minutes. So, if they start simultaneously at 12 noon, they will strike together again at 1:20 pm.

B. FINDING THE GREATEST COMMON FACTOR

Verify Skill

Objective 4.2 B

Find the greatest common factor of 60 and 72.

➜ **Find the greatest common factor of two or more natural numbers.**

Application

An orgami artist wants to cut squares from a hand painted sheet of paper which measures 126 cm wide by 210 cm long. He wants all the squares to be the same size. What size square should he cut so that he gets the largest possible squares without wasting any paper?

Illustration

Find the greatest common factor (GCF) of 63 and 108.

Method 1: **Listing of Factors Method.**

Factors of 63: **1**, **3**, 7, **9**, 21, 63

Factors of 108: **1**, 2, **3**, 4, 6, **9**, 12, 18, 27, 36, 54, 108

The GCF of 63 and 108 is **9**

Method 2: **Individual Prime Factoring Method.**

Since $63 = 3^2 \cdot 7$

and $108 = 2^2 \cdot 3^3$

The GCF of 63 and 108 is $3^2 = 9$

If your answer to this question is the same as given below then you may skip this objective.

Answer: $2^2 \cdot 3 = 12$

Discussion

The concept of **Greatest Common Factor (GCF)** is important when dealing with fractions. Knowing the greatest common factor helps to simplify, multiply and divide fractions. We discuss two different methods for finding the greatest common factor of natural numbers.

- **Listing of Factors Method**

The most important word in "greatest common factor" is factor. To find the GCF, first list the factors of each number.

For example, to find the GCF of 12 and 18.

Factors of 12 : **1**, **2**, **3**, 4, **6**, 12

Factors of 18 : **1**, **2**, **3**, **6**, 9, 18

Next, find the factors that are **common** to both lists.

The common factors are 1, 2, 3, and 6.

Finally, find the largest of the common factors. In this case, the largest common factor is 6. Thus, the GCF of 12 and 18 is 6.

Finding the GCF by this method has a drawback: some large numbers have many factors and listing them all can be tedious.

- **Prime Factoring Method**

To find the greatest common factor of 36 and 126, write the prime factorization of each.

$36 = \mathbf{2} \cdot 2 \cdot \mathbf{3} \cdot \mathbf{3}$

$126 = \mathbf{2} \cdot \mathbf{3} \cdot \mathbf{3} \cdot 7$

The GCF is the product of the common prime factors so the GCF is $2 \cdot 3 \cdot 3 = 18$

WARM-UP

> **Procedure** to find the greatest common factor of two or more natural numbers using the Listing of Factors Method.
>
> ***Step* 1** List the factors of each number.
>
> ***Step* 2** Find the largest number common to all the lists.

6. Find the GCF of 6 and 9 by listing their factors.

EXAMPLE 6 Find the GCF of 18 and 24.

Solution The factors of 18 are : 1, 2, 3, 6, 9 and 18

The factors of 24 are : 1, 2, 3, 4, 6, 8, 12, and 24

The largest number common to both lists is 6. Hence, the GCF of 18 and 24 is 6.

> **Procedure** to find the greatest common factor of two or more natural numbers using the prime factoring method.
>
> ***Step* 1** Find the prime factorization of each of the given numbers.
>
> ***Step* 2** Write the product of the common prime factors.

7. Find the GCF of 72 and 108 by the prime factoring method.

EXAMPLE 7 Find the GCF of 75 and 125 using the prime factorization.

Solution Prime Factoring Method

$$75 = 3 \times 5 \times 5$$

$$125 = 5 \times 5 \times 5$$

The common primes are 5 and 5.

Thus, the GCF of 75 and 125 is $5 \times 5 = 25$

8. Find the GCF of 112, 140 and 168 by the prime factoring method.

EXAMPLE 8 Find the GCF of 96, 108 and 180 using the prime factoring method.

Solution Prime Factoring Method

$$96 = 2 \cdot 2 \cdot 2 \cdot 2 \cdot 2 \cdot 3$$

$$108 = 2 \cdot 2 \cdot 3 \cdot 3 \cdot 3$$

$$180 = 2 \cdot 2 \cdot 3 \cdot 3 \cdot 5$$

Thus, the GCF of 96, 108 and 180 is $2 \cdot 2 \cdot 3 = 12$

Answers:

6. 3 7. 36 8. 28

Solution to the Application:

An orgami artist wants to cut squares from a hand painted sheet of paper which measures 126 cm wide by 210 cm long. He wants all the squares to be the same size. What size square should he cut so that he gets the largest possible squares without wasting any paper?

Solution: Since the artist wants no waste, the width of the square must be a factor of both 126 and 210. (The length and width of a square are equivalent.) Since he also wants the largest possible squares, the width of the square must be the greatest common factor of 126 and 210.

Finding the prime factorization of 126 and 210 yields

$126 = 2 \cdot 3 \cdot 3 \cdot 7$

$210 = 2 \cdot 3 \cdot 5 \cdot 7$

The common prime factors are 2, 3 and 7. So, the greatest common factor of 126 and 210 is $2 \cdot 3 \cdot 7 = 42$. Thus, the artist can cut 42 cm by 42 cm squares from the painted paper without wasting any paper.

EXERCISE 4.2

In exercises 1-10, list the first five multiples of the given natural number.

1. 3 **2.** 4 **3.** 5 **4.** 6 **5.** 7

6. 10 **7.** 11 **8.** 12 **9.** 19 **10.** 23

In exercises 11-15, determine whether the given number is a multiple of 2, 3 or 5.

11. 945 **12.** 6,816 **13.** 14,545 **14.** 17,370 **15.** 45,774

16. A mathematics instructor assigns all problems from 25 to 60 that are multiples of 3. Which problems are assigned?

17. A teacher assigns all problems from problem number 14 to 40 that are multiples of 5. Which problems are assigned?

18. A teacher assigns all problems from problem number 12 to 50 that are multiples of 6. Which problems are assigned?

In exercises 19-31, find the LCM of each group of whole numbers.

19. 2, 4 **20.** 6, 10 **21.** 9, 15 **22.** 8, 12 **23.** 12, 15

24. 10, 15 **25.** 24, 36 **26.** 18, 24 **27.** 16, 20 **28.** 15, 20

29. 55, 33 **30.** 49, 35 **31.** 26, 39

Applications

32. Find the smallest number which is exactly divisible by 70 and 80.

33. Two bells ring at intervals of 12 and 20 minutes respectively. At what time will they ring together again if they start ringing simultaneously at 4 a.m.

34. Coffee is to be packed in 100 or 250 gm packets. Find the least quantity of coffee required so that an exact number of any kind of packets can be made from it.

35. In a morning walk, two people step together. Their steps measure 80 cm and 90 cm respectively. At what distance from the starting point will they step together again?

36. Two different sized boxes can hold 24 lb and 54 lb respectively. Find the least amount of weight which will exactly fit any of these types of boxes.

37. Pete is selling candy bars. Each package he makes has **one** of each of the following types of candy bars: Three Musketeers, Snickers and Nutrageous. He buys the candy in bulk. Each bulk package of Three Musketeers contains 12 bars, each bulk package of Snickers contains 16 bars and each bulk package of Nutrageous contains 18 bars. How many bulk packages of each type must Pete buy in order to create his packages and have no candy bars left over?

In exercises 38-45, find the greatest common factor of each group of natural numbers.

38. 9, 18 **39.** 24, 36 **40.** 12, 18 **41.** 40, 56

42. 50, 140 **43.** 63, 81 **44.** 72, 90 **45.** 84, 132

Applications

46. In what ways can a radio station schedule 115 minutes of time if each program must last a whole number of minutes and if all programs must be of the same length?

47. A television station has 76 minutes of programming to fill. In what ways can the time be scheduled if each program must last a whole number of minutes and if all programs must be of the same length?

48. Find the prime factorization of your birth year.

49. Find the largest and the smallest prime factors of 1179.

50. The year 1993 was a prime number. What is the next year that is a prime number?

51. An artist wants to cut squares from a hand painted roll of paper which measures 270 in by 390 in. He wants all the squares to be the same size. What size square should be cut so that he gets the largest possible squares without wasting any paper?

INTEGERS AND FRACTIONS

This chapter is divided into the following five sections.

5.1 *Integers, Addition and Subtraction;*

5.2 *Multiplication, Division, Order of Operation on Integers;*

5.3 *Introduction to Fractions;*

5.4 *Reducing, Equivalent, and Comparing Fractions; and*

5.5 *Operations with Fractions.*

5.1 INTEGERS, ADDITION AND SUBTRACTION

VOCABULARY

1. **Positive numbers** are numbers greater than zero.

2. **Negative numbers** are numbers less than zero. The number zero is neither positive nor negative.

3. The **opposite** of a signed number is the number on the number line that is at the same distance from zero, but on the opposite side of zero. The opposite of 4 is written as – 4 and is read "the opposite of 4" or "negative 4". The number zero is its own opposite.

OBJECTIVES

After completing this section you will be able to:

A. Find the Opposite and absolute value of a signed number ; and

B. Add and Subtract integers.

4. All the positive whole numbers, zero, and their opposites are called **Integers.**

5. The **absolute value** of a signed number is the number of units between that number and zero on the number line. The absolute value of 2 is symbolically written as $|2| . |2| = 2$; $|-5.3| = 5.3$

(A.) OPPOSITES AND ABSOLUTE VALUES

Application

The temperature on a January morning in Detroit, Michigan was 5°F. By noon, it had fallen and was the opposite of the morning temperature. What was the temperature at noon?

Illustrations

- The opposite of 24 is –24.
- The opposite of –18 is – (–18) = 18.

Verify Skill

Objective 5.1A

Write the opposites of

1. – 50 **2.** 0 **3.** 117

If your answers to this question are the same as those given below, then you may skip this objective.

Answers:

1. 50 **2.** 0 **3.** – 117

Discussion

- Observe that in subtractions like

$$2 - 5, \qquad 7 - 11, \qquad 1 - 124$$

where the second number is larger than the first number, there is no whole number solution. The answers are found by introducing *negative* numbers.

Subtract 2 – 5 on a number line just as explained in Chapter 1.

Draw a line, and plot a point on it. Label it zero. Then, all the positive numbers are represented on the line to the right of zero. For 2 – 5, starting at zero move two positive units to the right to reach the point labelled '2'. Then move 5 units to the left of 2. (Figure 5.1).

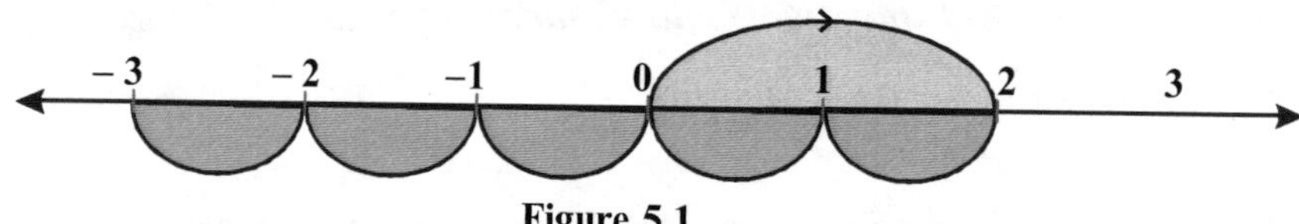

Figure 5.1

The point lies to the left of 0 by 3 units. This point is '– 3', read: "the opposite of 3" or "negative 3".

$$2 - 5 = -3.$$

Similarly, to compute 7 – 11, first go to the point 7. Then move 11 units to the left (Figure 5.2). The point lies 4 units to the left of 0.

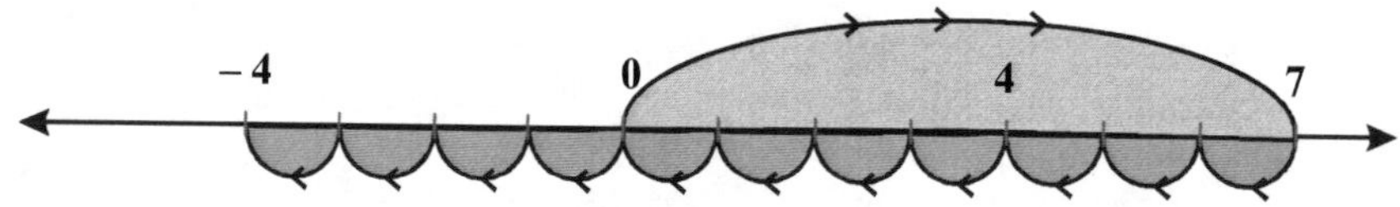

Figure 5.2

This point is "– 4" read: "the opposite of 4" or "negative 4."

$$7 - 11 = -4$$

The numbers to the left of 0 are **negative integers.**

The numbers to the right of 0 are **positive integers.**

The number zero (0) is neither positive nor negative.

Signed numbers include both positive and negative numbers as well as zero. A few signed numbers are shown in Figure 5.3

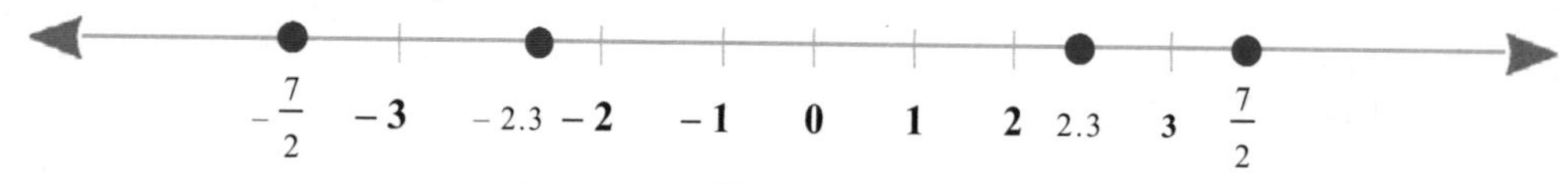

Figure 5.3

Observe that:

1. All positive numbers are *larger* than 0 and they all lie to the right of zero on the number line.
2. All negative numbers are *smaller* than 0 and they all lie to the left of zero on the number line.
3. Each negative number is smaller than every positive number. (Think, why?)

- In daily life, signed numbers are commonly used to represent quantities with opposite characteristics. For example,

Negative	*Positive*
Left of zero	**Right of zero**
(– 7)	(8)
Loss	**Profit**
(– $74)	($250)
Below sea level	**Above sea level**
(– 572 feet)	(3200 feet)
Fall in price	**Rise in price**
(– $1.25)	($2.50)
Temperature below zero	**Temperature above zero**
(– 4° F)	(32° F)
Bank withdraw	**Bank deposit**
(– $350)	($500)

Most quantities can be measured in both directions. Positive and negative numbers can be used to indicate direction.

- The symbol '–' before a number is used in two different ways:

27 – 12	means	subtract 12 from 27.
– 12	means	the opposite of 12 , or negative 12.

- To find the 'opposite' of a number, refer to a number line (Figure 5.4).

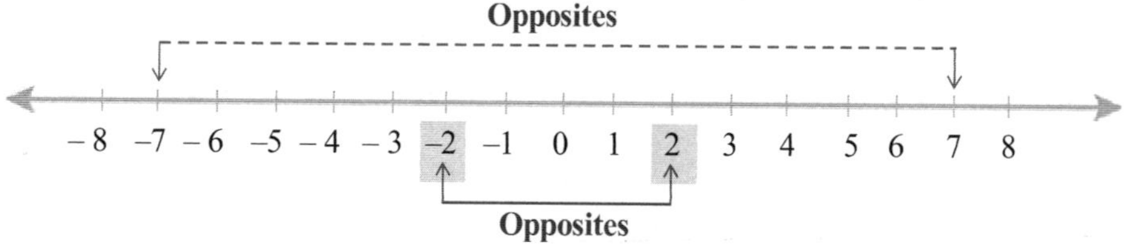

Figure 5.4

– (3) = –3		The opposite of 3 is negative 3
– (–8) = 8		The opposite of – 8 is positive 8
– (0) = 0		The opposite of 0 is 0.

Thus, the opposite of a *positive* number is a *negative* number and the opposite of a *negative* number is a *positive* number.

Procedure to find the opposite of a signed number.

***Step* 1** Locate the given number on a number line.

***Step* 2** Count the number of units between zero and the number.

***Step* 3** Count the same number of units from zero but on the opposite side of zero.

***Step* 4** Identify the number corresponding to the point where you stop. This is the opposite of the given number.

Warm-Up

1. Find the opposites of the signed numbers:

   (a) 58

   (b) – 85

   (c) $-\frac{16}{5}$

   (d) 7.25

2. Find the opposite of – (– 45)

Answers:

1. (a) –58 (b) 85 (c) $\frac{16}{5}$ (d) –7.25
2. – 45

EXAMPLE 1 Find the opposites of the signed numbers:

(a) 34 **(b)** – 27 **(c)** $-5\frac{2}{3}$ **(d)** 18.5

Solutions

(a) 34 is to the right of zero on the number line.

Therefore, its opposite is 34 units to the left of zero.

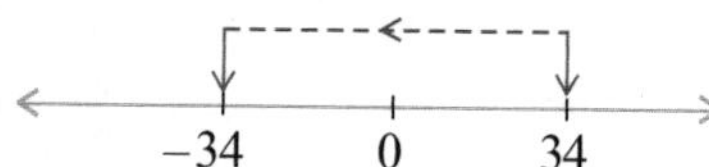

Thus, the opposite of 34 = – (34)

= – 34.

- Since there is no sign in front of 34, it is a positive number.
- 34 is 34 units to the right of zero.
- The opposite of 34 is 34 units to the left of zero.
- Since the opposite of 34 is to the left of zero, it is a negative number.

(b) – 27 is to the left of zero.

Therefore, the opposite of – 27 is 27 units to the right of zero.

–27 0 27

Thus, the opposite of – 27 = – (–27)

= 27

- The number has a ' ' sign in front of it.
- – 27 is 27 units to the left of zero.
- The opposite is 27 units to the right of zero.
- Since the opposite of 27 is to the right of zero, it is a positive number.

(c) The opposite of $-5\frac{2}{3}$

$= -\left(-5\frac{2}{3}\right)$

$= 5\frac{2}{3}$

$-5\frac{2}{3}$ is a negative number, therefore it is 'five whole units + two thirds of the sixth unit' to the left of zero. Thus, its opposite is the *same* number of units from zero, but to the right of zero.

(d) The opposite of 18.5

= – (18.5)

= – 18.5

18.5 is to the right of zero, so its opposite is to the left of zero. Hence, the opposite is a negative number.

EXAMPLE 2 Find the opposite of – (–12)

Solution

– (–12) is the opposite of –12 — The '–' sign before the parentheses is always read as "the opposite of ".

– (–12) is to the right of zero. — 12 is to the left of zero, so its opposite is to the right of zero.

Thus – (–12) = 12.

Since – (–12) is 12 units to the right of 0,

the opposite of – (–12) = – [– (–12)]

= – [12] = –12.

Solution to the Application:

The temperature on a January morning in Detroit, Michigan was 5°F. By noon, it had fallen and was the opposite of the morning temperature. What was the temperature at noon?

Solution: The temperature at noon was the opposite of the morning temperature, which was 5° F. Thus, it was the opposite of 5° F which is $-(5°\text{ F}) = -5°\text{ F}$ at noon.

B. Adding and Subtracting Integers

Application

Jacob starts the month with $500. During the month he spends $182 on clothes, $231 on food, and earns $187. Write each number as a signed number and add them to find Jacob's balance at the end of the month.

Illustrations

- $17 + (-28) = -(|-28| - |17|)$
  $= -(28 - 17) = -11$
- $-21 + 54 = +(|54| - |-21|)$
  $= (54 - 21) = 33.$
- $-42 + 37 = -(|42| - |37|)$
  $= -(42 - 37) = -5$

Verify Skill

Objective 5.1B

Evaluate the following:

(a) $-2 + (-1)$

(b) $15 + (-3)$

(c) $-72 + 48$

If your answers to this question are the same as those given below, then you may skip this objective.

Answers:
(a) -3 **(b)** 12 **(c)** -24

Discussion

- We will add two signed numbers with unlike, or opposite, signs.
  Positive and negative numbers are used to show opposite quantities:

  + 75 dollars may show 75 dollars earned,

  – 42 dollars may show 42 dollars spent.

  We shall use this idea to find the sum of positive and negative numbers.
- Suppose you earn $75 and then spend $42. You will have $33 left over.

  $75 + (-42) = 33.$

  To get this sum, subtract 42 (the absolute value of -42) from 75. The sum has the same sign as 75. Note that $|75| > |-42|$, that is, 75 has larger absolute value than -42.
- Suppose $35 is earned and $48 spent. The result is a deficit of $13.
  $35 + (-48) = -13.$

  To get this sum, subtract 35 from 48 (the absolute value of -48). The sum has the same sign as -48. Note that $|-48| > |35|$, that is, -48 has the larger absolute value than 35.

Similar reasoning can be used to find the sum.

$-23 + 12 = -11$

Subtract 12 from 23 (the absolute value of –23), and assign the sign of –23 to the difference, since –23 has a larger absolute value than 12.

> ***Rule* 1:**
>
> Two numbers with unlike signs are add***ed by* su**btracting the smaller absolute value from the larger and then assigning the sign of the number having the larger absolute value to the difference.

- *Adding two signed numbers with* ***like*** *signs.* The sum of two positive numbers is always positive.

  $15 + 9 = 24, \qquad 4 + 1 = 5, \qquad 3 + 1 = 4$

  To find the sum of two negative numbers, think of spending $12 and then another $25. The result is that $37 is spent.

  $-12 + (-25) = -37$

  To get this sum, add 12 and 25 (the absolute values of –12 and –25), and assign the common negative sign to the sum obtained.

> ***Rule* 2:**
>
> Two numbers with like signs are added by adding their absolute values and assigning the common sign to their sum.

- The sum of two integers can also be obtained on a number line. Positive and negative numbers indicate that the units are counted in the positive or negative directions.

  Adding 3 to a number means 'count 3 units to the right of the number'; adding – 4 to a number means 'count 4 units to the left of the number.'

  Thus, to find the sum 4 + (–7), that is to add –7 to 4, start at 4 then count 7 units to the left (Figure 5.5).

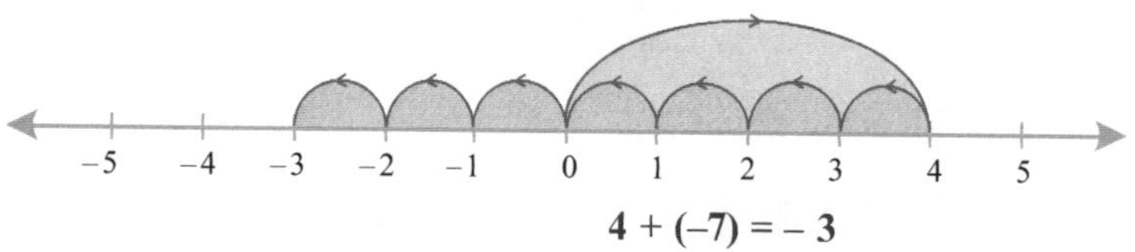

4 + (–7) = – 3

Figure 5.5

$4 + (-7) = -3$

The same answer can be obtained by using Rule 1: $4 + (-7) = -(|-7| - |4|) = -3$.

Similarly, to find the sum –3 + (–5), that is to add –5 to –3, start at –3, then count 5 units to the left of –3, since –5 is negative, (Figure 5.6).

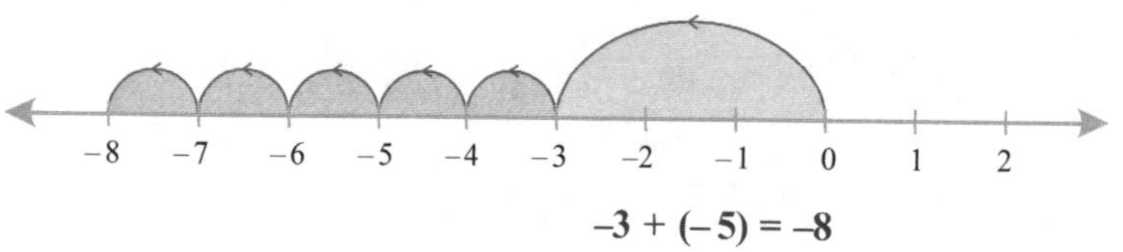

–3 + (– 5) = –8

Figure 5.6

$-3 + (-5) = -8.$

The same answer can be obtained by using Rule 2:
$-3 + (-5) = -(|-3| + |-5|) = -8.$

- To find the sum $-4 + 7$ start at -4, then count seven units to the right of -4 (since 7 is positive) (Figure 5.7)

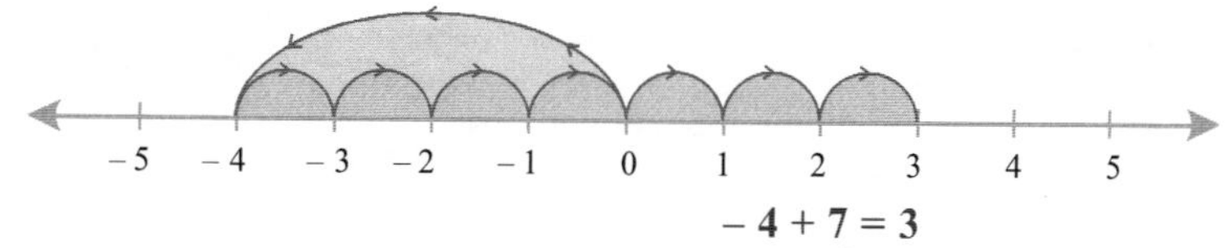

Figure 5.7

$-4 + 7 = 3.$

The same answer can be obtained by using Rule 1:
$-4 + 7 - + (|7| - -|4|) - + (7 - 4) - +(3) - 3.$

The sum of a number and its opposite is zero;

$$4 + (-4) = 0; \qquad -25.3 + 25.3 = 0; \qquad \frac{3}{5} + \left(\frac{-3}{5}\right) = 0$$

The sum of a signed number and zero is the number itself.

$$-5.7 + 0 = -5.7; \qquad 0 + \left(-\frac{1}{4}\right) = -\frac{1}{4}; \qquad -8 + 0 = -8.$$

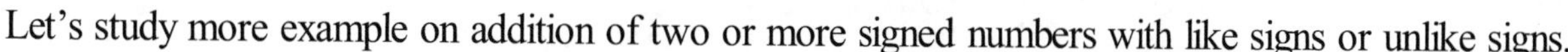

Let's study more example on addition of two or more signed numbers with like signs or unlike signs.

> **Procedure** to add two or more signed numbers with like signs.
>
> ***Step* 1** Find the absolute value of each number.
>
> ***Step* 2** Add the absolute values of signed numbers.
>
> ***Step* 3** The sign of the answer is the same as the sign of the number with the largest absolute value.

EXAMPLE 3 Add:

(a) $-10 + (-6)$ **(b)** $35 + 6$

(c) $-1 + (-2) + (-11)$

Solutions

(a) $|-10| + |-6| = 10 + 6$

$= 16$

- Add the absolute values of the numbers.

Therefore, $-10 + (-6) = -16$

- Assign the common sign ' ' to the sum.

(b) $35 + 6 = 41$

- $|35| + |6| = 35 + 6 = 41$
- Both the numbers are positive, therefore the sum is positive.

WARM-UP

3. Find the sum.

(a) $(-2) + (-6)$

(b) $345 + 78$

WARM-UP

(c) $-5 + (-1) + (-6)$

(c) $-1 + (-2) + (-11)$

$1 + 2 + 11 = 14$ • Add the absolute values.

$-1 + (-2) + (-11) = -14$ • Since all the numbers are negative, the sum is negative.

Note With practice, you should learn to use the common short-cut shown below.

Sum of the absolute values.

$-1 + (-2) + -11 =$

The common sign

$= -(14) = -14$

Procedure to add two signed numbers with unlike signs.

***Step* 1** Find the absolute values of the two numbers.

***Step* 2** Subtract the smaller absolute value from the larger one.

***Step* 3** The sign of the answer is the same as the sign of the number with the largest absolute value.

4. Add.

(a) $-1 + 4$

(b) $-72 + 56$

EXAMPLE 4 Add:

(a) $-35 + 52$ **(b)** $-7 + 3$ **(c)** $10 + (-7)$

(d) $41 + (-62)$ **(e)** $5 + (-3)$

Solutions

(a) $|-35| = 35,\ |52| = 52$ • Find the absolute values.

$52 - 35 = 17$ • Subtract the smaller absolute value (35) from the larger one (52).

$-35 + 52 = 17$ • The positive number has the larger absolute value, so the sum is positive.

The short-cut is:

Difference of the absolute values

$-35 + 52 = +(52 - 35) = 17$

Sign of the number that has larger absolute value.

(b) $|-7| = 7, |3| = 3$ • Find the absolute values.

$7 - 3 = 4$ • Find the difference of the absolute value.

Thus, $-7 + 3 = -4$ • The negative number has the larger absolute value, so the sum is negative.

The short-cut is:

$-7 + 3 = -(7 - 3) = -(4) = -4$

- The absolute value of –7.
- Sign of the number with the larger absolute value.
- The absolute value of 3.

(c) $10 + (-7) = +(10 - 7) = +3 = 3.$

- The absolute value of 10.
- The sign of the number with the larger absolute value (10).
- The absolute value of 7.

(d) $41 + (-62) = -(62 - 41) = -21$

- The absolute value of (– 62).
- The sign of the number with the larger absolute value (– 62).
- The absolute value of 41.

(e) $5 + (-3) = +(5 - 3)$
$= +(2) = 2$

> **Procedure** to add a group of signed numbers.
>
> ***Step* 1** Add all the positive and negative numbers separately.
>
> ***Step* 2** Add the two sums obtained in step 1.

EXAMPLE 5 Evaluate the following sums.

(a) $-44 + 37 + (-59) + 45$ **(b)** $56 + (-72) + 21$

Solutions

(a) First, add the negative numbers:

$-44 + (-59) = -(44 + 59) = \mathbf{-103}$

Next add the positive numbers: $37 + 45 = \mathbf{82}$

Now add the two sums obtained above:

$-103 + 82 = -(103 - 82)$
$= -21$

Hence, $-44 + 37 + (-59) + 45 = -21$

The short-cut is:

$-44 + 37 + (-59) + 45 = [-44 + (-59)] + [37 + 45]$

$= (-103) + (82)$ • Group the numbers having like signs.

$= -(103 - 82)$ • Add the numbers in each group.

$= -21.$ • Add the numbers having unlike signs as explained in example 2.

WARM-UP

(c) $8 + (-5)$

(d) $352 + (-500)$

(e) $2 + (-7)$

5. Evaluate the following sums.

(a) $-48 + 15 + (-17) + 26$

WARM-UP

(b) $3 + (-4) + 5$

(b) $56 + (-72) + 21$ • Group the numbers having like signs.

$= (56 + 21) + (-72)$ • Add the numbers in each group.

$= (77) + (-72)$ • Add the numbers having unlike signs.

$= + (77 - 72)$ Subtract the smaller absolute value from the larger one, and use the sign of the number having the larger absolute value.

$= 5$

6. Find the sum:

$26 + (-34.8) + (-15.2) + 19.3$

Answers:

3. (a) -8 (b) 423 (c) -12
4. (a) 3 (b) -16 (c) 3 (d) -148 (e) -5
5. (a) -24 (b) 4
6. -4.7

EXAMPLE 6 Compute the sum using a calculator.

$$-45 + 7.32 + (-12.6) + (-6.5)$$

Solution

The calculator takes care of the rules

-15 is entered as 15 [+/–], or [+/–] 15, or [( )] 15.

Determine how to enter signed numbers in your calculator, then add them. The result should be -56.78.

Thus, $-45 + 7.32 + (-12.6) + (-6.5) = -56.78$

Solution to the Application:

Jacob starts the month with \$500. During the month he spends \$182 on clothes, \$231 on food, and earns \$187. Write each number as a signed number and add them to find Jacob's balance at the end of the month.

Solution: The money Jacob has or earns is considered positive while the amount he spends is considered negative. Thus, Jacob's balance can be found by adding:

$500 + (-182) + (-231) + 187$

$= (500 + 187) + (-182 + (-231))$

$= 687 + (-413)$

$= 274$ So, Jacob's balance is \$274.

EXERCISE 5.1

In exercises 1-5, locate the opposite of the given signed number on a number line.

1. -7
2. 5
3. -1.25
4. 2
5. -9

In exercises 6-15, find the opposite of the given signed number.

6. 65
7. -4
8. -256
9. -175
10. $-(-11)$
11. 5
12. 12
13. -17
14. 125
15. $-(-1027)$

In exercises 16-20, write the opposite of the given statement.

16. A deposit of \$1000 in the checking account.
17. 560 yd above sea level
18. A loss of \$35
19. 15° F below zero
20. 1360 B.C.

In exercises 21-25, write the given statement using a signed number.

21. 1700 yd below sea level. **22.** A rise in the price by \$2.50 **23.** A deficit of \$350

24. A decrease of 35 lb **25.** A temperature of 17° C above 0° C

In exercises 26-35, find the absolute value.

26. $|-43|$ **27.** $|-6|$ **28.** $|-5|$ **29.** $|-85|$ **30.** $|125|$

31. $|-45|$ **32.** $|-(-3)|$ **33.** $|0|$ **34.** $|-12.6|$ **35.** $|17|$

Applications

36. If 60 miles east is represented by + 60, how would you represent 75 miles west?

37. On a thermometer, temperatures above zero are recorded as positive and those below zero recorded as negative. How will a reading of 3° C below zero be recorded?

38. In a bank, the amounts deposited are shown by using positive numbers, and the amounts withdrawn by negative numbers. If a man deposits \$375, on Monday and withdraws \$100 the next day, how will these transactions be shown in his pass book?

39. Two friends start from the same point and walk in the opposite directions. In 15 minutes, if one of them walks a distance of 2590 yd, and the other a distance of 3400 yd. Express the distances traveled by both of them using signed numbers. Also, find the distance in yards between them after 15 minutes.

In exercises 40-44, add the given numbers on a number line.

40. $-5+(-4)$ **41.** $2+(-7)$ **42.** $-10 + 8$ **43.** $-1+7$ **44.** $-3+(-8)$

In exercises 45-56, perform the addition.

45. $-2+(-5)$ **46.** $8+3$ **47.** $-14 + (-7)$ **48.** $-7+(-5)$

49. $-15+8$ **50.** $-7+1$ **51.** $-15 + 11$ **52.** $2+-4$

53. $3+(-4)$ **54.** $7+(-7)$ **55.** $-4+2+(-1)$ **56.** $-2+4-1$

In exercises 57-62, add the given group of numbers.

57. $5+(-9)+3+(-4)$ **58.** $-14+48+(-61)+(-63)$ **59.** $-1+5+(-3)+8$

60. $-5+3+(-8)+(-2)$ **61.** $92+(-53)+(-38)$ **62.** $1+(-2)+3+(-4)$

5.2 Multiplication, Division, Order of Operation on Integers

A. Multiply and Divide Two Integers With Like and Unlike Signs

Objectives

After completing this section you will be able to:

A. Multiply and Divide signed numbers with *unlike* signs; and

B. Simplify and Evaluate numerical expressions.

Application

The formula for converting a temperature measurement from Fahrenheit to Celsius is $C = \frac{5}{9}(F - 32)$. If at a particular time, the temperature is recorded as "13° F below zero", what is the Celsius measure of the temperature at that time.

Verify Skill

Objective 5.2A

Find the products:

(a) $2(-3)$ **(b)** $(-7)(2)$

(c) $4(-6)(1)$

If your answers to this question are the same as those given below, then you may skip this objective.

Answers:

(a) -6 **(b)** -14 **(c)** -24

Illustration

- $(-6)3 = -(6 \times 3) = -18$
- $5(-4) = -(5 \times 4) = -20$
- $2(1)(-6) = -(2 \times 1 \times 6) = -12$

Discussion

- Recall that multiplication is simply repeated addition.

  For instance, $3(7) = 7 + 7 + 7$ or 21

  Also recall that two numbers can be multiplied in any order (the *commutative* property of multiplication):

  $$4(5) = 5(4); \quad (2)(5) = (5)(2); \quad 3(15) = 15(3)$$

- Use the same ideas to multiply a positive and a negative number.

  $$5(-6) = (-6) + (-6) + (-6) + (-6) + (-6)$$ 5 times -6 means add -6 five times.

  $$= -30,$$ The product is negative.

The same result can be obtained by prefixing a negative sign to the product of 5 and 6.

Similarly, to find the product of -4 and 5,

$$(-4)(5) = 5(-4) = (-4) + (-4) + (-4) + (-4) + (-4)$$

$$= -20$$ The product is negative.

The same result can be obtained by prefixing a negative sign to the product of 4 and 5.

The product of a positive and a negative number is the opposite of the product of their absolute values.

This is sometimes stated as: "The product of two numbers with unlike signs is negative." That is,

$$(+)(-) = (-) \quad \text{and} \quad (-)(+) = (-).$$

Procedure to find the product of two numbers with *unlike* signs.

***Step* 1** Find the product of their absolute values.

***Step* 2** Attach a negative sign to the product.

EXAMPLE 1 Find the products.

(a) $12(-18)$ **(b)** $(-4)(3)$ **(c)** $7(-6)$

Solution

(a) $12(-18) = -(12 \times 18)$

The product is negative. The absolute value of the first factor. The absolute value of the second factor.

$= -216$

(b) $(-4)(3) = -[(4)(3)]$

The product is negative. The absolute value of the first factor. The absolute value of the second factor.

$= -12$

(c) $7(-6) = -(7 \times 6)$

The product is negative. The absolute value of the first factor. The absolute value of the second factor.

$= -42$

EXAMPLE 2 Multiply: $4(-5)(2)$

Solution

$4(-5)(2) = (-20)(2)$ Multiply the first two factors.

$= -40$ Multiply again.

WARM-UP

1. Find the product:

(a) $-1(4)$

(b) $24(-11)$

(c) $2(-15)$

2. Multiply: $3(-4)(2)$

Answers:

1. (a) -4 **(b)** -264 **(c)** -30

2. -24

Solution to the Application:

The formula for converting a temperature measurement from Fahrenheit to Celsius is $C = \frac{5}{9}(F - 32)$. If at a particular time, the temperature is recorded as "13 ° F below zero", what is the Celsius measure of the temperature at that time.

"13° F below zero" is the same as "–13° F".

$F = -13$ in the formula.

$$C = \frac{5}{9}(F - 32)$$

$$= \frac{5}{9}(-13 - 32)$$

$$= \frac{5}{9}(-45) = -\left(\frac{5}{9} \cdot 45\right) = -(25) = -25$$

Thus, the Celsius measure is – 25° C or 25° C below zero.

B. Simplifying and Evaluating Expressions for Integer Values

Verify Skill

Objective 5.2B

Evaluate the expression

$8(-9+5) - 45 \div (-3)^2$.

If your answer to this question is the same as given below, then you may skip this objective.

Answer: -37

Illustration

$$5(2)^3 + 25 \div (-5)^2(-7 + \mathbf{3})$$

$$= 5(2)^3 + 25 \div (\mathbf{-5})^2(-4)$$

$$= 5 \cdot 8 + 25 \div 25 \cdot (-4)$$

$$= 40 + \frac{25}{25}(-4)$$

$$= 40 + (-4) = 36$$

Discussion

- Recall that repeated multiplication of a number by itself can be written in exponential form (objective 1.5A). For example,

  $3 \cdot 3 \cdot 3 \cdot 3 \cdot 3$ is written as 3^5 ← Exponent (3: ↑ Base)

  and the value of $3^5 = 243$.

  This notation can be extended for signed numbers also. The product

  $(-4)(-4)(-4)$ is written as $(-4)^3$.

  In $(-4)^3$, -4 is the *base*, and 3 is the *exponent* or the *power*.

- To evaluate a number written in exponential form with a negative base, follow the same rules as for a positive base (objective 1.5A):

***Rule* 1:** If the exponent is zero and the base is not 0, the value is 1.

$(-4)^0 = 1, \qquad (-12)^0 = 1, \qquad (-1)^0 = 1$

***Rule* 2:** If the exponent is 1, the value is the base.

$(-3)^1 = -3, \qquad (-8)^1 = -8, \qquad (-150)^1 = -150.$

***Rule* 3:** If the exponent is a whole number larger than 1, multiply the base as many times as the exponent.

- $(-4)^3 = (-4)(-4)(-4) = -64$ — The product of an odd number of negative factors is negative.

and

- $(-3)^6 = (-3)(-3)(-3)(-3)(-3)(-3) = 729$ — The product of an even number of negative factors is positive.

Observe that when the base is a negative number, the sign of the exponential expression depends on whether the exponent is even or odd.

$(-3)^6 = 3^6$ — The exponent is an even number, so the value is positive.

$(-4)^3 = -(4^3)$ — The exponent is an odd number, so the value is negative.

- The order of operations for signed numbers is the same as that for whole numbers.

  i) Evaluate all the exponential expressions.

  ii) Perform multiplications and divisions in the order that they appear from left to right.

  iii) Perform additions and subtractions in the order that they appear from left to right.

If the expression involves any of the grouping symbols, such as parentheses, brackets, braces, etc., then the expressions within these grouping symbols are evaluated first in the above order starting at the innermost grouping symbol. For example, evaluate the following expression.

$4 - \{6 - [-2 + (7 - \mathbf{(1 + 5)})]\}$ — Evaluate (1 + 5) since this is the innermost grouping symbol.

$= 4 - \{6 - [-2 + \mathbf{(7 - 6)}]\}$ — Evaluate (7 – 6); the next innermost grouping symbol.

$= 4 - \{6 - \mathbf{[-2 + 1]}\}$ — Brackets, [ ].

$= 4 - \{6 - (-1)\}$ — Braces { }.

$= 4 - \{6 + 1\}$

$= 4 - 7$

$= -3$

Procedure to perform a combination of operations on signed numbers.

Step* 1** ***Grouping symbols: Perform the operations within the grouping symbols, in the order given in steps 2, 3, and 4, starting at the innermost grouping symbol.

***Step* 2** Evaluate all the **exponential** parts of the expressions.

***Step* 3** Perform all **multiplications and divisions** in order from left to right.

***Step* 4** Perform all **additions and subtractions** in order from left to right.

WARM-UP

3. Simplify the expressions.

(a) $-24 + (-65) \div 5$

(b) $-5(4) + 2\,[15 - 3(-2)^3]$

4. Simplify

(a) $\frac{2}{7} \div \left[\frac{5}{3}(7 - (-3)) - 4\right]$

EXAMPLE 3 Simplify the expressions.

(a) $-35 + (-18) \div 3$ **(b)** $-4(3) + 5\,[7 - 6(-4)^2]$

Solutions

(a) $-35 + \mathbf{(-18) \div 3} = -35 + \mathbf{(-6)}$ Perform division.

$= -41$ Perform addition.

(b) $-4(3) + 5\,[7 - \mathbf{6(-4)^2}]$

$= -4(3) + 5[7 - \mathbf{6(16)}]$ • Simplify the exponents within the grouping symbol.

$= -4(3) + 5[\mathbf{7 - 96}]$ • Perform multiplication.

$= -4(3) + 5[\mathbf{-89}]$ • Perform addition.

$= -12 + (-445)$

$= -457$

EXAMPLE 4 Simplify.

(a) $\frac{4}{5} \div \left[\frac{3}{4}(12 - (-4)) - 2\right]$ **(b)** $\frac{3(-5) - (-6)(-2)}{3^2\,(4-2)}$

Solutions

(a) $\frac{4}{5} \div \left[\frac{3}{4}(12 - (-4)) - 2\right]$

$= \frac{4}{5} \div \left[\frac{\mathbf{3}}{\mathbf{4}}\mathbf{(16)} - 2\right]$ • Simplify inside ( ).

$= \frac{4}{5} \div [\mathbf{12 - 2}]$ • Simplify inside [ ].

$= \frac{4}{5} \div \mathbf{10}$ • Perform division.

$= \frac{4}{5} \times \frac{\mathbf{1}}{\mathbf{10}} = \frac{2}{25}$ • Simplify.

(b) Simplify the numerator and the denominator separately and then divide.

Numerator: $3(-5) - (-6)(-2) = -15 - 12 = -27$

Denominator: $3^2(\mathbf{4-2}) = \mathbf{3^2}(2)$ • Evaluate within parentheses.

$= 9(2)$ • Evaluate the exponent.

$= 18$

Therefore, $\dfrac{3(-5) - (-6)(-2)}{3^2(4-2)} = \dfrac{-27}{18} = -\dfrac{3}{2}$

EXAMPLE 5 Evaluate $((-4)\,8 + 30)\,(-4) - 36 \div 12$ using a calculator.

Solution ***Note:*** On a calculator, each grouping symbol is entered as a parentheses.

ENTER  (4 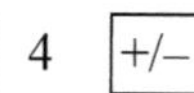 +/– 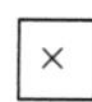 × 8  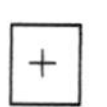 + 30 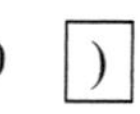) ×

ENTER 4 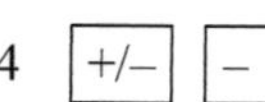 +/– – 36  ÷ 12  = or 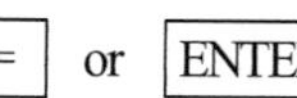 ENTER

The result should be 5.

Hence, the value of the given expression is 5.

WARM-UP

(b) $\dfrac{2(-7) - (-8)(-3)}{4^2\,(25-6)}$

5. Evaluate using a calculator.

$[(-12)4 + 6\cdot 8] + 26 \div (-2)(3)$

Answers:

3. (a) -37 **(b)** 58

4. (a) $\dfrac{3}{133}$ **(b)** $-\dfrac{1}{8}$ **5.** -39

EXERCISE 5.2

In exercises 1-30, find the product.

1.	$3(-9)$	**2.**	$(-8)5$	**3.**	$4(-7)$	**4.**	$(-5)(4)$	**5.**	$(-3)(7)$
6.	$4(-3)$	**7.**	$(3)(-4)$	**8.**	$(-16)(4)$	**9.**	$27(-4)$	**10.**	$-12(8)$
11.	$(-9)(-8)$	**12.**	$(-11)(-3)$	**13.**	$12(35)$	**14.**	$(-3)(-8)$	**15.**	$-25(-4)$
16.	$(-4)(-2)$	**17.**	$(-1)(-3)$	**18.**	$(-8)(-25)$	**19.**	$0(-82)$	**20.**	$-7(-5)$

21. $-18(-5)(2)$ **22.** $15(-10)(-9)(-8)$ **23.** $-8(-6)(-5)$ **24.** $-1(-1)(-1)(-1)(-279)$

25. $(3-1)(2-6)$ **26.** $-6(2)(-10)(-100)$ **27.** $4(-3)(-1)(9)$

28. $(-13)(42)(-7)(0)(1)$ **29.** $-18(-5)(-24)(-5)$ **30.** $(-2-12)(-12+24)$

Applications

31. The formula for converting a temperature measurement from Fahrenheit to Celsius is $C = \frac{5}{9}(F - 32)$. Find the Celsius measure that is equal to 23 °F.

32. Use the formula in exercise (31) to find the Celsius measure that corresponds to 4.9°F below zero. Round to the nearest tenth of a degree.

33. Use the formula in exercise (31) to find the Celsius measure equivalent to 78°F. Round to the nearest tenth of a degree.

34. Thriftway's loss leader is a hair shampoo that loses 14 cents per 500 ml bottle. They sell 154 of these bottles. Use signed numbers to find Thriftway's total loss.

35. Mrs. Brown goes on a diet for 15 consecutive weeks. She averages a weight loss of 1.75 lb each week. Represent this loss as a signed number, and use it to calculate her total weight loss for the 15 weeks.

In exercises 36-51, simplify.

36. $-4 + (-6) \div (2 \cdot 3)$

37. $-4 + (-6) \times 3 \div 2$

38. $-4 + (-6 \div 2) \times 3$

39. $-2 + 7 - 3 \div [(-2) - 1]$

40. $7 - 4[8 - 7(2 - 3)]$

41. $-9(4) - 24 \div (-6)$

42. $-7 + 3 - (5 + 1) \div 2$

43. $\left[\frac{1}{2} - \left(\frac{-3}{4}\right)\right] \div 5$

44. $-\frac{2}{3}\left(\frac{4}{7}\right) \div \left(4 - \frac{1}{3}\right)$

45. $4 \div (-0.8) + 2(-2.4)$

46. $\frac{30 - (-10)}{15 - (-5)}$

47. $\frac{-28 \div (-4)\,7 - 7^2}{(-2)^2 + 4(2)}$

48. $\frac{\left(4^2 - 3^2\right)(8) \div (9-7)^2}{\left(7^2 - 5^2\right)(3) \div (8-5)^2}$

49. $\frac{5 \times 3 \div (-2+7)}{5 \times 3 \div 5 + 1}$

50. $\frac{18 - 4(15 \div 3)}{7 \times 3 - 19}$

51. $\frac{6 \div 2 \times (7-6)}{6 \div 3 \times 2 - 1}$

In exercises 52-60, solve the given equation.

52. $x + 2 = -10$

53. $3 + y = -9$

54. $-18 = x - 44$

55. $-4x = 64$

56. $-7t = -18$

57. $\frac{x}{-5} = 6$

58. $x - \frac{2}{3} = -1$

59. $5x = -105$

60. $\frac{x}{-7} = -13$

5.3 Introduction to Fractions

Vocabulary

> **Objectives**
>
> After completing this section you will be able to:
>
> **A.** Understand the meaning of a fraction as a part of a unit and identify proper fractions or improper fractions;
>
> **B.** Convert improper fractions to mixed numbers or mixed numbers to improper fractions; and

1. A **fraction,** such as $\frac{3}{5}$ (read as **three - fifths**) has three components:

   (i) A horizontal line called the **fraction** or **division bar.**

   (ii) A number above the fraction bar called the **numerator** which indicates the number of parts being counted.

   (iii) A number below the fraction bar called the **denominator** which indicates the number of equal parts in the whole

   Division bar ⟵ $\frac{2}{7}$ ⟶ Numerator, ⟶ Denominator

2. A fraction whose numerator is smaller than the denominator is called a **proper fraction.**

   $\frac{2}{3}$ and $\frac{4}{9}$ are examples of proper fractions.

3. A fraction whose numerator is larger than or equal to the denominator is called an **improper fraction.**

   $\frac{7}{2}$ and $\frac{3}{3}$ are examples of improper fractions.

4. A **mixed number** is the sum of a whole number and a proper fraction.

   For example, $13 + \frac{2}{5}$ and $4 + \frac{1}{3}$ are mixed numbers.

   It is common to drop the plus sign when writing a mixed number:

   $13 + \frac{2}{5}$ is written as $13\frac{2}{5}$

   $4 + \frac{1}{3}$ is written as $4\frac{1}{3}$

A. Proper and Improper Fractions

➡ Understand the meaning of a fraction as a part of a unit and identify proper fractions or improper fractions

Application

Alisha wants to finish a novel as soon as possible. So far she has read only 54 pages. What fraction of the number of pages has she read if there are 180 pages in the novel?

> **Verify Skill**
>
> **Objective 5.3A**
>
> **1. (a)** Write the fraction represented by the figure.
>
> 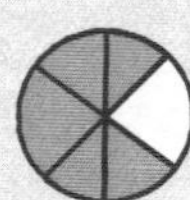

Verify Skill

(b) Write the fraction represented by the figure.

One Unit   One Unit

2. Identify the proper and the improper fractions.

$\frac{2}{7}, \frac{6}{5}, \frac{10}{3}, \frac{9}{13}$

If your answers to these questions are the same as given below then you may skip this objective.

Answers:

1. (a) $\frac{5}{6}$ (b) $\frac{4}{3}$

2. $\frac{2}{7}$, and $\frac{9}{13}$ are proper fractions.

$\frac{6}{5}$, and $\frac{10}{3}$ are improper fractions.

Illustrations

- What fraction of the figure is the shaded portion ?

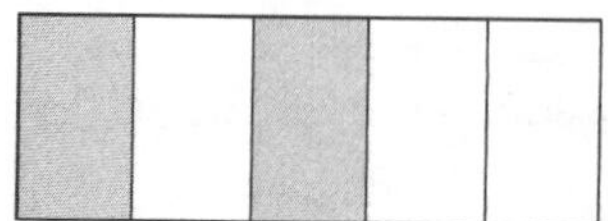

Two of the five equal parts of the figure are shaded, therefore the shaded portion is two-fifths (written as $\frac{2}{5}$) of the whole figure.

- What fraction of the figure is the shaded portion ?

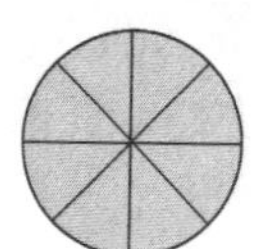

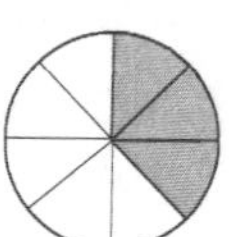

11 pieces are shaded and 8 pieces make up one circle (or unit).

Thus, the shaded portion is $\frac{11}{8}$ of a circle.

- Identify the following fractions as **proper** or **improper**.

$$\frac{2}{7}, \frac{4}{3}, \frac{5}{9}, \frac{14}{3}, \frac{19}{7}, \frac{8}{8}$$

A fraction is proper if the numerator is smaller than the denominator, otherwise it is improper.

$\frac{2}{7}$ and $\frac{5}{9}$ are proper fractions

$\frac{4}{3}, \frac{14}{3}, \frac{19}{7}$ and $\frac{8}{8}$ are improper fractions

Discussion

- A fraction is a part of a unit or several equal parts of a unit. In Figure 5.8, a unit is represented by a rectangle and divided into equal parts, (Figure 5.8).

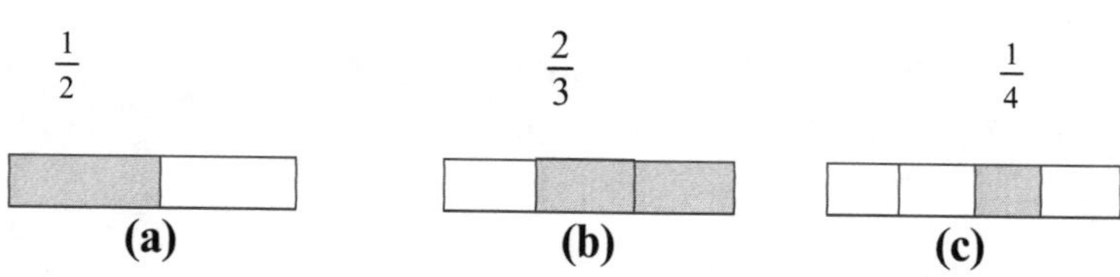

Figure 5.8

In Figure 5.8 (a), the rectangle is divided into 2 equal parts, and one part is shaded.

The fraction $\frac{1}{2}$ **(one-half)** represents the shaded part.

In Figure 5.8 (b), the rectangle is divided into 3 equal parts, and two parts are shaded.

The fraction $\frac{2}{3}$ **(two-thirds)** represents the shaded part.

In Figure 5.8 (c), the rectangle is divided into 4 equal parts, and one part is shaded.

The fraction $\frac{1}{4}$ **(one-fourth)** represents the shaded part.

Now, look at the Figure 5.9. Once again, unit rectangles are divided into *equal* parts.

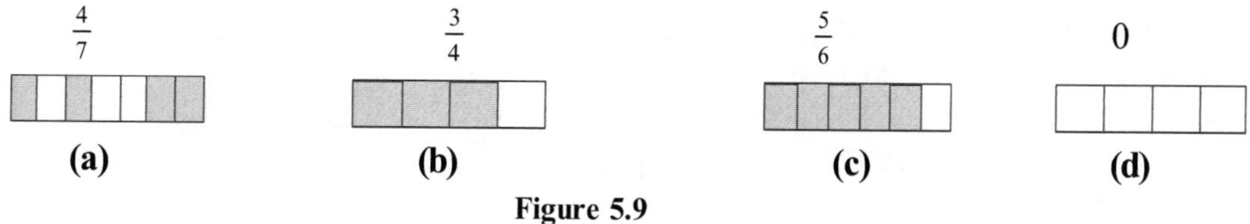

Figure 5.9

In Figure 5.9 (a), the rectangle is divided into 7 equal parts, and 4 parts are shaded.

The fraction $\frac{4}{7}$ **(four-sevenths)** represents the shaded area.

In Figure 5.9 (b), the rectangle is divided into 4 equal parts, and 3 parts are shaded.

The fraction $\frac{3}{4}$ **(three-fourths)** represents the shaded area.

In Figure 5.9 (c), the rectangle is divided into 6 equal parts, and 5 parts are shaded.

The fraction $\frac{5}{6}$ **(five-sixths)** represents the shaded area.

In Figure 5.9 (d), the rectangle is divided into 4 equal parts, but no part is shaded.

The fraction that represents the shaded area is $\frac{0}{4}$ or 0.

The fractions shown in Figure 5.8 and 5.9 have numerators smaller than their denominators. Such fractions are called **proper fractions**. The value of a proper fraction is always less than one.

In Figure 5.10 (a), the number of shaded parts (5) is equal to the total number of parts (5).

The shaded portion of the figure represents the fraction $\frac{5}{5}$ or 1.

When the numerator and the denominator of a fraction are equal, it represents the complete unit or the number 1.

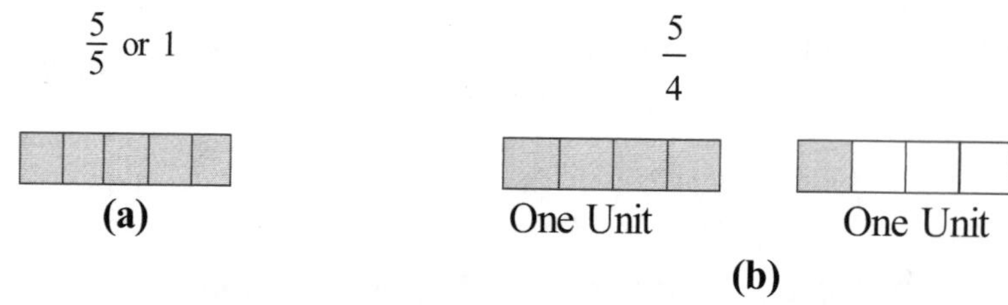

Figure 5.10

In Figure 5.10 (b), there are two units rectangles, each divided into 4 equal parts. Five parts (or one unit and one part of the other unit) have been shaded. The shaded area represents the fraction $\frac{5}{4}$.

The fractions, shown in Figure 5.10 have numerators greater than or equal to their denominators. Such fractions are called **improper fractions**. If the numerator of a fraction is equal to the denominator, then the value of the fraction is 1. If the numerator of a fraction is larger than the denominator, the value of the fraction is greater than 1.

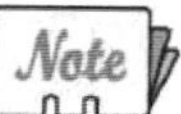

When a part of the unit is represented by a fraction, the unit must be divided into equal parts.

In Figure 5.11, because the unit is divided into unequal parts, the shaded part cannot be represented by a fraction using 4 as denominator.

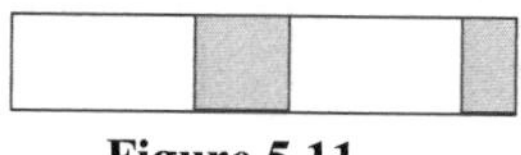

Figure 5.11

Caution: It is wrong to say that $\frac{2}{4}$ represents the shaded area in Figure 5.11.

Procedure to write a fraction from the shaded part of a unit, when the unit is divided into equal parts.

***Step* 1** Write the number of shaded parts as the numerator.

***Step* 2** Write the total number of equal parts in one unit as the denominator.

WARM-UP

1. Write the fraction represented by the shaded part of figure.

(a)

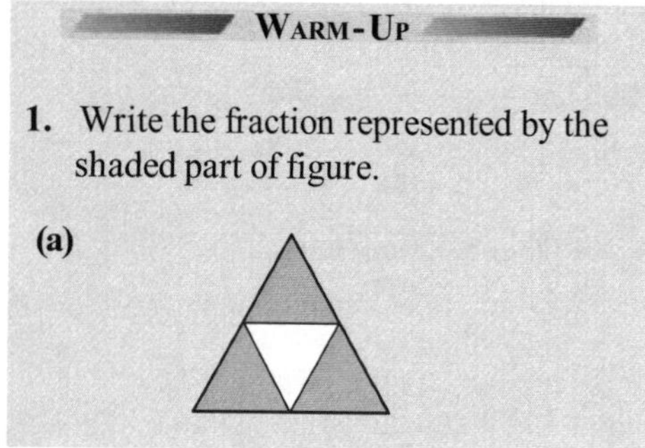

EXAMPLE 1 Write the fraction represented by the shaded portion of the figure.

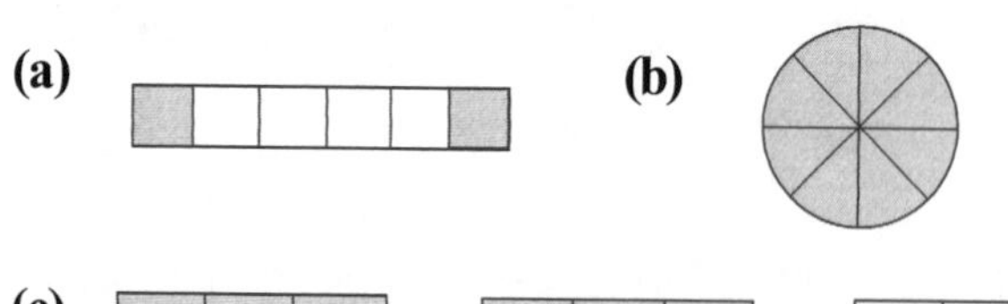

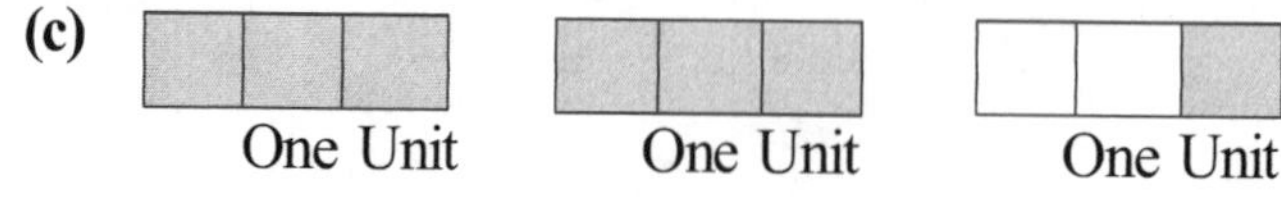

Solutions

(a) The numerator is 2; • Number of shaded parts is 2.

The denominator is 6 • Total number of parts in the unit is 6.

So, the shaded portion represents $\frac{2}{6}$.

(b) There is only one unit — The number of shaded parts is the same as the total number of parts.

The shaded portion represents $\frac{8}{8}$ or 1.

(c) There are three units, each divided into 3 equal parts. • Number of shaded parts is 7, so the numerator is 7.

The shaded portion represents $\frac{7}{3}$ • Total number of parts in each unit is 3, so the denominator is 3.

Procedure to determine whether a fraction is proper or improper.

***Step* 1** Compare the numerator with the denominator.

***Step* 2** If the numerator is smaller, the fraction is proper. Otherwise the fraction is improper.

EXAMPLE 2 Identify the proper and the improper fractions in the list.

[shaded 3 of 4 boxes], $\frac{27}{27}$, $\frac{41}{18}$, $\frac{6 \text{ over due books}}{11 \text{ total books checked out}}$

Solution

Numerator	**Denominator**	**Fraction Type**
3 is less than	4	Proper
27 is equal to	27	Improper
41 is greater than	18	Improper
6 is less than	11	Proper

Solution to the Application:

Alisha wants to finish a novel as soon as possible. So far she has read only 54 pages. What fraction of the number of pages has she read if there are 180 pages in the novel?

Solutions: The fraction is the number of pages read over the total number of pages, which is $\frac{54}{180}$.

(b)

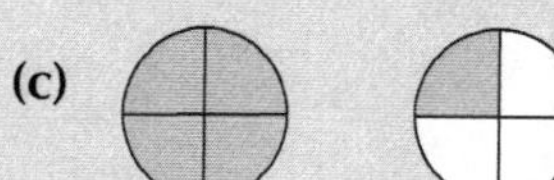

(c)

2. Identify the proper and the improper fractions in the list.

$\frac{4}{3}, \frac{1}{2}, \frac{0}{9}, \frac{6}{8}, \frac{8}{7},$ 

Answers:

1. (a) $\frac{3}{4}$ (b) $\frac{3}{3}$ or 1 (c) $\frac{5}{4}$

2. The proper fractions are $\frac{1}{2}, \frac{0}{9}, \frac{6}{8}$, and $\frac{2}{8}$

the improper fractions are $\frac{4}{3}$, and $\frac{8}{7}$

Verify Skill

Objective 5.3B

(a) Change $\frac{25}{6}$ to a mixed number.

(b) Express $13\frac{7}{9}$ as an improper fraction.

If your answers to these questions are the same as given below then you may skip this objective.

Answers:

(a) $4\frac{1}{6}$ (b) $\frac{124}{9}$

(B.) Improper Fractions and Mixed Numbers

➜ **Change improper fractions to mixed numbers or mixed numbers to improper fractions.**

Application

Ryan ate $\frac{27}{10}$ of pizza. Convert this to a mixed number and use this to determine the minimum whole number of pizzas that had to be ordered.

Illustration

- Change $\frac{41}{5}$ to mixed number.

$$\begin{array}{r} 8 \\ 5\overline{)41} \\ -40 \\ \hline 1 \end{array} \qquad \frac{41}{5} = 8 + \frac{1}{5} = \mathbf{8\frac{1}{5}}$$

- Change $2\frac{4}{5}$ to improper fraction.

$$2\frac{4}{5} = 2 + \frac{4}{5} = \frac{10}{5} + \frac{4}{5} = \frac{10+4}{5} = \frac{14}{5}$$

Discussion

- An improper fraction is equal to either a whole number or a mixed number.

Case 1: When an improper fraction is equal to a whole number.

Consider an improper fraction, say $\frac{12}{4}$. The denominator 4 suggests that a unit is divided into 4 equal parts. Also, $12 = 4 + 4 + 4$ suggests that all the four parts of three units are shaded (see the figure below).

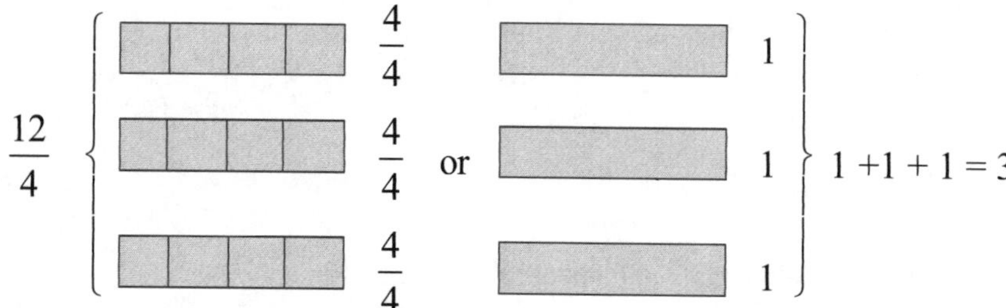

Figure 5.12

Thus, from the above Figure: $\frac{12}{4} = 3$

Observe that the denominator (4) divides evenly into the numerator (12): $12 \div 4 = 3$ with zero remainder.

In all such cases the improper fraction is a whole number.

Case 2: When an improper fraction is equal to a mixed number.

Consider the improper fraction $\frac{13}{5}$. The denominator is 5 so the unit is divided into five equal parts. To be able to shade 13 parts, we draw three complete units. Now we see that all five parts of the 1st and 2nd unit are shaded. But only 3 of the 5 parts are shaded in the third unit.

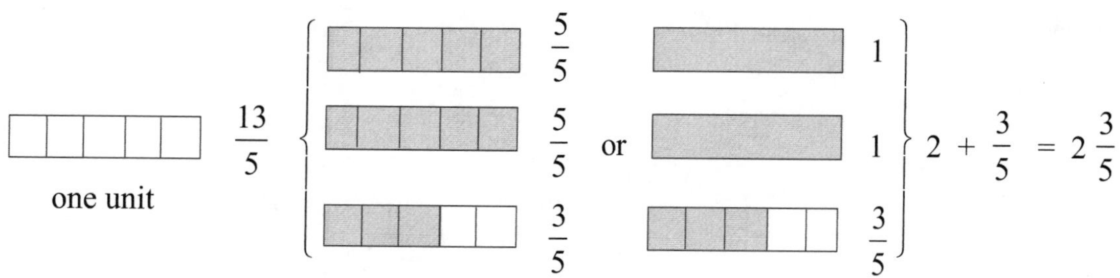

Figure 5.13

So $\frac{13}{5}$ is the same as $2+\frac{3}{5}$ which we write as $2\frac{3}{5}$.

We call $2\frac{3}{5}$ a **mixed number** because it is a "mix" of a **whole** number and a **proper** fraction.

Observe that when 13 is divided by 5, the quotient is 2 and the remainder is 3.

$$\frac{13}{5} = 2 + \frac{3}{5} = 2\frac{3}{5}$$

$$\frac{\text{Dividend}}{\text{Divisor}} = \text{Quotient} + \frac{\text{Remainder}}{\text{Denominator}} = \text{Quotient}\frac{\text{Remainder}}{\text{Denominator}}$$

Now, generalize the above observation for improper fractions that are not whole numbers.

$$\text{Improper fraction} = \frac{\text{Numerator}}{\text{Denominator}} \qquad (\text{Numerator} > \text{Denominator})$$

```
                 Quotient
Denominator )Numerator
             --------------
             --------------
             Remainder
```

$$\text{Improper fraction} = \textbf{Quotient}\ \frac{\textbf{Remainder}}{\textbf{Denominator}}$$

Notice that $13 \div 5 = 2 \text{ R } 3$

Thus $\dfrac{13}{5} = 2 + \dfrac{3}{5}$ $\quad 2\dfrac{3}{5}$

Improper fraction – Whole + proper fraction – Mixed number

Recall the notation: $16 \div 2 = \dfrac{16}{2}$. The fraction bar is also a division symbol. Thus, it makes sense to divide when changing an improper fraction to a mixed or whole number.

- We also have a procedure for changing a mixed number into an improper fraction. Consider the shaded portion in Figure 5.14.

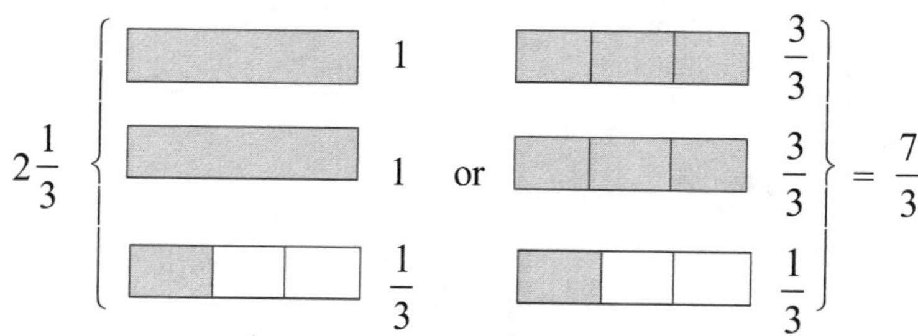

Figure 5.14

Figure 5.14 illustrates a method for changing a mixed number to an improper fraction.

Observe that: $2\dfrac{1}{3} = 1 + 1 + \dfrac{1}{3} = \dfrac{3}{3} + \dfrac{3}{3} + \dfrac{1}{3} = \dfrac{7}{3}$

$\longrightarrow$ $2 \times 3 + 1$

$2\dfrac{1}{3} = \dfrac{7}{3}$

Note The numerator of the improper fraction on the right = (whole number part) × (the denominator) + numerator.

Thus, to convert a mixed number to an improper fraction, the following short cut can be used.

$$\frac{(\text{Whole number part}) \times \text{Denominator} + \text{Numerator}}{\text{Denominator}}$$

- Every whole number can be written as an improper fraction. For example: $35 = \dfrac{35}{1}$.

Procedure to change an improper fraction to a mixed number.

***Step* 1** Divide the numerator by the denominator.

***Step* 2** **(a)** If there is no remainder, the fraction is a whole number, the quotient.

(b) If there is a remainder, the fraction is the sum of the quotient and a proper fraction : $\dfrac{\text{numerator}}{\text{denominator}} = \text{quotient} + \dfrac{\text{remainder}}{\text{divisor}}$.

EXAMPLE 3 Change the improper fraction to a mixed number.

(a) $\frac{9}{4}$, (b) $\frac{29}{3}$.

(c) $\frac{547}{11}$, (d) $\frac{483}{23}$.

Solutions

(a) $\frac{9}{4}$; $9 \div 4 = 2\,R\,1$

$$\frac{9}{4} = 2 + \frac{1}{4} = 2\frac{1}{4}$$

(b) $\frac{29}{3}$; $29 \div 3 = 9\,R\,2$

$$\frac{29}{3} = 9 + \frac{2}{3} = 9\frac{2}{3}$$

(c) $\frac{547}{11}$; $547 \div 11 = 49\,R\,8$

$$\frac{547}{11} = 49 + \frac{8}{11} = 49\frac{8}{11}$$

(d) $\frac{483}{23} = 483 \div 23 = 21$

Procedure to convert a mixed number into an improper fraction.

***Step* 1** Multiply the whole number by the denominator.

***Step* 2** Add the numerator to the product to get the numerator of the improper fraction.

***Step* 3** Write the improper fraction using this numerator. The denominator remains unchanged.

EXAMPLE 4 Convert each mixed number into an improper fraction:

(a) $7\frac{4}{9}$ (b) $3\frac{4}{5}$ (c) $53\frac{3}{4}$

Solutions

(a) $7\frac{4}{9} = \frac{7 \times 9 + 4}{9}$

$= \frac{63 + 4}{9}$

$= \frac{\mathbf{67}}{\mathbf{9}}$

- Multiply 7 by 9.
- Add 4.
- Retain the denominator.

(b) $3\frac{4}{5} = \frac{3 \times 5 + 4}{5} = \frac{\mathbf{19}}{\mathbf{5}}$

WARM-UP

3. Change to a mixed number.

(a) $\frac{14}{5}$

(b) $\frac{23}{4}$

(c) $\frac{112}{9}$

(d) $\frac{114}{6}$

4. Convert into improper fractions.

(a) $5\frac{3}{4}$

(b) $7\frac{5}{9}$

WARM-UP

(c) $13\frac{4}{7}$

Answers:

3. (a) $2\frac{4}{5}$ (b) $5\frac{3}{4}$ (c) $12\frac{4}{9}$ (d) 19

4. (a) $\frac{23}{4}$ (b) $\frac{68}{9}$ (c) $\frac{95}{7}$

(c) $$53\frac{3}{4} = \frac{53\times4+3}{4} = \frac{212+3}{4} = \frac{215}{4}$$

Note The denominator of a mixed number and its equivalent improper fraction are **always** equal, if both are reduced.

Solution to the Application:

Ryan ate $\frac{27}{10}$ of pizza. Convert this to a mixed number and use this to determine the minimum whole number of pizzas that had to be ordered.

Solution: $\frac{27}{10} = 2\frac{7}{10}$ because $27 \div 10 = 2\ R\ 7$

$2\frac{7}{10}$ is more than 2 so the minimum number of pizzas that had to be ordered is 3.

EXERCISE 5.3

In exercises 1-8, write the fraction represented by the shaded unit.

1. 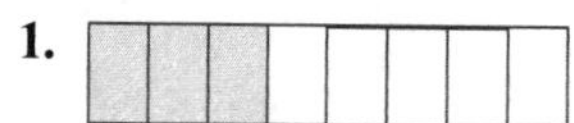

2. 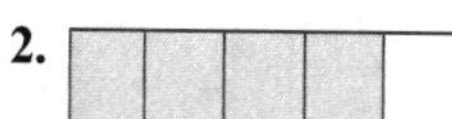

3. 

4. 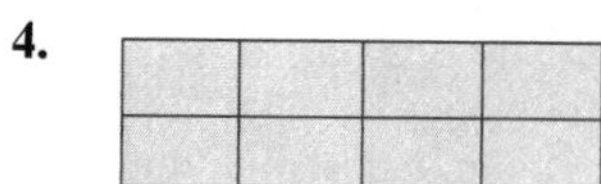

5. 

6. 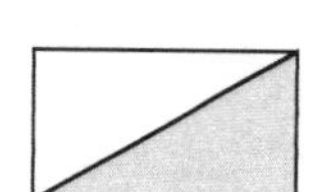

7. 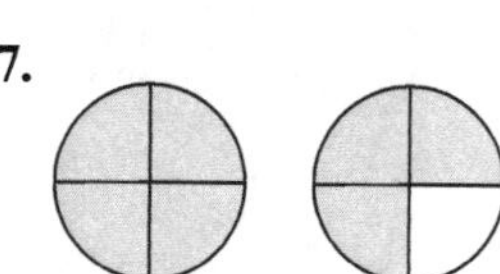

8.  

In exercises 9-11, identity the proper and the improper fractions from the list.

9. $\frac{7}{18}, \frac{13}{10}, \frac{4}{9}, \frac{5}{5}, \frac{2}{29}$ **10.** $\frac{21}{24}, \frac{20}{8}, \frac{7}{10}, \frac{13}{17}, \frac{16}{5}$ **11.** $\frac{105}{113}, \frac{23}{29}, \frac{97}{102}, \frac{0}{7}, \frac{5}{8}$

In exercises 12-20, change the improper fraction to a mixed number.

12. $\frac{19}{4}$ **13.** $\frac{15}{2}$ **14.** $\frac{25}{8}$ **15.** $\frac{49}{5}$ **16.** $\frac{135}{10}$

17. $\frac{83}{21}$ **18.** $\frac{155}{8}$ **19.** $\frac{1203}{8}$ **20.** $\frac{3754}{101}$

In exercises 21-29, change the mixed number to an improper fraction.

21. $1\frac{2}{3}$ **22.** $4\frac{3}{5}$ **23.** $7\frac{3}{8}$ **24.** $11\frac{5}{8}$ **25.** $187\frac{2}{3}$

26. $112\frac{5}{6}$ **27.** $80\frac{1}{3}$ **28.** $1\frac{7}{45}$ **29.** $13\frac{12}{23}$

5.4 Reducing, Equivalent, and Comparing Fractions

Vocabulary

1. **To simplify a fraction to lowest terms** means to write an equivalent fraction such that the numerator and denominator have no common factors other than 1.

2. **Equivalent fractions** *are fractions that have different names for the same number.*

   For example, $\frac{8}{12}$ and $\frac{10}{15}$ are equivalent, because both reduce to the same number $\frac{2}{3}$.

Objectives

After completing this section you will be able to:

A. Reducing fraction to lowest terms;

B. Build Equivalent Fractions; and

C. Comparing and Listing Fractions in Order.

A. Reducing Fractions to Lowest Terms

Application

Alisha wants to finish a novel as soon as possible. So far she has read only 54 pages. What fraction of the number of pages has she read if there are 180 pages in the novel? Simplify the fraction to lowest terms.

Illustration: Simplify $\frac{54}{36}$ to lowest terms.

$$\frac{54}{36} = \frac{2 \cdot 27}{2 \cdot 18}$$

$$= \frac{2 \cdot 3 \cdot 3 \cdot \mathbf{3}}{2 \cdot \mathbf{2} \cdot 3 \cdot 3} = \frac{3}{2}$$

Verify Skill

Objective 5.4A

Simplify $\frac{84}{210}$ to lowest terms.

If your answer to this question is the same as given below then you may skip this objective.

Answer : $\frac{2}{5}$

Discussion

Consider the four units shown below in Figure 5.15.

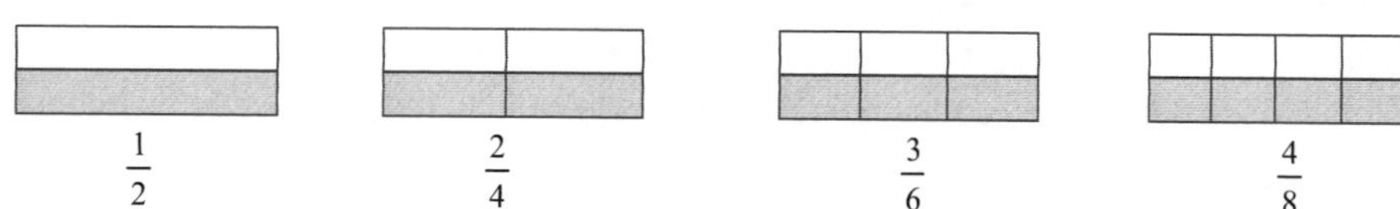

Figure 5.15

Since the shaded portion in each of the four units (rectangles) are of the same size, the fractions represented by the shaded portions are equal. That is,

$\frac{1}{2} = \frac{2}{4} = \frac{3}{6} = \frac{4}{8}$. Such fractions are called **equivalent fractions.**

Each of the above fractions can be derived by multiplying $\frac{1}{2}$ by a form of 1.

$$\frac{1}{2}=\frac{1}{2}\times\frac{\mathbf{2}}{\mathbf{2}}=\frac{2}{4};\qquad \frac{1}{2}=\frac{1}{2}\times\frac{\mathbf{3}}{\mathbf{3}}=\frac{3}{6};\qquad \frac{1}{2}=\frac{1}{2}\times\frac{\mathbf{4}}{\mathbf{4}}=\frac{4}{8}$$

> The value of a fraction is not changed if it is multiplied by a form of one.
>
> For example $\frac{1}{2}\cdot\frac{5}{5}=\frac{1}{2}\cdot 1=\frac{1}{2}$

Consider a few more fractions and their equivalents.

$$\frac{3}{5}=\frac{3}{5}\times\frac{\mathbf{4}}{\mathbf{4}}=\frac{12}{20};\qquad \frac{7}{6}=\frac{7}{6}\times\frac{\mathbf{5}}{\mathbf{5}}=\frac{35}{30};\qquad \frac{9}{11}=\frac{9}{11}\times\frac{\mathbf{4}}{\mathbf{4}}=\frac{36}{44}$$

This process of building equivalent fractions is called *changing the fraction to higher terms.*

- The fractions $\frac{2}{4}$, $\frac{3}{6}$, and $\frac{4}{8}$ in Figure 3.8 are equal to the fraction $\frac{1}{2}$.

$$\frac{2}{4}=\frac{1\cdot\mathbf{2}}{2\cdot\mathbf{2}}=\frac{1}{2};\qquad \frac{3}{6}=\frac{1\cdot\mathbf{3}}{2\cdot\mathbf{3}}=\frac{1}{2};\qquad \frac{4}{8}=\frac{1\cdot\mathbf{4}}{2\cdot\mathbf{4}}=\frac{1}{2}$$

> Common factors in the numerator and the denominator can be cancelled because 1 is the multiplicative identity: $\frac{2}{4}=\frac{1\cdot\mathbf{2}}{2\cdot\mathbf{2}}=\frac{1}{2}\cdot\frac{\mathbf{2}}{\mathbf{2}}=\frac{1}{2}\cdot\mathbf{1}=\frac{1}{2}$.

Consider a few more fractions and their equivalents.

$$\frac{35}{30}=\frac{7\cdot\mathbf{5}}{6\cdot\mathbf{5}}=\frac{7}{6};\qquad \frac{12}{20}=\frac{3\cdot\mathbf{4}}{5\cdot\mathbf{4}}=\frac{3}{5}$$

This process of cancelling common factors is called **simplifying the fraction to lower terms**, or **reducing the fraction.**

$$\frac{35}{30}=\frac{7\cdot\mathbf{5}}{6\cdot\mathbf{5}}=\frac{7}{6}$$ Cancel the common factor 5.

The fraction is said to have been **simplified to lowest terms** if the numerator and the denominator in the final fraction have no factor in common other than 1. Simplify the fraction $\frac{45}{120}$ to the lowest terms:

$$\frac{45}{120}=\frac{9\cdot\cancel{5}}{24\cdot\cancel{5}}$$ Cancel the common factor 5.

$$=\frac{9}{24}=\frac{3\cdot\cancel{3}}{8\cdot\cancel{3}}$$ Cancel the common factor 3.

$$= \frac{3}{8}$$ Stop, since the numerator and the denominator have no factor in common other then 1.

$$\frac{45}{120} = \frac{3}{8}$$ when reduced to lowest terms.

- Instead of cancelling the common factors one by one, there is another method for simplifying a fraction.

Write the numerator and the denominator as products of prime factors and cancel the common factors.

For example:

$$\frac{84}{144} = \frac{\not{2}\cdot\not{2}\cdot\not{3}\cdot 7}{\not{2}\cdot\not{2}\cdot 2\cdot 2\cdot\not{3}\cdot 3} = \frac{7}{2\cdot 2\cdot 3} = \frac{7}{12}$$

When the numerator and the denominator are large numbers, cancel the common factors that can be easily identified.

$$\frac{105}{135} = \frac{21\cdot 5}{27\cdot 5}$$ Both the numerator and the denominator are divisible by 5.

$$= \frac{21}{27} = \frac{7\cdot 3}{9\cdot 3}$$ Both the numerator and the denominator are divisible by 3.

$$= \frac{7}{9}$$ Stop; since 7 and 9 have no common factor other than 1.

Procedure to simplify a given fraction to lowest terms using prime factorization.

***Step* 1** Write the prime factorization of the numerator.

***Step* 2** Write the prime factorization of the denominator.

***Step* 3** Cancel common primes from the two factorizations. This is equivalent to cancelling common factors from the numerator and denominator.

EXAMPLE 1 Simplify the given fractions to lowest terms.

(a) $\frac{4}{12}$ **(b)** $\frac{12}{15}$ **(c)** $\frac{12}{35}$ **(d)** $\frac{84}{90}$

Solutions

(a) $\frac{4}{12} = \frac{\not{2}\cdot\not{2}}{\not{2}\cdot\not{2}\cdot 3} = \frac{1}{3}$

- $4 = 2\cdot 2$ (2 | 4, 2 | 2, 1)
- $12 = 2\cdot 2\cdot 3$ (2 | 12, 2 | 6, 3 | 3, 1)

(b) $\frac{12}{15} = \frac{2\cdot 2\cdot\not{3}}{\not{3}\cdot 5} = \frac{4}{5}$

- $12 = 2\cdot 2\cdot 3$ (2 | 12, 2 | 6, 3 | 3, 1)
- $15 = 3\cdot 5$ (3 | 15, 5 | 5, 1)

WARM-UP

1. Simplify the given fraction to lowest terms.

(a) $\frac{120}{35}$

(b) $\frac{15}{28}$

WARM-UP

(c) $\frac{25}{21}$

(d) $\frac{98}{126}$

2. Simplify the given fractions to lowest terms.

(a) $\frac{63}{84}$

(c) $\frac{12}{35} = \frac{2 \cdot 2 \cdot 3}{5 \cdot 7}$

$= \frac{12}{35}$

- 2 | 12, 2 | 6, 3 | 3, 1; $12 = 2 \cdot 2 \cdot 3$
- 5 | 35, 7 | 7, 1; $35 = 5 \cdot 7$
- There are no common factors. Fraction cannot be simplified.

(d) $\frac{84}{90} = \frac{\cancel{2} \cdot 2 \cdot \cancel{3} \cdot 7}{\cancel{2} \cdot \cancel{3} \cdot 3 \cdot 5}$

$= \frac{2 \cdot 7}{3 \cdot 5}$

$= \frac{14}{15}$

- 2 | 84, 2 | 42, 3 | 21, 7 | 7, 1; $84 = 2 \cdot 2 \cdot 3 \cdot 7$
- 2 | 90, 3 | 45, 3 | 15, 5 | 5, 1; $90 = 2 \cdot 3 \cdot 3 \cdot 5$
- 2 and 3 are common factors. They cancel.

Procedure to simplify a given fraction to lowest terms by cancelling common factors.

***Step* 1** Find a common factor of the numerator and the denominator by inspection, or divisibility tests, or by prime factorization.

***Step* 2** Cancel the common factor from both the numerator and the denominator.

***Step* 3** Repeat step 1 and 2 for the quotients, and continue until there are no common factors in the numerator and the denominator other than 1.

EXAMPLE 2 Simplify the given fractions to lowest terms.

(a) $\frac{525}{1125}$ (b) $\frac{6300}{10,500}$

Solutions

(a) $\frac{525}{1125} = \frac{5 \times 105}{5 \times 225}$

- 5 is a common factor of both the numerator and denominator. Factor each and cancel the common factor of 5.

$= \frac{5 \times 21}{5 \times 45}$

- Factor and cancel the common factor of 5.

$= \frac{3 \times 7}{3 \times 15}$

- Factor and cancel the common factor of 3.

$= \frac{7}{15}$

Stop, since 7 and 15 have no common factors other than 1.

(b) $\dfrac{6300}{10{,}500} = \dfrac{63 \times 100}{105 \times 100}$ • Factor and cancel the common factor of 100.

$= \dfrac{3 \times 21}{3 \times 35}$ • Factor and cancel the common factor of 3.

$= \dfrac{7 \times 3}{7 \times 5}$ • Factor and cancel the common factor of 7.

$= \dfrac{3}{5}$ Stop, since 3 and 5 have no common factors other than 1.

WARM-UP

(b) $\dfrac{750}{900}$

Answers:

1. (a) $\dfrac{24}{7}$ (b) $\dfrac{15}{28}$ (c) $\dfrac{25}{21}$ (d) $\dfrac{7}{9}$
2. (a) $\dfrac{3}{4}$ (b) $\dfrac{5}{6}$

Solution to the Application

Alisha wants to finish a novel as soon as possible. So far she has read only 54 pages. What fraction of the number of pages has she read if there are 180 pages in the novel? Simplify the fraction to lowest terms.

Solutions: The fraction is the number of pages read over the total number of pages, which is $\dfrac{54}{180}$.

$\dfrac{54}{180} = \dfrac{6 \times 9}{6 \times 30}$ • Factor and cancel the common factor of 6.

$= \dfrac{3 \times 3}{3 \times 10}$ • Factor and cancel the common factor of 3.

Stop, since 3 and 10 have no common factors other than 1.

$= \dfrac{3}{10}$

Alisha has read $\dfrac{3}{10}$ of the total number of pages.

B. BUILD EQUIVALENT FRACTIONS

➜ Understand forms of 1

Illustrations

(a) $\dfrac{12}{12}$ is a form of one because 12 divided by 12 is equivalent to 1.

(b) $\dfrac{7}{6}$ is not a form of one because 7 divided by 6 is not equivalent to 1.

Verify Skill

Objective 5.4B

Are the following forms of 1 ?

(a) $\dfrac{5}{5}$ **(b)** $\dfrac{6}{7}$

If your answers to these questions are the same as given below then you may skip this objective.

Answers: **(a)** Yes **(b)** No

Discussion

- Consider the fraction represented by the shaded area of each of the following :

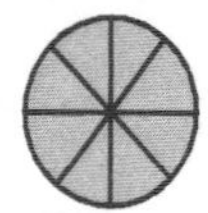
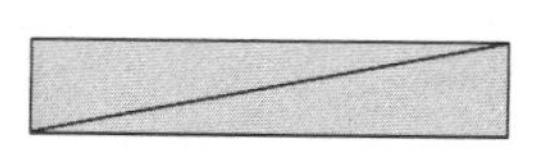
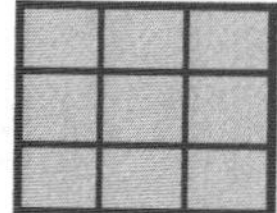

$\dfrac{\text{8 parts shaded}}{\text{8 parts total}}$ $\dfrac{\text{2 parts shaded}}{\text{2 parts total}}$ $\dfrac{\text{9 parts shaded}}{\text{9 parts total}}$

$\dfrac{8}{8}$ $\dfrac{2}{2}$ $\dfrac{9}{9}$

Notice that in each case, the numerator equals the denominator; the number of parts shaded equals the total number of parts. In each case, the value of the fraction is one, as in "*one whole unit is shaded*".

- We can extend this to many different fractions following the same pattern :

$\dfrac{15}{15}, \dfrac{7}{7}, \dfrac{2008}{2008}$

are all **FORMS OF ONE.**

- It is helpful to know different forms of one because the number one has a special property; in the real number system, 1 is the "multiplicative identity". This means that multiplying any number by 1 doesn't change the value of the number.

For example,

18×1 equals 18, 907×1 equals 907

Now lets look at some fractions multiplied by 1

$$\frac{7}{12} \times 1 \text{ equals } \frac{7}{12}$$

$$\frac{9}{5} \times 1 \text{ equals } \frac{9}{5}$$

What happens if we use one of our forms of one ?

Consider $\dfrac{1}{3}$ 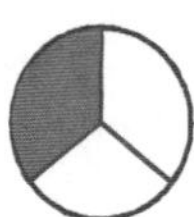

Now multiply $\dfrac{1}{3}$ by $\dfrac{2}{2}$, a form of 1.

$\dfrac{1}{3} \times \dfrac{2}{2} = \dfrac{2}{6}$ or 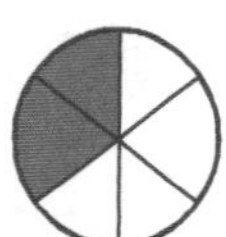

We have the same amount shaded. Though the fraction $\dfrac{1}{3}$ has been rewritten as $\dfrac{2}{6}$, its **value** is the **same.**

➜ Build equivalent fractions

Illustrations

- The fractions equivalent to $\frac{2}{5}, \frac{3}{2}$, and $\frac{3}{4}$, having 20 as the common denominator are obtained as follows:

$$\frac{2}{5} = \frac{2}{5} \times \frac{4}{4} = \frac{8}{20}$$

$$\frac{3}{2} = \frac{3}{2} \times \frac{10}{10} = \frac{30}{20}$$

$$\frac{3}{4} = \frac{3}{4} \times \frac{5}{5} = \frac{15}{20}$$

- To find the missing numerator in $\frac{2}{5} = \frac{?}{40}$.

$40 \div 5 = 8$

$\frac{2}{5} = \frac{2}{5} \cdot \frac{8}{8} = \frac{\mathbf{16}}{40}$.

- To find the missing denominator in $\frac{15}{13} = \frac{45}{?}$

$45 \div 15 = 3$, so multiply $\frac{15}{13}$ by $\frac{3}{3}$.

$\frac{15}{13} = \frac{15}{13} \cdot \frac{3}{3} = \frac{45}{\mathbf{39}}$.

Verify Skill

Objective 5.4B

1. Change $\frac{3}{7}, \frac{5}{3}, \frac{11}{6}$ into equivalent fractions, each with denominator 42.

2. Find the missing numerator or denominator in:

(a) $\frac{3}{8} = \frac{?}{32}$

(b) $\frac{7}{9} = \frac{14}{?}$

If your answers to these questions are the same as given below then you may skip this objective.

Answers:

1. $\frac{18}{42}, \frac{70}{42}, \frac{77}{42}$

2. (a) 12, (b) 18

Discussion

- As discussed, the fractions $\frac{1}{2}, \frac{2}{4}, \frac{3}{6}$, and $\frac{4}{8}$ are *equivalent fractions* since they all represent one half of a unit. In the same manner, the fractions $\frac{1}{3}, \frac{3}{9}$, and $\frac{8}{24}$ are equivalent fractions (Figure 5.16 below), as each of them represents one-third of a unit.

$\frac{1}{3}$ 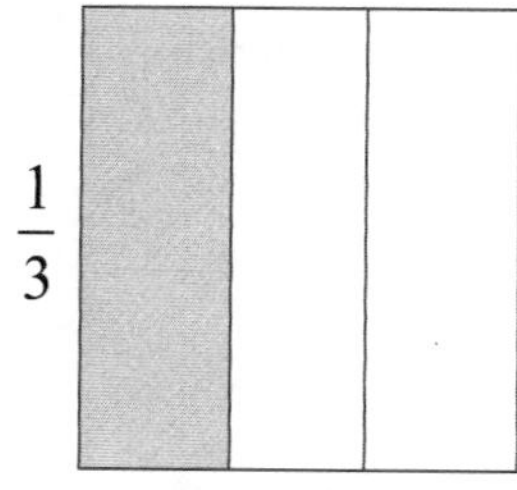 $\frac{3}{9}$  $\frac{8}{24}$ 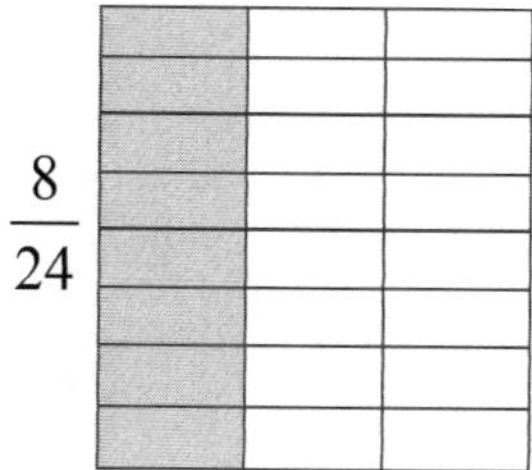

Figure 5.16

Equivalent Fractions

Multiply by :		$\frac{2}{2}$		$\frac{3}{3}$		$\frac{4}{4}$		$\frac{8}{8}$		$\frac{11}{11}$
$\frac{2}{3}$	=	$\frac{4}{6}$	=	$\frac{6}{9}$	=	$\frac{8}{12}$	=	$\frac{16}{24}$	=	$\frac{22}{33}$
$\frac{4}{5}$	=	$\frac{8}{10}$	=	$\frac{12}{15}$	=	$\frac{16}{20}$	=	$\frac{32}{40}$	=	$\frac{44}{55}$
$\frac{3}{7}$	=	$\frac{6}{14}$	=	$\frac{9}{21}$	=	$\frac{12}{28}$	=	$\frac{24}{56}$	=	$\frac{33}{77}$
$\frac{1}{4}$	=	$\frac{2}{8}$	=	$\frac{3}{12}$	=	$\frac{4}{16}$	=	$\frac{8}{32}$	=	$\frac{11}{44}$

- To find the missing numerator in $\frac{2}{7} = \frac{?}{42}$.

  This is the same as building an equivalent fraction from $\frac{2}{7}$ to get 42 as the denominator.

  Since $42 \div 7 = 6$, multiply $\frac{2}{7}$ by $\frac{6}{6}$. $\frac{2}{7} = \frac{2}{7} \cdot \frac{6}{6} = \frac{\mathbf{12}}{42}$.

  Therefore, the missing numerator is 12.

- To find the missing numerator in $\frac{7}{5} = \frac{?}{20}$, we build an equivalent fraction with 20 as the denominator.

  Since $20 \div 5 = 4$, multiply $\frac{7}{5}$ by $\frac{4}{4}$. So, $\frac{7}{5} = \frac{7}{5} \cdot \frac{4}{4} = \frac{\mathbf{28}}{20}$.

  Therefore, the missing numerator is 28.

- The process of finding missing denominators is similar. To find the missing denominator in $\frac{3}{4} = \frac{15}{?}$,

  build an equivalent fraction with 15 as the numerator. Since $15 \div 3 = 5$, multiply $\frac{3}{4}$ by $\frac{5}{5}$.

  $$\frac{3}{4} = \frac{3}{4} \cdot \frac{\mathbf{5}}{\mathbf{5}} = \frac{15}{\mathbf{20}}$$

  Therefore, the missing denominator is 20.

- To find the missing denominator in $\frac{7}{9} = \frac{35}{?}$, build an equivalent fraction with 35 as the numerator.

  Since $35 \div 7 = 5$, multiply $\frac{7}{9}$ by $\frac{5}{5}$. So, $\frac{7}{9} = \frac{7}{9} \cdot \frac{\mathbf{5}}{\mathbf{5}} = \frac{35}{\mathbf{45}}$.

  Therefore, the missing denominator is 45.

> **Procedure** to build equivalent fractions from given fractions.
>
> Multiply the fractions by 1 in the form $\frac{a}{a}$.

Among these fractions, the fraction $\frac{1}{3}$ is in lowest terms. The remaining two fractions, namely $\frac{3}{9}$ and $\frac{8}{24}$, can be obtained from $\frac{1}{3}$ by multiplying by a form of 1.

$$\frac{1}{3} = \frac{1}{3} \cdot 1 = \frac{1}{3} \cdot \frac{\mathbf{3}}{\mathbf{3}} = \frac{3}{9}$$

$$\frac{1}{3} = \frac{1}{3} \cdot 1 = \frac{1}{3} \cdot \frac{\mathbf{8}}{\mathbf{8}} = \frac{8}{24}$$

This process is called **building equivalent fractions.** It is the opposite of simplifying fractions. Study the following chart carefully to understand how to "build" equivalent fractions. The fractions in each row of the table are equivalent.

EXAMPLE 3

(a) Build a fraction equivalent to $\frac{7}{13}$ using $\frac{4}{4}$ for 1.

(b) Build three fractions equivalent to $\frac{5}{8}$ using $\frac{2}{2}$, $\frac{3}{3}$ and $\frac{5}{5}$ for 1.

Solutions

(a) $\mathbf{\frac{7}{13}} = \frac{7}{13} \cdot 1 = \frac{7}{13} \cdot \frac{4}{4} = \frac{7 \cdot 4}{13 \cdot 4} = \mathbf{\frac{28}{52}}$

The new fraction $\frac{28}{52}$ is equivalent to the given fraction $\frac{7}{13}$.

(b) $\mathbf{\frac{5}{8}} \cdot \frac{2}{2} = \mathbf{\frac{10}{16}}$; $\frac{5}{8} \cdot \frac{3}{3} = \mathbf{\frac{15}{24}}$; $\frac{5}{8} \cdot \frac{5}{5} = \mathbf{\frac{25}{40}}$

Each of the new fractions $\frac{10}{16}$, $\frac{15}{24}$, and $\frac{25}{40}$ is equivalent to the given fraction $\frac{5}{8}$.

> **Procedure** to find the missing numerator (denominator).
>
> ***Step* 1** Divide the larger denominator (numerator) by the smaller denominator (numerator).
>
> ***Step* 2** Multiply the original fraction by $\frac{\boldsymbol{a}}{\boldsymbol{a}}$, where $\boldsymbol{a}$ is the quotient obtained in step 1.

WARM-UP

3. (a) Build a fraction equivalent to $\frac{2}{5}$ using $\frac{11}{11}$ for 1.

(b) Build three fractions equivalent to $\frac{6}{7}$ using $\frac{2}{2}$, $\frac{4}{4}$, $\frac{5}{5}$.

4. Find the missing numerator.

(a) $\frac{5}{7} = \frac{?}{21}$

(b) $\frac{5}{8} = \frac{?}{72}$

5. Find the missing denominator.

(a) $\frac{9}{6} = \frac{108}{?}$

(b) $\frac{16}{11} = \frac{144}{?}$

Answers:

3. (a) $\frac{22}{55}$ (b) $\frac{12}{14}, \frac{24}{28}, \frac{30}{35}$
4. (a) 15 (b) 45
5. (a) 72 (b) 99

EXAMPLE 4 Find the missing numerator.

(a) $\frac{3}{4} = \frac{?}{20}$ **(b)** $\frac{3}{7} = \frac{?}{35}$

Solutions

(a) $\frac{3}{4} = \frac{?}{20}$

$20 \div 4 = 5$ Divide the denominators.

$\frac{3}{4} = \frac{3}{4} \cdot \frac{\mathbf{5}}{\mathbf{5}} = \frac{\mathbf{15}}{20}$ Multiply the fraction by $\frac{5}{5}$.

The missing numerator is 15.

(b) $\frac{3}{7} = \frac{?}{35}$

$35 \div 7 = 5$

$\frac{3}{7} = \frac{3}{7} \cdot \frac{\mathbf{5}}{\mathbf{5}} = \frac{\mathbf{15}}{35}$

The missing numerator is 15.

EXAMPLE 5 Find the missing denominator.

(a) $\frac{3}{4} = \frac{75}{?}$ **(b)** $\frac{7}{16} = \frac{147}{?}$

Solutions

(a) $\frac{3}{4} = \frac{75}{?}$

$75 \div 3 = \mathbf{25}$ Divide the numerators.

$\frac{3}{4} = \frac{3}{4} \cdot \frac{\mathbf{25}}{\mathbf{25}} = \frac{75}{\mathbf{100}}$ Multiply by $\frac{25}{25}$.

The missing denominator is 100.

(b) $\frac{7}{16} = \frac{147}{?}$

$147 \div 7 = 21$ Divide the numerators.

$\frac{7}{16} = \frac{7}{16} \cdot \frac{\mathbf{21}}{\mathbf{21}} = \frac{147}{\mathbf{336}}$ Multiply by $\frac{21}{21}$.

The missing denominator is 336.

Comparing and Listing Fractions in Order

➜ **(a) Compare two fractions.**

(b) List fractions in order.

Application

Data about 4 motorcycles from different companies is given below.

Company name	Gas consumption (in Gallons)	Distance traveled (in miles)
A	8	325
B	3	152
C	6	273
D	4	186

Which company's bike gives the best mileage?

Illustrations

- To check whether the fractions $\frac{8}{6}$ and $\frac{28}{21}$ are equal:

$$\frac{8}{6} \times \frac{28}{21} \quad \begin{array}{l} \rightarrow 8 \cdot 21 = 168 \\ \rightarrow 6 \cdot 28 = 168 \end{array} \quad \text{Equal}$$

$$\frac{8}{6} = \frac{28}{21}$$

- To list the fractions $\frac{7}{10}, \frac{5}{12}, \frac{3}{4}$ in ascending order, first change them to equivalent fractions with the LCD as the common denominator. The LCD = 60.

$$\frac{7}{10} = \frac{7}{10} \cdot \frac{6}{6} = \frac{42}{60}, \qquad 60 \div 10 = 6$$

$$\frac{5}{12} = \frac{5}{12} \cdot \frac{5}{5} = \frac{25}{60}, \qquad 60 \div 12 = 5$$

$$\frac{3}{4} = \frac{3}{4} \cdot \frac{15}{15} = \frac{45}{60}. \qquad 60 \div 4 = 15$$

Then, arrange the fractions in ascending order of the numerators.

Since $25 < 42 < 45$,

$$\frac{25}{60} < \frac{42}{60} < \frac{45}{60}; \quad \text{OR} \quad \frac{5}{12} < \frac{7}{10} < \frac{3}{4}$$

The list in the desired order is $\frac{5}{12}, \frac{7}{10}, \frac{3}{4}$

Verify Skill

Objective 5.4B

(a) Check whether $\frac{12}{13}$ and $\frac{7}{8}$ are equal? If not, which one is smaller?

(b) List the fractions $\frac{7}{3}, \frac{20}{8}, \frac{17}{20}$, and $\frac{12}{5}$ in descending order.

If your answers to these questions are the same as given below, then you may skip this objective.

Answers:

(a) Not equal, $\frac{7}{8}$ is smaller.

(b) $\frac{20}{8}, \frac{12}{5}, \frac{7}{3}, \frac{17}{20}$

Discussion

(a) Compare two fractions

First compare two fractions, say $\frac{2}{7}$ and $\frac{5}{7}$, having the same denominators but unequal numerators.

Figure 5.17 shows that the shaded portion representing the fraction $\frac{2}{7}$ is smaller than the shaded portion representing the fraction $\frac{5}{7}$.

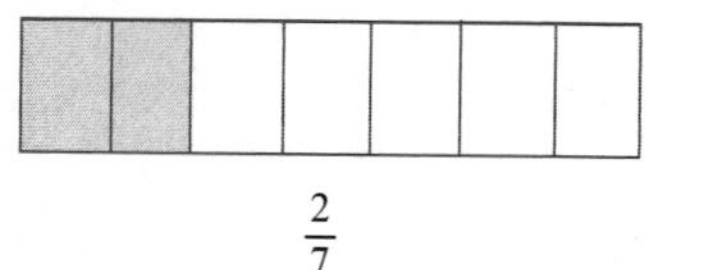

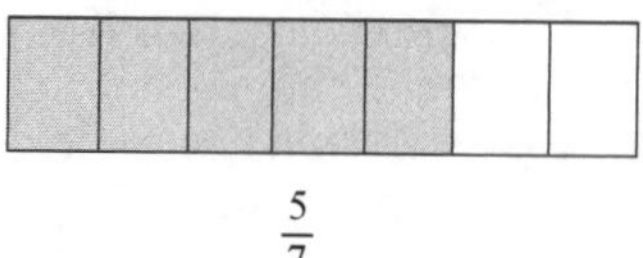

Figure 5.17

$\frac{2}{7}$ is less than $\frac{5}{7}$, written symbolically as $\frac{2}{7} < \frac{5}{7}$.

Also, $\frac{5}{7}$ is larger than $\frac{2}{7}$. This is written symbolically, $\frac{5}{7} > \frac{2}{7}$.

***Rule* 5 :** If two fractions have the same denominator, the one with larger numerator is larger.

$\frac{5}{9} > \frac{2}{9}$ because $5 > 2$

$\frac{13}{21} > \frac{8}{21}$ because $13 > 8$

$\frac{15}{91} > \frac{7}{91}$ because $15 > 7$

- If the fractions to be compared do not have common denominators then first convert the fractions to equivalent fractions with the LCD as the common denominator, then compare using Rule 5.

Compare $\frac{7}{9}$ and $\frac{5}{12}$.

First, convert these fractions to equivalent fractions with the LCD as the common denominator.

$\text{LCD} = \text{LCM of } 9 \text{ and } 12 = 36.$

$\frac{7}{\mathbf{9}} = \frac{7}{9} \cdot \frac{\mathbf{4}}{\mathbf{4}} = \frac{28}{\mathbf{36}}$, and $\frac{5}{\mathbf{12}} = \frac{5}{12} \cdot \frac{\mathbf{3}}{\mathbf{3}} = \frac{15}{\mathbf{36}}$,

Now, compare $\frac{28}{36}$ and $\frac{15}{36}$. Since $28 > 15$, $\frac{28}{36} > \frac{15}{36} \rightarrow \frac{7}{9} > \frac{5}{12}$.

- To compare fractions with whole numbers or mixed numbers, compare their whole number parts. The fraction with a larger whole number part is larger.

For example, $\mathbf{2}\frac{3}{4} > \mathbf{1}\frac{4}{5}$

Since whole number part $2 > 1$.

If, however, the whole number parts are equal, then compare their fractional parts using the above method. The fraction with the larger fractional part is larger.

For example, compare $2\frac{5}{12}$ and $2\frac{7}{16}$.

Since the whole number parts are equal, we compare their fractional parts.

$\frac{5}{12}$ and $\frac{7}{16}$

First convert these fractional parts to equivalent fractions with the LCD as the denominator.

LCD = LCM of 12 and 16 = 48.

$\frac{5}{12} = \frac{20}{\mathbf{48}}$ and $\frac{7}{16} = \frac{21}{\mathbf{48}}$, now compare.

Since 21 > 20.

$\frac{21}{48} > \frac{20}{48} \rightarrow \frac{7}{16} > \frac{5}{12}$ so $2\frac{7}{16} > 2\frac{5}{12}$.

- Recall that an improper fraction is always greater than or equal to 1 while a proper fraction is always less than 1. **Therefore, every improper fraction, whole number or mixed number, is larger than any proper fraction.**

$$2\frac{3}{4} > \frac{13}{53}\ ;\ \frac{17}{9} > \frac{201}{417}\ ;\ 2 > \frac{387}{388}$$

- To compare two improper fractions, first convert them to mixed numbers and then compare.

$\frac{11}{4}$ and $\frac{14}{5}$

Convert to mixed numbers $\frac{11}{4} = 2\frac{3}{4}$ and $\frac{14}{5} = 2\frac{4}{5}$.

To compare $2\frac{3}{4}$ and $2\frac{4}{5}$, compare the fractional parts $\frac{3}{4}$ and $\frac{4}{5}$ or $\frac{15}{20}$ and $\frac{16}{20}$.

Since $\frac{16}{20} > \frac{15}{20} \longrightarrow \frac{4}{5} > \frac{3}{4} \longrightarrow 2\frac{4}{5} > 2\frac{3}{4} \longrightarrow \frac{14}{5} > \frac{11}{4}$

(b) List fractions in order

When a group of fractions is arranged in order from smallest to largest, they are said to be in **ascending order**; and when arranged from the largest to smallest they are in **descending order.**

To list fractions in ascending or descending order, proceed the same way as comparing two fractions. Convert each fraction to an equivalent fraction with the LCD as the common denominator and then compare the numerators.

Arrange the fractions $\frac{2}{5}, \frac{3}{4}$, and $\frac{7}{10}$ in ascending order. The LCD = 20.

$$\frac{2}{5} = \frac{2}{5} \cdot \frac{\mathbf{4}}{\mathbf{4}} = \frac{8}{20}$$

$$\frac{3}{4} = \frac{3}{4} \cdot \frac{\mathbf{5}}{\mathbf{5}} = \frac{15}{20}$$

$$\frac{7}{10} = \frac{7}{10} \cdot \frac{\mathbf{2}}{\mathbf{2}} = \frac{14}{20}.$$

Now arrange these equivalent fractions each with denominator 20 in ascending order of the numerators:

Since $8 < 14 < 15$,

$\frac{8}{20} < \frac{14}{20} < \frac{15}{20}$ The equivalent fractions with common denominators are arranged in ascending order.

$\frac{2}{5} < \frac{7}{10} < \frac{3}{4}$ The original fractions are arranged from smallest to largest.

Hence, the list in ascending order is $\frac{2}{5}, \frac{7}{10}, \frac{3}{4}$.

- To arrange the given fractions in descending order, arrange the equivalent fractions with common denominators in descending order of their numerators.

Since, $15 > 14 > 8$, $\frac{15}{20} > \frac{14}{20} > \frac{8}{20}$ so $\frac{3}{4} > \frac{7}{10} > \frac{2}{5}$.

Hence, the given fractions arranged in descending order are $\frac{3}{4}, \frac{7}{10}, \frac{2}{5}$.

Procedure to compare two fractions, and write the inequality statement between them.

***Step* 1** Change the given fractions to equivalent fractions with the LCD as the common denominator.

***Step* 2** Compare the new fractions.

***Step* 3** Replace the new fractions by the original ones.

WARM-UP

6. Identify the smaller of the two fractions.

(a) $\frac{5}{6}$ or $\frac{3}{4}$

EXAMPLE 6 Identify the larger of the two fractions.

(a) $\frac{2}{9}, \frac{5}{12}$ **(b)** $2\frac{3}{4}, \frac{17}{36}$

Write an inequality in each case.

Solutions

(a) *Step* 1 The LCD of 9 and 12 is 36.

$$\frac{2}{9} = \frac{2}{9} \cdot \frac{\mathbf{4}}{\mathbf{4}} = \frac{8}{\mathbf{36}},$$

$$\frac{5}{12} = \frac{5}{12} \cdot \frac{\mathbf{3}}{\mathbf{3}} = \frac{15}{\mathbf{36}}$$

Step 2 $\frac{15}{36}$ is larger than $\frac{8}{36}$ since $15 > 12$.

Step 3 $\frac{5}{12}$ is larger than $\frac{2}{9}$.

The inequality statement is: $\frac{5}{12} > \frac{2}{9}$.

(b) The two fractions $2\frac{3}{4}$ and $\frac{17}{36}$ can be compared with the knowledge of proper and improper fractions.

The fraction $2\frac{3}{4}$ is a mixed number.

The fraction $\frac{17}{36}$ is a proper fraction. Since every mixed number or improper fraction is greater than every proper fraction $2\frac{3}{4}$ is greater than $\frac{17}{36}$.

The inequality statement is: $2\frac{3}{4} > \frac{17}{36}$

EXAMPLE 7 Identify the statement as True or False.

(a) $\frac{2}{5} > \frac{3}{4}$ **(b)** $\frac{11}{30} < \frac{7}{18}$

Solutions

(a) The LCD equals LCM of 4 and 5 equals 20.

$$\frac{2}{5} = \frac{2}{5} \cdot \mathbf{\frac{4}{4}} = \frac{8}{20}$$

$$\frac{3}{4} = \frac{3}{4} \cdot \mathbf{\frac{5}{5}} = \frac{15}{20}.$$

$$\frac{2}{5} > \frac{3}{4} \text{ means } \frac{8}{20} > \frac{15}{20} \rightarrow 8 > 15 \text{ False}$$

The statement is False.

(b) The LCD equals LCM of 30 and 18 equals 90.

$$\frac{11}{30} = \frac{11}{30} \cdot \mathbf{\frac{3}{3}} = \frac{33}{90}$$

$$\frac{7}{18} = \frac{7}{18} \cdot \mathbf{\frac{5}{5}} = \frac{35}{90}$$

$30 = 2 \times 3 \times 5$
$18 = 2 \times 3 \times 3 = 2 \times 3^2$
The least common multiple of 30 and 18 is $2 \times 3^2 \times 5$

$$\frac{11}{30} < \frac{7}{18} \text{ means } \frac{33}{90} < \frac{35}{90} \rightarrow 33 < 35 \text{ True}$$

The statement is True.

WARM-UP

(b) $5\frac{4}{9}$ or $\frac{47}{11}$

7. Identify the statement as True or False.

(a) $\frac{3}{4} > \frac{7}{9}$

(b) $\frac{11}{16} < \frac{13}{20}$

Procedure to list a group of fractions in ascending or descending order.

***Step* 1** Find the LCD.

***Step* 2** Convert each fraction to an equivalent fraction with the LCD as the common denominator.

***Step* 3** Arrange the new fractions in the desired order of numerators.

***Step* 4** Replace each of the new fractions by the original fractions.

8. List the following in ascending order.

$\frac{9}{12}, \frac{17}{20}, \frac{11}{15}$

EXAMPLE 8 Arrange the following fractions in descending order.

$$\frac{3}{4}, \frac{7}{12}, \frac{12}{15}.$$

Solution LCD = LCM of 4, 12, 15 = 60 (verify)

- Build the fractions to the common denominator 60.

$$\frac{3}{4} = \frac{3}{4} \cdot \frac{\mathbf{15}}{\mathbf{15}} = \frac{45}{\mathbf{60}}$$

$$\frac{7}{12} = \frac{7}{12} \cdot \frac{\mathbf{5}}{\mathbf{5}} = \frac{35}{\mathbf{60}}$$

$$\frac{12}{15} = \frac{12}{15} \cdot \frac{\mathbf{4}}{\mathbf{4}} = \frac{48}{\mathbf{60}}$$

The fractions equivalent to the given fractions with the common denominator are:

$$\frac{45}{60}, \frac{35}{60}, \frac{48}{60}$$

The numerators, from largest to smallest, are

- List the new fractions in the descending order of the numerators.

$$48 > 45 > 35$$

therefore, $\frac{48}{60} > \frac{45}{60} > \frac{35}{60}$

- Replace each fraction by the original fraction.

So, $\frac{12}{15} > \frac{3}{4} > \frac{7}{12}$

The desired list order is : $\frac{12}{15}, \frac{3}{4}, \frac{7}{12}$

Answers:

3. (a) $\frac{3}{4}$ (b) $\frac{47}{11}$

4. (a) False (b) False

5. $\frac{11}{15}, \frac{9}{12}, \frac{17}{20}$

Solution to the Application

Data about 4 motorcycles from different companies is given below.

Company name	Gas consumption (in gallons)	Distance travelled (in miles)
A	8	325
B	3	152
C	6	273
D	4	186

Which company's motorcycle gives the best mileage?

Mileage means miles per gallon of gas = $\dfrac{\text{Distance travelled in miles}}{\text{Gas consumed in gallons}}$.

The mileage of Company A's motorcycle is $= \dfrac{325}{8} = 40\dfrac{5}{8}$.

The mileage of Company B's motorcycle is $= \dfrac{152}{3} = 50\dfrac{2}{3}$.

The mileage of Company C's motorcycle is $= \dfrac{273}{6} = 45\dfrac{1}{2}$.

The mileage of Company D's motorcycle is $= \dfrac{186}{4} = 46\dfrac{1}{2}$.

To find the best mileage means to find the largest of these fractions.

As discussed in this section, compare these fractions by converting them to mixed numbers and comparing the whole number parts. Since $\dfrac{152}{3}$ or $50\dfrac{2}{3}$ is the largest fraction, the motorcycles of company B gives the best mileage.

EXERCISE 5.4

A. **In exercises 1-12, simplify the given fraction to lowest terms.**

1. $\frac{18}{30}$ 2. $\frac{12}{20}$ 3. $\frac{63}{90}$ 4. $\frac{60}{144}$ 5. $\frac{32}{50}$ 6. $\frac{45}{120}$

7. $\frac{108}{144}$ 8. $\frac{75}{125}$ 9. $\frac{172}{236}$ 10. $\frac{200}{240}$ 11. $\frac{260}{900}$ 12. $\frac{242}{264}$

B. **In exercises 13-18, build three equivalent fractions by multiplying by $\frac{3}{3}, \frac{4}{4}$, and $\frac{6}{6}$.**

13. $\frac{3}{5}$ 14. $\frac{2}{7}$ 15. $\frac{4}{5}$ 16. $\frac{5}{9}$ 17. $\frac{8}{11}$ 18. $\frac{18}{13}$

In exercises 19 - 30, find the missing numerator or denominator.

19. $\frac{1}{5} = \frac{2}{?}$ 20. $\frac{1}{6} = \frac{?}{24}$ 21. $\frac{4}{5} = \frac{?}{60}$ 22. $\frac{3}{7} = \frac{15}{?}$ 23. $\frac{4}{7} = \frac{20}{?}$ 24. $\frac{5}{11} = \frac{30}{?}$

25. $\frac{7}{12} = \frac{42}{?}$ 26. $\frac{21}{40} = \frac{42}{?}$ 27. $\frac{13}{25} = \frac{?}{100}$ 28. $\frac{15}{21} = \frac{?}{84}$ 29. $\frac{?}{147} = \frac{16}{7}$ 30. $\frac{22}{15} = \frac{198}{?}$

In exercises 31-40, identify the fraction with the larger value.

31. $\frac{5}{4}$ or $\frac{13}{10}$ 32. $\frac{2}{3}$ or $\frac{4}{5}$ 33. $\frac{1}{3}$ or $\frac{3}{10}$ 34. $\frac{2}{5}$ or $\frac{4}{11}$ 35. $2\frac{2}{3}$ or $3\frac{2}{5}$

36. $2\frac{1}{3}$ or $2\frac{3}{10}$ 37. $25\frac{1}{2}$ or $25\frac{1}{3}$ 38. $\frac{17}{35}$ or $\frac{6}{14}$ 39. $12\frac{5}{16}$ or $12\frac{3}{8}$ 40. $\frac{15}{20}$ or $\frac{11}{15}$

In exercises 41-46, identify whether the statement is *True* or *False*.

41. $\frac{17}{20} < \frac{13}{8}$ 42. $\frac{7}{3} = 6\frac{2}{5}$ 43. $5\frac{2}{7} = \frac{74}{14}$ 44. $\frac{13}{17} > \frac{12}{17}$ 45. $\frac{7}{10} < \frac{7}{12}$ 46. $\frac{6}{9} = \frac{24}{45}$

In exercises 47-56, insert appropriate symbol (>, <, or =) to make the statement true.

47. $\frac{5}{6} \square \frac{3}{4}$ 48. $\frac{16}{5} \square \frac{10}{3}$ 49. $\frac{5}{7} \square \frac{7}{9}$ 50. $\frac{3}{8} \square \frac{9}{24}$ 51. $\frac{9}{13} \square \frac{9}{16}$

52. $\frac{56}{72} \square \frac{105}{135}$ 53. $9\frac{1}{2} \square 8\frac{3}{2}$ 54. $5\frac{1}{2} \square \frac{5}{2}$ 55. $\frac{15}{4} \square 3\frac{4}{3}$ 56. $\frac{5}{12} \square \frac{9}{14}$

In exercises 57-61, arrange the given fractions in ascending order.

57. $\frac{2}{3}, \frac{13}{15}, \frac{11}{20}$ **58.** $\frac{3}{7}, \frac{5}{6}, \frac{2}{14}$ **59.** $\frac{17}{35}, \frac{13}{28}, \frac{6}{14}$ **60.** $15\frac{3}{4}, 15\frac{2}{5}, 15\frac{4}{7}$ **61.** $\frac{3}{8}, \frac{5}{8}, \frac{1}{4}, \frac{7}{16}$

In exercises 62-66 arrange the given fractions in descending order.

62. $\frac{5}{6}, \frac{7}{8}, \frac{2}{3}$ **63.** $\frac{2}{9}, \frac{1}{3}, \frac{5}{27}$ **64.** $\frac{4}{7}, \frac{3}{4}, \frac{2}{5}$ **65.** $\frac{7}{8}, 1\frac{1}{16}, \frac{3}{4}$ **66.** $\frac{2}{5}, \frac{7}{18}, \frac{11}{30}$

Applications

67. If 65 pieces of candy out of a box of 120 pieces have been distributed, what fraction of the total pieces of candy is left? Simplify to lowest terms.

68. Deandra has solved only 15 problems out of 75 problems. What fraction (in lowest terms) of the problems has she solved?

69. The load capacities of four pickup trucks are $\frac{7}{8}$ ton, $\frac{1}{2}$ ton, $\frac{2}{3}$ ton, and $\frac{5}{6}$ ton. Which capacity is the smallest, and which is the largest?

70. Mary spends $\frac{1}{4}$ of her monthly salary on food and clothing, $\frac{4}{13}$ on gasoline, and $\frac{5}{26}$ on books and magazines. Where does she spend the most out of these three categories?

71. The weights of three newborn babies at a maternity hospital are recorded as $7\frac{1}{8}$ lb, $7\frac{3}{16}$ lb, and $7\frac{1}{4}$ lb. Arrange the weights of the these babies from smallest to largest.

72. The male-female ratios in senior citizens's residences are found to be $\frac{53}{77}$, and $\frac{15}{22}$ respectively. List the ratios from largest to the smallest.

5.5 OPERATIONS WITH FRACTIONS

OBJECTIVES

After completing this section you will be able to:

A. Multiply fractions;

B. Divide fractions.

C. Adding and Subtracting like or unlike fractions;

D. Adding and Subtracting mixed numbers; and

E. Perform any combination of operations.

VOCABULARY

1. A **product** is the result obtained by multiplication.

2. If the product of two fractions is 1, either fraction is said to be the **reciprocal** of the other. For example, $\frac{3}{5}$ is the reciprocal of $\frac{5}{3}$.

2. **Like fractions** are fractions with common denominators.

   $\frac{7}{5}, \frac{13}{5}, \frac{25}{5}$ are like fractions.

3. **Unlike fractions** are fractions with different denominators.

   $\frac{3}{5}$ and $\frac{4}{7}$ are unlike fractions.

The symbols of grouping are:

Parentheses	( );
braces	{ };
brackets	[ ];
fraction bar	$\frac{\square}{\square}$

A fraction bar is commonly used to indicate division;

$$\frac{5-3}{7+4} \quad \text{means} \quad (5-3) \div (7+4)$$

Verify Skill

Objective 5.5 A

Multiply the fractions $\frac{3}{4}, \frac{15}{34}, \frac{51}{70}$ and simplify the product to lowest terms.

If your answer to the above question is the same as given below then you may skip this objective.

A. MULTIPLYING FRACTIONS

Application

A recipe which serves two people calls for $\frac{3}{4}$ cups of water. How much water is needed if the cook wants to make enough to serve ten people?

Illustration

- Multiply fractions and reduce the product to lowest terms.

$$\frac{2}{3}\times\frac{4}{15}\times\frac{18}{7}$$

$$\frac{2}{3}\times\frac{4}{15}\times\frac{18}{7} = \frac{2\times4\times18}{3\times15\times7} = \frac{\mathbf{2}\times\mathbf{2}\times\mathbf{2}\times\mathbf{2}\times3\times3}{3\times3\times\mathbf{5}\times\mathbf{7}} = \frac{16}{35}$$

Since 16 and 35 have no common factor other than 1, this fraction cannot be simplified further.

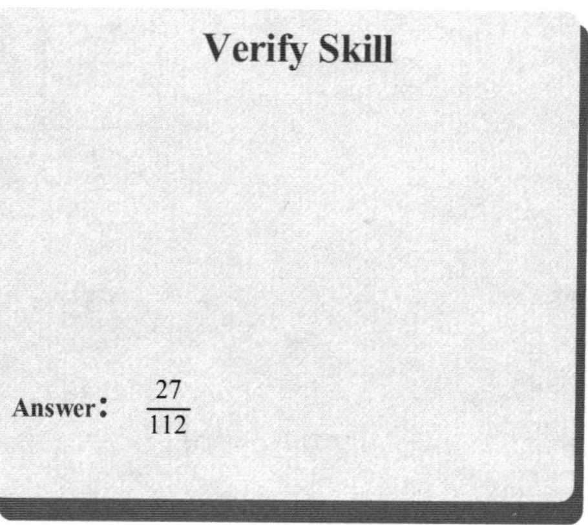

Discussion

- In Figure 5.18 (a) the rectangular unit is divided into five equal parts. Four parts, are shaded. They represent $\frac{4}{5}$ of the rectangle.

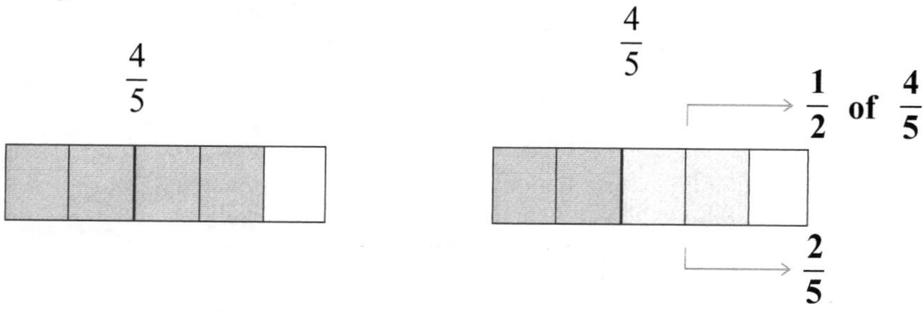

Figure 5.18 (a) **Figure 5.18 (b)**

In Figure 5.18 (b), observe that one-half $\left(\frac{1}{2}\right)$ of the shaded part $\left(\frac{4}{5}\right)$ is actually $\frac{2}{5}$ of the rectangular unit.

$$\frac{1}{2} \text{ of } \frac{4}{5} = \frac{2}{5}$$

$\downarrow$

A fraction of a fraction is the product of the fractions.

$$\frac{1}{2}\cdot\frac{4}{5} = \frac{2}{5}$$

Observe that when multiplying the two fractions $\frac{1}{2}$ and $\frac{4}{5}$ as follows, the product is the same as $\frac{2}{5}$.

$$\frac{1}{2}\cdot\frac{4}{5} = \frac{1\cdot4}{2\cdot5} = \frac{\text{Product of the numerators}}{\text{Product of the denominators}}$$

$$= \frac{4}{10} = \frac{2\cdot2}{5\cdot2} = \frac{2}{5}$$

In Figure 5.19(a), the rectangle is divided into three equal parts, and the shaded part is represented by $\frac{1}{3}$.

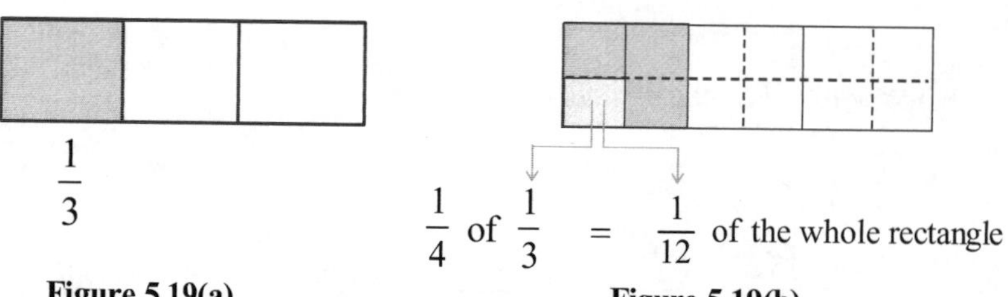

Figure 5.19(a) **Figure 5.19(b)**

In Figure 5.19(b) observe that one fourth $\left(\frac{1}{4}\right)$ of the shaded part $\left(\frac{1}{3}\right)$ is the same as $\left(\frac{1}{12}\right)$ of the rectangular unit.

$$\frac{1}{4} \text{ of } \frac{1}{3} = \frac{1}{12}$$

↓

A fraction of a fraction is the product of the fractions.

$$\frac{1}{4} \cdot \frac{1}{3} = \frac{1}{12} = \frac{\text{Product of the numerators}}{\text{Product of the denominators}}$$

***Rule* 1** To multiply two (or more) fractions, multiply the numerators together for the numerator of the product, and multiply the denominators together for the denominator of the product.

For example: $\frac{24}{30} \cdot \frac{3}{8} = \frac{24 \cdot 3}{30 \cdot 8} = \frac{\text{Product of the numerators}}{\text{Product of the denominators}}$

$$\frac{72}{240} = \frac{2 \cdot 2 \cdot 2 \cdot 3 \cdot \mathbf{3}}{2 \cdot 2 \cdot 2 \cdot \mathbf{2} \cdot 3 \cdot \mathbf{5}}$$

Find the prime factorization of the numerator and the denominator

$$= \frac{3}{10}$$

Cancel the common prime factors to simplify the fractions.

72
$2 \cdot \mathbf{36}$
$2 \cdot 2 \cdot \mathbf{18}$
$2 \cdot 2 \cdot 2 \cdot \mathbf{9}$
$2 \cdot 2 \cdot 2 \cdot 3 \cdot \mathbf{3}$

240
$24 \cdot 10$
$3 \cdot \mathbf{8} \cdot 2 \cdot 5$
$3 \cdot \mathbf{2} \cdot \mathbf{2} \cdot \mathbf{2}$

OR, simplify before multiplying.

$$\frac{24}{30} \cdot \frac{3}{8} = \frac{\overset{4}{\cancel{24}}}{\underset{5}{\cancel{30}}} \cdot \frac{3}{8}$$

First divide 24 and 30 by 6, and

$$= \frac{\overset{1}{\cancel{4}}}{5} \cdot \frac{3}{\underset{2}{\cancel{8}}}$$

then divide 4 and 8 by 4.

$$= \frac{1 \cdot 3}{5 \cdot 2} = \frac{3}{10}$$

- To multiply a fraction and a whole number, first write the whole number as an improper fraction and then perform multiplication as above.

$$\frac{7}{25} \cdot 15 = \frac{7}{\underset{5}{\cancel{25}}} \cdot \frac{\overset{3}{\cancel{15}}}{1} = \frac{21}{5} \text{ or } 4\frac{1}{5}$$

- To multiply mixed numbers, convert the mixed numbers to improper fractions and then perform multiplication.

$$\left(3\frac{4}{7}\right)\left(\frac{14}{15}\right) = \frac{25}{7}\cdot\frac{14}{15} \qquad 3\frac{4}{7} = \frac{21+4}{7} = \frac{25}{7}$$

$$= \frac{25\cdot 14}{7\cdot 15}$$

$$= \frac{5\cdot \mathbf{5}\cdot \mathbf{2}\cdot 7}{7\cdot \mathbf{3}\cdot 5} = \frac{5\cdot 2}{3} = \frac{10}{3} = 3\frac{1}{3}$$

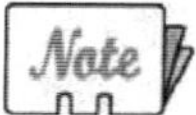

If a question has mixed numbers in it, it is common to give the answer as a mixed number, when possible.

Procedure to multiply two or more fractions.

***Step* 1** Cancel the common factors, between the numerators and denominators.

***Step* 2** Multiply by Rule 1.

EXAMPLE 1 Multiply, and reduce.

(a) $\frac{3}{4}\cdot\frac{5}{6}$ **(b)** $\frac{15}{24}\cdot\frac{16}{40}$ **(c)** $\frac{243}{1000}\cdot\frac{25}{81}\cdot\frac{40}{45}$

Solutions

(a) $\frac{3}{4}\cdot\frac{5}{6} = \frac{\overset{1}{\cancel{3}}}{4}\cdot\frac{5}{\underset{2}{\cancel{6}}}$ • Divide 3 and 6 by 3.

$= \mathbf{\frac{5}{8}}$ • Multiply by Rule 1.

(b) $\frac{15}{24}\cdot\frac{16}{40} = \frac{\overset{\overset{1}{\cancel{3}}}{\cancel{15}}}{\underset{\cancel{8}}{\cancel{24}}}\cdot\frac{\overset{2}{\cancel{16}}}{\underset{8}{\cancel{40}}}$
- Divide 15 and 40 by 5;
- Divide 3 and 24 by 3;
- Divide 16 and 8 by 8.

$= \frac{2}{8} = \frac{1}{4}$

(c) $\frac{243}{1000}\cdot\frac{25}{81}\cdot\frac{40}{45}$
- Divide 40 and 1000 by 10.
- Divide 25 and 100 by 25.
- Cancel out the 4's.

$= \frac{243}{\underset{\cancel{4}}{\underset{\cancel{100}}{\cancel{1000}}}}\cdot\frac{\overset{1}{\cancel{25}}}{81}\cdot\frac{\overset{\cancel{4}}{\cancel{40}}}{45}$

$= \frac{243}{81\cdot 45}$ • Multiply

WARM-UP

1. Multiply, and reduce.

(a) $\frac{12}{25}\cdot\frac{15}{16}$

(b) $\frac{9}{64}$ and $\frac{80}{27}$

(c) $\frac{4}{5},\frac{15}{10}$ and $\frac{7}{12}$

WARM-UP

2. Multiply, and simplify the product to lowest terms.

(a) $\frac{18}{4}\cdot 12$

(b) $\frac{3}{2}\cdot\frac{7}{5}\cdot 13$

3. Simplify

$3\frac{2}{3}\times\frac{5}{4}$

$$= \frac{\cancel{3}\cdot\cancel{3}\cdot\cancel{3}\cdot\cancel{3}\cdot\cancel{3}}{\cancel{3}\cdot\cancel{3}\cdot\cancel{3}\cdot\cancel{3}\cdot\cancel{3}\cdot 3\cdot 5}$$

- Since the numbers are large, do prime factorization and cancel the common factors.

$$= \frac{1}{15}$$

EXAMPLE 2 Find the product in lowest terms.

(a) $\frac{7}{9}\cdot\frac{18}{5}\cdot\frac{10}{21}\cdot 15$ **(b)** $\frac{11}{2}\cdot\frac{3}{5}\cdot 7$

Solutions

(a) $\frac{7}{9}\cdot\frac{18}{5}\cdot\frac{10}{21}\cdot 15$

$$= \frac{\cancel{7}^{1}}{\cancel{9}_{1}}\cdot\frac{\cancel{18}^{2}}{\cancel{5}_{1}}\cdot\frac{\cancel{10}^{2}}{\cancel{21}_{\cancel{3}_1}}\cdot\frac{\cancel{15}^{5}}{1}$$

- Write 15 as an improper fraction.

$$= \frac{7}{9}\cdot\frac{18}{5}\cdot\frac{10}{21}\cdot\frac{15}{1}$$

- Simplify:
  Divide 7 and 21 by 7.
  Divide 18 and 9 by 9.
  Divide 5 and 10 by 5.
  Divide 15 and 3 by 3.

$$= \frac{2\cdot 2\cdot 5}{1}$$

- Multiply.

$$= \frac{20}{1} = 20$$

(b) $\frac{11}{2}\cdot\frac{3}{5}\cdot 7 = \frac{11}{2}\cdot\frac{3}{5}\cdot\frac{7}{1}$

- Write 7 as an improper fraction.

$$= \frac{11\cdot 3\cdot 7}{2\cdot 5\cdot 1}$$

- No common divisors, Multiply.

$$= \frac{231}{10} = 23\frac{1}{10}$$

- Divide by 10 to change to a mixed number.
  231 ÷ 10 – 23 R 1

EXAMPLE 3 Simplify: $18\frac{2}{3}\times 4\frac{1}{6}\times\frac{3}{5}$

Solution

$$18\frac{2}{3}\times 4\frac{1}{6}\times\frac{3}{5} = \frac{56}{3}\cdot\frac{25}{6}\cdot\frac{3}{5}$$

- $18\frac{2}{3} = \frac{18\cdot 3+2}{3} = \frac{56}{3}$
  $4\frac{1}{6} = \frac{4\cdot 6+1}{6} = \frac{25}{6}$

$$= \frac{56\cdot 25\cdot \cancel{3}^{1}}{{}_{1}\cancel{3}\cdot 6\cdot 5}$$

- Cancel 3.

$$= \frac{2\cdot 2\cdot\cancel{2}\cdot 7\cdot 5\cdot\cancel{5}}{3\cdot\cancel{2}\cdot\cancel{5}}$$

- Replace by prime factors and cancel common factors.

$$= \frac{2\cdot 2\cdot 7\cdot 5}{3}$$

- Multiply.

$$= \frac{140}{3}$$

$$= 46\frac{2}{3}$$

• D ⟵ 3) 140 (quotient 46 ⟶ Q)

$$\begin{array}{r} 46 \\ 3\overline{)140} \\ \underline{12} \\ 20 \\ \underline{18} \\ 2 \end{array}$$

D ⟵ 3; 46 ⟶ Q; 2 ⟶ R

> *Rule 2* To find some part of a number, multiply the number by the fraction expressing that part.

EXAMPLE 4 A committee of 150 members meets for an election. Two thirds of the committee members must be present to hold the meeting. How many members must be present for the meeting to take place?

Solution The goal is to find $\frac{2}{3}$ of 150.

$$\frac{2}{3} \times 150 = \frac{2}{3} \times \frac{150}{1} = \frac{2 \cdot \cancel{150}^{50}}{\cancel{3}_{1}} = 100$$

So, 100 members must be present for the meeting to take place.

Solution to the Application:

A recipe which serves two people calls for $\frac{3}{4}$ cups of water. How much water is needed if the cook wants to make enough to serve ten people?

Solution: If the cook wants to serve ten people instead of two, then he must make 5 times as much food.

So, he will need $\left(\frac{3}{4} \times 5\right)$ cups of water

$$\frac{3}{4} \times 5 = \frac{3}{4} \times \frac{5}{1} = \frac{15}{4} = 3\frac{3}{4}$$

Thus, he needs $3\frac{3}{4}$ cups of water.

B. Dividing Fractions

Application

The distance a nut moves vertically on a bolt in one complete turn is $\frac{3}{16}$ inch. How many turns are needed to make the nut move $7\frac{1}{2}$ inches?

Warm-Up

4. There are 40 students in a Basic Mathematics class. Two-fifth of the class received an *A* on the final. How many students received an *A* ?

Answers:

1. (a) $\frac{9}{20}$ (b) $\frac{5}{12}$ (c) $\frac{7}{10}$
2. (a) 54 (b) $\frac{273}{10}$ or $27\frac{3}{10}$
3. $\frac{55}{12}$ or $4\frac{7}{12}$ 4. 16

Verify Skill

Objective 5.5B

Divide:

(a) $\frac{7}{5}$ by $\frac{3}{10}$ (b) $\frac{14}{3}$ by 7

(c) 42 by $\frac{6}{5}$

Verify Skill

If your answers to these questions are the same as given below then you may skip this objective.

Answers:

(a) $\frac{14}{3}$ **(b)** $\frac{2}{3}$ **(c)** 35

Illustrations

- Divide and simplify to lowest terms.

$$\frac{24}{36} \div \frac{8}{9}$$

$$\frac{24}{36} \times \frac{9}{8} = \frac{\overset{3}{\cancel{24}} \cdot \overset{1}{\cancel{9}}}{\underset{4}{\cancel{36}} \cdot \underset{1}{\cancel{8}}}$$

$$= \frac{3 \cdot 1}{4 \cdot 1} = \frac{3}{4}$$

- $\frac{12}{5} \div 3$

$$\frac{12}{5} \div 3 = \frac{12}{5} \div \frac{3}{1} = \frac{\overset{4}{\cancel{12}}}{5} \times \frac{1}{\underset{1}{\cancel{3}}} = \frac{4}{5}.$$

Discussion

- Two fractions are said to be **reciprocals** of each other if their product is 1. The reciprocal of $\frac{2}{5}$ is $\frac{5}{2}$, because $\frac{2}{5} \cdot \frac{5}{2} = \frac{10}{10} = 1$

  Finding the reciprocal means "inverting" the fraction or swapping the numerator and the denominator.

  The reciprocal of $\frac{17}{15}$ is $\frac{15}{17}$.

Rule 3 To find the reciprocal of a fraction, simply interchange the numerator and the denominator.

- To find the reciprocal of a whole number or a mixed number, first write the number as an improper fraction and then interchange the numerator and the denominator.

  The reciprocal of 15 or $\frac{15}{1}$ is $\frac{1}{15}$.

  The reciprocal of $14\frac{2}{3}$ or $\frac{44}{3}$ is $\frac{3}{44}$.

Caution: The number zero "0" does not have a reciprocal, because the product of 0 and any other number is always 0; never 1.

- Recall that *division* is the inverse of *multiplication*. To divide a number by a second number is to ask "How many times is the second number contained in the first?"

In	*We ask*	*Answer*
$15 \div 3$	How many threes are in 15?	5
$12 \div 4$	How many fours are in 12?	3
$\frac{5}{6} \div \frac{1}{12}$	How many one-twelfths are in five-sixths?	See Figure 5.12

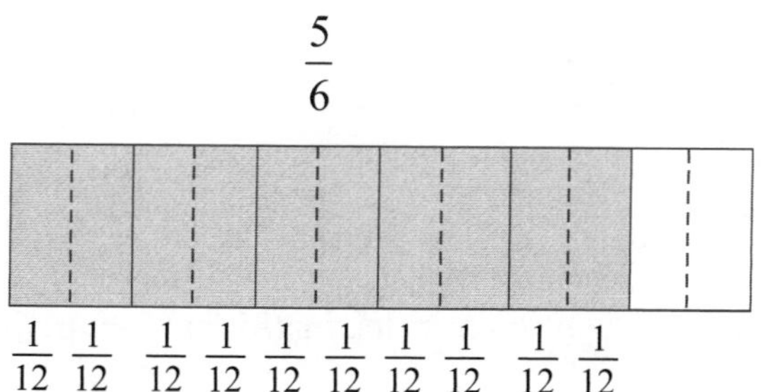

Figure 5.20

In Figure 5.20, there are ten one-twelfths in five-sixths. Therefore,

$$\underset{\text{Dividend}}{\underset{\downarrow}{\frac{5}{6}}} \div \underset{\text{Divisor}}{\underset{\downarrow}{\frac{1}{12}}} = \underset{\text{Quotient}}{\underset{\downarrow}{10}}$$

To check by multiplication (Quotient · Divisor = Dividend),

$$10 \cdot \frac{1}{12} = \frac{10}{1} \cdot \frac{1}{12} = \frac{10 \cdot 1}{1 \cdot 12} = \frac{10}{12} = \frac{5 \cdot 2}{6 \cdot 2} = \frac{5}{6}$$

The answer can also be obtained by multiplying the dividend $\frac{5}{6}$ by the reciprocal of the divisor $\frac{1}{12}$.

$$\frac{5}{6} \div \frac{\mathbf{1}}{\mathbf{12}} = \frac{5}{6} \cdot \frac{\mathbf{12}}{\mathbf{1}} = \frac{5 \cdot \overset{2}{\cancel{12}}}{\underset{1}{\cancel{6}}} = \frac{10}{1} = 10$$

This gives us the following rule to divide one fraction by another.

> ***Rule* 4** To divide a fraction by another fraction, multiply the first fraction (the dividend) by the reciprocal of the second (the divisor).

For example : $\frac{12}{5} \div \frac{\mathbf{10}}{\mathbf{3}} = \frac{\overset{6}{\cancel{12}}}{5} \cdot \frac{\mathbf{3}}{\underset{5}{\cancel{\mathbf{10}}}} = \frac{6 \cdot 3}{5 \cdot 5} = \frac{18}{25}$

- This rule is also applicable when the dividend and the divisor are whole numbers.

  For example, $7 \div 5 = \frac{7}{1} \div \frac{\mathbf{5}}{\mathbf{1}} = \frac{7}{1} \cdot \frac{\mathbf{1}}{\mathbf{5}} = \frac{7}{5}$

  This illustrates why the fraction bar is also referred to as the division bar.

  This observation is very useful in expressing a part of the whole as a fraction. For example, if 4 students in a class of 30 are absent, then the fraction that represents the part of the class that is absent is:

  $$4 \div 30 \text{ or } \frac{4}{30} = \frac{2}{15}$$

- If a whole number is in the division problem, write the whole number as an improper fraction, and then divide.

For example: $\frac{2}{5} \div 4 = \frac{2}{5} \div \frac{\mathbf{4}}{\mathbf{1}} = \frac{2}{5} \cdot \frac{\mathbf{1}}{\mathbf{4}} = \frac{2}{20} = \frac{1}{10}$;

$$14 \div \frac{7}{3} = \frac{14}{1} \div \frac{\mathbf{7}}{\mathbf{3}} = \frac{14}{1} \cdot \frac{\mathbf{3}}{\mathbf{7}} = \frac{42}{7} = 6$$

- If division involves mixed numbers, convert the mixed numbers to improper fractions before dividing.

For example: $6\frac{1}{4} \div 7\frac{1}{2} = \frac{25}{4} \div \frac{\mathbf{15}}{\mathbf{2}}$ $\qquad 6\frac{1}{4} = \frac{24+1}{4} = \frac{25}{4};\quad 7\frac{1}{2} = \frac{14+1}{2} = \frac{15}{2}$

$$= \frac{25}{4} \cdot \frac{\mathbf{2}}{\mathbf{15}} = \frac{25 \cdot 2}{4 \cdot 15} = \frac{5 \cdot \mathbf{5} \cdot 2}{2 \cdot \mathbf{2} \cdot \mathbf{3} \cdot 5} = \frac{5}{6}$$

Procedure to find the reciprocal of a number.

***Step* 1** **(a)** If the number is a proper fraction, find the reciprocal by interchanging the numerator and the denominator.

(b) If the number is a non-zero whole number or a mixed number, first write it as an improper fraction, then interchange the numerator and the denominator.

***Step* 2** Check by showing that the product of the fraction and its reciprocal is 1.

WARM-UP

5. Find the reciprocal of:

(a) 210

(b) $\frac{1}{79}$

(c) $15\frac{2}{7}$

EXAMPLE 5 Find the reciprocal of

(a) 87, **(b)** $\frac{1}{135}$, **(c)** $3\frac{7}{9}$

Solutions

(a) First write 87 as an improper fraction. $87 = \frac{87}{1}$

The reciprocal of $\frac{87}{1}$ is $\frac{1}{87}$.

(b) The reciprocal of $\frac{1}{135}$ is $\frac{135}{1}$ or 135.

(c) First convert $3\frac{7}{9}$ into an improper fraction.

$3\frac{7}{9} = \frac{34}{9}$ $\qquad 3\frac{7}{9} = \frac{3 \cdot 9 + 7}{9} = \frac{34}{9}$

The reciprocal of $\frac{34}{9}$ is $\frac{9}{34}$.

Procedure to divide a fraction by another fraction.

***Step* 1** Multiply the first fraction by the reciprocal of the second fraction (divisor).

***Step* 2** Simplify the product to lowest terms.

EXAMPLE 6 Divide:

(a) $\frac{7}{20} \div \frac{14}{15}$ (b) $\frac{16}{81} \div \frac{8}{108}$

Solutions

(a) $\frac{7}{20} \div \frac{14}{15} = \frac{\overset{1}{\cancel{7}}}{\underset{4}{\cancel{20}}} \cdot \frac{\overset{3}{\cancel{15}}}{\underset{2}{\cancel{14}}}$

- Change division to multiplication by inverting the divisor.

$= \frac{7}{20} \cdot \frac{15}{14}$

- Simplify.

$= \frac{3}{8}$

(b) $\frac{16}{81} \div \frac{8}{108} = \frac{\overset{2}{\cancel{16}}}{81} \cdot \frac{108}{\underset{1}{\cancel{8}}}$

$108 = 2 \cdot 2 \cdot 3 \cdot 3 \cdot 3$

$81 = 3 \cdot 3 \cdot 3 \cdot 3$

$= \frac{16 \cdot 108}{81 \cdot 8}$

$= \frac{2 \cdot 2 \cdot 2 \cdot 3 \cdot 3 \cdot 3}{3 \cdot 3 \cdot 3 \cdot 3} = \frac{8}{3}$

EXAMPLE 7 Divide.

(a) 1480 by $9\frac{1}{4}$ (b) $12\frac{3}{7} \div \frac{3}{7}$

Solutions

(a) $1480 \div 9\frac{1}{4} = \frac{1480}{1} \div \frac{37}{4}$

- Change the whole number and mixed number to improper fractions.

$= \frac{1480}{1} \cdot \frac{4}{37}$

- Change division to multiplication by inverting the divisor.
- Find prime factors of 1480.

$= \frac{(2 \cdot 2 \cdot 2 \cdot 5 \cdot 37)}{1} \cdot \frac{(2 \cdot 2)}{37}$

2	1480
2	740
2	370
5	185
37	37
	1

$= \frac{160}{1}$

$= 160$

(b) $12\frac{3}{7} \div \frac{3}{7} = \frac{87}{7} \div \frac{3}{7}$

$= \frac{87}{7} \cdot \frac{7}{3}$

$= \frac{3 \cdot 29}{7} \cdot \frac{7}{3}$

WARM-UP

6. Divide:

(a) $\frac{4}{5} \div \frac{2}{3}$

(b) $\frac{70}{63} \div \frac{154}{33}$

7. Divide:

(a) 320 by $1\frac{5}{11}$

(b) $\frac{21}{52}$ by 7

WARM-UP

Answers:

5\. (a) $\frac{1}{210}$ (b) 79 (c) $\frac{7}{107}$

6\. (a) $\frac{6}{5}$ (b) $\frac{5}{21}$

7\. (a) 220 (b) $\frac{3}{52}$

$$= \frac{29}{1}$$

$$= 29$$

Solution to the Application:

The distance a nut moves vertically on a bolt in one complete turn is $\frac{3}{16}$ inch. How many turns are needed to make the nut move $7\frac{1}{2}$ inches?

Solution: The solution is the number of $\frac{3}{16}$ inches contained in $7\frac{1}{2}$ inches.

$$7\frac{1}{2} \div \frac{3}{16} = \frac{15}{2} \div \frac{3}{16}$$

$$= \frac{\overset{5}{\cancel{15}}}{\underset{1}{\cancel{2}}} \cdot \frac{\overset{8}{\cancel{16}}}{\underset{1}{\cancel{3}}}$$

$$= 40$$

Thus, the nut needs to be turned 40 times.

C. ADDING AND SUBTRACTING LIKE/UNLIKE FRACTIONS

Add like or unlike fractions.

Illustration

- $\frac{2}{7} + \frac{3}{7} = \frac{2+3}{7} = \frac{5}{7}$

$$\frac{2}{5} + \frac{7}{10} + \frac{3}{4} = \frac{8}{20} + \frac{14}{20} + \frac{15}{20} \qquad \text{LCD} = 20$$

$$= \frac{8+14+15}{20}$$

$$= \frac{37}{20} = 1\frac{17}{20}$$

Verify Skill

Objective 5.5C

Find the sum

(a) $\frac{3}{8} + \frac{7}{8}$, (b) $\frac{2}{15} + \frac{7}{24} + \frac{5}{12}$

If your answers to these questions are the same as given below then you may skip this objective.

Answers: (a) $\frac{5}{4}$ (b) $\frac{101}{120}$

Discussion

- Observe that in Figure 5.21 a rectangular unit is divided into 5 equal parts. Each part represents the fraction $\frac{1}{5}$.

  One part is shaded on the right, and two parts are shaded on the left.

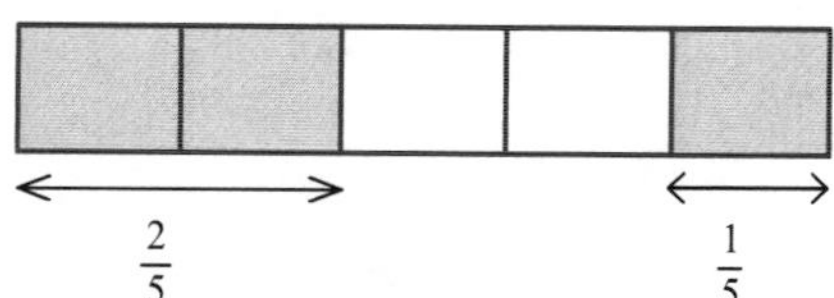

Figure 5.21

The left shaded parts represent the fraction $\frac{2}{5}$; the right shaded part represents the fraction $\frac{1}{5}$.

The total number of shaded parts are 3, and together they represent the fraction $\frac{3}{5}$.

Therefore, $\frac{2}{5} + \frac{1}{5} = \frac{3}{5}$ $\longrightarrow 2 + 1$

Find the sum of $\frac{3}{7} + \frac{5}{7}$. The common denominator represents the number of parts in a unit. The numerators represents the number of shaded parts (Figure 5.22). Since all pieces are of the same size, the parts can be rearranged to have one whole unit shaded leaving one extra $\frac{1}{7}$ shaded.

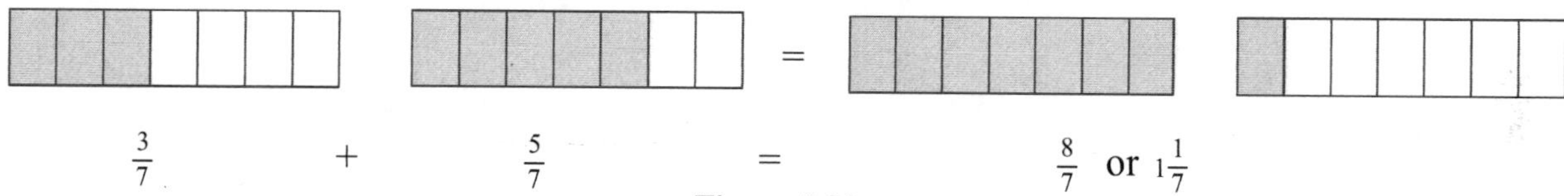

Figure 5.22

$\frac{3}{7} + \frac{5}{7} = \frac{8}{7} = 1\frac{1}{7}$

Addition of like fractions can also be explained with the help of a number line.

To add $\frac{3}{7}$ and $\frac{5}{7}$ on a number line, see Figure 5.23

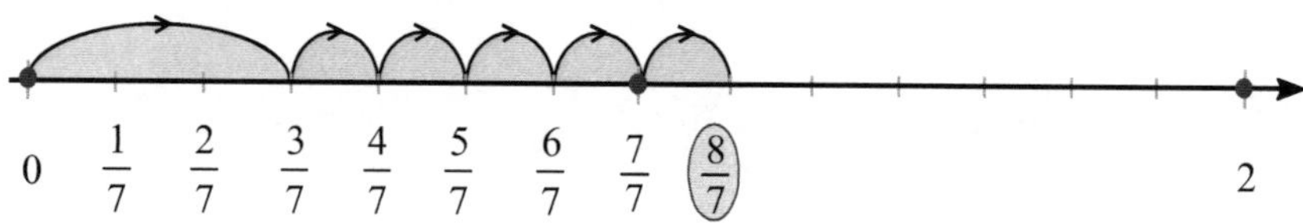

Figure 5.23

Each unit is divided into 7 equal parts. From the third part $\left(\frac{3}{7}\right)$, move five parts to the right $\left(\frac{5}{7}\right)$ to reach $\frac{8}{7}$. Recall that adding on a number line means moving to the right. $\frac{3}{7} + \frac{5}{7} = \frac{8}{7} = 1\frac{1}{7}$

The above observations can be generalized in the form of a rule to add like fractions.

> ***Rule* 6** The sum of like fractions $= \dfrac{\text{Sum of the numerators}}{\text{Common denominator}}$.

For example: $\frac{3}{5} + \frac{4}{5} = \frac{3+4}{5} = \frac{7}{5}$

$\frac{4}{7} + \frac{2}{7} + \frac{5}{7} = \frac{4+2+5}{7} = \frac{11}{7}$

- **Unlike fractions** cannot be added in the manner explained above. Consider the shaded parts of the first two rectangles in Figure 5.24. These parts cannot be added directly because of their **different sizes.**

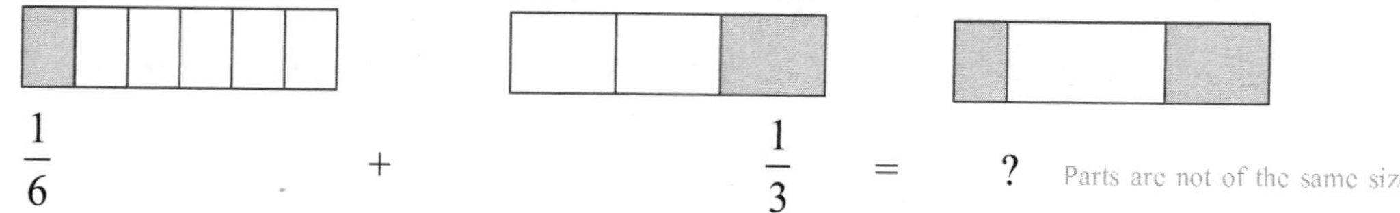

$\frac{1}{6}$ + $\frac{1}{3}$ = ? Parts are not of the same size

Figure 5.24

Figure 5.25 illustrates how unlike fractions can be added. These parts can now be added because their **sizes** are made the same by dividing the second rectangular unit to as many parts as the LCD of $\frac{1}{6}$ and $\frac{1}{3}$, which is 6. Since $\frac{1}{3} = \frac{2}{6}$.

$\frac{1}{6}$ + $\frac{2}{6}$ = $\frac{3}{6}$

Figure 5.25

To add $\frac{1}{6}$ and $\frac{1}{3}$, first convert to equivalent fractions with the LCD as the common denominator.

Procedure to add like fractions.

***Step* 1** Add the numerators.

***Step* 2** Write the sum over the common denominator.

***Step* 3** Simplify the sum, if possible

WARM-UP

8. Add the fractions and reduce.

(a) $\frac{2}{7} + \frac{1}{7} + \frac{3}{7}$

(b) $\frac{6}{15} + \frac{3}{15} + \frac{7}{15}$

EXAMPLE 8 Add the fractions and reduce.

(a) $\frac{3}{5} + \frac{4}{5}$ **(b)** $\frac{3}{8} + \frac{7}{8} + \frac{5}{8} + \frac{1}{8}$

Solutions

(a) $\frac{3}{5} + \frac{4}{5} = \frac{3+4}{5} = \frac{7}{5}$

- Add the numerators.
- Retain the common denominator.
- The sum is already in lowest terms.

(b) $\frac{3}{8} + \frac{7}{8} + \frac{5}{8} + \frac{1}{8} = \frac{3+7+5+1}{8}$

$$= \frac{16}{8}$$

$$= \frac{2}{1} = 2.$$

Warm-Up

Procedure to add unlike fractions.

***Step* 1** Find the LCD of the given fractions.

***Step* 2** Convert the fractions to equivalent fractions with the LCD as the common denominator.

***Step* 3** Add the converted like fractions by adding the numerators and retaining the common denominator.

***Step* 4** Simplify.

EXAMPLE 9 Add the following fractions:

(a) $\frac{4}{5} + \frac{3}{10}$ (b) $\frac{1}{21} + \frac{5}{14}$

Solutions

(a) $\mathbf{\frac{4}{5} + \frac{3}{10}}$: LCD = 10

$\frac{4}{5} = \frac{4}{5} \cdot \frac{2}{2} = \frac{8}{10}$, and $\frac{3}{10} = \frac{3}{10}$ — Convert each fraction to equivalent fraction with LCD of 10 as the common denominator.

$$\frac{4}{5} + \frac{3}{10} = \frac{8}{10} + \frac{3}{10} = \mathbf{\frac{11}{10}}$$

(b) $\mathbf{\frac{1}{21} + \frac{5}{14}}$ — Factor denominators

$= \frac{1}{3 \cdot 7} + \frac{5}{2 \cdot 7}$ — Determine the missing factor

$= \frac{1}{3 \cdot 7} \cdot \frac{2}{2} + \frac{5}{2 \cdot 7} \cdot \frac{3}{3}$ — Write the missing factor as a unit of one

$= \frac{2}{42} + \frac{15}{42}$ — Multiply

$= \frac{17}{42}$ — Add the numerators and retain the denominator

Warm-Up

9. Add the following fractions:

(a) $\frac{3}{4} + \frac{5}{6}$

(b) $\frac{7}{33} + \frac{5}{22}$

Answers:

8. (a) $\frac{6}{7}$ (b) $\frac{16}{15}$ or $1\frac{1}{15}$

9. (a) $\frac{19}{12}$ or $1\frac{7}{12}$ (b) $\frac{29}{66}$

Verify Skill

Objective 5.5C

Find the difference.

(a) $\dfrac{6}{11} - \dfrac{4}{11}$

(b) $\dfrac{25}{48} - \dfrac{13}{80}$

If your answers to these questions are the same as given below then you may skip this objective

Answers: **(a)** $\dfrac{2}{11}$ **(b)** $\dfrac{43}{120}$

Subtract like or unlike fractions.

Illustrations

(a) $\dfrac{7}{13} - \dfrac{5}{13} = \dfrac{7-5}{13} = \dfrac{2}{13}$

(b) $\dfrac{4}{5} - \dfrac{2}{3} = \dfrac{12}{15} - \dfrac{10}{15}$

$= \dfrac{12-10}{15}$

$= \dfrac{2}{15}$

Discussion

- To understand the subtraction of like fractions, compute $\frac{5}{7} - \frac{3}{7}$. The common denominator represents the number of parts in a unit. The numerators represent the number of shaded parts (Figure 5.26). Subtract the numerators to find the number of shaded parts that remain.

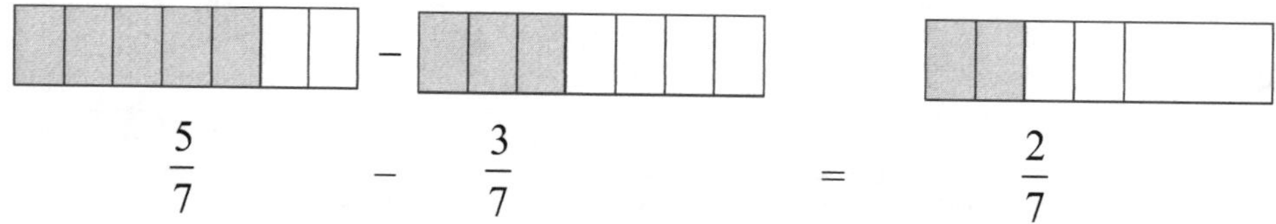

$\dfrac{5}{7} - \dfrac{3}{7} = \dfrac{2}{7}$

Figure 5.26

In the first unit five parts are shaded. In the second unit three parts are shaded. The third unit in the figure shows that three shaded parts have been taken away leaving two of the five shaded parts.

Hence, $\dfrac{5}{7} - \dfrac{3}{7} = \dfrac{2}{7} \longrightarrow 5-3$

To obtain the difference of two like fractions, subtract the numerators and retain the common denominator. Observe that this process is similar to that for addition of fractions.

Subtraction of like fractions can also be explained with the help of a number line.

To subtract $\frac{3}{5}$ from $\frac{7}{5}$ on a number line, see Figure 5.27.

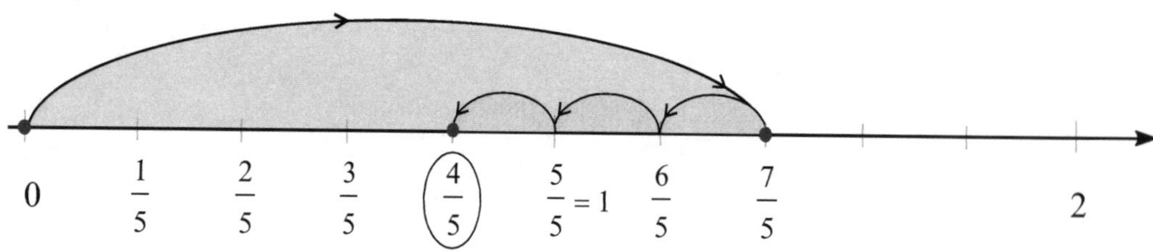

Figure 5.27

Each unit is divided into 5 equal parts. From the seventh part move three parts to the left to reach $\frac{4}{5}$. Recall that subtracting on a number line means moving to the left.

$$\frac{7}{5} - \frac{3}{5} = \frac{4}{5}$$

The above observations can be generalized in the form of a rule to subtract like fractions.

> ***Rule 7*** The difference of like fractions $= \dfrac{\text{the difference of the numerators}}{\text{the common denominator}}$

- Unlike fractions can be subtracted, just as in addition, by converting fractions to equivalent fractions with the LCD as the common denominator.

For example: $\quad \frac{2}{3} - \frac{1}{2} = \frac{4}{6} - \frac{3}{6} = \frac{4-3}{6} = \frac{1}{6}.$

Procedure to subtract fractions.

> ***Step* 1** Build each fraction to a common denominator (the LCD).
>
> ***Step* 2** Subtract the numerators of the new fractions, and retain the common denominator.
>
> ***Step* 3** Simplify the resulting fraction to lowest terms.

EXAMPLE 10 Subtract $\frac{3}{4}$ from $\frac{7}{8}$

Solution To find the difference $\frac{7}{8} - \frac{3}{4}$,

$\frac{7}{8} = \frac{7}{8} \cdot \frac{\mathbf{1}}{\mathbf{1}} = \frac{7}{8}$ • The LCD is 8.

$\frac{3}{4} = \frac{3}{4} \cdot \frac{\mathbf{2}}{\mathbf{2}} = \frac{6}{8}$ • Build the fractions to the common denominator 8.

Thus, $\frac{7}{8} - \frac{3}{4}$ • Subtract the numerators of the new fractions, and retain the common denominator.

$= \frac{7}{8} - \frac{6}{8}$

$= \frac{1}{8}$

EXAMPLE 11 Simplify : $\frac{16}{21} - \frac{4}{35}$

Solution $\frac{16}{21} - \frac{4}{35}$

WARM-UP

10. Subtract:

$\frac{32}{35} - \frac{17}{20}$

11. Simplify:

$\frac{7}{25} - \frac{2}{15}.$

Answers:

10. $\frac{9}{140}$ 11. $\frac{11}{75}$

$$= \frac{16}{3\cdot 7} - \frac{4}{5\cdot 7}$$

• Factor denominators.

$$= \frac{16}{3\cdot 7}\cdot\frac{5}{5} - \frac{4}{5\cdot 7}\cdot\frac{3}{3}$$

• Write in missing factors as units of one.

$$= \frac{80}{105} - \frac{12}{105}$$

• Multiply.

$$= \frac{68}{105}$$

• Add numerators and retain denominator.

Verify Skill

Objective 5.5D

Find the sum:

$$9\frac{7}{15} + 5\frac{2}{5} + 4 + 3\frac{2}{3}$$

If your answer to this question is the same as given below then you may skip this objective.

Answer: $22\frac{8}{15}$

D. ADDING AND SUBTRACTING MIXED NUMBERS

Illustration

$$2\frac{3}{4} + 3\frac{4}{5} = \left(2 + \frac{3}{4}\right) + \left(3 + \frac{4}{5}\right)$$

$$= \left(2+3\right) + \left(\frac{3}{4} + \frac{4}{5}\right)$$

$$= 5 + \left(\frac{15}{20} + \frac{16}{20}\right)$$

$$= 5 + \frac{31}{20} = 5 + 1\frac{11}{20}$$

$$= 5 + 1 + \frac{11}{20} = 6\frac{11}{20}$$

Discussion

Add $1\frac{2}{5}$ and $2\frac{1}{5}$.

The common denominator tells the number of parts in a unit. In Figure 5.28 (a) & (b), the fractions $1\frac{2}{5}$ and $2\frac{1}{5}$ are represented by the shaded parts.

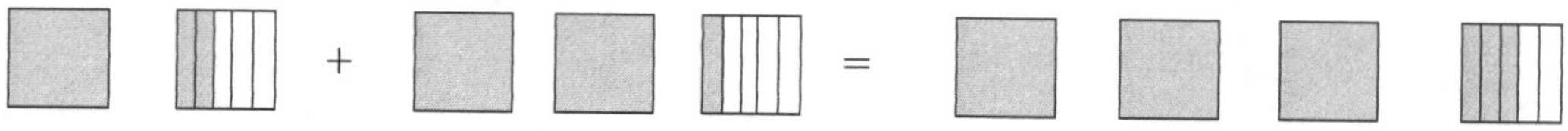

$1\frac{2}{5}$ + $2\frac{1}{5}$ = $3\frac{3}{5}$

(a) (b) (c)

Figure 5.28

When these shaded parts are combined as in Figure 5.28 (c), we get three shaded units and three shaded parts out of the five parts in the fourth unit. The number representing the sum of shaded parts in Figure 5.28 is $3\frac{3}{5}$.

Therefore, $1\frac{2}{5} + 2\frac{1}{5} = 3\frac{3}{5}$.

To add two or more mixed numbers, add the whole numbers and fractions separately. Then write the two sums together to get the required sum of the given numbers.

When the mixed numbers are added, it is possible that the sum of the fractional parts is an improper fraction. In this case, the improper fraction should be changed to a mixed number, and the whole number part can then be added to the sum of the whole numbers already obtained. For example,

$$
\begin{aligned}
5\frac{1}{2} + 7\frac{2}{3} &= \left(5 + \frac{1}{2}\right) + \left(7 + \frac{2}{3}\right) \\
&= (5 + 7) + \left(\frac{1}{2} + \frac{2}{3}\right) \\
&= 12 + \left(\frac{3}{6} + \frac{4}{6}\right) \\
&= 12 + \frac{7}{6} \\
&= 12 + \left(1 + \frac{1}{6}\right) \\
&= (12 + 1) + \frac{1}{6} \\
&= 13 + \frac{1}{6} \\
&= 13\frac{1}{6}
\end{aligned}
$$

An alternative method to add mixed numbers is to first change them to improper fractions, and then add by the method explained in Objective 5.5 A.

For example,

$$
\begin{aligned}
5\frac{1}{2} + 7\frac{2}{3} &= \frac{11}{2} + \frac{23}{3} \\
&= \frac{33}{6} + \frac{46}{6} \\
&= \frac{33 + 46}{6} \\
&= \frac{79}{6} \\
&= 13\frac{1}{6}
\end{aligned}
$$

This method often involves computation of larger numbers.

Procedure to add mixed numbers.

***Method* 1**

***Step* 1** Add the whole number parts.

***Step* 2** Add the proper fraction parts. If the sum of the proper fractions is greater or equal to 1 (Numerator ≥ Denominator), change the fraction to a whole or mixed number and add the whole number parts again.

***Step* 3** Write the answer as a whole or mixed number.

***Method* 2**

***Step* 1** Change the mixed numbers to improper fractions.

***Step* 2** Add the improper fractions and simplify the answer.

WARM-UP

12. Add, and write the sum as a reduced mixed number.

(a) $2\frac{3}{5} + 3\frac{2}{3}$

(b) $21\frac{3}{4} + 17\frac{2}{3}$

EXAMPLE 12 Add, and write the sum as a reduced mixed number.

(a) $4\frac{2}{3} + 1\frac{3}{4}$ **(b)** $18\frac{3}{4} + 17\frac{7}{8}$

Solutions

(a) $4\frac{2}{3} + 1\frac{3}{4}$

$= \left(4 + \frac{2}{3}\right) + \left(1 + \frac{3}{4}\right)$

- Write the mixed numbers in expanded form.

$= (4 + 1) + \left(\frac{2}{3} + \frac{3}{4}\right)$

- Add the whole numbers and the fractions separately.

$= 5 + \left(\frac{8}{12} + \frac{9}{12}\right)$

- Add the fractions using 12 as the common denominator.

$= 5 + \frac{17}{12}$

$= 5 + 1\frac{5}{12}$

$= 6\frac{5}{12}$

(b) $18\frac{3}{4} + 17\frac{7}{8}$

$= \left(18 + \frac{3}{4}\right) + \left(17 + \frac{7}{8}\right)$

- Write the mixed numbers in expanded form.

$= (18 + 17) + \left(\frac{3}{4} + \frac{7}{8}\right)$

- Add the whole numbers and fractions separately.

$= 35 + \left(\frac{6}{8} + \frac{7}{8}\right)$

- LCD = 8.

$= 35+\left(\frac{6+7}{8}\right)$

$= 35+\frac{13}{8}$

$= 35+1\frac{5}{8}$

$= 36\frac{5}{8}$

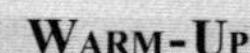

WARM-UP

Answers :

10. (a) $6\frac{4}{15}$ (b) $39\frac{5}{12}$

E. SIMPLIFYING EXPRESSIONS INVOLVING FRACTIONS

Illustration

Evaluate the following numerical expressions.

$\frac{3}{8}\div\left(\frac{1}{4}+\frac{2}{15}\div\frac{4}{25}\right)+\frac{5}{2}$	First, consider the operations within the grouping symbols.
$=\frac{3}{8}\div\left(\frac{1}{4}+\frac{\not{2}^{1}}{\not{15}_{3}}\cdot\frac{\not{25}^{5}}{\not{4}_{2}}\right)+\frac{5}{2}$	Change division to multiplication.
$=\frac{3}{8}\div\left(\frac{1}{4}+\frac{5}{6}\right)+\frac{5}{2}$	Multiply.
$=\frac{3}{8}\div\left(\frac{3}{12}+\frac{10}{12}\right)+\frac{5}{2}$	Change to equivalent fractions for addition.
$=\frac{3}{8}\div\frac{13}{12}+\frac{5}{2}$	Add.
$=\frac{3}{8}\cdot\frac{12}{13}+\frac{5}{2}$	Change division to multiplication.
$=\frac{9}{26}+\frac{5}{2}$	Multiply.
$=\frac{9}{26}+\frac{65}{26}$	Change to equivalent fraction for addition.
$=\frac{74}{26}=\frac{37}{13}$	Add and reduce the result.
$=2\frac{11}{13}$	Change to mixed fraction.

Verify Skill

Objective 5.5E

Evaluate the following expression.

$\frac{9}{20}\div\left(\frac{8}{5}-\frac{7}{10}\right)-\frac{1}{3}$

If your answer to this question is the same as given below, then you may skip this objective.

Answer: $\frac{1}{6}$

Discussion

Recall the rules for order of operations on whole numbers. The same rules are used while performing various combinations of operations on fractions. First evaluate exponents, then perform multiplication and division in the order in which they appear from left to right and last perform addition and subtraction in the order in which they appear from left to right.

If the expression involves grouping symbol(s), then the operations within the grouping symbols should be carried out first in the same order, starting with the innermost grouping symbols.

Procedure to simplify a numerical expression involving more than one operation.

***Step* 1** Perform operations within the grouping symbols in the order given in steps 2, 3, and 4, starting from the innermost grouping symbol.

***Step* 2** Simplify exponents by performing repeated multiplications indicated by exponents.

***Step* 3** Perform multiplications and divisions as they appear from left to right.

***Step* 4** Perform additions and subtractions as they appear from left to right.

Study the following examples carefully.

EXAMPLE 13 Perform the indicated operations: $\frac{1}{4} + \frac{3}{8} \div \frac{1}{2}$

Solution

$$\frac{1}{4} + \frac{3}{8} \div \frac{\mathbf{1}}{\mathbf{2}}$$

$$\frac{1}{4} + \frac{3}{\mathbf{8}} \times \frac{\mathbf{2}}{1} = \frac{1}{4} + \frac{3}{4} = 1$$

EXAMPLE 14 Evaluate the following numerical expression:

$$\left(\frac{1}{2} + \frac{2}{5}\right) \div \frac{5}{11}$$

Solution

$$\left(\frac{\mathbf{1}}{\mathbf{2}} + \frac{\mathbf{2}}{\mathbf{5}}\right) \div \frac{5}{11}$$

$$= \left(\frac{5}{10} + \frac{4}{10}\right) \div \frac{5}{11}$$

$$= \frac{9}{10} \div \frac{\mathbf{5}}{\mathbf{11}} = \frac{9}{10} \cdot \frac{\mathbf{11}}{\mathbf{5}}$$

$$= \frac{99}{50} \text{ or } 1\frac{49}{50}$$

WARM-UP

13. Perform the indicated operations

$$\frac{1}{3} + \frac{5}{4} \div \frac{15}{8}$$

14. Simplify:

$$\left(\frac{2}{3} + \frac{5}{9}\right) \div \frac{22}{27}$$

Answers:

13. 1

14. $\frac{3}{2}$ or $1\frac{1}{2}$

EXERCISE 5.5

In exercises 1-27, multiply and reduce.

1. $\frac{2}{3}\cdot\frac{3}{4}$ **2.** $\frac{4}{5}\cdot\frac{10}{12}$ **3.** $\frac{2}{5}\cdot\frac{10}{12}$ **4.** $\frac{15}{16}\cdot\frac{12}{21}$ **5.** $\frac{4}{5}\cdot\frac{5}{16}$ **6.** $\frac{7}{40}\cdot\frac{16}{7}$

7. $\frac{8}{15}\cdot\frac{9}{16}$ **8.** $\frac{20}{63}\cdot\frac{21}{40}$ **9.** $\frac{70}{27}\cdot\frac{18}{35}$ **10.** $\frac{16}{45}\cdot\frac{9}{7}$ **11.** $\frac{4}{5}\cdot\frac{10}{21}$ **12.** $\frac{9}{10}\cdot\frac{40}{81}$

13. $\frac{15}{42}\cdot\frac{21}{30}$ **14.** $\frac{12}{75}\cdot\frac{8}{9}$ **15.** $\frac{4}{3}\cdot\frac{11}{3}\cdot\frac{9}{4}$ **16.** $\left(2\frac{3}{5}\right)\cdot\frac{4}{9}$ **17.** $2\frac{3}{4}\times\frac{16}{11}$ **18.** $12\cdot\frac{5}{6}$

19. $2\frac{5}{8}\cdot\frac{4}{15}$ **20.** $\left(3\frac{3}{4}\right)\cdot\left(1\frac{4}{5}\right)$ **21.** $2\frac{5}{6}\cdot\frac{4}{9}$ **22.** $\frac{4}{9}\cdot\left(1\frac{3}{5}\right)$ **23.** $\left(2\frac{3}{4}\right)\left(1\frac{1}{47}\right)$

24. $5\cdot 0\cdot\left(2\frac{4}{109}\right)$ **25.** $\left(4\frac{2}{7}\right)\cdot 42$ **26.** $\left(5\frac{4}{9}\right)\left(3\frac{2}{7}\right)$ **27.** $\frac{7}{9}\cdot\left(4\frac{5}{7}\right)$

In exercises 28-31, find a part from the whole.

28. Two-ninths of 36. **29.** Five-sixths of 120. **30.** Three-halves of 120. **31.** Seven-fifths of 155.

In exercises 32-38, find the reciprocal and check by multiplication.

32. $3\frac{6}{13}$ **33.** $\frac{4}{19}$ **34.** $\frac{15}{39}$ **35.** $\frac{79}{100}$ **36.** $1\frac{4}{5}$

37. $14\frac{2}{3}$ **38.** $\frac{1052}{2931}$

In exercises 39-63, add and simplify, if possible.

39. $\frac{2}{5}+\frac{3}{5}$ **40.** $\frac{2}{7}+\frac{4}{7}$ **41.** $\frac{4}{3}+\frac{2}{3}+\frac{1}{3}$ **42.** $\frac{4}{5}+\frac{2}{5}+\frac{3}{5}$ **43.** $\frac{5}{6}+\frac{1}{6}+\frac{3}{6}$

44. $\frac{2}{9}+\frac{4}{9}$ **45.** $\frac{3}{5}+\frac{2}{5}$ **46.** $\frac{2}{15}+\frac{7}{15}$ **47.** $\frac{5}{18}+\frac{4}{15}$ **48.** $\frac{3}{10}+\frac{4}{5}$

49. $\frac{7}{6}+\frac{2}{3}$ **50.** $\frac{4}{9}+\frac{1}{3}$ **51.** $\frac{3}{4}+\frac{1}{2}$ **52.** $\frac{2}{3}+\frac{7}{15}$ **53.** $\frac{5}{38}+\frac{1}{57}$

54. $\frac{2}{35}+\frac{5}{49}$ **55.** $\frac{5}{22}+\frac{3}{55}$ **56.** $\frac{2}{14}+\frac{5}{21}$ **57.** $\frac{5}{35}+\frac{2}{49}$ **58.** $\frac{1}{3}+\frac{1}{5}$

59. $\frac{7}{8}+\frac{5}{12}$ **60.** $\frac{1}{3}+\frac{1}{2}+\frac{1}{16}$ **61.** $\frac{9}{20}+\frac{8}{15}+\frac{19}{30}$ **62.** $\frac{1}{4}+\frac{1}{8}+\frac{5}{12}$ **63.** $\frac{7}{12}+\frac{5}{16}+\frac{19}{24}$

In exercises 64-78, add the given numbers. Write the answer as a mixed number where possible.

64. $2\frac{1}{4} + 1\frac{3}{4}$ **65.** $1\frac{2}{3} + 2\frac{1}{3}$ **66.** $2\frac{2}{5} + 1\frac{1}{5}$ **67.** $3\frac{1}{2} + 1\frac{1}{3}$ **68.** $2\frac{1}{5} + 3\frac{1}{2}$

69. $1\frac{1}{3} + 3\frac{2}{5}$ **70.** $4\frac{2}{5} + 3\frac{3}{4}$ **71.** $7\frac{2}{5} + 4\frac{7}{15}$ **72.** $4\frac{3}{8} + 11\frac{11}{16}$ **73.** $5\frac{5}{6} + 17$

74. $2\frac{3}{4} + 3\frac{4}{5}$ **75.** $\frac{1}{2} + 7\frac{16}{25}$ **76.** $\frac{7}{10} + 2\frac{3}{5}$ **77.** $3\frac{3}{4} + 5\frac{1}{2}$ **78.** $5\frac{2}{3} + 2\frac{4}{5}$

In exercises 79-98, subtract and simplify where possible.

79. $\frac{5}{4} - \frac{3}{4}$ **80.** $\frac{6}{7} - \frac{3}{7}$ **81.** $\frac{12}{5} - \frac{8}{5}$ **82.** $\frac{7}{8} - \frac{3}{8}$ **83.** $\frac{7}{10} - \frac{4}{10}$ **84.** $\frac{9}{10} - \frac{2}{10}$

85. $\frac{7}{24} - \frac{2}{24}$ **86.** $\frac{15}{19} - \frac{7}{19}$ **87.** $\frac{2}{5} - \frac{1}{3}$ **88.** $\frac{11}{13} - \frac{5}{13}$ **89.** $\frac{5}{12} - \frac{1}{6}$ **90.** $\frac{2}{3} - \frac{1}{4}$

91. $\frac{4}{5} - \frac{3}{4}$ **92.** $\frac{5}{7} - \frac{2}{5}$ **93.** $\frac{9}{10} - \frac{7}{20}$ **94.** $\frac{4}{15} - \frac{7}{30}$ **95.** $\frac{17}{57} - \frac{5}{38}$ **96.** $\frac{27}{35} - \frac{5}{49}$

97. $\frac{23}{22} - \frac{23}{33}$ **98.** $\frac{19}{14} - \frac{19}{21}$

In exercises 99-114, perform the indicated operations.

99. $\frac{5}{9} + \frac{7}{3} \times \frac{9}{5}$ **100.** $\frac{1}{2} + \frac{1}{4} \cdot \frac{4}{5}$ **101.** $\frac{2}{3} + \frac{4}{5} \cdot \frac{5}{12}$ **102.** $\frac{2}{5} + \frac{3}{4} \div \frac{9}{16}$

103. $\frac{4}{5} + \frac{4}{15} \div \frac{16}{25}$ **104.** $\frac{2}{5} \div \frac{3}{10} + \frac{2}{3}$ **105.** $\frac{3}{10} \times \frac{15}{24} - \frac{3}{16}$ **106.** $\frac{3}{4} + \frac{5}{8} \div \frac{3}{16}$

107. $\frac{1}{3} \div \frac{1}{2} + \frac{5}{12} \cdot \frac{2}{5} - \frac{1}{6}$ **108.** $\frac{7}{12} - \frac{1}{2} \cdot \frac{3}{4} + \left(\frac{3}{4}\right)^2$ **109.** $\frac{2}{3} \div \frac{3}{5} \cdot \frac{5}{9}$ **110.** $\frac{2}{3} \cdot \frac{3}{5} \div \frac{5}{9}$

111. $\frac{2}{3} \div \left(\frac{3}{5} \cdot \frac{5}{9}\right)$ **112.** $\frac{1}{4} - \frac{2}{27} \div \frac{8}{3}$ **113.** $\frac{5}{6} \div \frac{3}{4} + \frac{4}{5} \cdot \frac{25}{16}$ **114.** $\frac{5}{6} + \frac{3}{4} - \frac{4}{5} \div \frac{2}{3}$

In exercises 115-122, evaluate the given numerical expression.

115. $\left(\frac{24}{35} \div \frac{1}{7} + \frac{5}{9}\right) \cdot \frac{3}{4}$ **116.** $\frac{2}{3}\left(\frac{1}{2} - \frac{1}{3}\right)$ **117.** $\frac{4}{5}\left(\frac{3}{5} + \frac{7}{10}\right)$ **118.** $\frac{4}{9} \div \left(\frac{5}{3} - \frac{2}{3}\right)$

119. $\frac{7}{15} \div \left(\frac{2}{3} + \frac{3}{5}\right)$ **120.** $\frac{3}{4} + \left(\frac{1}{2}\right)^2$ **121.** $\left(2\frac{1}{2} + 1\frac{1}{4}\right) \div 7\frac{1}{2}$ **122.** $\frac{4}{9} \div \frac{2}{3} - \left(\frac{1}{3}\right)^2$

DECIMALS, RATIONAL AND IRRATIONAL NUMBERS

6

INTRODUCTION

This chapter involves reading decimals and performing basic operations (+, –, ×, ÷) on decimals. The chapter is divided into nine sections.

6.1	*Decimals, Place Values, Read, Write, and Rounding Decimals ;*
6.2	*Operations and Decimals ;*
6.3	*Fractions to Decimals, Compare Decimals ;*
6.4	*Multiplication/Division by Powers of 10 and Scientific Notation ;*
6.5	*Find Fraction Notation for a Ratio or a Rate ;*
6.6	*Percents, Conversion to Decimals and Fractions ;*
6.7	*Percent Problems using Percent Equations ;*
6.8	*Rational Numbers: Identifying and Graphing ; and*
6.9	*Operations on Real Numbers.*

6.1 DECIMALS, PLACE VALUES, READ, WRITE, AND ROUNDING DECIMALS

VOCABULARY

1. The digits and a dot, ".", called a **decimal point** are used to write numbers called **decimals**, such as 32.715.
2. The number of digits on the right of the decimal point are called **decimal places**; for example, 27.016 has three decimal places.
3. The **digit value** is equal to the digit times its place value.
4. The digits and a dot, ".", called a **decimal point** are used to write numbers called **decimals**, such as 32.715.
5. The number of digits on the right of the decimal point are called **decimal places**; for example, 27.016 has three decimal places.
6. The **digit value** is equal to the digit times its place value.
7. Like whole numbers, decimals can also be **rounded** to any required place value. 25.7469 rounded to the nearest hundredth is 25.75.

↑ approximately equal to.

OBJECTIVES

Upon completion of this section you will study about:

A. Determine the place value of a digit in a decimal number, and identify a digit that has a given place value;
B. Write a decimal number in its expanded form; and
C. Rounding decimals.

DETERMINING PLACE VALUE AND EXPANDED FORM OF DECIMALS

Verify Skill

Objective 6.1 A

(a) Determine the place value of the 3 in 0.38.

(b) Identify the digit in 4329.0125 whose place value is ten-thousandths.

If your answers to the above questions are the same as given below, then you may skip this objective

Answers:

(a) Tenths (b) 5

➜ **Determine the place value of a digit in a decimal and identify a digit that has a given place value.**

Illustrations

- The place value of the digit 7 in 8.247 is **thousandths** $\left(\frac{1}{1000}\right)$.

- The digit in 45.609 whose place value is **hundredths** $\left(\frac{1}{100}\right)$ is 0.

Discussion

- A fraction whose denominator is 10 or a power of 10 is called a **decimal fraction**.

  $\frac{3}{10}$, $\frac{15}{100}$, and $\frac{47}{1000}$ are examples of decimal fractions. These denominators are powers of 10 because $10^1 = 10$, $10^2 = 100$, and $10^3 = 1000$.

  Decimal fractions can be **written** as decimals. Decimals are written without denominators. The denominator is determined by placement. For example,

  $\frac{3}{\mathbf{10}}$ is written as **0.3** and is read "three tenths",
  ↓
  Decimal point

  $\frac{15}{\mathbf{100}}$ is written as **0.15** and is read "fifteen - hundredths",
  ↓
  Decimal point

  Caution: It is **wrong** to read .15 as "decimal fifteen".

  $\frac{45}{\mathbf{1000}}$ is written as **0.045** and is read as "forty five-thousandths",
  ↓
  Decimal point

- Improper fractions and mixed numbers whose fractional parts are decimal fractions can also be written using a decimal point.

  $\frac{25}{10} = 2\frac{5}{10}$ is written as 2.5 and is read as "two **and** five tenths",
  ↓
  Decimal point

$24\frac{35}{100}$ is written as 24.35 and is read as "twenty-four **and** thirty-five hundredths"

↓

Decimal point

- Numbers written using a decimal point are called **decimals**. The number of digits to the right of the decimal point are called **decimal places**. For example, the number 1.527 has three decimal places.

Some Facts to Remember

1. A decimal consists of three parts - a whole number, a decimal point, and a **decimal part** or fraction.

   In 57.629, the whole number part is 57 and the decimal part is .629.

   Thus,

57.629	=	57	.	629
		whole number		decimal part

2. In the case of a whole number, the decimal point is understood to be present to the right of the digit at the ones place.

   Thus, 75 = 75.   180 = 180.   5 = 5.

   ↓ Decimal point   ↓ Decimal point   ↓ Decimal point

3. The number formed by the digits is the numerator of the decimal fraction, and the number of decimal places determines the denominator of the decimal fraction.

   Thus,

   $$0.\mathbf{23} = \frac{23}{\mathbf{100}} \quad ; \quad 27.\mathbf{023} = \frac{27023}{\mathbf{1000}}$$

- The advantage of decimal fractions over other fractions lies in the fact that they are based on the same number scale as are the whole numbers.

Therefore, decimals are written by using a standard place value in the same way as whole numbers.

$0.3 = \frac{3}{10}$ is read as "**three tenths**". 3 has a place value of "**tenths**".

The digit 3 is located in the *first* place after the decimal point.

$0.03 = \frac{3}{100}$ is read as "**three hundredths**". The digit 3 in 0.03 has a place value of **hundredths**, because the 3 is in the *second* place to the right of the decimal point.

Similarly, in 0.003, the digit 3 is placed at the *third* decimal place. Therefore, its place value is

thousandths. Note that $0.003 = \frac{3}{1000}$ and is read as "**three thousandths**".

Consider the number 0.745.

7 has a place value of **tenths** $\left(\frac{1}{10}\right)$, since 7 is in the *first* decimal place .

4 has a place value of **hundredths** $\left(\frac{1}{100} \text{ or } \frac{1}{10^2}\right)$, since 4 is in the *second* decimal place.

5 has a place value of **thousandths** $\left(\frac{1}{1000} \text{ or } \frac{1}{10^3}\right)$, since 5 is in the *third* decimal place.

- The place values for the digits to the left of the decimal points are the same as those for whole numbers. Consider, for example, the number 45.231.

The place value of **4** is '**ten**' (10)

The place value of **5** is '**one**' (1)

The place value of **2** is '**tenths**' $\left(\frac{1}{10}\right)$, and so on.

- The place value for the digits of a decimal is provided in the following chart.

PLACE VALUE CHART FOR DECIMALS

Whole number part						**•**	**Decimal part**				
HUNDRED THOUSANDS	TEN THOUSANDS	THOUSANDS	HUNDREDS	TENS	ONES		TENTHS	HUNDREDTHS	THOUSANDTHS	TEN - THOUSANDTHS	HUNDRED - THOUSANDTHS
100,000	10,000	1000	100	10	1		$\frac{1}{10}$	$\frac{1}{100}$	$\frac{1}{1000}$	$\frac{1}{10,000}$	$\frac{1}{100,000}$
10^5	10^4	10^3	10^2	10^1	10^0		$\frac{1}{10^1}$	$\frac{1}{10^2}$	$\frac{1}{10^3}$	$\frac{1}{10^4}$	$\frac{1}{10^5}$

Figure 6.1

This chart is an extension of the place value chart for whole numbers.

Procedure to determine the place value of a digit.

a. If the digit appears to the left of the decimal point, consider the entire group of digits to the left of the decimal points a whole number. The place value of this digit is the same as its place value in the whole number.

b. If the digit appears to the right of the decimal point, its place value is determined by counting the number of decimal places for the digit being considered. Its place value is $\frac{1}{10^n}$ where n is the number of decimal places for the digit.

EXAMPLE 1 Determine the place value of the following digits in 1752.3609.

(a) 6 **(b)** 0 **(c)** 7

Solutions

(a)
- The digit 6 appears to the right of the decimal point.
- 6 is in the **second** decimal place.
- Hence, the place value of 6 in 1752.3609 is

$$\frac{1}{10^2} \text{ or } \frac{1}{100} \text{ or hundredths.}$$

(b) The place value of 0 in 1752.3609 is

$$\frac{1}{10^3} \text{ or } \frac{1}{1000} \text{ or thousandths}$$

- 0 appears to the right of the decimal point.
- 0 is in the **third** decimal place.
- The place value of 0 is $\frac{1}{10^3}$.

(c) The place value of 7 in 1752.3609 is hundreds.

Since 7 appears to the left of the decimal point, its place value is the same as in the whole number 1752.

Procedure to identify the digit that has a given place value.

***Step* 1** Identify the position of the given place value using the place value chart (Figure 6.1)

***Step* 2** Identify the digit in that position.

EXAMPLE 2 Identify the digit in the

(a) hundredths place in 72.061

(b) thousands place in 4312.56

(c) ten thousandths place in 0.0045.

WARM-UP

1. Determine the place value of the following digits in 250.1243.

(a) 5 **(b)** 1 **(c)** 3

2. Identify the digit in the

(a) tenths place in 25.14

(b) hundreds place in 250.5

(c) thousandths place in 25.0561

Answers:

1. (a) Ten (b) Tenth (c) Ten-thousandths
2. (a) 1 (b) 2 (c) 6

Solutions

(a) The 'hundredths' place is the second place to the right of the decimal point. The digit in the hundredths place in

72.0**6**1 is 6.

(b) The 'thousands' place is the fourth place to the left of the decimal point. The digit in the thousands place in

4312.56 is 4.

(c) The 'ten thousandths' place is the fourth place to the right of the decimal point. The digit in the ten-thousandths place in

0.004**5** is 5.

Verify Skill

Objective 6.1 A

(a) Write the number 9.5021 in expanded form.

(b) Write as a decimal:

$$70+6+\frac{1}{10}+\frac{5}{1000}$$

If your answers to these questions are the same as given below then you may skip this objective.

Answers:

(a) 9 + .5 + .002 + .0001 **(b)** 76.105

➡ **Write the expanded form of a decimal or write the decimal numbers from the expanded form.**

Illustrations

- The expanded form of 35.246 is

  3 tens + 5 ones + 2 tenths + 4 hundredths + 6 thousandths.

  or $30 + 5 + \frac{2}{10} + \frac{4}{100} + \frac{6}{1000}$

  or $30 + 5 + .2 + .04 + .006$

- The decimal number with expanded form

  $$\frac{9}{10} + \frac{3}{100} + \frac{5}{10,000}$$

  is 0.9305.

Discussion

As in the case of whole numbers, the expanded form of a decimal shows the value of each digit. It is the indicated sum of the digit values of each digit taken in order. Recall that digit values are obtained by multiplying the digits with their respective place values.

Thus, the expanded form of .475 (or 0.475) is,

4 tenths + 7 hundredths + 5 thousandths

or $4\times\frac{1}{10} + 7\times\frac{1}{100} + 5\times\frac{1}{1000}$

which is the same as $\frac{4}{10} + \frac{7}{100} + \frac{5}{1000}$ or $.4 + .07 + .005$

The following chart shows some decimal numbers with their expanded forms.

Decimal Number	Expanded form
5.01	$5 + \frac{1}{100}$
742.565	$700 + 40 + 2 + \frac{5}{10} + \frac{6}{100} + \frac{5}{1000}$
0.493	$\frac{4}{10} + \frac{9}{100} + \frac{3}{1000}$
25	$20 + 5$

Procedure to write a number in expanded form.

***Step* 1** Obtain the digit value of each digit.

***Step* 2** Write the sum of the digit values.

EXAMPLE 3 Write the following numbers in expanded form:

(a) 82.573 **(b)** 0.9653.

Solutions

(a) 82.573 = 8 tens + 2 ones + 5 tenth + 7 hundredths + 3 thousandths

$$= 80 + 2 + \frac{5}{10} + \frac{7}{100} + \frac{3}{1000}$$

$$= 80 + 2 + 0.5 + 0.07 + 0.003$$

(b) 0.9653 = 9 tenths + 6 hundredths + 5 thousandth + 3 ten-thousandths

$$= \frac{9}{10} + \frac{6}{100} + \frac{5}{1000} + \frac{3}{10{,}000}$$

$$= 0.9 + 0.06 + 0.005 + 0.0003.$$

Procedure to write the decimal from its expanded form.

***Step* 1** Find the sum of the numbers.

***Step* 2** Write the sum as a decimal.

WARM-UP

3. Write the following numbers in expanded form:

(a) 43.508

(b) 0.3579

WARM-UP

4. Write the decimal number from the expanded form:

(a) $20+3+\frac{8}{10}+\frac{5}{1000}$

(b) $\frac{1}{10}+\frac{3}{100}+\frac{2}{1000}$

Answers:

3. (a) 40 + 3 + .5 + .008

(b) .3 + .05 + .007 + .0009

4. (a) 23.805 **(b)** 0.132

EXAMPLE 4 Write the decimal number from the given expanded form:

(a) $50 + 5 + \frac{3}{10} + \frac{4}{100} + \frac{8}{1000}$

(b) $4 + \frac{7}{100} + \frac{5}{1000}$

Solutions

(a) $50 + 5 + \frac{3}{10} + \frac{4}{100} + \frac{8}{1000}$

$= (50+5) + \left(\frac{3}{10}+\frac{4}{100}+\frac{8}{1000}\right)$

- LCD is 1000. Build the fractions to the common denominator.

$= (50+5) + \left(\frac{300}{1000}+\frac{40}{1000}+\frac{8}{1000}\right)$

- Add the whole numbers and the fractions separately.

$= 55 + \frac{348}{1000} = 55 + 0.348$

- Write the whole number for the whole number part, and then the decimal part.

$= 55.348$

(b) $4 + \frac{7}{100} + \frac{5}{1000}$

$= 4 + \left(\frac{70+5}{1000}\right)$

$= 4 + \frac{75}{1000} = 4 + .075 = 4.075$

B. WORD NAMES OF DECIMALS

➜ **Write the word names of decimals and write decimals from their word names.**

Application

Mr. Lane wants to write a check for \$58.06 to pay for his groceries. What word name should he write on the check?

Stephen Lane 0953
479-294-2975 64-1/610
295 PIEDMONT AVE 493
ATLANTA, GA 30308 02/09/2004
PAY TO THE
ORDER OF *Value Plus Supermarket* \$ 58.06
________________________________ DOLLARS
Wachovia Bank of Georgia, N.A.
Atlanta, GA 30383
For ____________
1:061000010: 01 669 034 "' 0953

Illustrations

- The word name of **154 . 25** is

One hundred fifty - four and twenty - five hundredths

- The decimal number for

is **256 . 074**

two hundred fifty six and seventy - four thousandths

> **Verify Skill**
>
> **Objective 6.1 B**
>
> **(a)** Write the word name for 19.56.
>
> **(b)** Write the decimal number for: "Twenty-six and fifty-nine thousandths"
>
> **If your answers to these questions are the same as given below, then you may skip this objective**
>
> Answers:
>
> **(a)** Ninteen and fifty six hundredths
>
> **(b)** 26.059

Discussion

There are four things to do when writing the word name for a decimal number. **First**, read the word name for the whole number part. **Second**, write the word "and" for the decimal point. **Third**, write the word name for the number following the decimal point. **Fourth**, write place value of the right most digit. Thus, 23.095 is read as: "**Twenty-three and ninety-five thousandths**".

The following table explains the method to write the word name of a decimal number.

	Number to the left of the decimal point	Decimal point	Number to the right of the decimal point	Place value of the right most digit
Number:	23	.	095	$\frac{1}{1000}$
	↓	↓	↓	↓
Word name:	twenty-three	and	ninety-five	thousandths

The word name of **23.095** is "twenty three and ninety-five thousandths."

Similarly, to write the word name of 8.2345, visualize the following table:

	Number to the left of the decimal point	Decimal point	Number to the right of the decimal point	Place value of the right most digit
Place-value:	8	.	2345	$\frac{1}{10000}$
	↓	↓	↓	↓
Word name of each:	eight	and	two thousand, three hundred forty-five	ten-thousandths

The word name of 8.2345 is

"eight and two thousand, three hundred forty five ten thousandths."

- If the number to the left of the decimal point is zero, it is not necessary to say the words "zero and" in the word name. For example, the word name of 0.73 is "seventy three hundredths". Similarly, if the number to the right of the decimal point is zero, it is not necessary to say the words "and zero…" in the word name. For example, the word name of 105.0 is "one hundred five".

Procedure to write the word name for a decimal number.

***Step* 1** Write the word name for the whole number to the left of the decimal point.

***Step* 2** Write "**and**" for the decimal point.

***Step* 3** Write the whole number word name for the digits to the right of the decimal point.

***Step* 4** Write the word name for the place value of the right most digit in the number.

If the decimal has only zero or no digit to the left of the decimal point, omit writing the whole number part.

If the decimal has only zero(s) or no digit to the right of the decimal point, write only the whole number part.

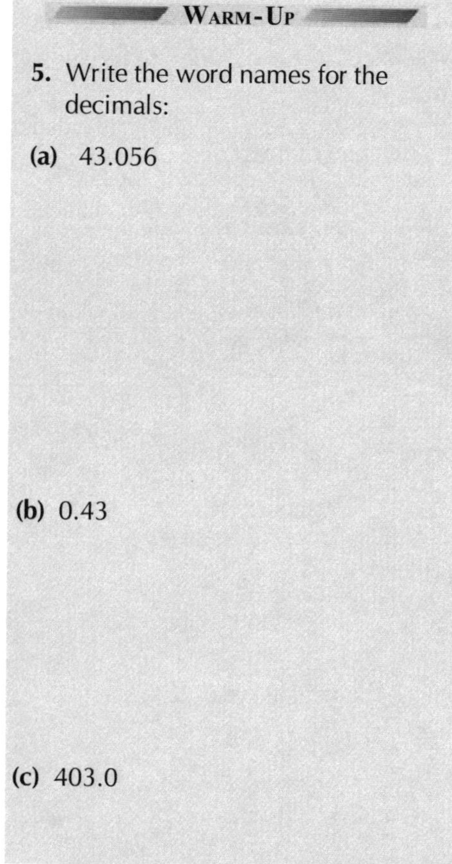

EXAMPLE 5 Write the word names for the decimals:

(a) 27.005 **(b)** 0.725 **(c)** 275.00

Solutions

(a) 27 . 005

twenty - seven and five thousandths

The word name for 27.005 is

"twenty-seven and five thousandths."

- The word name for 27 is Twenty-seven.
- The word name for the decimal point is and
- The word name for 005 is Five
- The place-value of the right most digit 5 is thousandths.

(b) The word name for 0.725 is

"seven hundred twenty-five thousandths".

- The number has only a zero to the left of the decimal point, so omit the whole number part as well as the word "and".
- The word name for 725 is seven hundred twenty-five.
- The word name for the place value of the right most digit 5 is thousandths.

(c) 275.00 has only zeros to the right of the decimal point, so the word name of 275.00 is the same as that of 275:

"two hundred seventy-five".

Procedure to write a decimal number from its word name.

***Step* 1** Write the number preceding "and" as the whole number part of the decimal.

***Step* 2** Replace the word "and" with a decimal point.

***Step* 3** Write the number for the word name after the word "and" to the right of the decimal point so that the digit in the right most place occupies the decimal place suggested by the word name.

***Step* 4** If necessary, write zero(s) to fill out the vacant decimal places.

EXAMPLE 6 Write the decimals from their word names:

(a) seven hundred twelve and thirty-five hundredths.
(b) forty-nine and twenty-five thousandths.
(c) five hundred seven hundred-thousandths.

Solutions

(a) seven hundred twelve and thirty – five hundredths

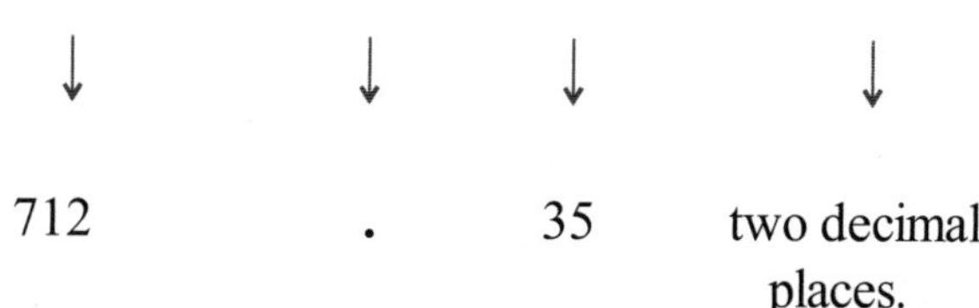

Thus, "seven hundred twelve and thirty five hundredths" when written as a decimal number is 712.35

(b) forty nine and twenty five thousandths

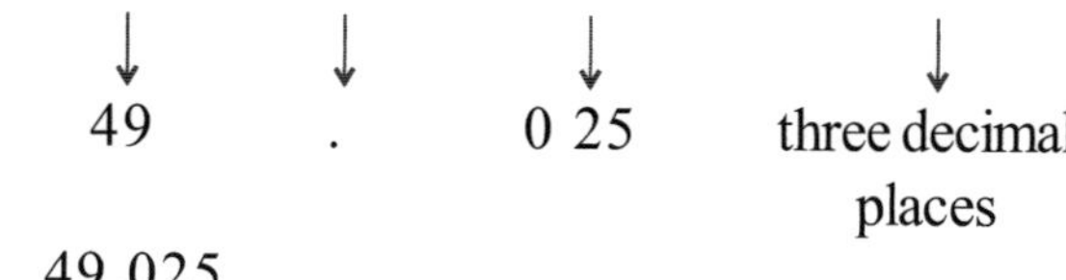

= 49.025

(c) five hundred seven hundred - thousandths.

The whole number part is zero.

The number to the right of decimal point is 507.

The place of the 7 in 507 is hundred thousandths (five decimal places). Therefore "five hundred seven hundred thousandths"

= .00507

WARM-UP

6. Write the decimals from their word names:

(a) four hundred five and fifteen hundred-thousandths.

(b) seventy two and four thousandths.

(c) twenty one thousandths.

Answers:

5. (a) Forty three and fifty six thousandths
(b) Forty three hundredths.
(c) Four hundred three.

6. (a) 405.00015 **(b)** 72.004 **(c)** .021

Solution to the Application

Mr. Lane wants to write a check for $58.06 to pay for his groceries. What word name should he write on the check ?

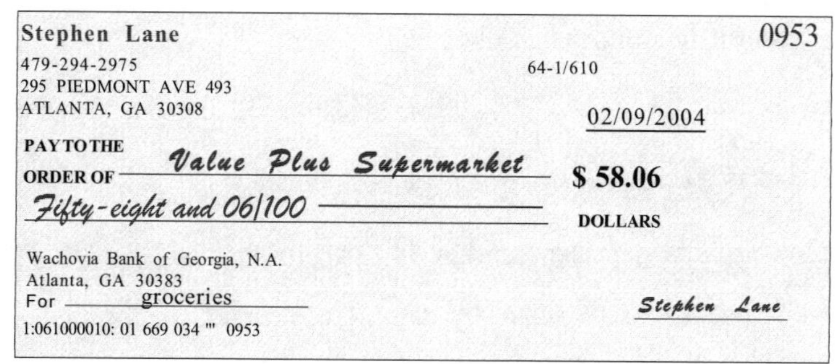
Stephen Lane
479-294-2975
295 PIEDMONT AVE 493
ATLANTA, GA 30308
0953
64-1/610
02/09/2004
PAY TO THE ORDER OF Value Plus Supermarket $ 58.06
Fifty-eight and 06/100 DOLLARS
Wachovia Bank of Georgia, N.A.
Atlanta, GA 30383
For groceries
Stephen Lane
1:061000010: 01 669 034 ''' 0953

To write the word name for $58.06, he should write: "Fifty-eight and 6/100".

Note To prevent theft, it is customary to fill the entire space given for the word name on a check.

Verify Skill

Objective 6.1 C

Round the number 41.3579 to the nearest

(a) ten

(b) hundredth

(c) thousandth

If your answers to these questions are the same as given below then you may skip this objective.

Answers:

(a) 40 **(b)** 41.36 **(c)** 41.358

C. Rounding Decimals

➜ **Round a decimal to a given place of accuracy**

Application

Charles plans to deduct \$385.65 for union dues when he files his tax return. If the instructions are that the amount should be rounded to the nearest dollar, how much can he deduct?

Illustration

$15.459 \approx 15$	rounded to the nearest unit.
$15.479 \approx 15.5$	rounded to the nearest tenth.
$15.479 \approx 15.48$	rounded to the nearest hundredth.
$15.479 \approx 20$	rounded to the nearest ten.

Discussion

Decimals are rounded the same way as whole numbers.

To round 235.6473 to the **nearest tenth**, draw an arrow under the digit in **tenths place.**

235.6473

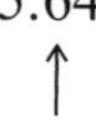

Since the digit to the right of the arrow is 4, *round down* by replacing each digit to the right of the arrow with zero.

Thus, 235.**6473** ≈ 235.**6** rounded to the nearest tenth.

Similarly, to round the same number to the nearest hundredth, draw an arrow under 4, the digit in the hundredths place.

235.6**473**

↑

Since the digit to right of the arrow is 7, *round up* by adding 1 to hundredths place and replacing each digit to the right of the hundredths place with a zero.

$$235.6473 \approx 235.6500 = 235.65 \text{ to the nearest hundredth.}$$

Procedure to round a decimal to a given place.

***Step* 1** Draw an arrow under the digit in the rounding place.

***Step* 2** Round up or round down by inspecting the digit to the right of the rounding place.

***Step* 3** Drop the unnecessary zeros to the right of the arrow.

EXAMPLE 7 Round the following decimals to the nearest thousandth.

(a) 15.43281 **(b)** 0.084413 **(c)** 251.629601

Solutions

(a) *Step* 1 15.43281 — Draw an arrow under the digit in the thousandths place.
↑

Step 2 15.43300 — Since the first digit to the right of the arrow is 8, round up.
↑

Step 3 15.433 — Drop the unnecessary zeros.

15.43281 ≈ 15.433 to the nearest thousandth.

(b) 0.084413 — Draw an arrow under the digit in the thousandths place.
↑

0.084000 — Since the first digit to the right of the arrow is 4 (less than 5), round down.
↑

0.084 — Drop the unnecessary zeros.

0.084413 ≈ 0.084 to the nearest thousandth.

(c)

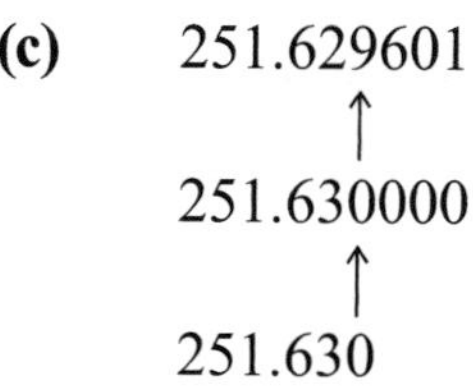

Caution: Do not drop the zero in the rounding place. It is required to display the place of accuracy.

251.629601 ≈ 251.630 to the nearest thousandth.

WARM-UP

7. Round the following decimals to the second decimal place.

(a) 537.4139

(b) 21.72564

(c) 0.29985

Answers:
7. **(a)** 537.41 **(b)** 21.73 **(c)** 0.30

Solution to the Application:

Charles plans to deduct $385.65 for union dues when he files his tax return. If the instructions are that the amount should be rounded to the nearest dollar, how much can he deduct?

Solution: Since 385.65 ≈ 386 rounded to the nearest whole number, Charles can deduct $386 for union dues.
↑

EXERCISE 6.1

In exercises 1-20, determine the place value of the bold faced digit.

1. 2.73**8** **2.** 295.**8**5 **3.** 4927.0**5**21 **4.** 4.1**7**582 **5.** 5**2**.001

6. 35.43**2** **7.** 132.0572**1**6 **8.** 0.59**5** **9.** 197.752**6** **10.** 0.0**3**7

11. 47.62**5** **12.** 75.375 **13.** 21.**2**5 **14.** **1**0.428 **15.** **3**7.5901

16. 0.032**5** **17.** 74.**0**225 **18.** 835.279**1**5 **19.** 4.5**4**2 **20.** 13.26**8**

In exercises 21-36, identify the digit that has the given place value.

21. 28.589; hundredths **22.** 327.0912; tenths **23.** 20.5029; tens

24. 2.9295; ten-thousandths **25.** 4092.631; hundreds **26.** 0.24513; thousandths

27. 75.0025; tenths **28.** 49.987654; hundred-thousandths **29.** 20.78125; ten-thousandths

30. 0.00456 ; hundred- thousandths **31.** 3152.891; thousands **32.** 75.0026; ones

33. 425.0063; thousandths **34.** 9.873; hundredths **35.** 12.49705; tenths **36.** 83.729; tens

In exercises 37-48, write the given number in expanded form.

37. 54.271 **38.** 7.235 **39.** 47.22 **40.** .009 **41.** 107.405 **42.** 0.2359

43. 27.326 **44.** 298.05 **45.** 13.7984 **46.** 0.3014 **47.** 9.32051 **48.** 50.0234

In exercises 49-58, write the given number in expanded form using the word names for the place values.

49. 51.139 **50.** 2.395 **51.** 16.954 **52.** 4.0093 **53.** 5.143

54. 7.1054 **55.** 35.782 **56.** 18.0235 **57.** 105.36 **58.** 6.375

In exercises 59-70, write the decimal number from the given expanded form.

59. $200 + 30 + 9 + \frac{0}{10} + \frac{3}{100} + \frac{4}{1000}$ **60.** $\frac{5}{10} + \frac{3}{100} + \frac{2}{1000}$ **61.** $9 + \frac{0}{10} + \frac{0}{100} + \frac{9}{1000}$

62. $4 + \frac{5}{10} + \frac{0}{100} + \frac{3}{1000}$ **63.** $20 + 5 + \frac{0}{10} + \frac{1}{100} + \frac{3}{1000} + \frac{5}{10000}$

64. $\frac{0}{10} + \frac{0}{100} + \frac{4}{1000} + \frac{7}{10000}$

65. 9 tens + 2 ones + 4 tenths + 3 hundredths + 2 thousandths + 5 ten-thousandths.

66. 4 tenths + 9 hundredths + 1 thousandth. **67.** 6 ten-thousandths.

68. 4 thousandths + 8 ten-thousandths **69.** 3 tens + 5 ones + 0 tenths + 6 hundredths + 2 thousandths.

70. 0 tenths + 5 hundredths + 7 thousandths + 3 ten-thousandths.

In exercises 71-85, write the word names for the given decimals.

71. 4005.083 **72.** 2.643 **73.** 12.064 **74.** 8.650 **75.** 7.2354

76. 23.15 **77.** 16.135 **78.** 435.7 **79.** 5.0007 **80.** 28.35

81. 8.009 **82.** 40.01 **83.** 103.007 **84.** 758.6 **85.** 413.305

In exercises 86-93, write the decimal number from the given word name.

86. Two hundred seventeen and three hundredths.

87. Twenty-nine and five tenths.

88. One thousand nine and three hundred forty-nine thousandths.

89. Five and twenty-five hundredths.

90. Four thousand, five hundred thirty-two and ninety-two thousandths.

91. Eight and eight ten-thousandths.

92. One million, ninety-two and twelve hundredths.

93. Eight and eight tenths.

Applications

94. Maria buys a transistor that has a marked price of $95.35. What word name does she write on the check?

95. Heather wants to write a check for $322.17. What word name for this amount should be written on the check?

96. Roza has five hundred sixty-four dollars and twenty-eight cents to spend on holiday gifts this year. Write the amount she has to spend as a decimal number.

In exercises 97-106, round the number as indicated.

97. 275.57 to the tenths place

98. 63.4531 to two decimal places.

99. 17.036 to the nearest hundredth

100. 569.692 to the nearest unit

101. 43.0091 to three decimal places

102. 0.9521 to one decimal place

103. 15.0049 to two decimal places

104. 2564.99 to the nearest ten

105. 0.05962 to the nearest thousandth

106. 754.93102 to the nearest hundred

In exercises 107 and 108, complete the chart by rounding the number as indicated.

	Number \ Round to nearest	Ten	Unit	Tenth	Hundredth
107.	26.1095				
108.	399.563				

Applications

109. The computer at Joan's savings company shows that her account, including the interest she has earned, has a value of $2073.50433391. What is the value of the account to the nearest cent?

110. Elizabeth worked for 162 days in a fashion designer's company and received a check for $8654 as her pay. To know the average payment per day, she divided the figure 8654 by 162 on her calculator and found the answer 53.419753. Round the value of the average payment per day to the nearest dollar.

111. Round the number 5499.999 to the nearest hundredth; tenth; unit and ten. What do you observe?

112. One store manager offered a discount of 0.15 percent on the marked price of an article, while the other store offers 0.155 percent. Which of the two stores is offering a better discount?

113. One basket of oranges weighs 14.059 pounds and another weighs 14.0589 pounds. Which of the two baskets is heavier?

6.2 Operations and Decimals

Objectives

After completing this section you will be able to:

A. Adding Decimals;

B. Subtracting Decimals;

C. Estimating the Sum and Difference of Decimals;

D. Multiplying Decimals;

E. Dividing Decimals by Whole Numbers;

F. Dividing Decimals by Decimals; and

G. Estimate Products and Quotients (/-).

Verify Skill

Objective 6.2 A

Find the sum of 53.724, 13.9 and 564.976.

If your answer to this question is the same as given below, then you may skip this objective.

Answer:

632.6

Vocabulary

1. Decimals having the same number of decimal places are called **like decimals**. 426.05 and 1.37 are like decimals.
2. Decimals having different numbers of decimal places are called **unlike decimals**. 3.2, 5.03, 7.609 are unlike decimals.

(A.) Adding Decimals

➜ **Add two or more decimals.**

Application

Maria's rectangular kitchen measure 5.6 meters by 7.9 meters. She wishes to replace the baseboard in her kitchen. In order to determine how much baseboard she will need, she must calculate the perimeter. How much baseboard will she need?

Illustration

Find the sum of 2.31, 0.045, and 15.3:

$$\begin{array}{r} 2.31 \\ 0.045 \\ +\ 15.3 \\ \hline \end{array} \quad \text{may be written as} \quad \begin{array}{r} 2.310 \\ 0.045 \\ +\ 15.300 \\ \hline \text{Sum } = 17.655 \end{array}$$

2.31 + 0.045 + 15.3 = 17.655

Discussion

The addition of decimal numbers is very similar to the addition of whole numbers, extra care is needed in aligning the decimal points and digits with the same place value.

Compare the following two additions:

Whole Numbers

$$\begin{array}{r} 1\ 1\ \ \ \ \\ 2\ 3\ 9\ 5 \\ +\ \ \ 9\ 3\ 2 \\ \hline 3\ 3\ 2\ 7 \end{array}$$

Decimal Numbers

$$\begin{array}{r} 1\ 1\ \ \ \ \ \ \\ 2\ 3\ .\ 9\ 5 \\ +\ 9\ .\ 3\ 2 \\ \hline 3\ 3\ .\ 2\ 7 \end{array}$$

5 hundredths + 2 hundredths
= 7 hundredths
9 tenths + 3 tenths = 12 tenths
= 1 unit + 2 tenths

To add a group of decimals first, change them to like decimals, then, write the decimals in columns lining up the decimal points and the corresponding place values on either side of the decimal points: tenths under tenths, hundredths under hundredths, and so on.

```
     2.400   <——   2.4  = 2.400          ]  Change each decimal to three
+   15.000   <——   15   = 15. = 15.000   ]  decimal places since the largest
+    0.050   <——   0.05 = 0.050          ]  number of decimal places in
+    1.215                                  the group is three.
   -------
    18.665
```

With practice it may become unnecessary to change the decimals to like decimals. It is only necessary to align the decimal points, and to write each digit in its proper place.

Procedure to add a group of decimals.

***Step* 1** Write the decimals in columns so that the decimal points and the corresponding place values on either side of the decimal points are lined up.

***Step* 2** Add the decimals as if they were whole numbers.

***Step* 3** Place the decimal point in the sum just below those in the addends and drop unnecessary zeros, if any.

EXAMPLE 1 Add:

5.21, 13.719, 0.06, 103.15

Solution

```
          1 1   1
Step 1      5. 2 1 0  <——   5.21 = 5.210
           1 3. 7 1 9
            0. 0 6 0  <——   0.06 = 0.060
         1 0 3. 1 5 0  <——   103.15 = 103.150
         ------------
Step 2   1 2 2. 1 3 9       Add
               ↑
Step 3         └——————————  Place the decimal point.
```

The sum is 122.139

EXAMPLE 2 Add the following numbers

824.6, 53.0484, 17.9736, 275.47

Solution

```
  1 2 2    1 1 1
  8 2 4 . 6 0 0 0   <——   Note this step.
    5 3 . 0 4 8 4
    1 7 . 9 7 3 6
  2 7 5 . 4 7 0 0   <——   Note this step.
 ----------------
1 1 7 1 . 0 9 2 0         Add
```

The sum of the given numbers is 1171.0920 or 1171.092.

WARM-UP

1. Add:

2.7, 17.45, 0.034, and 24.5

2. Find the sum of 43.55, 9.005, 215.25, and 5.085.

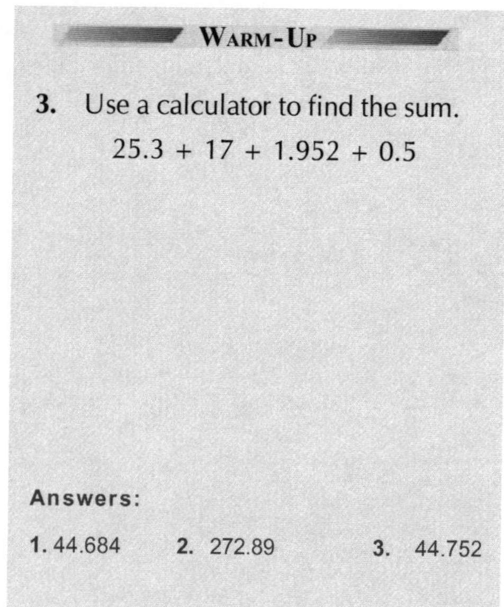

WARM-UP

3. Use a calculator to find the sum.

$25.3 + 17 + 1.952 + 0.5$

Answers:

1. 44.684 2. 272.89 3. 44.752

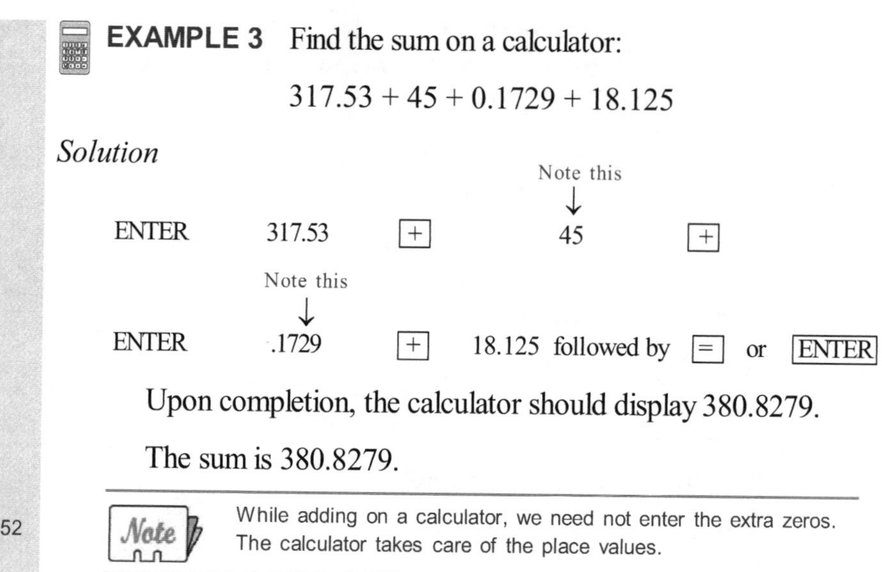

EXAMPLE 3 Find the sum on a calculator:

$$317.53 + 45 + 0.1729 + 18.125$$

Solution

ENTER 317.53 [+] 45 (Note this) [+]

ENTER .1729 (Note this) [+] 18.125 followed by [=] or [ENTER]

Upon completion, the calculator should display 380.8279.

The sum is 380.8279.

Note While adding on a calculator, we need not enter the extra zeros. The calculator takes care of the place values.

Solution to the Application:

Maria's rectangular kitchen measure 5.6 meters by 7.9 meters. She wishes to replace the baseboard in her kitchen. In order to determine how much baseboard she will need, she must calculate the perimeter. How much baseboard will she need?

Solution: Maria will need baseboard on all four walls, so she needs 5.6 m + 5.6 m + 7.9 m + 7.9 m = 27 m of baseboard.

B. SUBTRACTING DECIMALS

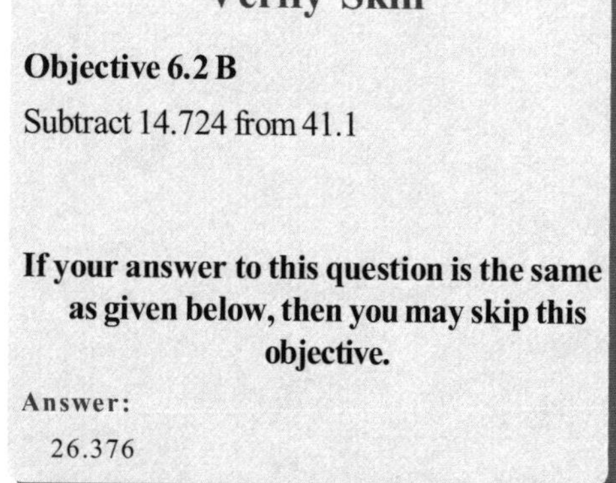

Verify Skill

Objective 6.2 B

Subtract 14.724 from 41.1

If your answer to this question is the same as given below, then you may skip this objective.

Answer:

26.376

➜ **Subtract decimals.**

Application

George writes four checks in the amounts of \$774.94, \$2150.35, \$1379.75, and \$155.80. He has \$4450.00 in his checking account. Does he have enough money to cover the four checks? If not, how much more, to the nearest dollar, must he deposit in order to cover the four checks? The bank requires, him to have a minimum balance of \$100.00 in his account.

Illustration

Find the difference 25.32 – 16.295:

$$\begin{array}{r} 25.320 \\ -\ 16.295 \\ \hline 9.025 \end{array}$$

Discussion

- Like addition of decimals, subtraction of decimals is performed in the same way as subtraction of whole numbers; just line up the decimal points so that the digits with the same place values are aligned.

Compare the following two subtractions:

Whole Numbers	Decimal Numbers	
$\begin{array}{r} 2987 \\ -\ \ 352 \\ \hline 2635 \end{array}$	$\begin{array}{r} 29.87 \\ -\ \ 3.52 \\ \hline 26.35 \end{array}$	7 hundredths − 2 hundredths = 5 hundredths 8 tenths − 5 tenths − 3 tenths, and so on.

- If the subtraction in any column cannot be performed, simply regroup as in the case of whole numbers. For example, to subtract 19.249 from 75.46, write 75.46 = 75.460 and subtract.

$$\begin{array}{r} 75.46 \\ -\ 19.249 \\ \hline \end{array} \longrightarrow \begin{array}{r} \overset{6}{\not7}\,\overset{15}{\not5}.4\overset{5}{\not6}\overset{10}{\not0} \\ -\ 19.249 \\ \hline 56.211 \end{array}$$

- Change to like decimals.
- Subtract.

Check the answer by addition.

$$\begin{array}{r} 19.249 \\ +\ 56.211 \\ \hline 75.460 \end{array} = 75.46$$

Procedure to subtract decimals.

***Step* 1** Write the decimals in columns so that the decimal points and the corresponding place values on either side of the decimal points are lined up. Attach zeros, to convert the decimals to like decimals, if necessary.

***Step* 2** Subtract the decimals as if they were whole numbers.

***Step* 3** Place the decimal point in the difference just below other decimal points and drop unnecessary zeros, if any.

EXAMPLE 4 Find the difference:

32.189 − 5.069

Solutions

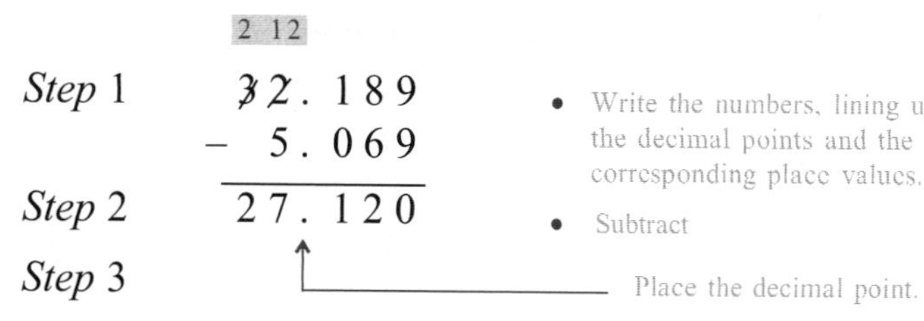

WARM-UP

4. Find the difference:

13.55 − 2.34

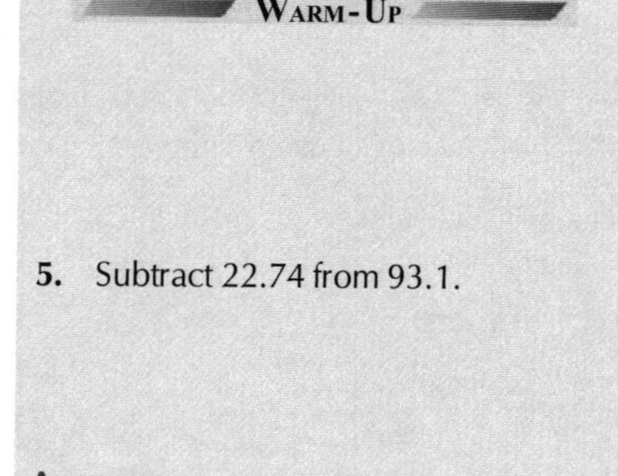

WARM-UP

5. Subtract 22.74 from 93.1.

Answers:

4. 11.21   5. 70.36

Check:

$$\begin{array}{r} 5.069 \\ +\ 27.120 \\ \hline 32.189 \end{array}$$

The difference 27.120, or 27.12, is correct.

 **EXAMPLE 5** Subtract 59.6758 from 263.

Solution

ENTER 263 [−] 59.6758 followed by [=] or [ENTER]

Upon completion, the calculator should display 203.3242.

The difference is 203.3242.

Solution to the Application:

George writes four checks in the amount of \$774.94, \$2150.35, \$1379.75, and \$155.80. He has \$4450.00 in his checking account. Does he have enough money to cover the four checks? If not, how much more, to the nearest dollar, must he deposit in order to cover the four checks? The bank requires him to have a minimum balance of \$100 in his account.

Solution: The money in the bank must equal the total amount of the four checks plus the \$100 minimum.

This sum is 774.94 + 2150.35 + 1379.75 + 155.80 + 100 = \$4560.84.

Thus, George does **not** have enough money to cover the four checks and leave a minimum balance of \$100.

Let x represent the money George must deposit.

$x + 4450.00$ will be in the bank.

$$\begin{aligned} x + 4450.00 &= 4560.84 \\ -\ 4450.00 &\quad -\ 4450.00 \\ x &= 110.84 \\ x &\approx 111 \end{aligned}$$

Rounded to the nearest whole dollar.

George must deposit \$111 more in order to cover the four checks and retain a balance of at least \$100.

Verify Skill

Objective 6.2 C

(a) Estimate the sum of 31.92, 41.3, and 57 to the nearest whole number.

(b) Estimate the difference 217.35 − 85.903 to the nearest whole number.

C. ESTIMATING THE SUM AND DIFFERENCE OF DECIMALS

➜ **Estimate the sum or difference to the nearest whole number.**

Application 

Rhonesha is shopping. She picks up a six pack of soda for \$2.98, some beef for \$8.16, some butter for \$3.68 and a candy bar for \$.79. Estimate her total purchase. Rhonesha has \$20.00 in her pocket. Do you think this will be enough for her purchases?

Illustration

- Estimate the sum of 52.861, 0.25, 8.1 and 57.37 to the nearest whole number:

52.861	≈	53	to the nearest whole number
0.25	≈	0	
8.1	≈	8	
+ 57.37	≈	+ 57	
118.581		118	

The estimated sum is 118, which is close to the actual sum 118.581.

Verify Skill

If your answers to these questions are the same as given below, then you may skip this objective.

Answers:

(a) 130 **(b)** 131

Discussion

- To estimate the sum or difference of decimals to the nearest whole number, first round each of the given numbers to the nearest whole number, and then add or subtract.

For example, to estimate the sum of 572.617, and 126.3415:

572.**6**17 ≈ 573 to the nearest whole number
↑

126.**3**415 ≈ 126 to the nearest whole number
↑

Find the actual sum and the estimated sum.

572.617	≈	573
126.3415	≈	126
698.9585	≈	699

The estimate of the sum, 699, is close to the actual sum 698.9585.

- Similarly, to estimate the difference 72.815 – 37.9272 , first round each number to a whole number and then take the difference.

72.**8**150	≈	73
–37.**9**272	≈	–38
34.8878	≈	35

The actual difference (34.8878) is close to the estimate (35).

Procedure to estimate the sum or difference of decimals to the nearest whole number.

***Step* 1** Round each of the given decimals to the nearest unit (ones place).

***Step* 2** Add or subtract the rounded numbers.

EXAMPLE 6 Estimate the sum to the nearest whole number.

(a) 4.732 + 19.894

(b) 107.309 + 19.07 + 137.5 + 259.825.

Solutions

WARM-UP

6. Estimate the sum of 12.92, 9.783, and 187.045 to the nearest whole number.

WARM-UP

7. Estimate the difference 384.543 – 270.295 to the nearest whole number.

Answers:

6. 210 7. 115

(a) 4.732 + 19.894

4.732	≈	5	• Round each of the given numbers to the nearest whole number.
19.894	≈	20	• Add the rounded numbers.
Sum	≈	25	

The estimated sum is 25

(b)

107.309	≈	107	• Round each of the given numbers to the nearest whole number.
19.07	≈	19	
137.5	≈	138	
259.825	≈	260	
Sum	≈	524	• Add the rounded numbers.

The estimated sum is 524.

EXAMPLE 7 Estimate the difference 2953.109 – 729.51 to the nearest whole number.

Solution

2953.109	≈	2953	• Round each of the given numbers to the nearest whole number.
729.51	≈	730	• Subtract the rounded numbers.
difference	≈	2223	

The estimated difference is 2223.

Solution to the Application:

Rhonesha is shopping. She picks up a six pack of soda for $2.98, some beef for $8.16, some butter for $3.68 and a candy bar for $.79. Estimate her total purchase. Rhonesha has $20.00 in her pocket. Do you think this will be enough for her purchases?

Solution: To estimate the sum of $2.98, $8.16, $3.68 and $.79, add 3 + 8 + 4 + 1 = 16. Her total is approximately $16. Not only does Rhonesha have enough to cover her purchases, she probably has enough to cover tax as well.

Verify Skill

Objective 6.2 D

Find the product of 24.13 and 7.25.

D. MULTIPLYING DECIMALS

➔ **Multiply two decimal numbers.**

Application 

Myra's rectangular kitchen measures 17.25 feet by 12.75 feet. To figure out how much tile is needed to cover the floor, the area of the floor must be calculated. How many square feet of tile does Myra need? Round the answer to the nearest unit.

Illustration

Compute the product (3.71) (4.5):

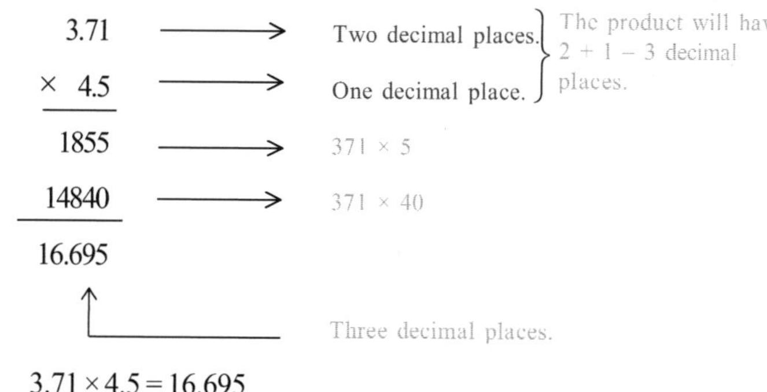

3.71 × 4.5 = 16.695

Verify Skill

If your answer to this question is the same as given below, then you may skip this objective.

Answer: 174.9425

Discussion

The multiplication of two decimals is performed in almost the same way as the multiplication of whole numbers. The only additional step is to locate the decimal point in the product. To understand how to place the decimal point in 2.37 × 1.5, change the decimals to fractions:

$$2.37 \times 1.5 = \frac{237}{100} \times \frac{15}{10} = \frac{237 \times 15}{1000} = \frac{3555}{1000} = 3.555$$

Observe that the factor 2.37 has *two* decimal places, and

the factor 1.5 has *one* decimal place.

Note the relationship of the zeros in the denominators.

The product 2.37 × 1.5 has *three* (2 + 1) decimal places.

Similarly, to multiply 2.3 and 0.04:

$$2.3 \times 0.04 = \frac{23}{10} \times \frac{4}{100} = \frac{23 \times 4}{1000} = \frac{92}{1000} = 0.092$$

The short cut is to multiply 23 × 4. Then, locate the decimal point in the product by counting the number of decimal places in both of the factors. In this case, the total number of decimal places in both factors is 3, and the product of the factors is 92. As the product must have *three* decimal places, we insert zeros to the left of 92 to have three decimal places.

Thus, 2.3 × 0.04 = 0.092

The usual method of finding the product of 2.738 × 13.5 is shown below:

```
   2.738   ———>  Three decimal places  } The product will have 3 + 1 = 4 decimal places.
  ×13.5    ———>  One decimal place     } Multiply the numbers ignoring the decimal points.
  13690    <———  2738 × 5
  82140    <———  2738 × 30
 273800    <———  2738 × 100
 36.9630
 ↑_______________ Position the decimal point so the product has 4 decimal places.
```

$$2.738 \times 13.5 = 36.9630$$
$$= 36.963.$$

Drop the unnecessary zeros.

Caution: Do not drop zeros before locating the decimal point.

To find 1.125×0.08, first find the product $1125 \times 8 = 9000$.

The number of decimal places in the product is $3 + 2 = 5$.

Insert zeros to the left of 9000 in order to locate the decimal point 5 decimal places from the right.

$$1.125 \times 0.08 = 0.09000$$
$$= 0.09$$

Drop the unnecessary zeros.

Procedure to multiply two or more decimals.

***Step* 1** Multiply the numbers as if they were whole numbers ignoring the decimal point.

***Step* 2** Count the number of decimal places in each of the factors and find their sum. This sum is the number of decimal places in the product.

***Step* 3** Locate the decimal point in the product by counting from the right the number of decimal places obtained. Insert zeros to the left of the product, if necessary, to have enough digits for decimal places.

***Step* 4** Drop the unnecessary zeros, if any.

WARM-UP

8. Multiply by inspection

(a) 0.7×0.05

(b) 2.73×0.006

EXAMPLE 8 Multiply by inspection.

(a) 0.8×0.04 **(b)** 13.25×0.07

Solutions

(a) $\mathbf{0.8 \times 0.04}$

$8 \times 4 = 32$

- Multiply as whole numbers.

Therefore,

$0.8 \times 0.04 = 0.032$

- The number of decimal places in 0.8 is 1. The number of decimal places in 0.04 is 2.

  The number of decimal places in 0.8×0.04 is $1 + 2 = 3$.
- Insert zeros to the left of 32, and locate the decimal point three places from the right.

(b) 13.25×0.07,

13.25	⟶	1325	The factor 13.25 has 2 decimal places.
× 0.07		× 7	The factor 0.07 has 2 decimal places.
		9275	The product must have 2 + 2 = 4 decimal places.

$13.25 \times 0.07 = 0.9275$

EXAMPLE 9 Compute the indicated products: (216.03) (35)

Solutions

$$\begin{array}{r} 216.03 \\ \times 35 \\ \hline \end{array} \longrightarrow \begin{array}{r} 21603 \\ \times 35 \\ \hline 108015 \\ 648090 \\ \hline 756105 \end{array}$$

- Ignore decimal point and multiply.
- The product must have 2 decimal places.

$216.03 \times 35 = 7561.05$

- Locate the decimal point.

EXAMPLE 10 Multiply

(a) 2.31×0.032 **(b)** 7.42×0.205

Solutions

(a)

$$\begin{array}{r} 2.31 \\ \times 0.032 \\ \hline \end{array} \longrightarrow \begin{array}{r} 231 \\ \times 32 \\ \hline 462 \\ 6930 \\ \hline 7392 \end{array}$$

$2.31 \times 0.032 = 0.07392$

The product must have 5 decimal places, so insert a zero to the left of 7392 to allow for 5 decimal places.

(b)

$$\begin{array}{r} 7.42 \\ \times 0.205 \\ \hline 3710 \\ 148400 \\ \hline 1.52110 \end{array}$$

7.42 ⟶ 2 decimal places; × 0.205 ⟶ 3 decimal places; 2 + 3 = 5

3710 ⟵ 742 × 5

148400 ⟵ 742 × 200

Count five places from right to left and locate decimal point.

$7.42 \times 0.205 = 1.52110 = 1.5211$

> ***Caution***: Do not drop the zero before locating the decimal point.

EXAMPLE 11 Multiply:

(1.45) (2.1) (0.065)

Solution

$$\begin{array}{r} 1.45 \\ \times 2.1 \\ \hline 145 \\ +2900 \\ \hline 3.045 \end{array}$$

- First multiply 1.45 and 2.1 ignoring the decimal points. (Recall that numbers can be multiplied in any order.)
- The product has 3 decimal places.

$$\begin{array}{r} 3.045 \\ \times 0.065 \\ \hline 15225 \\ +182700 \\ \hline 0.197925 \end{array}$$

- Next multiply the product of 1.45 and 2.1 (3.045) by 0.065.
- The product has 6 decimal places.

WARM-UP

9. Compute the indicated products.

503.18 × 2.7

10. Multiply

(a) 8.97 × 0.61

(b) 3.04 × 0.75

11. Multiply:

(2.5) (1.43) (0.015)

WARM-UP

12. Multiply 3.04 and 0.75 on calculator and verify the answer obtained in warm up (b), example 3.

Answers:

8. (a) 0.035 (b) 0.01638
9. 1358.586
10. (a) 5.4717 (b) 2.28
11. 0.053625
12. 2.28

Hence, $(1.45)(2.1)(0.065) = 0.197925$

EXAMPLE 12 Multiply 7.42 and 0.205, and verify the product in Example 3 (b).

Solution

ENTER 7.42 [×] .205 followed by [=] or [ENTER]

The result should be 1.5211

$7.42 \times 0.205 = 1.5211$, which is the same as obtained in Example 3 (b).

Solution to the Application:

Myra's rectangular kitchen measures 17.25 feet by 12.75 feet. To figure out how much tile is needed to cover the floor, the area of the floor must be calculated. How many square feet of tile does Myra need? Round the answer to the nearest unit.

Solution: The area can be calculated by multiplying the length by the width.

$$\begin{array}{r} 17.25 \\ \times\ 12.75 \\ \hline 8625 \\ 120750 \\ 345000 \\ 1725000 \\ \hline 219.9375 \end{array}$$

Thus, Myra needs approximately 220 square feet of tile.

Verify Skill
Objective 6.2 E

Divide $50.4 \div 11$ and find the quotient rounded to the thousandths place.

If your answer to this question is the same as given below, then you may skip this objective.

Answer: 4.582

E. DIVIDING DECIMALS BY WHOLE NUMBERS

➜ **Divide a decimal by a whole number.**

Application 

The tab at a restaurant came to $132.65 after a 15% tip was added. If there were five diners, how much did each pay in order to split the bill, including tip, equally?

Illustration

To find the quotient in $25.3 \div 9$ rounded to the hundredths place:

$$
\begin{array}{r}
2.811 \\
9\,\overline{)\,25.300} \\
\underline{-18} \\
73 \\
\underline{-72} \\
10 \\
\underline{-9} \\
10 \\
\underline{-9} \\
1
\end{array}
$$

To round the quotient to the hundredths place, it is necessary to add zeros to the right of the decimal point so that the quotient has a digit at the thousandth place.

$25.3 \div 9 \approx \mathbf{2.81}$

Verify Skill

If your answer to this question is the same as given below, then you may skip this objective.

Answer: 4.582

Discussion

- The division of a decimal by a whole number is performed in almost the same way as the division of whole numbers. The only additional step is to locate the decimal point in the quotient.

Compare the following two divisions:

Whole numbers

$$
\begin{array}{r}
258 \\
16\,\overline{)\,4128} \\
\underline{-32} \\
92 \\
\underline{-80} \\
128 \\
\underline{-128} \\
0
\end{array}
$$

Decimal numbers

Divisor → 16; 2.58 → Quotient; 41.28 → Dividend

$$
\begin{array}{r}
2.58 \\
16\,\overline{)\,41.28} \\
\underline{-32} \\
9\,2 \\
\underline{-8\,0} \\
1\,2\,8 \\
\underline{-1\,2\,8} \\
0
\end{array}
$$

Place the decimal point in the quotient just above the decimal point in the dividend.

Check the answer by multiplication. $16 \times 2.58 = 41.28$

This verifies that the decimal point is correctly placed in the quotient.

- In a division problem, the division process may not leave a remainder of zero. For example, divide: $14.527 \div 25$

$$
\begin{array}{r}
.581 \\
25\,\overline{)\,14.527} \\
\underline{-125} \\
202 \\
\underline{-200} \\
27 \\
\underline{-25} \\
2
\end{array}
$$

At this step, we can insert zeros to the right of the digit 7 in the dividend, since 14.527 = 14.5270 = 14.52700 = 14.527000, and so on.

$$
\begin{array}{r}
.58108 \\
25\,\overline{)\,14.52700} \\
\underline{-125} \\
202 \\
\underline{-200} \\
27 \\
\underline{-25} \\
200 \\
\underline{-200} \\
0
\end{array}
$$

Thus, the remainder zero is obtained by inserting two zeros in the dividend.

$14.527 \div 25 = 0.58108$

In both these examples , the quotient is a **terminating decimal.**

- At times, the process of inserting zeros and dividing may continue endlessly. For example, divide: $3.29 \div 13$

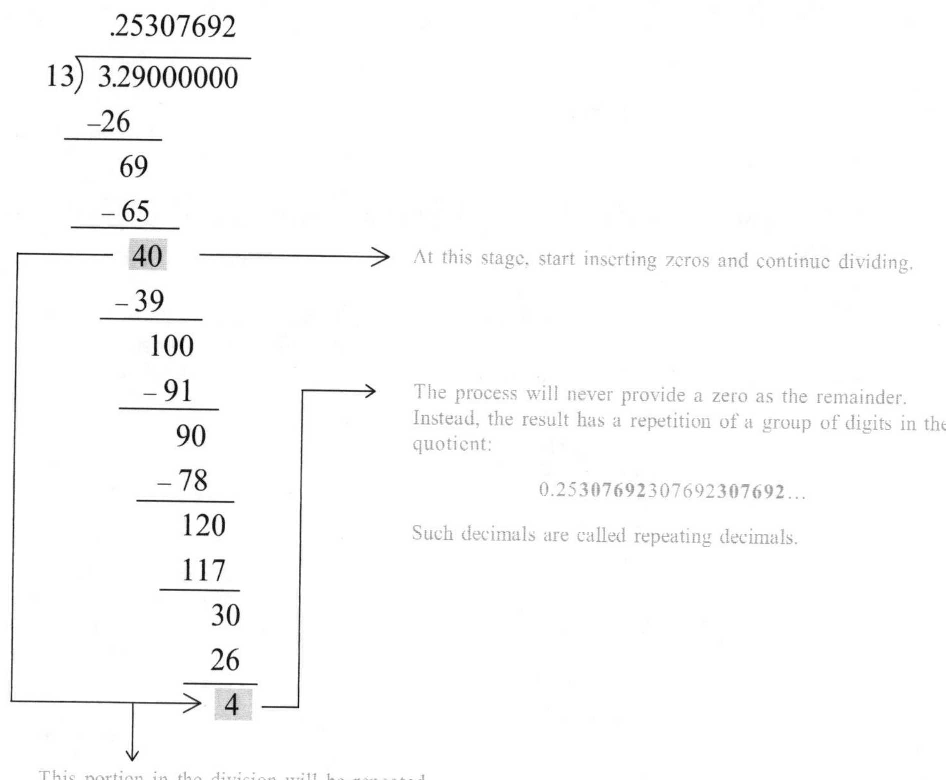

Such decimals can be written in a compact form by grouping the digits that repeat. For example, the above decimal is written as:

$0.25\overline{307692}$

The bar written above the group of digits, 307692, indicates that these digits are repeated, in order, endlessly.

- Usually, the quotient is only needed up to a given place. In that case, stop the division process one place value beyond the required place, and then round the decimal number to the place.

$3.29 \div 13 = 0.25\overline{307692}$, therefore

$3.29 \div 13$	$\approx$	0.3	rounded to the nearest tenth;
$3.29 \div 13$	$\approx$	0.25	rounded to the nearest hundredth;
$3.29 \div 13$	$\approx$	0.2531	rounded to the nearest ten-thousandth.

Procedure to divide a decimal by a whole number.

***Step* 1** Use long division. Place the decimal point in the quotient just above the decimal point in the dividend.

***Step* 2** Divide as if both numbers were whole numbers, adding zeros after the decimal point in the dividend when necessary.

***Step* 3** Round to the given place by dividing one place beyond the given place and then rounding. If no rounding place is given, divide until the remainder is zero or until some digits in the quotient repeat.

EXAMPLE 13 Divide:

(a) $6.846 \div 21$ **(b)** $1.664 \div 32$

Solutions **(a) 6.846 ÷ 21**

$$21\overline{)6.846}$$ (decimal point placed above)

- Place the decimal point in the quotient just above the decimal point in the dividend.

$$\begin{array}{r} 0.326 \\ 21\overline{)\,6.846} \\ -63 \\ \hline 54 \\ -42 \\ \hline 126 \\ -126 \\ \hline 0 \end{array}$$

- Divide as whole numbers. The whole number part, that is 6, is less than 21. Write a zero above 6 in the quotient. Include the next digit, 8, in the group to be divided first, and continue dividing.

$6.846 \div 21 = 0.326$

(b) 1.664 ÷ 32

$$32\overline{)1.664}$$ (decimal point placed above)

- Write the decimal point in the quotient just above the decimal in the dividend.

$$\begin{array}{r} 0.052 \\ 32\overline{)\,1.664} \\ -160 \\ \hline 64 \\ -64 \\ \hline 0 \end{array}$$

- Start dividing. The whole number part , 1, is less than 32, so write a zero in the quotient, above the 1. Now consider the group 16. This is also less than 32, so write a zero in the quotient above 6.

  Include the next digit in the group to get 166. Divide 166 by 32, and continue dividing until the remainder is zero.

$1.664 \div 32 = 0.052.$

EXAMPLE 14 Divide and round the quotient to the nearest hundredth.

$68.9 \div 35$

Solution

WARM-UP

13. Divide:

(a) $13.28 \div 64$

(b) $0.48 \div 75$

14. Divide, and round the quotient to the nearest thousandth.

$13.2 \div 7.$

WARM-UP

Answers:

13. (a) 0.2075 (b) 0.0064
14. 1.886

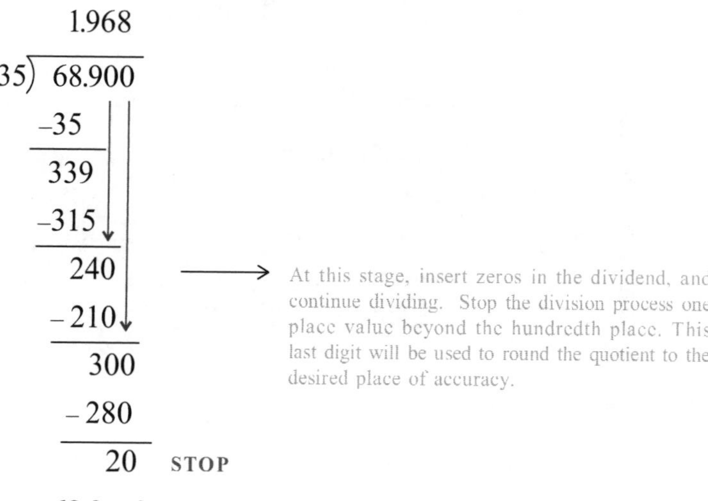

$68.9 \div 35 \approx 1.968 \approx 1.97$ to the nearest hundredth.

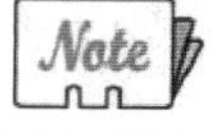

IIf division can continue, it is incorrect to just stop without rounding. The last digit in the answer must be accurate.

Solution to the Application

The tab at a restaurant came to \$132.65 after a 15% tip was added. If there were five diners, how much did each pay in order to split the bill, including tip, equally?

Solution: Amount per diner = \$132.65 ÷ 5 = \$26.53

Amount each paid \$26.53

F. DIVIDING DECIMALS BY DECIMALS

➜ **Divide a decimal by a Decimals.**

Application

William travels 789.6 miles in 16.37 hours. What is his average speed to the nearest tenth of a mile per hour?

Use the formula: $\text{speed} = \dfrac{\text{distance}}{\text{time}}$

Verify Skill

Objective 6.2 F

Find the quotient $7.2 \div 0.23$ to the nearest hundredth.

Illustration

Find the quotient $2.375 \div 0.75$, rounded to the nearest tenth

$$\frac{2.375}{0.75} = \frac{237.5}{75}$$

$$\begin{array}{r} 3.16 \\ 75\overline{)\,237.50} \\ \underline{-225} \\ 125 \\ \underline{-75} \\ 500 \\ \underline{-450} \\ 50 \end{array}$$

→ **Stop** after obtaining the digit in the hundredths place needed to round the quotient to tenths place.

$2.375 \div 0.75 \approx 3.16 \approx 3.2$ to the nearest tenth.

Verify Skill

If your answer to this question is the same as given below then you may skip this objective.

Answer: 31.30

Discussion

Consider the division:

$$2.53 \div 1.2 = \frac{2.53}{1.2} = \frac{2.53}{1.2} \times \frac{10}{10}$$

Note this step. The divisor has one decimal place, so multiply by $\frac{10}{10}$.

$$= \frac{2.5.3}{1.2.}$$

To multiply by 10 means move the decimal point to the right by one place.

 **Observe that :**

1. Multiplication by $\frac{10}{10}$ is equivalent to multiplication by 1, therefore it does not change the division.

2. Multiplication by $\frac{10}{10}$ is equivalent to shifting the decimal point by one digit to the right in both the dividend and the divisor.

3. Shifting the decimal by one digit to the right in both the dividend and the divisor changes the divisor to a whole number.

4. If the divisor is whole number, we can perform division as in the previous discussion.

$$\frac{2.53}{1.2} = \frac{2.5.3}{1.2.}$$

Similarly:

$$\frac{15.753}{2.54} = \frac{15.753}{2.54} \times \frac{100}{100}$$

→ The divisor has **two** decimal places, so multiply by $\frac{100}{100}$.

$$= \frac{15.75.3}{2.54.} = \frac{1575.3}{254}$$

→ Shift the decimal two places to the right.

$$\frac{1.7354}{.034} = \frac{1.7354}{.034} \times \frac{1000}{1000}$$ ⟶ Divisor has **three** decimal places, so we multiply by $\frac{1000}{1000}$

$$= \frac{1.735.4}{.034.} = \frac{1735.4}{34}$$ ⟶ Shift the decimal by three places to the right.

To change the divisor to a whole number, shift the decimal points in both the divisor and the dividend to the right as many places as is necessary to make the divisor a whole number.

For example:

$$\frac{47.375}{3.82} = \frac{4737.5}{382}$$

$$\frac{23.45}{.043} = \frac{23450}{43}$$

In each of the above examples, to divide a decimal by another decimal, we first changed the divisor to a whole number by shifting the decimal point in both the divisor and the dividend by the number of decimal places in the divisor.

Procedure to divide a number by a decimal.

***Step* 1** Change the divisor to a whole number by shifting the decimal point in both the divisor and the dividend. Place the decimal point in the quotient directly above its final position in the dividend.

***Step* 2** Divide the resulting numbers.

WARM-UP

15. Find quotient to the nearest tenth.

(a) 0.05677 ÷ 0.007

(b) 42.679 ÷ 5.45

EXAMPLE 15 Find the quotient:

(a) 2.4 ÷ 1.2 **(b)** 91.586 ÷ 3.62 **(c)** 9158.6 ÷ 0.362

Solutions

(a) $\frac{2.4.}{1.2.} = \frac{24}{12} = 2$

(b) $3.62\overline{)91.586} = 362.\overline{)9158.6}$

$$= 362\overline{)9158.6}$$ quotient 25.3

```
       25.3
362 ) 9158.6
     - 724
       1918
      -1810
       1086
      -1086
          0
```

91.586 ÷ 3.62 = 25.3

(c) $0.362\overline{)9158.6} = 0\,362.\overline{)9158\ 600.}$

$$\begin{array}{r} 25300 \\ = 362\overline{)\ 9158600} \\ -724 \\ \hline 1918 \\ -1810 \\ \hline 1086 \\ -1086 \\ \hline 000 \end{array}$$

$9158.6 \div 0.362 = 25{,}300$

EXAMPLE 16 Divide, and round the quotient to the nearest hundredth.

$0.08919 \div 0.0046$

Solution $0.0046\overline{)0.08919}$

$00046.\overline{)00891.9}$

$$\begin{array}{r} 19.389 \\ 46\overline{)\ 891.900} \\ -46 \\ \hline 431 \\ -414 \\ \hline 179 \\ -138 \\ \hline 410 \\ -368 \\ \hline 420 \\ -414 \\ \hline 6 \end{array}$$

Divide the resulting numbers.

Start inserting zeros in the dividend.

Stop: The quotient is needed only to the thousandths place.

$0.08919 \div 0.0046 \approx 19.389$

≈ 19.39 to the nearest hundredth.

EXAMPLE 17 Verify the answer in example 4 with a calculator.

Solution

ENTER .08919 [÷] .0046 followed by [=] or [ENTER]

The reslt should be approximately 19.38913

$0.08919 \div 0.0046 \approx 19.38913$,

≈ 19.39 to the nearest hundredth.

WARM-UP

(c) $2517.9 \div 0.125$

16. Divide, and round the quotient to the nearest tenths.

$4.753 \div 1.24$

17. Verify the answer in exercise 4 with calculator.

Answers:

15. (a) 8.1 **(b)** 7.8 **(c)** 20143.2

16. 3.8 **17.** 3.8

Solution to the Application

William travels 789.6 miles in 16.37 hours. What is his average speed to the nearest tenth of a mile per hour. Speed = $\dfrac{\text{Distance}}{\text{Time}}$

Solution:

$$x = \frac{789.6}{16.37}$$

$$\frac{789.60.}{16.37.} = \frac{78960}{1637}$$

$$x = 48.23$$

```
              48.23
16.37.)789.60.00
      -6548
       13480  ——> Insert zeros in the dividend at this stage.
      -13096
         3840
        -3274
          5660  Stop, since the quotient is to be rounded
         -4911  to the nearest tenth.
           749
```

Average speed ≈ 48.23 ≈ 48.2 to the nearest tenth of a mile per hour.

Hence, William's average speed is 48.2 mph.

G. Estimate Products and Quotients(/-)

➡ Estimating Products and Quotients

- **Estimating a Product**

It is very important to have an estimate of the product or quotient in mind before actually performing multiplication or division. The estimate can be used to keep a check on placing the decimal point in the product and in the quotient. To estimate a product, **front end round each number using the first non-zero digit and then multiply using these rounded numbers.** For example, let us first estimate and then compute the actual product (0.463) (7.2):

Estimate

```
0.463 ≈  0.5
  7.2 ≈ × 7
        ----
         3.5  ——> Estimate.
```

Actual Product

```
   0.463
  × 7.2
  ------
     926  } Multiply ignoring
   32410  } the decimal points.
  ------
  3.3336  ——> The actual product.
```

The estimated product 3.5 helps us place the decimal point correctly in the product 3.3336. Thus, an answer of 33.336 or 0.33336 would indicate an error in the placement of the decimal point, since the answer should be close to 3.5 (or between 3 and 4).

Note: Estimates in multiplication/division are not always as close as they are in addition or subtraction. A small change in rounding can make a big change in the estimate.

Procedure to estimate a product involving decimals

Step 1 Front-end round each factor using the first non-zero digit.

Step 2 Multiply the rounded factors.

EXAMPLE 18 First estimate the product and then find the actual product on a calculator.

(a) (2.579) (4.978) **(b)** 421×0.0542

(c) (–0.008956) (201.67)

Solutions

(a) **(2.579) (4.978)**

i) ***Estimate:***

Step 1 **2**.579 ≈ 3.0 or **3**

↑

4.978 ≈ 5.0 or **5**

↑

Step 2 The estimate of the product (2.579) (4.978) is $3 \times 5 = 15$.

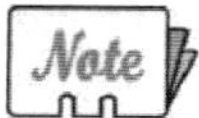

This is a high estimate, since both factors were rounded up. But it serves our purpose for placement of the decimal in the actual product.

ii) ***Actual Product:*** (2.579) (4.978) = 12.838262

The actual product, 12.838262, is close to 15.

(b) **421 × 0.0542**

i) ***Estimate:***

421 ≈ 400 • Front-end round each factor.

↑

0.0542 ≈ 0.05

↑

$421 \times 0.0542 \approx 400 \times 0.05 = 20$ • Multiply: 400 × 0.05 = 20.00

The estimate of the product is 20.

ii) ***The Actual Product:*** $421 \times 0.0542 =$ **22.8182**.

22.8182 is close to 20.

(c) **(–0.008956)(201.67)**

***Estimate*:**

–0.00**8**956 ≈ – .009

201.67 ≈ 200

Estimate = –1.800

The actual product is –1.80615652.

WARM-UP

18. First estimate the product and then find the actual product on a calculator.

(a) 5.973×3.45

(b) 0.128×0.036

(c) (–0.00078234)(4907.72)

- **Estimating a Quotient**

Estimating a quotient of rational numbers in decimal form is similar to estimating a quotient of integers. No rounding is necessary in finding a good estimate.

To estimate a quotient, carefully position the decimal point in the quotient. Locate and place the first non-zero digit in the quotient. Enter zeros for any remaining places between the digit and the decimal point.

Estimate the quotient $2.055 \div 0.047$.

- Move the decimal point in the divisor and the dividend to make the divisor a whole number.

$$\frac{2.055}{0.047} = \frac{2055.}{047.} = \frac{2055.}{47}$$

- Position the decimal point in the quotient.

$$47\overline{)2055.}$$

- Divide and identify the first non-zero digit of the quotient.

$$\begin{array}{r} 4\;\;. \\ 47\overline{)2055.} \end{array}$$

- Insert zeros between the digit in the quotient and the decimal point

$$\begin{array}{r} 40. \\ 47\overline{)2055.} \end{array}$$ ← Estimate of the quotients.

- The quotient thus obtained is the estimate.

  Thus, $2.055 \div 0.047 \approx 40$.

- The exact value is 43.7234, which is quite close to the estimate.

The process discussed in this illustration leads us to the following procedure.

Procedure to estimate a quotient involving decimals:

***Step* 1** Move the decimal point in the divisor and the dividend to make the divisor a whole number.

***Step* 2** Position the decimal in the quotient

***Step* 3** Divide and identify the first non-zero digit of the quotient and its correct place.

***Step* 4** Insert zeros between that digit and the decimal point.

WARM-UP

19. Estimate the quotient. Compare to the actual quotients.

(a) $0.031765 \div 8.36$

EXAMPLE 19 Estimate the quotient. Compare to the actual quotients.

(a) $-0.00284 \div 9.12$ **(b)** $2.0863 \div 0.193$

Solution

(a)

$$9.12\overline{)-0.00284} \longrightarrow 912\overline{)-0.2840}$$ quotient estimate -0.0003

Position the decimal point in the quotient. The first digit in the quotient is 3, which is positioned above the 0 in the dividend. Zeros are inserted in the three places in the quotient between the decimal point and the digit 3. The estimate is -0.0003.

The actual quotient is obtained with calculator.

ENTER [(−)] [.00284] [÷] [9.12] [=] **−0.000311404**

The estimate, -0.0003, is very close to the actual quotient -0.000311404.

Position the decimal point in the quotient. Dividing 193 into 208 give us 1 in the quotient placed above 8 in the dividend. Insert zero between 1 and the decimal point. The estimate, 10, is very close to the actual quotient 10.80984.

WARM-UP

(b) 5.47123÷0.349

Answers:

17. (a) −0.0274 **(b)** 21900 **(b)** 0.0124
18. (a) 18 ; 20.60685 **(b)** 0.004 ; 0.004608
(c) −4.0; −3.8393093
19. (a) 0.004 ; 0.0037996
(b) 10 ; 15.676876

EXERCISE 6.2

In exercises 1-15, add the given decimals.

1. 24.4 + 16.6 + 8.7 **2.** 1.2 + 2.3 + 5 **3.** 2.5 + 4.8

4. 0.2 + 1 + 2.4 **5.** 14.7 + 8.1 + 9.7 **6.** 3.05 + 12.86 + 17.29

7. 17.005 + 23.067 + 5.108 **8.** 123.043 + 72.006 + 9.104 **9.** 0.125 + 0.813 + 0.061

10.
```
712.650
 45.304
168.512
```

11.
```
 3.410
 6.3975
23.251
```

12.
```
 1.4003
13.5
27.251
 0.0042
```

13.
```
28.92
 3.49
45.788
36.066
```

14.
```
41.8
39.24
 5.01
62.67
```

15.
```
 68.39 lb
141.45 lb
 87.3  lb
213.09 lb
```

In exercises 16-18, add the given numbers on a calculator.

16. 441.03 + 2.59 + 73.123 + 0.9925 **17.** 13.715 + 25.25 + 75.025 + 105.05 **18.** 18.624 + 0.0116 + 3.410 + 6.3975

In exercises 19-37, find the difference.

19. 85.294 − 36.079 **20.** 27.476 − 17.376 **21.** 7.9367 − 1.7347 **22.** 765.32 − 204.96 **23.** 75.755 − 5.650

24. 19 – 7.45 25. 191 – 71.02 26. 8.201 – 7.09 27. 17.946 – 0.37 28. 227 – 75.7429

29. 39 – 15.4 30. 27 – 26.8383 31. 72 – 24.642 32. 603.042 – 246.3

33. 0.3 – 0.135 34. 100 – 73.678 35. 979.84 – 425.69

36. 254.345 – 129.4 37. 4921.475 – 3198.91

38. Subtract 218.765 from 300.

39. Subtract 573.0958 from 1069.75 and round the difference to the nearest hundredth.

40. Solve exercises 19-37 on a calculator and verify your answers.

In exercises 41-49, estimate the answer by rounding each number to a whole number.

41. The sum of 25.791, 40.003, and 107.49.

42. The sum of $79.82, $26.7, and $ 43.39.

43. The difference of 2759.543 and 874.099.

44. The difference of 678.499 and 57.61009.

45. The difference of 47.0987 lb and 23.601 lb.

46. 2.79 + 19.23 + 15.8 47. 77.9 + 18.42 – 9.89 48. 1099.9 + 2154.23 – 819.72 49. 1999,999.84 – 70.9

Applications

50. Subtract the difference of 111.051 and 72.63 from the sum of 135.065 and 205.

51. Add the difference of 2.0593 and 0.655 to the difference of 0.555 and 0.55.

52. Maurice goes shopping with $117 in his pocket. He pays $27.15 for a shirt, $53.75 for a jacket and $1.65 for candy bars. How much cash does he have left?

53. Mrs. Berg writes three checks in the amount of $43.95, $125.73, and $89.68. She has $315 in her checking account. Does she have enough money to cover the three checks?

54. George has a gross income, before deductions, of $1975 per month. He has the following monthly deductions: health insurance $75.50; union dues $28; retirement contribution $65.37; and income tax $197.50. Find his actual take home pay.

In exercises 55-94, find the product.

55. 0.2 × 0.4 56. 0.02 × 0.4 57. 0.03 × 0.05 58. 7.3 × 0.2 59. 1.002 × 0.06

60. 3.5 × 0.003 61. 15.4 × 3 62. 4.5 × 0.6 63. 12.35 × 0.03 64. 45.32 × 0.05

65. 14.3 × 0.4 66. 2.37 × 0.07 67. 12.54 × 0.8 68. 0.8 × 7 69. 4.9 × 5

70. 0.013 × 0.5 71. 8.3 × 5 72. 27.14 × 0.06 73. 0.016 × 0.03 74. 0.2 × 24.5

75. 0.2 × 0.3 × 0.8 76. 1.2 × 0.4 × 0.07 77. 12.4 × 0.03 × 0.2 78. 4.9 × 0.4 × 0.3

79. 0.5 × 0.3 × 7.25 80. 1.6 × 0.7 × 1.1 81. 2.8 × 0.11 × 0.03 82. 11.23 × 0.5 × 1.1

83. 0.4 × 47.13 × 0.8 **84.** 8.3 × 5 × 0.6 **85.** 2.4 × 5 × 0.3 **86.** 13.4 × 3 × 1.2

87. 0.4 × 2.37 × 0.6 **88.** 0.145 × 4 × 0.7 **89.** 25.3 × 0.4 × 0.11 **90.** 7.5 × 1.1 × 0.5

91. 0.7 × 1.5 × 0.4 **92.** 39.2 × 0.2 × 0.5 **93.** 0.002 × 0.03 × 0.8 **94.** 4.25 × 0.003 × 0.02

In exercises 95-106, multiply.

95. $\begin{array}{r} 36.8 \\ \times 5.7 \\ \hline \end{array}$ **96.** $\begin{array}{r} 0.456 \\ \times 0.23 \\ \hline \end{array}$ **97.** $\begin{array}{r} 34.5 \\ \times 0.37 \\ \hline \end{array}$ **98.** $\begin{array}{r} 28.65 \\ \times 25 \\ \hline \end{array}$ **99.** $\begin{array}{r} 4739 \\ \times 0.27 \\ \hline \end{array}$ **100.** $\begin{array}{r} 3.207 \\ \times 29 \\ \hline \end{array}$

101. $\begin{array}{r} 6.23 \\ \times 1.7 \\ \hline \end{array}$ **102.** $\begin{array}{r} 4.01 \\ \times 2.02 \\ \hline \end{array}$ **103.** $\begin{array}{r} 14.25 \\ \times 6.4 \\ \hline \end{array}$ **104.** $\begin{array}{r} 6.04 \\ \times 5.05 \\ \hline \end{array}$ **105.** $\begin{array}{r} 9.423 \\ \times 1.1 \\ \hline \end{array}$ **106.** $\begin{array}{r} 8.43 \\ \times 2.7 \\ \hline \end{array}$

 **107.** Multiply the numbers in exercises 95-106 on a calculator, and verify your answer.

In exercises 108-127, divide.

108. 6.8 ÷ 4 **109.** 3.2 ÷ 2 **110.** 72.5 ÷ 5 **111.** 4.8 ÷ 12 **112.** 51.6 ÷ 24

113. 34.56 ÷ 3 **114.** 14.1 ÷ 3 **115.** 3.62 ÷ 8 **116.** 12.35 ÷ 5 **117.** 46.816 ÷ 11

118. 23.52 ÷ 6 **119.** 1.305 ÷ 9 **120.** 121.8 ÷ 7 **121.** 21.6 ÷ 12 **122.** 1.384 ÷ 4

123. $5\overline{)0.4325}$ **124.** $12\overline{)1.524}$ **125.** $11\overline{)37.84}$ **126.** $7\overline{)91.28}$ **127.** $12\overline{)36.9}$

In exercises 128-147, divide and round the quotient to the nearest hundredth.

128. 35.836 ÷ 62 **129.** 25.24 ÷ 12 **130.** 29.47 ÷ 11 **131.** 19.524 ÷ 12

132. 3.564 ÷ 11 **133.** 29.064 ÷ 21 **134.** 0.6446 ÷ 22 **135.** 32.07 ÷ 15

136. 60.176 ÷ 16 **137.** 57.365 ÷ 11 **138.** 1.575 ÷ 21 **139.** 33.8 ÷ 25

140. 128.01 ÷ 30 **141.** 27.04 ÷ 20 **142.** 4.96 ÷ 40 **143.** 187.75 ÷ 50

144. 58.32 ÷ 24 **145.** 212.49 ÷ 31 **146.** 1562.3 ÷ 125 **147.** $34\overline{)375.42}$

In exercises 148-162, find the quotient.

148. 316.96 ÷ 2.8 **149.** 21.04 ÷ 0.4 **150.** 27.12 ÷ 0.06 **151.** 29.82 ÷ 0.006

152. 0.31696 ÷ 0.0002 **153.** 0.2 ÷ .0005 **154.** 6.3 ÷ 0.007 **155.** 0.81 ÷ 0.9

156. 0.5625 ÷ 1.5 **157.** 35.08 ÷ 0.04 **158.** 189.32 ÷ 0.8 **159.** 0.0025 ÷ 0.004

160. 0.0144 ÷ 0.00012 **161.** 72.548 ÷ 0.4 **162.** 0.0001 ÷ 0.04

In exercises 163-172, divide using a calculator and round the quotient to the nearest hundredths.

163. $0.035\overline{)2.567}$ **164.** $7.8\overline{)0.14369}$ **165.** $5.2\overline{)64.319}$ **166.** $0.07\overline{)149.3}$ **167.** $13.5\overline{)0.8}$

168. 0.06221 ÷ 0.0013 **169.** 63.04 ÷ 0.017 **170.** 0.166313 ÷ 0.023 **171.** 20.7375 ÷ .0056 **172.** 8.0376 ÷ 0.7

173. Divide the numbers in Exercises 108-162 on *calculator*, and verify your answers.

In exercises 174-183, find the quotient accurate to the given place.

174. $0.02 \div 1.1$; hundredths **175.** $3.05 \div 0.9$; hundredths **176.** $14.23 \div 0.06$; tenths **177.** $785.87 \div 0.11$; ones

178. $5.63 \div 2.2$; tenths **179.** $35.719 \div 0.33$; ones **180.** $2.354 \div 1.4$; tenths **181.** $0.011 \div 6$; thousandths

182. $234.17 \div 0.3$; ones **183.** $45.6782 \div .03$; tens

Applications

184. What is the cost per ounce of a 12 ounce package of potato chips that costs $2.16?

185. Robin travels 75.34 miles on a bicycle in 8.6 hours. What is his average speed to the nearest tenth?

186. A 613.5 yard long cloth is to be divided into pieces, each measuring 2.15 yards in length. How many pieces can be obtained measuring the exact length? How much cloth is wasted?

187. What is the approximate weight of one box of apples if 68 such boxes weigh 1479.68 pounds?

188. Ohm's law is given by the formula $E = I R$ where E is the voltage (number of volts), I is the current (number of amperes), and R is the resistance (number of ohms). What is the resistance, to the nearest thousandth, if the voltage is 220 volts, and the current is 7.85 amperes?

In exercises 189-222, first estimate the product or quotient, then compute the actual product or quotient on a calculator.

189. 5.414×2.8 **190.** 8.28×7.12 **191.** 6.07×21.52 **192.** 7.05×145 **193.** 67.3×42.44

194. 0.64×9.71 **195.** 34.6×3.577 **196.** $0.03\overline{)6.275}$ **197.** $0.3\overline{)0.6275}$ **198.** $3.1\overline{)0.0636}$

199. $3.6\overline{)282.4}$ **200.** $3.1\overline{)6.36}$ **201.** $18.2\overline{)132.9}$ **202.** $3.8\overline{)0.0676}$ **203.** 8.2×9.75

204. 1.62×0.03 **205.** $0.1\overline{)211.5}$ **206.** $162(-0.03)$ **207.** $17.3 \times (-0.67)$ **208.** -19.4×0.897

209. $15.6 \div (-0.78)$ **210.** $0.08\overline{)18.346}$ **211.** $-13.8 \times (-7.91)$ **212.** $-16.8 \div (-0.79)$ **213.** $1.2\overline{)0.985}$

214. $-18.7 \times (9.67)$ **215.** $-21.7 \times (-19.79)$ **216.** $23.8 \times (-14.567)$ **217.** $2.89\overline{)0.0867}$ **218.** $-31.7 \div (-1.98)$

219. $28.8 \times (-0.0094)$ **220.** $-35.8 \times (-0.0379)$ **221.** $-34.8 \div (-4.879)$ **222.** $11.65\overline{)34.569}$

6.3 Fractions to Decimals, Compare Decimals

Vocabulary

Objectives

After completing this section you will be able to:

A. Converting Decimals to Fractions;

B. Listing Decimals in Order.

1. Decimals having the same number of decimal places are called **like decimals**. 426.05 and 1.37 are like decimals.
2. Decimals having different numbers of decimal places are called **unlike decimals**. 3.2, 5.03, 7.609 are unlike decimals.
3. Decimals are either **exact** or **approximate**. For example, decimals that count money are usually exact. The figure $375.50 shows an exact amount.

   Decimals that represent measurements generally give approximations of measurements. For example, 40.6 m represents a length measured to the nearest tenth.
4. Like whole numbers, decimals can also be **rounded** to any required place value. 25.7469 rounded to the nearest hundredth is 25.75.

   ↑ approximately equal to.
5. Decimals which have a last non-zero digit are called **terminating decimals**. 3.5 and 0.724 are terminating decimals.
6. Decimals which are not terminating and have a series of repeating digits are called **repeating decimals**.

   3.222... and 4.2876876876... are repeating decimals. Since we cannot write the representation down completely, we use a bar to indicate the digits that repeat. Thus,

   3.222... = $3.\overline{2}$ and 4.2876876876... = $4.2\overline{876}$
7. Terminating and repeating decimals are each equivalent to some fraction and are called **rational numbers**.
8. Decimals which do not repeat and do not terminate are called **irrational numbers**. 1.01001000100001... is an irrational number.

(A.) Converting Decimals to Fractions

➜ **Change a decimal to a fraction or mixed number.**

Application

A machine manual notes that the size of a bolt head is 0.375 inches. A mechanic needs to remove the bolt, but her wrenches are labeled in fractions of an inch. What size wrench will she need to remove the bolt?

Verify Skill

Objective 6.3 A

Write the following decimals as fractions or mixed numbers.

(a) 45.42 **(b)** 0.325

If your answers to these questions are the same as given below, then you may skip this objective.

Answers: **(a)** $45\frac{21}{50}$ **(b)** $\frac{13}{40}$

Illustrations

- $0.24 = \frac{24}{100} = \frac{6}{25}$
- $37.5 = 37\frac{5}{10} = 37\frac{1}{2}$

Discussion

Recall: 0.25 is read as "twenty-five hundredths."

$$0.25 = \frac{25}{100}$$

→ The number without the decimal point.
→ 1 followed by 2 zeros since there are 2 decimal places.

0.025 is read as "twenty-five thousandths".

$$0.025 = \frac{25}{1000}$$

→ The number without the decimal point.
→ 1 followed by 3 zeros, since there are 3 decimal places.

23.15 is read as "twenty three and fifteen hundredths.

$$23.15 = \frac{2315}{100}$$

Thus

$$23.15 = 23\frac{15}{100}$$

→ The decimal part without the decimal point.
→ 1 followed by 2 zeros, since there are 2 decimal places.
→ The whole number part.

Procedure to change a decimal to a fraction.

***Step* 1** If there is a whole number part, retain it.

***Step* 2** Drop the decimal point and write the decimal part as the numerator of the fraction.

***Step* 3** Write the denominator as 1 followed by zeros. The number of zeros written is equivalent to the number of decimal places in the decimal.

***Step* 4** Simplify the resulting fraction, if possible.

WARM-UP

1. Convert the given decimals to fractions or mixed numbers.

(a) 0.35

EXAMPLE 1 Change the given decimals to fractions or mixed numbers.

(a) 0.365 **(b)** 21.14

Solutions

(a) $0.365 = \frac{365}{1000}$

$= \frac{73}{200}$

- Drop the decimal point. The numerator is 365.
- There are three decimal places, so the denominator is 1000.
- Simplify the fraction.

(b) 21.14 $= 21 + 0.14$ • Retain the whole number portion.

$= 21 + \frac{14}{100}$ • Drop the decimal point. The numerator is 14.

$= 21\frac{14}{100}$ • There are two decimal places, so the denominator is 100.

$= 21\frac{7 \cdot \cancel{2}}{50 \cdot \cancel{2}} = 21\frac{7}{50}$

(b) 421.6

2. Convert the given decimal to a fraction or mixed numbers: 0.0035

EXAMPLE 2 Convert the given decimal to a fraction or mixed number: 0.045

Solution $0.045 = \frac{45}{1000}$ • The numerator is 45, and the denominator is 1000 since there are three decimal places.

$= \frac{9}{200}$ • Simplify the fraction.

Answers:

1. (a) $\frac{7}{20}$ (b) $421\frac{3}{5}$ 2. $\frac{7}{2000}$

Solution to the Application:

A machine manual notes that the size of a bolt head is 0.375 inches. A mechanic needs to remove the bolt, but her wrenches are labeled in fractions of an inch. What size wrench will she need to remove the bolt?

Solution: To determine the size as a fraction, it is necessary to convert 0.375 to a fraction.

$0.375 = \frac{375}{1000}$ The denominator has three zeros since there are three decimal places.

$= \frac{3 \cdot \cancel{125}}{8 \cdot \cancel{125}} = \frac{3}{8}$

Thus, the mechanic needs a $\frac{3}{8}$ inch wrench to remove the bolt.

➜ **Change fractions to decimals.**

Application 

Jacob's teacher asks him to draw the following figure in his note book. His ruler is marked in tenths.

Change all the measurements to tenths so that he may draw a figure with the best estimates.

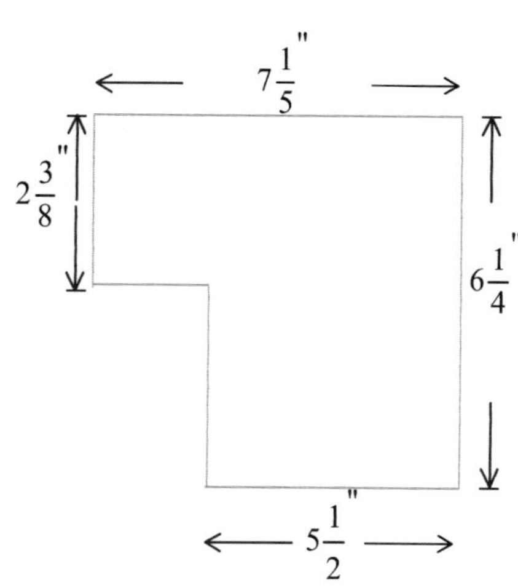

Illustrations

- To express $\frac{21}{4}$ as a decimal:

$\frac{21}{4} = 21 \div 4 = 5.25$

$$\begin{array}{r} 5.25 \\ 4\overline{)21.0} \\ \underline{20} \\ 10 \\ \underline{8} \\ 20 \\ \underline{20} \\ 0 \end{array}$$

Verify Skill

Objective 6.3 A

Express as decimals

(a) $\frac{31}{16}$ **(b)** $\frac{7}{12}$

If your answers to these questions are the same as given below, then you may skip this objective.

Answers:

(a) 1.9375 **(b)** $0.5\overline{83}$

- To express $\frac{11}{6}$ as a decimal:

$\frac{11}{6} = 1.8\overline{3}$ a repeating decimal

$\frac{11}{6} \approx 1.8$ to the nearest tenth

$\frac{11}{6} \approx 1.83$ to the nearest hundredth

$$\begin{array}{r} 1.833 \\ 6\overline{)\,11.000} \\ -6 \\ \hline 50 \\ -48 \\ \hline 20 \\ -18 \\ \hline 20 \\ -18 \\ \hline \leftarrow 2 \end{array}$$

Discussion

To convert a fraction to a decimal, divide the numerator by the denominator. For fractions whose denominators have only 2 or 5 as prime factors, the division process terminates at some stage. In these cases, we keep adding zeros after the decimal point until the remainder is 0.

$\frac{14}{25} = 0.56$

because

$$\begin{array}{r} 0.56 \\ 25\overline{)\,14.00} \\ -12\,5 \\ \hline 1\,50 \\ -1\,50 \\ \hline 0 \end{array}$$

$\frac{51}{16} = 3.1875$

because

$$\begin{array}{r} 3.1875 \\ 16\overline{)\,51.0000} \\ -48 \\ \hline 30 \\ -16 \\ \hline 140 \\ -128 \\ \hline 120 \\ -112 \\ \hline 80 \\ -80 \\ \hline 0 \end{array}$$

For fractions whose denominators have prime factors other than 2 or 5, the division process does not end, and the remainder is never zero. In these cases, we keep adding zeros after the decimal point until we either find the digits that repeat or, more commonly, until one place beyond the desired rounding place.

To convert $\frac{5}{3}$ to an exact decimal, we divide and find:

$\frac{5}{3} = 1.6666... = 1.\overline{6}$ ⟶ The bar means the 6 is repeated.

To convert $\frac{23}{7}$ to a decimal accurate to the hundredths, we divide to the thousandths and find that

$\frac{23}{7} = 3.285 \approx 3.29$

- There are two ways to change a mixed number to a decimal. One method is to change the fraction part to a decimal and then attach the fraction to the whole number part of the fraction. The other method is to change the mixed number to an improper fraction and then divide. To change $15\frac{3}{5}$ to a decimal, use either of the following two methods.

***Method* 1**

$\frac{3}{5} = 3 \div 5 = 0.6$

So, $15\frac{3}{5} = 15 + \frac{3}{5} = 15 + 0.6 = 15.6$

***Method* 2**

$15\frac{3}{5} = \frac{78}{5}$

$= 78 \div 5$

$= 15.6$

Procedure to change a fraction to a decimal.

***Step* 1** Divide the numerator by the denominator.

***Step* 2** Stop the division process as soon as there are enough decimal places to attain the required accuracy by rounding or to write the answer as a repeating decimal.

Note When asked to round to a specific place, it is only necessary to divide one place *beyond* the specified place.

EXAMPLE 3 Change $\frac{42}{11}$ to a repeating decimal.

Solutions

$$\begin{array}{r} 3.818 \\ 11\overline{)\,42.000} \\ -33 \\ \hline 90 \\ -88 \\ \hline 20 \\ -11 \\ \hline 90 \\ -88 \\ \hline 20 \end{array}$$

- Divide.
- Stop, The remainders 9 and 2 have started repeating.

$\frac{42}{11} = 3.8181... = 3.\overline{81}$ is a repeating decimal.

WARM-UP

3. Write $\frac{23}{6}$ as a repeating decimal.

WARM-UP

4. Find the decimal representation of the given fractions accurate to the nearest hundredth.

(a) $\frac{3}{7}$

(b) $15\frac{2}{3}$

5. Express $\frac{271}{513}$ as a decimal rounded to the nearest thousandth.

Use a calculator

Answers:

3. $3.8\bar{3}$

4. (a) 0.43 (b) 15.67 5. 0.528.

EXAMPLE 4 Find the decimal representation of the given fractions accurate to the nearest hundredth.

(a) $\frac{3}{16}$ (b) $5\frac{6}{13}$

Solutions

(a)

$$\begin{array}{r} 0.187 \\ 16 \overline{)\, 3.000} \\ -16 \\ \hline 140 \\ -128 \\ \hline 120 \\ -112 \\ \hline 8 \end{array}$$

- Divide.
- Stop here, since the requirement is to round the answer to two places only.

$$\frac{3}{16} \approx 0.187 \approx 0.19$$

(b) Convert $5\frac{6}{13}$ to a decimal accurate to the nearest hundredth.

$$\begin{array}{r} 0.461 \\ 13 \overline{)\, 6.000} \\ -52 \\ \hline 80 \\ -78 \\ \hline 20 \\ -13 \\ \hline 7 \end{array}$$

Express $\frac{6}{13}$ as a decimal.

Stop here to round to two places.

$$\frac{6}{13} \approx 0.46$$

$$5\frac{6}{13} \approx 5 + 0.46 = 5.46$$

EXAMPLE 5 Compute $\frac{379}{413}$ to the nearest thousandths.

Solution

ENTER 379 [÷] 413 [=] or [ENTER]

The calculator should display 0.9176755.

$$\frac{379}{413} \approx 0.918 \text{ to the nearest thousandths.}$$

Solution to the Application :

Jacob's teacher asks him to draw the following figure in his note book. His ruler is marked in tenths. Change all the measurements to tenths so that he may draw a figure with the best estimates.

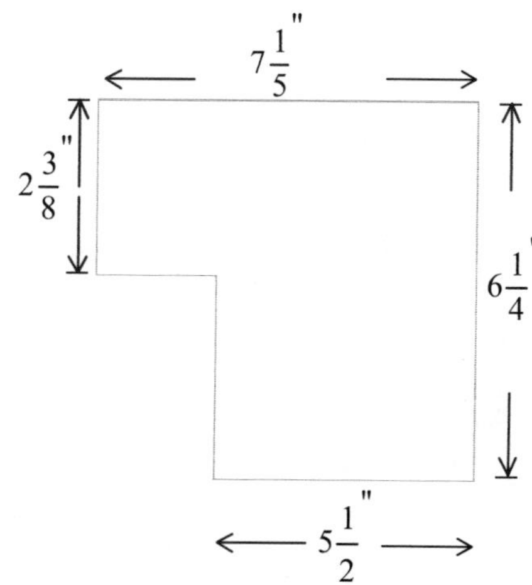

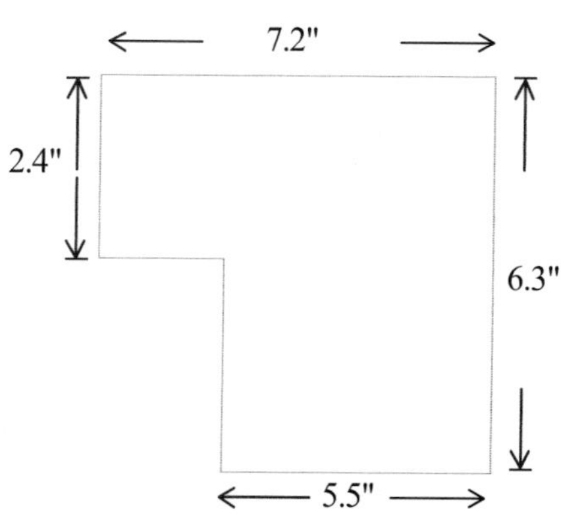

In order for Jacob to use his ruler, each fraction is changed to a decimal rounded to the nearest tenth.

$$7\frac{1}{5} = 7 + \frac{1}{5} = 7 + \frac{2}{10} = 7 + 0.2 = 7.2$$

$$6\frac{1}{4} = 6 + \frac{1}{4} = 6 + \frac{1}{4}\cdot\frac{25}{25} = 6 + \frac{25}{100} = 6 + 0.25 = 6.25 \approx 6.3$$

$$5\frac{1}{2} = 5 + \frac{1}{2} = 5 + \frac{5}{10} = 5 + 0.5 = 5.5$$

$$2\frac{3}{8} = 2 + \frac{3}{8} = 2 + 0.375 = 2.375 \approx 2.4, \text{ because } 3 \div 8 = 0.375$$

B. Listing Decimals in Order

➔ **List decimals in ascending or descending order.**

Applications

A two liter bottle of soda costs \$2.39. Roberto has \$2.64. Does he have enough to buy the soda?

Illustration

To list 0.89, 1.23, and 0.109 in ascending order, convert the decimals to like decimals, then compare the like decimals

0.890, 1.230, and 0.109.

Since $109 < 890 < 1230$,

$0.109 < 0.89 < 1.23$

Therefore, the desired list is 0.109, 0.89, 1.23.

> **Verify Skill**
>
> **Objective 6.3 B**
>
> List the decimals 12.05, 1.205, 120.5, and 12.5 in descending order.
>
> **If your answer to this question is the same as given below, then you may skip this objective.**
>
> **Answer:** 120.5, 12.5, 12.05, 1.205

Discussion

- Comparing like decimals (decimals having the same number of decimal places) can be easily done by ignoring the decimal points and comparing the resulting numbers.

  Thus, to compare 8.67 and 9.34

  First compare 867 and 934. Since $867 < 934$,

  $8.67 < 9.34$

  The reason the decimal points can be ignored in this case is because the fractional forms of like decimals have common denominators and, when comparing fractions with common denominators, it is sufficient to compare only numerators.

  Since $8.67 = \frac{867}{100}$ and $9.34 = \frac{934}{100}$, to compare $\frac{867}{100}$ and $\frac{934}{100}$ it suffices to compare the numerators: 867 and 934

  In general, **to compare like decimals, compare the whole numbers obtained by dropping the decimal point.**

- To list three or more like decimals in ascending or descending order, proceed in a similar manner.

  Thus, to list 13.75, 6.93, and 12.96 in ascending order, list the whole numbers 1375, 693 and 1296 in ascending order.

  Since $693 < 1296 < 1375$, the desired list is 6.93, 12.96, 13.75.

- To compare **unlike decimals** (decimals having an unequal number of decimal places), first convert them to like decimals and then compare. This conversion is based on the fact that the value of a decimal number does not change if zeros are appended to the right of the last decimal place.

  $0.24 = \frac{24}{100} = \frac{24}{100} \cdot \frac{10}{10} = \frac{240}{1000} = 0.240$ Thus, $\mathbf{0.24 = 0.240}$

  $1.6 = \frac{16}{10} = \frac{16}{10} \cdot \frac{100}{100} = \frac{1600}{1000} = 1.600$ Thus, $\mathbf{1.6 = 1.600}$

  $0.05 = \frac{5}{100} = \frac{5}{100} \cdot \frac{10}{10} = \frac{50}{1000} = 0.050$ Thus, $\mathbf{0.05 = 0.050}$

  Observe that attaching zero(s) to the right of the last decimal digit does not change the value of the decimal number.

  Thus, $28.5 = 28.50 = 28.500 = 28.5000$, and so on.

  To convert two or more unlike decimals to like decimals, simply append zero(s) to the right of the decimal parts in order to have the **same** number of decimal places in each decimal. Compare the unlike decimals 0.37 and 0.345. Since 0.345 has three decimal places, first write $0.37 = 0.370$ so that it also has three decimal places. Then compare the like decimals 0.370 and 0.345

  Since, $370 > 345$, $0.370 > 0.345$

  Therefore, $0.37 > 0.345$.

- To list 5.515, 5.15, 55.51, and 55.1 in ascending order, first write each decimal to *three* decimal places, since the maximum number of decimal places in this group is three.

$5.515 = 5.515$

$5.15 = 5.150$ Attach one zero to the right.

$55.51 = 55.510$ Attach one zero to the right.

$55.1 = 55.100$ Attach two zeros to the right.

Since $5150 < 5515 < 55100 < 55510$,

$5.150 < 5.515 < 55.100 < 55.510$

The numbers listed in ascending order are: 5.15, 5.515, 55.1, 55.51.

Procedure to compare two decimals.

***Step* 1** Write the given decimals as like decimals by appending zeros, to the right of the decimal part, if necessary.

***Step* 2** Compare the digit values, starting from the left most, one at a time for each number.

- If they are the same, go to the next place value on the right.
- If they are different, the number with the larger digit value is greater.

***Step* 3** State the comparison without the extra zeros.

EXAMPLE 6 Compare the following decimals to find which number is greater.

(a) 0.627 and 0.62 **(b)** 7.919 and 7.92

Solutions

(a)

$0.62 = 0.620$

- Write the decimals as like decimals.

$0.627 > 0.62\mathbf{0}$

- Compare:

$0.627 > 0.62$

0.627 is greater in the thousandths place.

(b)

$7.92 = 7.920$

- Write each decimal to three decimal places.

$7.919 < 7.920$

- Compare:

$7.919 < 7.92$

7.920 is greater in the hundredths place.

WARM-UP

6. Compare 1.005 and 1.01 to find which number is greater.

Procedure to list a group of decimals in ascending or descending order.

***Step* 1** Write all the decimals in the group as like decimals by appending zeros, to the right of the decimal part, if necessary.

***Step* 2** Compare and list the numbers in the desired order ignoring the decimal point.

***Step* 3** Write the corresponding list dropping extra zeros.

WARM-UP

7. List the numbers in descending order.

   3.5, 3.499, 4.39, 4.09.

EXAMPLE 7 List the numbers in descending order.

2.04, 2.2, 4.02, 2.404

Solution

2.04 = 2.**0**40

2.2 = 2.**2**00

4.02 = 4.020

2.404 = 2.**4**04

- Write all the decimals with three decimal places, the largest number of decimal places in this group.
- 4.020 has the greatest whole part. The other numbers differ at tenths.

$4.020 > 2.404 > 2.200 > 2.040$

The desired list in descending order is
4.02, 2.404, 2.2 and 2.04

- Drop the extra zeros.

8. List the numbers in ascending order.

   2.47, 24.7, 3.049, 0.39

EXAMPLE 8 List the numbers in ascending order.

2.59, 25.9, 3.402, .034

Solution

2.59 = 2.590

25.9 = 25.900

3.402 = 3.402

.034 = 0.034

- Convert to like decimal.

$0.034 < 2.590 < 3.402 < 25.900$

- Compare the numbers.

.034 , 2.59 , 3.402 , 25.9
is the list in ascending order

- List, dropping extra zeros.

Answers:

6. 1.01 is larger
7. 4.39, 4.09, 3.5, 3.499
8. 0.39, 2.47, 3.049, 24.7

Solution to the Application:

A two liter bottle of soda costs $2.39. Roberto has $2.64. Does he have enough to buy the soda?

Solution: First, compare 2.39 and 2.64. The first place these numbers differ is in the tenths place. Since $3 < 6$, $2.39 < 2.64$. Thus, Roberto has more than enough money to buy the soda.

EXERCISE 6.3

In exercises 1-16, change the decimal to a fraction of mixed number.

1. 12.075	**2.** 0.15	**3.** 17.28	**4.** 0.125	**5.** 0.0125	**6.** 1256.003
7. 6.736	**8.** 7.305	**9.** 0.007	**10.** 542.0008	**11.** 67.034	**12.** 15.135
13. 0.95	**14.** 417.15	**15.** 0.004	**16.** 1040.004		

In exercises 17-31, express the fraction as an exact decimal. (Without using calculator)

17. $\frac{27}{40}$	**18.** $\frac{11}{5}$	**19.** $\frac{1}{2}$	**20.** $\frac{17}{2}$	**21.** $\frac{21}{4}$
22. $\frac{32}{5}$	**23.** $\frac{234}{10}$	**24.** $\frac{7}{100}$	**25.** $\frac{21}{8}$	**26.** $\frac{5}{8}$

27. $\frac{1}{32}$ 28. $\frac{234}{16}$ 29. $\frac{27}{25}$ 30. $\frac{17}{20}$ 31. $\frac{21}{75}$

In exercises 32-46, express as a decimal to the nearest tenth.

32. $\frac{105}{128}$ 33. $\frac{19}{25}$ 34. $\frac{27}{25}$ 35. $\frac{75}{14}$ 36. $\frac{143}{40}$

37. $\frac{984}{16}$ 38. $\frac{463}{21}$ 39. $\frac{179}{8}$ 40. $\frac{39}{40}$ 41. $\frac{93}{125}$

42. $\frac{566}{11}$ 43. $\frac{287}{135}$ 44. $\frac{79}{12}$ 45. $\frac{55}{24}$ 46. $\frac{265}{30}$

In exercises 47-61, change the given fraction or mixed number to a decimal and identify whether it is a terminating or a repeating decimal.

47. $\frac{8}{15}$ 48. $\frac{11}{16}$ 49. $4\frac{37}{50}$ 50. $\frac{5}{16}$ 51. $\frac{14}{15}$

52. $\frac{542}{25}$ 53. $23\frac{5}{7}$ 54. $2\frac{11}{12}$ 55. $16\frac{7}{8}$ 56. $115\frac{9}{4}$

57. $10\frac{5}{24}$ 58. $\frac{22}{3}$ 59. $1\frac{29}{32}$ 60. $\frac{157}{24}$ 61. $3\frac{11}{15}$

In exercises 62-76, change to a decimal. Round as indicated. (Use a calculator wherever necessary).

62. $\frac{2}{9}$, tenths 63. $\frac{24}{11}$; tenths 64. $\frac{5}{11}$; hundredths 65. $\frac{22}{7}$; tenths

66. $\frac{5}{12}$; tenths 67. $13\frac{17}{40}$; tenths 68. $\frac{99}{125}$; hundredths 69. $\frac{32}{35}$; hundredths

70. $\frac{4375}{135}$; thousandths 71. $4\frac{17}{20}$; hundredths 72. $12\frac{8}{9}$; tenths 73. $\frac{135}{42}$; hundredths

74. $\frac{18}{23}$; hundredths 75. $8\frac{7}{15}$; tenths 76. $17\frac{5}{6}$; tenths

In exercises 77-82, write as a decimal accurate to the nearest thousandth. (Use a calculator, wherever necessary).

77. $\frac{73}{192}$ 78. $\frac{1903}{291}$ 79. $\frac{105}{153}$

80. $73\frac{78}{81}$ 81. $\frac{147}{57}$ 82. $15\frac{5}{18}$

Applications

83. Mrs. Brown needs $4\frac{3}{8}$ glasses of milk and $2\frac{1}{5}$ cups of sugar to prepare a sweet dish. What are the decimal equivalents for these two numbers?

84. Annie is asked to draw a line measuring $6\frac{3}{5}$ inches in her note book. Her ruler is marked in tenths. Change the measurement to tenths so she can draw the line measuring the length required.

85. Oliver wants to buy a TV. Two shops offer discounts of $5\frac{7}{8}$ percent and $5\frac{13}{15}$ percent. Convert to decimals to find which offer is better.

86. Ellen needs $\frac{9}{16}$ yard of a fabric. What is the decimal equivalent?

87. George wants to draw a triangle whose sides measure $2\frac{1}{10}$ inches, $3\frac{2}{5}$ inches, and $4\frac{1}{12}$ inches. Change all the measurements to the nearest tenth so he may use a ruler which is marked in tenths of an inch.

In exercises 88-96, compare the given decimals.

88. 21.513 and 21.509

89. 0.432 and 0.48

90. 139.25 and 132.95

91. 65.825 and 65.8247

92. 29.799 and 30.001

93. 3.489 and 3.524

94. 9.378 and 93.78

95. 84.35 and 84.3495

96. 17.3564 and 17.3556

In exercises 97-100, identify whether the statement is True or False.

97. $43.2 > 4.32 > 4.23$

98. $2.91 < 2.807$

99. $103.1023 > 103.1203$

100. 0.902 and 145.315 are like decimals.

In exercises 101-106, list the numbers in descending order.

101. 8.9, 12.6, 3.08, 18.001

102. 10.01, 100.1, 1.001, 10.001

103. 0.011, 0.22, 0.033, 0.4

104. 7.36, 7.3599,7.3401,7.2975

105. 2.609, 9.01, 8.76, 12.6, 2.34

106. 1.05, 1.053, 1.53, 10.05

In exercises 107-114, list the numbers in ascending order.

107. 0.32, 0.337, 0.3139, 0.321

108. 2.75, 2.65, 0.975, 1.99, 2.72

109. 55.55, 5.55, 555.5, 55.05, 5.85

110. 6.049, 6.06, 6.1, 6.12, 6.058

111. 143.15, 134.015, 143.51, 115.34, 314.5

112. 7.09, 7.009, 7.9, 9.79, 7.099

113. 0.07, 7.77, 43.3, 4.33, 5.67

114. 14.35, 10.95, 14.056, 13.925, 10.951

6.4 Multiplication/Division by Powers of 10 and Scientific Notation

Vocabulary

1. A **power of ten** is a number of the type 10^n where n is a positive or negative whole number.

   For example: $10^1 = 10$, $10^2 = 10 \times 10 = 100$,
   $10^3 = 10 \times 10 \times 10 = 1000$,

   $10^0 = 1$ by definition

Objectives

After completing this section you will be able to:

A. Multiplying or Dividing Decimals by Powers of 10;

B. Express Numbers in Scientific Notation and Conversion; and

C. Application: Using Scientific Notations

A. Multiplying or Dividing Decimals by Powers

Illustrations

- $4.3724 \times 10^3 = 4.372.4$ or 4372.4
- $0.04 \times 10^5 = .04000.$ or 4000
- $\dfrac{25.78}{10^2} = 0.25.78$ or 0.2578
- $\dfrac{9.314}{10^3} = 0.009.314$ or 0.009314

Verify Skill

Objective 6.4 A

1. Multiply:

(a) 2.3485×10^3; **(b)** 23.485×10^4;

2. Divide:

(a) $\dfrac{234.85}{10^3}$; **(b)** $\dfrac{23.485}{10^4}$.

If your answers to these questions are the same as given below, then you may skip this objective.

Answers:

1. (a) 2348.5 **(b)** 234,850

2. (a) 0.23485 **(b)** 0.0023485

Discussion

- Multiplying a decimal by 10 or by a power of 10 is equivalent to moving the decimal point to the right one or more places. To understand this, we will multiply 345.832 by 10, 10^2, 10^3, and 10^4.

$345.832 \times 10 = 3458.320$

The exponent of 10 is 1.

$= 3458.32$

- Multiply as whole numbers ignoring the decimal point.
- Locate the decimal point. The product must have 3 decimal places. Why?
- Drop the unnecessary zeros.

The decimal point has moved one place to the right.

$345.832 \times 10^2 = 345.832 \times 100 = 34583.200 = 34583.2$

The exponent of 10 is 2.

The decimal point has moved two places to the right.

$345.832 \times 10^3 = 345.832 \times 1000 = 345832.000 = 345832.$

The exponent of 10 is 3.

The decimal point has moved 3 places to the right.

$345.832 \times 10^4 = 345.832 \times 10{,}000$

The exponent of 10 is 4.

$= 3458320\,.\,000$ — Note this product. A zero has been inserted to the right of the number 345.832.

$= 3458320.$ — The decimal point has moved 4 places to the right.

These observations can be generalized in the following rule.

> ***Rule* 1:**
>
> To multiply a decimal number by a power of 10, move the decimal point to the right by as many places as the exponent or power of 10.

Examples: $2.735 \times 10^2 = 273.5$ $154.739 \times 10^3 = 154739.$

- **Dividing** a decimal by 10 or by a power of 10 is equivalent to moving the decimal point **to the left.** Consider the division of 47.205 by 10, 10^2, 10^3, ...

$$47.205 \div 10 = 47.205 \times \frac{1}{10}$$ Multiply by the reciprocal of 10.

$$= \frac{47025}{1000} \times \frac{1}{10}$$ Change the decimal to fraction.

$$= \frac{47025}{1000 \times 10}$$ Multiply the fractions.

$$= \frac{47025}{10000}$$ ← Four zeros in the denominator.

$$= 4.7205$$

The decimal point has moved left by one place.

$$47.205 \div 10 = 4.7205$$

$$47.205 \div 10^2 = \frac{47205}{1000} \times \frac{1}{100} = \frac{47205}{100000} = .47205$$

$$47.205 \div 10^2 = 0.47205$$

The decimal point in 47.205 has moved left by *two* places.

$$47.205 \div 10^3 = 47.205 \times \frac{1}{1000} = \frac{47205}{1000} \times \frac{1}{1000} = \frac{47205}{1{,}000{,}000} = .047205$$

$$47.205 \div 10^3 = 0.047205$$

The decimal point has moved left by *three* places.

These observations can be generalized in the following rule.

Rule 2:

To divide a decimal number by a power of 10, the quotient is obtained by moving the decimal point in the dividend to the left by as many places as is the exponent of 10.

Examples: $43.473 \div 10^2 = .43473$, $\quad 2.42 \div 10^3 = .00242$

Procedure to multiply a decimal by a power of 10.

***Step* 1** Multiply by powers of ten by moving the decimal point to the right. Insert zeros, if necessary, to have enough decimal places to move the decimal point.

***Step* 2** Drop the unnecessary zeros, if any.

EXAMPLE 1 Multiply as indicated.

(a) 0.0054×10^3 **(b)** $127.03 \times (10^5)$ **(c)** 2.76×10

Solutions

(a) $0.0054 \times 10^3 = 0005.4$ • Multiply: Move the decimal point to the right by 3 places since the exponent of 10 is 3.

$= 5.4$ • Drop the unnecessary zeros.

$0.0054 \times 10^3 = 5.4$

(b) 127.03×10^5

$= 12703000.$ • The exponent of 10 is 5, so move the decimal point to the *right* 5 places. Insert three zeros to make 5 moves possible.

$127.03 \times 10^5 = 12{,}703{,}000$ • There are no unnecessary zeros.

(c) $2.76 \times 10 = 27.6$ Move the decimal point to the right by one place since the exponent of ten is 1.

$2.76 \times 10 = 27.6$

Procedure to divide a decimal by a power of 10.

***Step* 1** Divide by powers of ten by moving the decimal point to the left. Insert zeros, if necessary, to have enough decimal places to move the decimal point.

***Step* 2** Drop the unnecessary zeros, if any.

EXAMPLE 2 Divide as indicated.

(a) $2458.1 \div 10^2$ **(b)** $71.5 \div 10^3$ **(c)** $0.5 \div 10$

WARM-UP

1. Multiply as indicated.

(a) 0.0069×10^3

(b) $45.09\,(10^4)$

(c) $3.52\,(10)$

2. Divide as indicated.

(a) $3495.25 \div 10^3$

(b) $0.8 \div 10^2$

(c) $0.4 \div 10$

Answers:

1. (a) 6.9, (b) 450900, (c) 35.2

2. (a) 3.49525, (b) 0.008, (c) 0.04

Solutions

(a) $2458.1 \div 10^2$

$= 24.581$

- Divide. Move the decimal point to the *left* by 2 places since the exponent of 10 is 2.
- There are no unnecessary zeros.

Therefore, $2458.1 \div 10^2 = 24.581$

(b) $71.5 \div 10^3$

$= 0.0715$

- The exponent of 10 is 3. Move the decimal point to the *left* by 3 places. Insert zeros to make 3 moves possible.

Therefore, $71.5 \div 10^3 = 0.0715$

(c) $0.5 \div 10 = 0.05$ Move the decimal point to the left by one place.

B. Express Numbers in Scientific Notation and Conversion

Scientific notation is a convenient way of expressing very large or very small numbers. In scientific notation numbers are written in the form $a \times 10^n$ where $1 \leq |a| < 10$ and a is written in decimal form. Hence 4.32×10^{15} is the scientific notation for 4,320,000,000,000,000. Numbers in the form $1 \leq |a| < 10$ have exactly one place to the left of the decimal point.

Express Numbers in Scientific Notation

Observe that: **a)** $53.9 = 5.39 \times 10$ **b)** $539.72 = 5.3972 \times 10^2$

c) $.053 = 5.3 \times 10^{-2}$ **d)** $5.39 = 5.39 \times 10^0$

In each case the number on the right side of the equal sign is the scientific notation version of the number on the left side of the equal sign. These observations lead us to the following rule.

Rule: ***To convert a number from standard notation to scientific notation,***

***Step* 1** Move the decimal to the right of the first non zero digit.

***Step* 2** **a)** If the decimal was moved n places to the left then multiply by 10^n.

b) If the decimal was moved n places to the right then multiply by 10^{-n}.

Warm-Up

3. Convert to scientific notation.

a) 4384

b) 43.84

EXAMPLE 3 Convert the following to scientific notation.

a. 37.54 **b.** 375.4 **c.** –3754

d. .3754 **e.** .03754 **f.** –.003754

Solutions:

a. 37.54: Move the decimal **to the left 1** digit and **multiply by 10^1.** Thus, $37.54 = 3.754 \times 10^1$

b. 375.4: Move the decimal **to the left 2** digits and **multiply by 10^2.** Thus, $375.4 = 3.754 \times 10^2$.

c. –3754.0: Move the decimal **to the left 3** digits and **multiply by 10^3.** Thus, $-3754 = -3.754 \times 10^3$.

d. .3754: Move the decimal **to the right 1** digit and **multiply by 10^{-1}.** Thus, $.3754 = 3.754 \times 10^{-1}$.

e. .03754: Move the decimal **to the right 2** places and **multiply by 10^{-2}.** Thus, $.03754 = 3.754 \times 10^{-2}$.

f. –.003754: Move the decimal **to the right 3** places and **multiply by 10^{-3}.**
Thus, $-.003754 = -3.754 \times 10^{-3}$.

We may verify the answers with a calculator.

c) 438.4

d) .4384

e) –0.00543

f) 0.0000345

Answers:

3. a) 4.384×10^3 b) 4.384×10^1
c) 4.384×1^2 d) 4.384×10^{-1}
e) -5.43×10^{-3} f) 3.45×10^{-5}

C. Application: Using Scientific Notations

EXAMPLE 4 Light travels 300,000,000 meters per second. A light year is the distance that light travels in one year. Use scientific notation to express the number of meters traveled in one light year.

Solution:

$300{,}000{,}000 = 3.0 \times 10^8$

Number of seconds in one year $= 365 \times 24 \times 60 \times 60$

$= 31536000 = 3.1536 \times 10^7$ Express in scientific notation.

Number of meters traveled in one light year:

= (Number of meters traveled in one second) × (Number of seconds in one year)

$= (3 \times 10^8) \times (3.1536 \times 10^7)$

$= (3 \times 3.1536)10^{15} = \mathbf{9.4608 \times 10^{15}}$ **meters**

4. A plane travels at 3,000 miles per hour. Express this value in scientific notation.

Answer:
4. 3×10^3 mi/hr

Exercise 6.4

In exercises 1-20, multiply.

1. 0.3257×10^4	**2.** 1.758 (100)	**3.** $0.0421\,(10^3)$	**4.** 0.534×10^5
5. 0.005×100	**6.** 75.235×10	**7.** 2.851×10^5	**8.** 2.3781×10^3
9. 0.00123(10)	**10.** 0.0052×10^6	**11.** 75.789×10^1	**12.** 75.789×10^2

13. 75.789×10^3 **14.** 75.789×10^4 **15.** 0.00312×10^3 **16.** 9.7562×10^5

17. 27.54×10^6 **18.** 87.253×10^4 **19.** 72.548×10^2 **20.** 0.00042×10^4

In exercises 21-40, divide.

21. $0.5 \div 10^2$ **22.** $0.7 \div 10$ **23.** $473.5 \div 100$ **24.** $27 \div 10^3$

25. $322.56 \div 1000$ **26.** $7.4 \div 10^2$ **27.** $198,345 \div 10^4$ **28.** $65.4 \div 10$

29. $5.5 \div 10^6$ **30.** $35.35 \div 100$ **31.** $356.9 \div 10^1$ **32.** $356.9 \div 10^2$

33. $356.9 \div 10^3$ **34.** $356.9 \div 10^4$ **35.** $2.25 \div 10^4$ **36.** $18.137 \div 10^2$

37. $7406.25 \div 10^5$ **38.** $75.64 \div 10$ **39.** $0.0625 \div 10^3$ **40.** $427.175 \div 10^6$

In exercises 41-65, write the given number in scientific notation.

41. 4501 **42.** 230.6 **43.** 95.37 **44.** 9.573 **45.** -847.509 **46.** -83.759

47. 400.09 **48.** 305.09 **49.** 0.034 **50.** 0.0027 **51.** 0.00809 **52.** 0.0207

53. 2,456,000 **54.** $-75,000$ **55.** 0.000043 **56.** 0.000076 **57.** $-819,000,000$

58. 0.00000093 **59.** 0.0529×10^5 **60.** 0.0238×10^4 **61.** 775×10^5 **62.** 17.23×10^4

63. 0.0037×10^{-3} **64.** 0.027×10^{-2} **65.** 0.000000678

In exercises 66-69, use scientific notation to express the answer.

66. In chemistry, the molar mass = atomic mass × Avogadro's constant. Suppose the atomic mass of an element is 2.3244×10^{-26} kg and Avogardo's constant is $\frac{6.023 \times 10^{23}}{\text{mol}}$. Find the molar mass in terms of $\frac{\text{kg}}{\text{mol}}$.

67. Light travels 300,000,000 meters per second. Find the number of kilometers traveled in one hour.

Hint: Change $\frac{3 \times 10^8 \text{ m}}{\text{sec}}$ to $\frac{\text{kilometers}}{\text{hour}}$.

68. If E = energy emitted by an oscillation and V = frequency of oscillation, then $E = kV$ where k is Planck's constant 6.626×10^{-24} J. Find E if V = 1.25 E 15/s in J (Joules).

69. The density of an object is $\frac{\text{weight}}{\text{volume}}$. If the density of an object is $3.25 \times 10^{-7}\ \frac{\text{oz}}{\text{ft}^3}$, and the volume is 2.2×10^3 ft^3, then find the weight.

6.5 Find Fraction Notation for a Ratio or a Rate

Vocabulary

Objectives

After completing this section you will be able to:

A. Converting Ratios/Rates to Fraction;

B. Express a Rate as a Unit Rate.

1. A **measurement** is written with a number and a unit of measure.
2. **Like measurements** have the same units of measurement.

   5 yards and 12 yards are *like* measurements.

   9 gallons and 105 dollars are **unlike measurements.**

3. A **ratio** is a comparison by division of two numbers or quantities expressed as a fraction.

   The quantities have like measurements.

   For example The ratio 5 inches to 2 ft can be written as,

   $$\frac{5\text{ in}}{2\text{ ft}} = \frac{5\cancel{\text{in}}}{24\cancel{\text{in}}} = \frac{5}{24}.$$

4. A **rate** is a comparison by division of two unlike measurements.

A. Converting Ratios/Rates to Fraction

➜ **Express the ratio comparison of two numbers or like measurements as a fraction.**

Application

To make a certain shade of green paint, Juan mixed 6 quarts of yellow paint with 2 gallons of blue paint. He used all the green paint and needs a little more. Find the ratio of yellow paint to blue paint so that Juan can buy the proper amounts of each to make the shade of green he wants.

Illustration

- John earns $6500 per month, and his son Robin earns $2600 per month.

  The ratio of their monthly earnings is

  $$\frac{\$6500}{\$2600} = \frac{6500}{2600}$$ The units are the same, so they are dropped.

  $$= \frac{65}{26} = \frac{5}{2}$$ Simplify to lowest terms.

Verify Skill

Objective 6.5 A

(a) There are 7000 books in a library, of which 2000 are on mathematics. Find the ratio of the mathematics books to the total number of books in the library.

(b) Write the ratio of 2 minutes to 50 seconds.

If your answer to this question is the same as given below then you may skip this objective.

Answer:

(a) $\frac{2}{7}$ **(b)** $\frac{12}{5}$

Discussion

- Rational number, ratio and rate are all closely related. Recall that a rational number can be expressed as a whole number divided by a natural number. This division can look either like a fraction or, equivalently, a decimal.

  When comparing two numbers or like measurements by division, a **ratio** of the two numbers or like quantities is formed.

  Thus, $15 \div 3$ or $\frac{15}{3}$ is called the *ratio* of 15 and 3.

  The quotient $\frac{15}{3}$ is used to express the ratio of 15 and 3. It is read as '15 to 3'.

  It should be noted that when comparing 15 to 3, 15 is written first. Fifteen and three are the terms of the ratio.

- The concept of a *ratio* can be used to compare any two like measurements.

  The ratio of 20 dollars to 25 dollars is $\frac{\$20}{\$25}$ or $\frac{20}{25}$. The units are cancelled if they are the same.

  The ratio of 36 yards to 27 yards is $\frac{36 \text{ yds}}{27 \text{ yds}}$ or $\frac{36}{27}$.

- Since the ratio is expressed as a fraction, it can be reduced. The ratio $\frac{24}{15}$ in lowest terms is $\frac{8}{5}$.

  $$9 \text{ books to } 5 \text{ books} = \frac{9 \text{ books}}{5 \text{ books}} = \frac{9}{5}$$

  The units are the same, so they are dropped.

  $$\$20 \text{ to } \$25 = \frac{\$20}{\$25} = \frac{4 \times 5}{5 \times 5} = \frac{4}{5}$$

  The common units are dropped and the fraction is simplified.

  Similarly, $36 \text{ yds to } 27 \text{ yds} = \frac{36 \text{ yds}}{27 \text{ yds}} = \frac{4}{3}$

- When finding the ratio of two unlike measurements, convert them to like measurements whenever possible.

  The ratio of 3 quarters to 7 dimes is

  $$\frac{3 \text{ quarters}}{7 \text{ dimes}} = \frac{75 \text{ c}}{70 \text{ c}} = \frac{75}{70} = \frac{15}{14}$$

Note Generally, a ratio is expressed in lowest terms and is written as a proper or improper fraction.

Procedure to write the ratio of two numbers or like measurements as a fraction.

***Step* 1** Write the ratio as a fraction.

***Step* 2** Drop the common units.

***Step* 3** Reduce the fraction.

EXAMPLE 1 Write the ratio of 234 to 36 in lowest terms.

Solution

234 appears first in the comparison, therefore it is written in the numerator.

The ratio of 234 to 36 $= \dfrac{234}{36}$ Write the ratio as a fraction.

$= \dfrac{13}{2}$ Simplify.

The ratio of 234 to 36 is $\dfrac{13}{2}$.

EXAMPLE 2 The length of a rod is 45 inches, and that of another rod is 54 inches. Compare the length of the *second* rod to that of the *first* and express the result as a ratio.

Solution

The length of the second rod, which is 54 in, is written in the numerator because it is mentioned first in the ratio.

$\dfrac{54 \text{ inches}}{45 \text{ inches}}$ • Express as a fraction.

$= \dfrac{54}{45}$ • Drop the common units.

$= \dfrac{6}{5}$ • Simplify.

The ratio of the length of the second rod to the first rod is 6 to 5.

Procedure to write the ratio of two unlike measurements as a ratio of like measurements.

***Step* 1** Write the ratio as a fraction.

***Step* 2** Convert to like measurements.

***Step* 3** Drop the common units.

***Step* 4** Reduce the fraction.

EXAMPLE 3 Write the ratio of 7 feet to 3 yards in simplest form.

Solution

The ratio of 7 feet to 3 yards.

WARM-UP

1. Write the ratio of 250 to 375 in simplest form.

2. Jolly and Ela went on a picnic. Jolly spent \$35 and Ela spent \$20. Compare Ela's expenditure to that of Jolly's in ratio form.

3. Write the ratio of 4 inches to 2 feet in simplest form.

$$\frac{7\text{ ft}}{3\text{ yd}}$$ • Write the ratio as a fraction.

$$= \frac{7\text{ ft}}{9\text{ ft}}$$ • Convert 3 yds to 9 ft.

$$= \frac{7}{9}$$ • Cancel common measurements.

EXAMPLE 4 Write the ratio of 3 dimes to 3 quarters in simplest form.

Solution

The ratio of 3 dimes to 3 quarters.

$$\frac{3\text{ dimes}}{3\text{ quarters}}$$ • Write the ratio as a fraction.

$$= \frac{30¢}{75¢}$$ • Convert to like measurements.

$$= \frac{2}{5}$$ • Cancel common measurements and simplify.

WARM-UP

4. John has 4 dimes and 7 nickels. Write the ratio of nickels to dimes.

Answers:

1. $\frac{2}{3}$ 2. $\frac{4}{7}$

3. $\frac{1}{6}$ 4. $\frac{7}{8}$

Solution to the Application :

To make a certain shade of green paint, Juan mixed 6 quarts of yellow paint with 2 gallons of blue paint. He used all the green paint and needs a little more. Find the ratio of yellow paint to blue paint so that Juan can buy the proper amounts of each to make the shade of green he wants.

Solution: The ratio of yellow paint to blue paint

$$= \frac{6\text{qt}}{2\text{gal}}$$ Write the ratio as a fraction.

$$= \frac{6\text{qt}}{8\text{qt}}$$ Convert 2 gallons to 8 quarts.

$$= \frac{3}{4}$$ Cancel common measurements and reduce.

Thus, the required ratio of yellow paint to blue paint is 3 to 4.

Verify Skill

Objective 6.5 B

(a) If it takes 15 gallons of gasoline to travel 325 miles, what is the rate of miles traveled to gallons of gasoline used?

➡ **Express the rate of two unlike measurements as a fraction.**

Illustration

- There are 15 apples for 6 children: Express this information as a rate:

$$\frac{15 \text{ apples}}{6 \text{ children}} = \frac{5 \text{ apples}}{2 \text{ children}}$$

The units are **not** dropped since they are not the same.

Verify Skill

If your answer to this question is the same as given below then you may skip this objective.

Answer:

(a) 65 gallon to 3 miles

Discussion

- Fractions are also used to compare *unlike* quantities or measurements. To make the comparison of 38 chairs to 19 students, write:

$\frac{38 \text{ chairs}}{19 \text{ students}}$ and read it as the **ratio** or **rate** of 38 chairs to 19 students.

Since $\frac{38 \text{ chairs}}{19 \text{ students}} = \frac{2 \text{ chairs}}{1 \text{ student}}$ = 2 chairs to 1 student. This means there are two chairs for every one student.

- The definitions of rate and ratio are not universally agreed upon. We will define a rate to be a type of ratio where the comparison is between unlike quantities or measurements. Thus, all rates could also be called ratios. However, for all future comparisons, if the quantities have unlike measurements, we will call the comparison a rate. We will not be considering other types of rates which might not have measurements such as slope expressed as a rate or interest rates.

- If a car travels 350 miles on 20 gallons of gas, it can be expressed as a **rate.**

$$\frac{350 \text{ miles}}{20 \text{ gallons}} = \frac{35 \text{ miles}}{2 \text{ gallons}} = 35 \text{ miles to 2 gallons.}$$

Procedure to make a comparison of two unlike units and express it as a rate.

***Step* 1** Write the first unit in the numerator and the second unit in the denominator.

***Step* 2** Reduce the fraction and retain the unlike units.

EXAMPLE 5 Write as a rate : 80 boys to 55 girls.

Solution

The first unit (80 boys) is written in the numerator, and the second unit (55 girls) is written in the denominator.

$\frac{80 \text{ boys}}{55 \text{ girls}}$ Simplify the fraction.

$= \frac{16 \text{ boys}}{11 \text{ girls}}$ or 16 boys to 11 girls

***Caution*:** Do not drop the unlike units.

WARM-UP

5. Write 384 men to 360 chairs as a rate.

WARM-UP

6. There are 25 roses and 20 lilies in a garden. What is the rate of:

(a) the lilies to the roses.

(b) the roses to the lilies.

(c) the rose plants to the total number of flower plants in the garden.

(It is assumed that there are only two kinds of flowers in the garden.)

EXAMPLE 6 A library has 8,750 books, of which 1750 are mathematics books, and the rest are literature books. What are the rates of:

(a) The number of mathematics books to the number of literature books.

(b) The number of literature books to the number of mathematics books.

(c) The number of mathematics books to the total number of books in the library.

Interpret the rate in each case.

Solution

Total number of books in the library = 8750

The number of mathematics books = 1750

So, the number of literature books = 8750 – 1750

= 7000

(a) Write the first term (1750 mathematics books) in the numerator, and the second term (7000 literature books) in the denominator. The desired rate is

$$\frac{1750 \text{ mathematics books}}{7000 \text{ literature books}}$$ Simplify.

$$= \frac{1 \text{ mathematics book}}{4 \text{ literature books}}$$ Retain the unlike units.

(b) The required rate $= \frac{\text{the number of literature books}}{\text{the number of mathematics books}}$

$$= \frac{7000 \text{ literature books}}{1750 \text{ mathematics books}}$$ Simplify.

$$= \frac{4 \text{ literature books}}{1 \text{ mathematics book}}$$

(c) The rate of the number of mathematics books to the total number of books is

$$= \frac{1750 \text{ mathematics books}}{8750 \text{ total books}}$$ Simplify.

$$= \frac{1 \text{ mathematics book}}{5 \text{ total books}}$$ Retain the unlike units.

EXAMPLE 7 A typist types 84 words in 1.4 minutes. Find his typing speed

Solution

$$\frac{84 \text{ words}}{1.4 \text{ minutes}} = \frac{84 \times 10 \text{ words}}{1.4 \times 10 \text{ minutes}}$$

$$= \frac{840 \text{ words}}{14 \text{ minutes}}$$ Simplify.

$$= \frac{60 \text{ words}}{1 \text{ minute}}$$

The typist types 60 words in 1 minute.

WARM-UP

7. A typist types 75 words in 1.5 minutes. Find the typing speed.

Answers:

5. $\frac{16 \text{ men}}{15 \text{ chairs}}$

6. (a) $\frac{4 \text{ lilies}}{5 \text{ roses}}$ (b) $\frac{5 \text{ roses}}{4 \text{ lilies}}$ (c) $\frac{5 \text{ roses}}{9 \text{ flowers}}$

7. 50 words in one minute.

B. Express a Rate as a Unit Rate

Application

The population of city A is 12,834 and its area is 1520 square miles, while the population of city B is 14,500 and the area is 1600 square miles. Which city is more densely populated?

Illustration

- If a car travels 255 miles on 15 gallons of gasoline, then the unit rate of the miles travelled per gallon of gas (called the mileage) is:

$$\frac{255 \text{ miles}}{15 \text{ gallons}} = 255 \div 15 \text{ miles per gallon}$$

$$= 17 \text{ miles per gallon.}$$

Verify Skill

Objective 6.5 C

The area of a town is 1200 square miles, and the population is 15,950. Find the population density (a unit rate of the population per square mile) of the town, rounded to the nearest whole number.

If your answer to this question is the same as given below then you may skip this objective.

Answer:

13 people square mile.

Discussion

The rates we have been looking at are comparisons of quantities with unlike measurements. We expressed these rates as either fractions or whole numbers. When the rate is a whole number or when the fraction representing the rate is converted to a decimal by dividing, the rate is called a **unit rate**. For example, consider the ratio 15 apples to 12 children. To change this to a **unit rate**, divide the numerator by the denominator.

$$\frac{15 \text{ apples}}{12 \text{ children}} = (15 \div 12) \text{ apples per child} = 1.25 \text{ apples per child}$$ 15 ÷ 12 = 1.25

Convert the ratio 18 students to 16 chairs to a unit rate.

$$\frac{18 \text{ students}}{16 \text{ chairs}} = \frac{9 \text{ students}}{8 \text{ chairs}} = (9 \div 8) \text{ students per chair}$$ 9 ÷ 8 = 1.125

$$= 1.125 \text{ students per chair}$$ The rate.

The rate, 1.125 students per chair, is a comparison. It is impossible to have 1.125 students.

- The concept of a unit rate is very important as it facilitates comparison. Speed (distance travelled per time unit); mileage (miles covered per gallon of gasoline); population density (number of people per square mile) are some examples of rates which are frequently used in daily life. For example, if one car travels 27 miles on 1.5 gallons of gasoline, and another car travels 35 miles on 2 gallons of gasoline, to find which car gets better mileage, we compute the unit rates.

The rate for the first car is $\dfrac{27 \text{ miles}}{1.5 \text{ gallons}} = 18$ miles per gallon. $27 \div 1.5 = 18$ (verify)

The rate for the second car is $\dfrac{35 \text{ miles}}{2 \text{ gallons}} = 17.5$ miles per gallon. $35 \div 2 = 17.5$

Since the first car travels 18 miles per gallon and the second 17.5 miles per gallon, the first car gets better mileage.

Procedure to write a unit rate.

***Step* 1** Write the rate as a fraction.

***Step* 2** Divide the numerator by the denominator. *Caution*: Do not drop the units.

WARM-UP

8. Write as a unit rate: 18 computers to 6 printers.

9. Jacob reads 87 pages of his text book in 35 minutes. Find his reading rate of speed. Round the answer to the nearest tenth.

EXAMPLE 8 Write as a unit rate: 340 feet to 8 seconds.

Solution

$$340 \text{ feet to } 8 \text{ seconds} = \frac{340 \text{ feet}}{8 \text{ seconds}}$$ Write as a fraction.

$$= (340 \div 8)\frac{\text{ft}}{\text{sec}}$$ Divide the numerator by the denominator.

$$= 42.5\frac{\text{ft}}{\text{sec}}$$

The rate is 42.5 feet per second.

EXAMPLE 9 George drives his car and covers a distance of 123 miles in 2.2 hours. Find his rate of speed (the distance covered per hour). Round the answer to the nearest tenth.

Solution

$$\text{Speed} = \frac{123 \text{ miles}}{2.2 \text{ hours}}$$ Divide the numerator by the denominator.

$$= (123 \div 2.2)\frac{\text{mi}}{\text{hr}} \approx 55.9\frac{\text{mi}}{\text{hr}}$$

The rate is $55.9\dfrac{\text{mi}}{\text{hr}}$ Rounded to the nearest tenth.

The speed to the nearest tenth is 55.9 miles per hour.

EXAMPLE 10 $245 buys 4 shirts of a certain brand. Find the cost per shirt.

Solution

The ratio of **cost** to **quantity**

$= \dfrac{\$245}{4 \text{ shirts}}$ Divide to find the rate.

$= (245 \div 4)\dfrac{\$}{\text{shirt}}$

$= \$\ 61.25$ per shirt.

The cost per shirt is $ 61.25.

WARM-UP

10. A package of 12 underwear costs $45. Find the cost per underwear.

Answers:

8. 3 computers per printer

9. 2.5 pages per minute

10. $3.75 per underwear

Solution to the Application :

The population of city A is 12,834 and its area is 1520 square miles, while the population of city B is 14,500 and its area is 1600 square miles. Which city is more densely populated?

Solution: First find the density (a unit rate of population per square mile) of each city.

Density of city A $= \dfrac{12{,}834 \text{ people}}{1520 \text{ square miles}}$ Divide the numerator by the denominator.

$= (12{,}834 \div 1520)\dfrac{\text{people}}{\text{mi}^2}$ Divide.

$= 8.443421$

≈ 8.4 people per square mile. Rounded to the nearest tenth.

Density of city B $= \dfrac{14{,}500 \text{ people}}{1600 \text{ square miles}} \approx 9.1$ people per square mile.

Comparison:

Since the density of city A is 8.4 people per square mile and that of city B is 9.1 people per square mile, city B is more densely populated.

EXERCISE 6.5

In exercises 1-20, write as a ratio or a rate in the simplest form.

1. 76 miles to 54 miles

2. 12 hours to 8 hours

3. 124 to 86

4. 135 dollars to 65 dollars

5. 42 men to 90 men

6. 17 inches to 1 foot

7. 42 seconds to 2 minutes

8. 7 quarters to 4 nickels

9. 3 hours to 75 minutes

10. 14 dimes to 17 nickels

11. 64 feet to 12 seconds

12. 15 cows to 25 cows

13. 10 chairs to 13 people

14. 15 miles to 10 miles

15. 2 hours to 135 minutes

16. 15 gallons to 80 dollars

17. 45 days to 30 days

18. 2 yards to 18 feet

19. 15 oak trees to 35 birch trees

20. 234 people to 26 sq. miles

In exercises 21-40, write as a unit rate.

21. 25 candy bars to 10 children

22. 65 feet to 5 seconds

23. 125 dollars to 10 books

24. 35 miles to 10 days

25. 36 trees to 5 cows

26. 16 gallons to 10 miles

27. 34 apples to 10 men

28. 35 books to 7 students

29. 12 children to 5 families

30. 42 Russian books to 20 German books

31. 10,540 people to 100 sq. miles

32. 729 miles to 27 gallons of gasoline

33. 228 pages to 30 minutes

34. 234 feet to 36 seconds

35. 49.5 dollars to 21.6 gallons (Round to the nearest tenth)

36. $216 to 16 shirts

37. 137 miles to 3 hours, rounded

38. 3000 books to 750 students to the nearest tenth

39. 31 children to 10 families

40. 22,450 people to 230 square miles (Round to the nearest tenth)

Applications

41. A store buys a camera for $80 and sells it for $155. What is the ratio of the cost to the selling price?

42. In a library, out of 7500 books there are 1350 Russian books and 2450 German books. What is the ratio of the number of German books to the number of Russian books?

43. What is the population density of a town if the population is 8750 and the area is 1090 square miles? Round to the nearest whole number.

44. A car uses 15.2 gallons of gasoline to travel 266 miles, while another uses 21 gallons to travel 324 miles. Which car gets better mileage?

45. City A has 16,775 people and its area is 1600 square miles. City B has 12,650 people and its area is 1200 square miles. Which city is more densely populated?

46. To mix a certain shade of orange paint, Kelly needs 7 quarts of red paint and 3 gallons of yellow paint. Find the ratio of red paint to yellow paint.

6.6 Percents, Conversion to Decimals and Fractions

Vocabulary

> **Objectives**
>
> After completing this section you will be able to:
>
> **A.** Understand the meaning of percent;
>
> **B.** Convert percent-fraction-decimal.

1. When ratio comparisons are expressed as fractions, the denominator is called the **base** and the numerator is called the **amount**. In comparing 5 to 20, as in the ratio $\frac{5}{20}$, 20 is the base and 5 is the amount.

2. The **percent comparison,** or just the **percent,** is a ratio with a base unit of 100. The percent $\frac{40}{100} = 40 \cdot \frac{1}{100}$ is usually written as 40%.

The symbol %, read "percent", is used for the factor $\frac{1}{100}$. Thus, $1\% = \frac{1}{100} = 0.01$.

As we have seen, "per" means divide (as in miles per hour). Cent means 100 (as in century).

So percent means divide by 100. Thus $40\% = 40 \div 100 = \frac{40}{100}$.

A. Understanding Percents

> **Verify Skill**
>
> **Objective 6.6 A**
>
> What percent of the region is not shaded ?
>
> 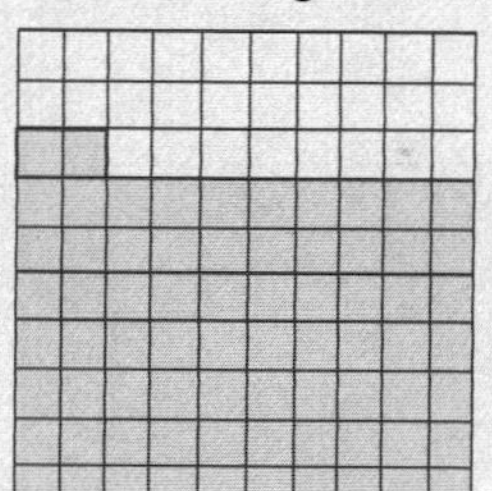
>
> **If your answer to this question is the same as given below then you may skip this objective**
>
> Answer: 72%

➜ Understand the meaning of "percent".

Illustration

In the following figure, 53 of the 100 parts are shaded.

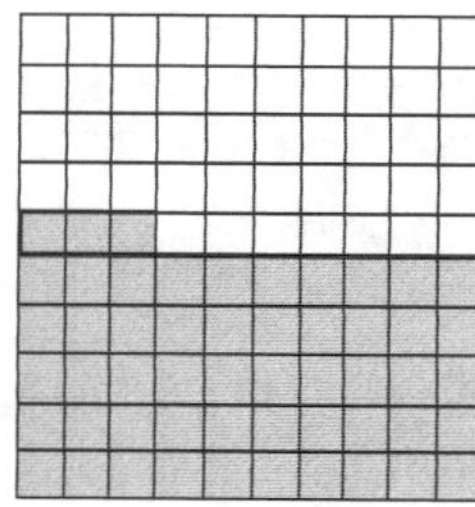

Since $\frac{53}{100} = 53\%$

53% of the region is shaded.

Discussion

The term **percent** (an abbreviation of the Latin phrase "per centum") means a hundredth part, or by the hundred. It is used in expressing interest rates, taxes, discount rates, and in many other situations in daily life.

- Basically, a **percent** is a fraction whose denominator is one hundred. Consider the square in Figure 6.2. It is divided into 100 equal parts with 35 of these shaded.

  35 percent of the unit square is shaded.
  Symbolically, write 35 percent as 35%.

$$\mathbf{35\%} = \frac{35}{100}$$

  The symbol % (read as percent) indicates "divide by 100".

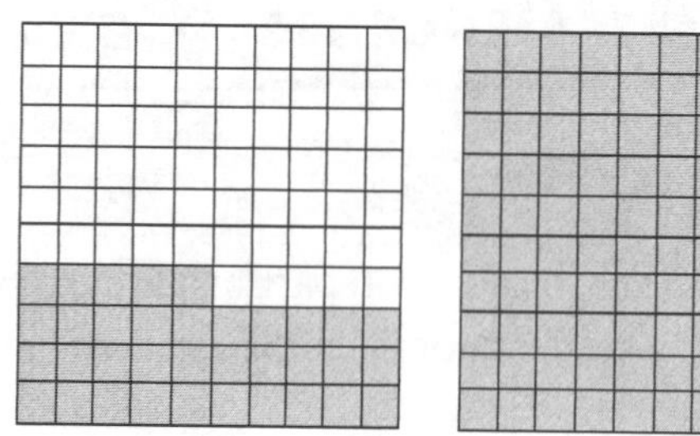

Figure 6.2 Figure 6.3

- If all one hundred parts are shaded, the entire unit will be shaded (See Figure 6.3). In this case, **100% of the unit is shaded**. Note that

$$100\% = \frac{100}{100} = 1$$

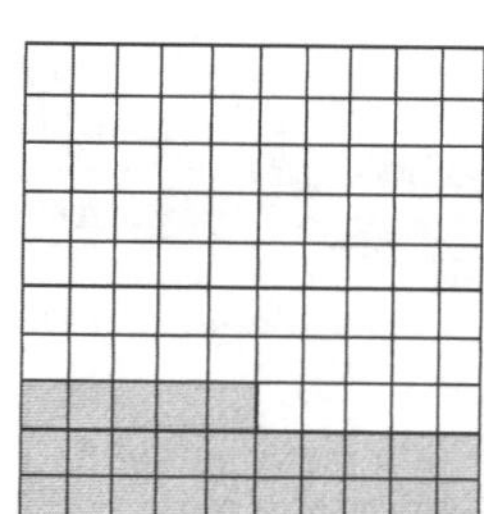

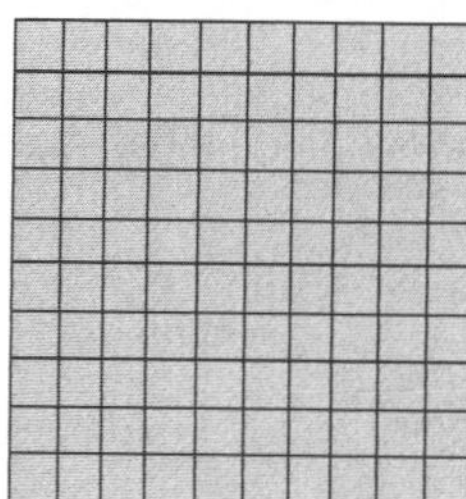

Figure 6.4

- In Figure 6.4 there are two units. Each unit is divided into 100 equal parts. The shaded part is $\frac{100}{100}+\frac{25}{100}=\frac{125}{100}$, so 125% of the region is shaded. The shaded region is **more than 100%** of a single unit.

> **Procedure** to express the shaded region of a 100 grid block as a percent.
>
> ***Step* 1** Write the number of blocks that have been shaded.
>
> ***Step* 2** Attach a percent symbol to the number found in step 1.

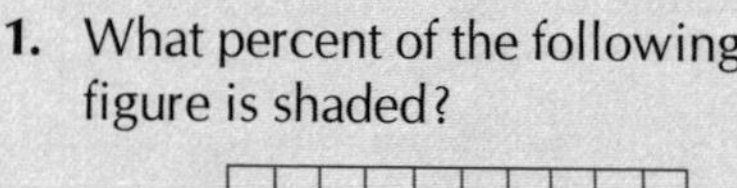

WARM-UP

1. What percent of the following figure is shaded?

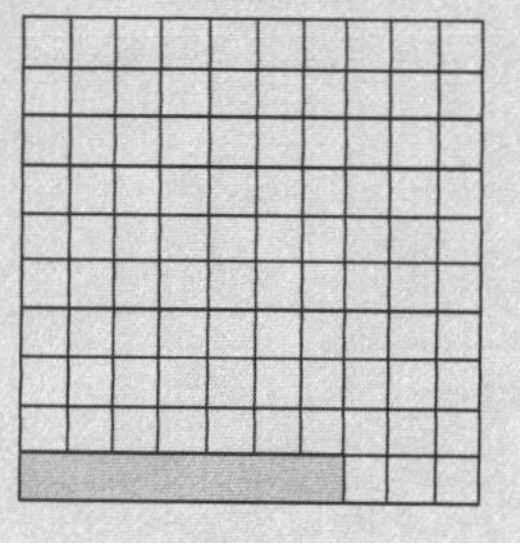

Answer:

1. 7%

EXAMPLE 1 What percent of the following figure is shaded?

Solution

14 out of 100 blocks are shaded, so

14 % of the region is shaded.

B. CONVERT PERCENT - FRACTION - DECIMAL

Verify Skill

Objective 6.6 B

Change 4.8% to a fraction.

If your answer to this question is same as given below then you may skip this objective

Answer: $\frac{6}{125}$

➡ Convert a percent to a fraction.

Illustration

- To change 52% to a fraction:

$$52\% = 52 \div 100 = \frac{52}{100} = \frac{13}{25}$$

$$52\% = \frac{13}{25}$$

Discussion

- Percent means per 100 or divide by 100. Thus, $93\% = \frac{93}{100}$.
- Similarly, to change $12\frac{2}{3}\%$ to a fraction:

$$12\frac{2}{3}\% = 12\frac{2}{3} \div 100 \qquad \text{Replace "\%" with } \div 100.$$

$$= \frac{38}{3} \div \frac{100}{1} \qquad \text{Change to improper fractions.}$$

$$= \frac{38}{3} \times \frac{1}{100} = \frac{38}{300} = \frac{19}{150} \qquad \text{Multiply by the reciprocal and reduce.}$$

- To convert a decimal percent to a fraction, we can write the decimal part as a fraction and divide that fraction by 100. Thus,

$$7.25\% = 7.25 \div 100 \qquad \text{Replace "\%" with } \div 100.$$

$$= \frac{725}{100} \div \frac{100}{1} \qquad \text{Change to fractions.}$$

$$= \frac{725}{100} \times \frac{1}{100} = \frac{725}{10000} = \frac{29}{400} \qquad \text{Multiply by the reciprocal and reduce.}$$

Procedure to change a percent to a fraction

***Step* 1** Replace the symbol % with ÷ 100.

***Step* 2** If necessary, perform the division by rewriting the numbers as improper fractions.

***Step* 3** Simplify.

WARM-UP

2. Write the following as fractions:

(a) 4%

(b) 156%

(c) 2.06%

3. Change the following to fractions.

(a) $4\frac{2}{5}\%$ (b) $7\frac{1}{4}\%$

(c) $12\frac{4}{9}\%$

Answers:

2. (a) $\frac{1}{25}$ (b) $\frac{39}{25}$ (c) $\frac{103}{5000}$

3. (a) $\frac{11}{250}$ (b) $\frac{29}{400}$ (c) $\frac{28}{225}$

EXAMPLE 2 Write the following percents as fractions (or mixed numbers)

(a) 16 % (b) 428 % (c) 0.5 %

Solutions

(a) $\mathbf{16\%} = 16 \div 100 = \frac{16}{100} = \mathbf{\frac{4}{25}}$

(b) $\mathbf{428\%} = 428 \div 100 = \frac{428}{100} = \frac{107}{25} = \mathbf{4\frac{7}{25}}$

(c) $\mathbf{0.5\%} = 0.5 \div 100 = \frac{5}{10} \times \frac{1}{100} = \mathbf{\frac{1}{200}}$

EXAMPLE 3 Change the following percents to fractions.

(a) $2\frac{1}{2}\%$ (b) $5\frac{3}{4}\%$ (c) $27\frac{3}{7}\%$

Solutions

(a) $\mathbf{2\frac{1}{2}\%} = \frac{5}{2}\% = \frac{5}{2} \div 100 \rightarrow = \frac{5}{2} \cdot \frac{1}{100} = \mathbf{\frac{1}{40}}$

(b) $\mathbf{5\frac{3}{4}\%} = \frac{23}{4}\% = \frac{23}{4} \div 100$

$= \frac{23}{4} \cdot \frac{1}{100} = \mathbf{\frac{23}{400}}$

(c) $\mathbf{27\frac{3}{7}\%} = \frac{192}{7}\% = \frac{192}{7} \div 100$

$= \frac{192}{7} \cdot \frac{1}{100} = \frac{192}{700} = \mathbf{\frac{48}{175}}$

- Since percent means divide by 100, to change a percent to a decimal, we divide by 100, just as we did to change the percent to a fraction. The difference is that we do not leave the division as a fraction, but carry out the division, inserting a decimal point where necessary. You can verify that dividing a decimal by 100 is equivalent to moving the decimal point to the left by two places.

Thus, $\mathbf{16.5\%} = 16.5 \div 100 = .1\,6\,5 = \mathbf{0.165}$

Observe that the decimal point is moved to the left by two places and that the percent symbol is dropped.

Sometimes it is necessary to insert zero(s) to make places available for shifting the decimal point. For example, to write 0.5% as a decimal:

$\mathbf{0.5\%} = 0.5 \div 100$

$= .0\,0\,5$ Move the decimal to the left by two places. It is necessary to insert zeros.

$= \mathbf{0.005}$

Procedure to change a percent to a decimal.

***Step* 1** Rewrite the percent symbol as ÷ 100.

***Step* 2** Divide by moving the decimal point to the left by two places. Insert zeros, if necessary.

***Step* 3** Drop the unnecessary zeros, if any.

EXAMPLE 4 Change the given percents to decimals.

(a) 12.4% **(b)** 0.21% **(c)** 80%

Solutions

(a) $12.4\% = 12.4 \div 100$ • Rewrite "%" as "÷ 100".

$= .124$ • Move the decimal point to the left two places.

$= 0.124$

Therefore, 12.4% = 0.124

(b) $0.21\% = 0.21 \div 100$ • Rewrite "%" as "÷ 100".

$= .0021$ • Move the decimal point to the left two places, inserting two zeros.

$= 0.0021$

Therefore, 0.21% = 0.0021

(c) $80\% = 80 \div 100 = 0.80 = 0.8$ • Rewrite "%" as "÷ 100".

Therefore, 80% = 0.8

• Move the decimal point (assumed to be after the right most digit) to the left two places.

• Drop the unnecessary zero.

EXAMPLE 5 Convert the following percents to decimals. Round to the nearest thousandth, if necessary.

(a) $35\frac{1}{2}\%$ **(b)** $27\frac{1}{6}\%$ **(c)** $3\frac{3}{5}\%$

Solutions

(a) $35\frac{1}{2}\% = 35.5\%$ • Rewrite "%" as "÷ 100".

$= 35.5 \div 100$ • Change the fraction to decimal $\left(\frac{1}{2} = 0.5\right)$.

$= 0.355$ Move the decimal point to the left two places.

Therefore, $35\frac{1}{2}\% = 0.355$

WARM-UP

4. Change the percents to decimals.

(a) 45.6%

(b) 0.15%

(c) 110%

5. Convert the following percents to decimals, rounding to the nearest thousandths if necessary.

(a) $6\frac{1}{2}\%$

WARM-UP

(b) $14\frac{2}{3}\%$

(c) $54\frac{1}{2}\%$

Answers:

4. (a) 0.456 (b) 0.0015 (c) 1.1

5. (a) 0.065 (b) » 0.147 (c) 0.545

(b) $27\frac{1}{6}\% = 27.16\overline{6}\%$ $\quad \frac{1}{6} = 0.166\overline{6}$

$= 27.16\overline{6} \div 100$ • Rewrite "%" as "÷ 100".

$= 0.2716\overline{6}$ • Move the decimal point to the left two places.

≈ 0.272 • Round to the nearest thousandth.

(c) $3\frac{3}{5}\% = 3.6\%$ $\quad \frac{3}{5} = 0.6$

$= 3.6 \div 100 = 0.036$

Therefore, $3\frac{3}{5}\% = 0.036$

➡ **Convert fractions and Decimals to percent.**

Application

Fifteen out of the forty students in a class received an A on the final examination. Write the fraction of students who received an A on the final examination. Convert this fraction to a percent.

Verify Skill

Objective 6.6 C

Change $\frac{7}{13}$ to a percent, rounded to the nearest tenth of a percent.

If your answer to this question is the same as given below then you may skip this objective.

Answer: 53.8%.

Illustration

- To change $4\frac{2}{3}$ to a percent:

$4\frac{2}{3} = \frac{14}{3}$ Recall 100% = 1

$= \frac{14}{3} \times 100\%$ Multiply by 100%.

$= \frac{14}{3} \times \frac{100}{1}\%$ $\quad 100 = \frac{100}{1}$

$= \frac{1400}{3}\%$ Multiply the fractions.

$= 466\frac{2}{3}\%$ Change the improper fraction to a mixed number.

Therefore, $4\frac{2}{3} = 466\frac{2}{3}\%$ or $466.\overline{6}\ \% \approx 466.7\ \%$

Discussion

- The term "percent" as well as the symbol "%" mean **divide by 100**. Thus, $100\% = 100 \div 100 = 1$.
- 1 is the multiplicative identity. That is, any number multiplied by 1 is the number itself. Since $100\% = 1$, any number multiplied by 100% is equal to the number expressed as a percent. For example,

$$\frac{4}{5} = \frac{4}{5} \times 100\%$$ Multiply by 100%

$$= \frac{4}{5} \times \frac{100}{1}\%$$ $100 = \frac{100}{1}$

$$= \frac{400}{5}\%$$ Multiply fractions.

$$= 80\%$$ Reduce the fraction.

- In some cases, the result reduces to a whole number. In other cases, the result may be written as a mixed number percent. For example, to write $1\frac{1}{6}$ as a percent:

$$1\frac{1}{6} = 1\frac{1}{6} \times 100\%$$ Multiply by 100%

$$= \frac{7}{6} \times \frac{100}{1}\%$$ Convert whole and mixed numbers to improper fractions.

$$= \frac{700}{6}\%$$ Multiply fractions.

$$= 116\frac{2}{3}\%$$ Convert to a mixed number and reduce.

> **Procedure** to convert a fraction or a mixed number into a percent.
>
> ***Step* 1** Multiply by 100%.
>
> ***Step* 2** Reduce the result.

EXAMPLE 6 Change each of the following fractions to percents.

(a) $2\frac{3}{4}$ **(b)** $\frac{11}{20}$ **(c)** $7\frac{3}{25}$

Solutions

(a) $$2\frac{3}{4} = 2\frac{3}{4} \times 100\%$$ Multiply by 100%.

$$= \frac{11}{4} \times \frac{100}{1}\%$$ Convert to improper fractions.

$$= \frac{1100}{4}\% = \mathbf{275\ \%}$$ Multiply and reduce.

(b) $$\frac{11}{20} = \frac{11}{20} \times 100\%$$ Multiply by 100%.

$$= \frac{11}{20} \times \frac{100}{1}\%$$ Convert to improper fractions.

$$= \frac{1100}{20}\% = \mathbf{55\%}$$ Multiply and reduce.

WARM-UP

6. Express the given numbers as percents.

(a) $\frac{3}{5}$

(b) $4\frac{3}{10}$

(c) $\dfrac{4}{125}$

(c) $7\dfrac{3}{25} = 7\dfrac{3}{25} \times 100\%$ Multiply by 100%.

$= \dfrac{178}{25} \times \dfrac{100}{1}\%$ Convert to improper fractions.

$= \dfrac{17800}{25}\% = \mathbf{712\%}$ Multiply and reduce.

7. Write the number as a percent and round to the nearest tenth of a percent.

(a) $\dfrac{23}{256}$

(b) $1\dfrac{9}{35}$

Answers:

6. (a) 60% (b) 430% (c) 3.2%
7. (a) 9.0% (b) 125.7%

EXAMPLE 7 Change the given number to a percent and round to the nearest tenth of a percent.

(a) $\dfrac{43}{160}$ (b) $4\dfrac{5}{48}$

Solutions

(a) $\dfrac{43}{160}$

ENTER 43 [÷] 160 [×] 100 followed by [=] or [Enter]

The result should be 26.875.

Thus, $\dfrac{43}{160} = 26.875\%$

$\approx 26.9\%$ to the nearest tenth of a percent

(b) $4\dfrac{5}{48} = \dfrac{197}{48}$ Convert the mixed number to an improper fraction.

ENTER 197 [÷] 48 [×] 100 followed by [=] or [Enter]

The result should be about 410.416667.

$4\dfrac{5}{48} \approx 410.416667\%$

$\approx 410.4\%$ to the nearest tenth of a percent

Solution to the Application:

Fifteen out of the forty students in a class received an A on the final examination. Write the fraction of students who received an A on the final examination. Convert this fraction to a percent.

Solution: The fraction of students who got an A in class is $\dfrac{15}{40}$.

To write the fraction as a percent, we multiply by 100%.

$\dfrac{3}{8} \times 100\% = \dfrac{3}{8} \times \dfrac{100}{1}\%$

$$\frac{300}{8}\% = \left(\frac{75 \times \not{4}}{2 \times \not{4}}\right)\%$$

$$= \left(\frac{75}{2}\right)\% = 37\frac{1}{2}\%$$

$37\frac{1}{2}\%$ of the class received an A.

➔ **Convert a decimal to a percent.**

Verify Skill

Objective 6.6.3

Write 3.2 as a percent.

If your answer to this question is the same as given below then you may skip this objective.

Answer:

320%

Illustration

- To change 0.056 to a percent:

$0.056 = 0\,0\,5\,.\,6\%$ Move the decimal point to the right by two places and affix a percent symbol.

$= 5.6\%$ Drop the unnecessary zeros.

$0.056 = 5.6\%$

Discussion

- The method of changing a decimal to a percent is similar to that of changing a fraction to a percent. Since 100% = 100 ÷ 100 = 1, we multiply by 1 in the form of 100%. For example,

  $0.2575 = 0.2575 \times 1 = 0.2575 \times 100\% = 25.75\%$

- Recall to multiply by a power of 10, we move the decimal point to the right by as many places as is the exponent of 10. Thus, multiplying by 100 is the same as moving the decimal two places to the right.

  For example:

  $15 = 15 \times 100\% = 15.00 \times 100\% = 1500\%$

  and $0.5 = 0.5 \times 100\% = 0.50 \times 100\% = 50\%$

Procedure to write a given decimal as a percent.

***Step* 1** Multiply by 100%. (This is the same as moving the decimal two places to the right.)

***Step* 2** Drop the unnecessary zeros, if any.

EXAMPLE 8 Change the given decimals to percents.

(a) 0.75 **(b)** 0.05 **(c)** 2.7

Solutions

(a) 0.75

WARM-UP

8. Write as a percent:

(a) 0.34

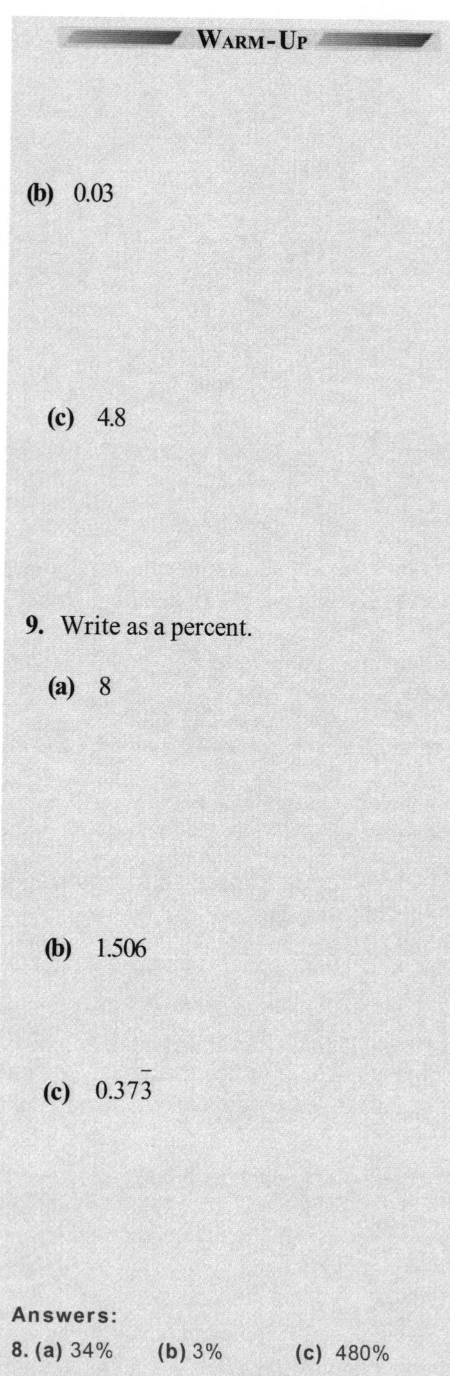

$= 0.75 \times 100\%$ Multiply by 100%.

$= 75\%$

Therefore, $0.75 = 75\%$

(b) 0.05

$= 0.05 \times 100\%$ Multiply by 100%.

$= 5\%$

Therefore, $0.05 = 5\%$

(c) 2.7

$= 2.7 \times 100\%$ Multiply by 100%.

$= 270\%$

Therefore, $2.7 = 270\%$

EXAMPLE 9 Express the following numbers as percents.

(a) 6 **(b)** 4.315 **(c)** $0.15\overline{6}$

Solutions

(a) $6 = 6 \times 100\%$ Multiply by 100%.

$= 600\%$

(b) $4.315 = 4.315 \times 100\%$ Multiply by 100%.

$= 431.5\%$

(c) $0.15\overline{6} = 0.15\overline{6} \times 100\%$

$015.\overline{6}\ \% = 15\frac{2}{3}\%$ $\quad .\overline{6} = \frac{2}{3}$

$15.\overline{6}\% = 15\frac{2}{3}\%$ exact

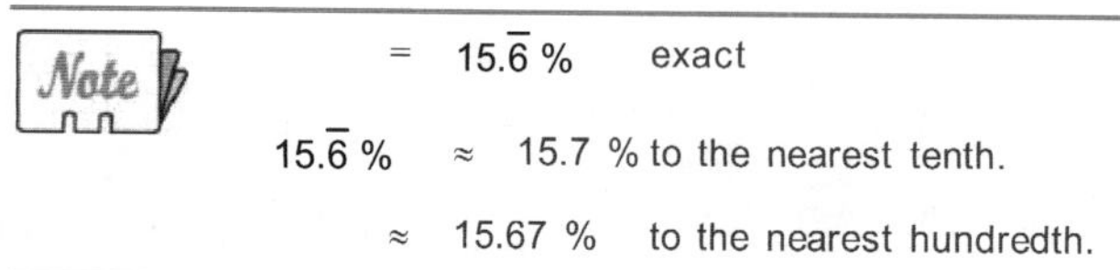

➔ Equivalence of fractions, decimals and percents

Discussion

In previous sections, fractions, decimals and percents were shown to be mutually related concepts. Any of these three forms of a number can be expressed in terms of the other two forms. Below is a summary of the procedures for conversion.

- **Fraction to Decimal** $\longrightarrow$ Divide the numerator by the denominator.

$$\frac{13}{5} = 5\overline{)13.0} = 2.6$$

(Long division: 2.6; 10; 30; 30; 0)

- **Fraction to Percent** $\longrightarrow$ Convert the fraction to a percent, by multiplying by 1 in the form of 100%.

$$\frac{13}{5} = \frac{13}{5} \times 100\% = \frac{13}{5} \cdot \frac{100}{1}\% = 260\%$$

- **Decimal to Fraction** $\longrightarrow$ Remove the decimal point and divide the resulting number by 10^n, where n is the number of decimal places. Reduce the fraction.

$$2.45 = \frac{245}{10^2} = \frac{245}{100}$$
$$= \frac{49}{20}$$
$$= 2\frac{9}{20}$$

- **Decimal to Percent** $\longrightarrow$ Multiply by 1 in the form of 100% and simplify.

$$3.45 = 3.45 \times 100\% = 345\ \%$$

- **Percent to Decimal** $\longrightarrow$ Change the percent symbol to $\div$ 100 and simplify.

$$15.2\ \% = 15.2 \div 100 = 0.152$$

- **Percent to Fraction** $\longrightarrow$ Replace the % symbol with $\div$ 100 and simplify.

$$2.4\ \% = 2.4 \div 100 = \frac{24}{10} \div \frac{100}{1}$$
$$= \frac{24}{10} \times \frac{1}{100} = \frac{3}{125}$$

EXAMPLE 10 Complete the following table with the related equivalent forms.

Fraction	Decimal	Percent
$\frac{3}{8}$		
	0.625	
		4.5%

WARM-UP

10. Complete the following table:

Solutions

Fraction	Decimal	Percent	Solution
$\frac{3}{8}$	0.375	37.5%	$\frac{3}{8} = \mathbf{0.375} = \mathbf{37.5\%}$
$\frac{5}{8}$	**0.625**	62.5%	$0.625 = \mathbf{62.5\%} = \frac{625}{10}\% = \frac{\overset{5}{\cancel{625}}}{\underset{8}{\cancel{1000}}} = \mathbf{\frac{5}{8}}$
$\frac{9}{200}$	0.045	**4.5%**	$4.5\% = \mathbf{0.045} = \frac{45}{1000} = \mathbf{\frac{9}{200}}$

Warm-Up

Fraction	Decimal	Percent
	0.875	
		$5\frac{1}{2}$ %
$2\frac{1}{4}$		

Answers:

10. $\frac{7}{8}$, 0.875, 87.5%

$\frac{11}{200}$, 0.055, $5\frac{1}{2}$%

$\frac{9}{4}$, 2.25, 225%

Exercise 6.6

In exercise 1-2, what percent of each figure is shaded?

1. 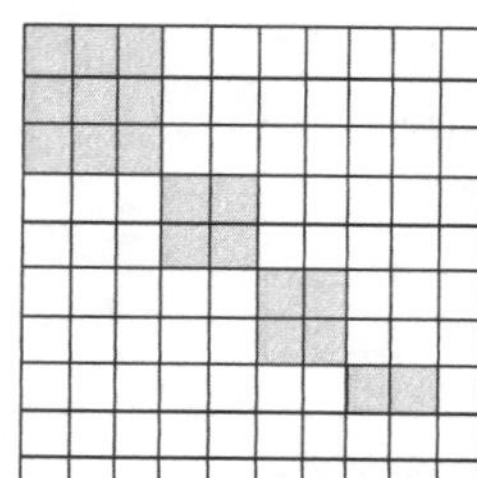

2. 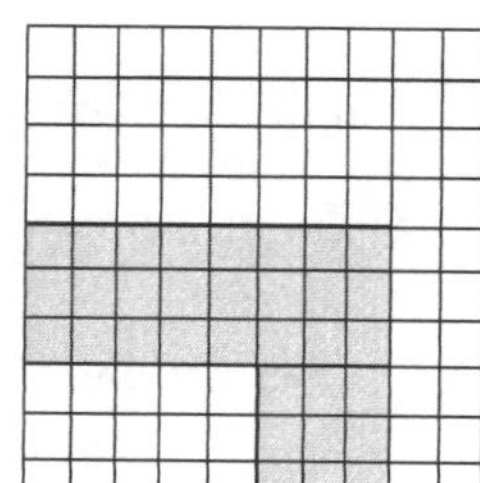

In exercises 3-14, change the given percent to a fraction and reduce to lowest terms.

3. 37% **4.** 25% **5.** 36% **6.** 15%

7. 64% **8.** $5\frac{3}{4}$ % **9.** $32\frac{5}{16}$ % **10.** $42\frac{3}{20}$ %

11. $4\frac{8}{15}$ % **12.** $27\frac{3}{7}$ % **13.** 22.5% **14.** 1.25%

In exercises 15-34, write the given percent as a decimal.

15. 6.6% **16.** 271.5% **17.** 0.01% **18.** 400% **19.** 40%

20. 4% **21.** 0.4% **22.** 32% **23.** 500% **24.** 125%

25. 0.04% **26.** 0.0035% **27.** 7% **28.** 2.5% **29.** 12.375%

30. 2.125% **31.** 0.24% **32.** 1.063% **33.** 0.75% **34.** 48%

Applications

35. Fifteen percent of Smith's salary is spent on food. What fraction of his salary is spent on food?

36. Twenty percent of a class received an A. What fraction of the class received an A?

37. Over a ten year period, property values in a certain city increased by 11.5%. What fraction describes this increase?

38. The population of a city in a particular year increased by $10\frac{5}{7}\%$. What fraction describes the increase?

39. The cost of living increased by 1.2% from January 1999 to December 1999. Express this increase as a decimal.

40. Which rate of interest is better for an investment, $\frac{11}{6}\%$ or 0.0182?

41. Wachovia Bank charges 8.3% interest on auto loans, while the Citibank charges a rate of 0.09.

(a) Which of the two rates is higher? **(b)** Which is better for a loan?

42. Which rate of interest is better for an investment, $6\frac{2}{3}\%$ or 0.068?

In exercises 43-57, convert the fraction or mixed number to a percent.

43. $\frac{2}{5}$ **44.** $1\frac{13}{25}$ **45.** $\frac{3}{10}$ **46.** $\frac{13}{20}$ **47.** $\frac{7}{50}$

48. $\frac{7}{16}$ **49.** $\frac{1}{8}$ **50.** $1\frac{3}{4}$ **51.** $\frac{17}{20}$ **52.** $2\frac{13}{200}$

53. $\frac{23}{400}$ **54.** $\frac{19}{160}$ **55.** $\frac{21}{50}$ **56.** $1\frac{3}{40}$ **57.** $\frac{41}{50}$

In exercises 58-76, use a calculator to write the given number as a percent and round to the nearest tenth of a percent.

58. $\frac{13}{6}$ **59.** $\frac{2}{3}$ **60.** $1\frac{9}{11}$ **61.** $\frac{4}{7}$ **62.** $1\frac{3}{14}$ **63.** $3\frac{7}{15}$ **64.** $1\frac{4}{9}$

65. $\frac{7}{11}$ **66.** $\frac{3}{2500}$ **67.** $\frac{53}{100}$ **68.** $\frac{5}{7}$ **69.** $\frac{1}{15}$ **70.** $\frac{4}{11}$ **71.** $\frac{10}{13}$

72. $\frac{7}{20}$ **73.** $\frac{103}{500}$ **74.** $\frac{178}{300}$ **75.** $1\frac{7}{9}$ **76.** $\frac{8}{11}$

In exercises 77-96, write the given decimal as a percent.

77. 0.505 **78.** 0.25 **79.** 2.58 **80.** 0.444 **81.** 35

82. 0.08 **83.** 0.659 **84.** 0.0015 **85.** 4 **86.** 0.02

87. 2.043 **88.** 1.007 **89.** 0.064 **90.** 0.09 **91.** 0.016

92. 0.65 **93.** 2.05 **94.** 0.275 **95.** 0.063 **96.** 1.2

In exercises 97-110, complete each row in the following table with an equivalent fraction, decimal, or percent.

	Fraction	Decimal	Percent
97.	$\frac{9}{10}$		
98.			$66\frac{2}{3}\%$
99.		1.75	
100.			50%
101.	$\frac{3}{25}$		
102.		$0.33\overline{3}$	
103.	$\frac{5}{12}$		

	Fraction	Decimal	Percent
104.			100%
105.		0.0526	
106.	$2\frac{1}{2}$		
107.			118.75%
108.		$2.9\overline{090}$	
109.	$\frac{3}{7}$		
110.			$62\frac{1}{2}\%$

Applications

111. Brooks and Foster form a partnership. If Brook's investment is $\frac{9}{16}$ of the total, find his investment as a percent.

112. An airline sold 435 tickets for a certain flight and only 412 passengers boarded the plane. What percentage of tickets sold were used for that flight. Round to the nearest tenth.

113. In an election, 50,000 out of 75,000 eligible voters cast their votes. What percent of eligible voters cast their votes? Round to the nearest tenth.

114. Mrs. Brown earns $1200 per month and saves $112. What percent of her monthly income does she save?

115. In a bulb manufacturing factory, 11 out of every 275 bulbs are found to be defective. What percent of the bulbs produced are defective?

116. There are 13 girls and 37 boys in a class. What percent of the class are girls? What percent are boys?

117. Four students are absent in a class of 30. What percent of the class is absent?

118. A mortgage interest is quoted in decimal form, as 0.03. What is this interest in percent?

6.7 PERCENT PROBLEMS USING PERCENT EQUATIONS

VOCABULARY

1. The statement "P% of B is A" is equivalent to the proportion

   $\frac{P}{100} = \frac{A}{B}$ where

   P is the **rate** or percent,

   B is the **base** representing the 'whole', and

   A is the **amount** representing the part of the whole.

   We call this the **percent proportion**.

2. The statement "P% of B is A" is equivalent to $\frac{P}{100} \cdot B = A$.

   We call this the **percent formula**.

3. To **solve** a percent problem means to find either P, B, or A when the other two are known.

4. The **complement** of a percent, P, is 100% – P.

OBJECTIVES

After completing this section you will be able to:

A. Solve problems using the percent proportion; or

B. Solve problems using the percent formula.

C. Solve general percent applications; and

D. Solve various kinds of business related percent problems.

(A.) SOLVE PROBLEMS USING THE PERCENT PROPORTION/FORMULA

➜ **Solve problems using the percent proportion.**

Illustration

- 42% of 60 is what number?

  This translates to the percent proportion:

  $\frac{42}{100} = \frac{x}{60}$, which results in

  $100x = 2520$ after you cross multiply

  So, $x = 25.2$

Verify Skill

Objective 6.7 A

What percent of 65 is 13 ?

If your answer to this question is the same as given below then you may skip this objective.

Answer: 20%.

Discussion

- There are many real life applications to percentages. In preparation to solving these, it is useful to first learn how to solve the percent proportion or the percent equation.

- Consider the statement "6% of 500 is 30".

  This statement involves three numbers:

  One: We denote 6 by P for the **percent**.

  Two: The number 500 expresses the 'whole' or the **Base** and is represented by B. The base is the number that usually follows the word "**of**" in the statement.

  Three: The number 30 is represented by A, the **Amount**.

Thus, the above statement can now be formulated as: $\frac{P}{100} = \frac{A}{B}$ or,

$$\frac{P}{100} \times B = A.$$

The equations, $\frac{\mathbf{P}}{\mathbf{100}} = \frac{\mathbf{A}}{\mathbf{B}}$ and $\frac{\mathbf{P}}{\mathbf{100}} \times \mathbf{B} = \mathbf{A}$, will be referred to as the **percent proportion** and the **percent formula** respectively.

These equations enable us to find any one of the three quantities P, B, and A when the other two are known. Thus, a percent proportion or formula can be used to answer the following types of questions:

Type I P percent of B is what number? Find A.

For example, to find 9% of 150, substitute $P = 9$ and $B = 150$ into the percent proportion. Next, solve the proportion by cross multiplying and dividing.

$\frac{9}{100} = \frac{A}{150}$ The proportion

$100A = 1350$ Cross multiply

$A = 13.5$ Divide

Thus, 9% of 150 is **13.5.**

Type II What percent of B is A? Find P%.

For example, what percent of 150 is 13.5?

Substitute $B = 150$ and $A = 13.5$ into the percent proportion.

$\frac{P}{100} = \frac{13.5}{150}$ The proportion

$150P = 1350$ Cross multiply

$P = 9\%$ Divide

Thus, 13.5 is **9%** of 150.

Type III P percent of what number is A? Find the base number B.

For example, if 9% of a number is 13.5, what is the number?

Substitute $P = 9$, and $A = 13.5$ into the percent proportion.

$\frac{9}{100} = \frac{13.5}{B}$ The proportion

$9B = 1350$ Cross multiply

$B = 150$ Divide

Thus, the desired number is **150**.

Procedure to solve percent problems using the percent proportion.

***Step* 1** Determine which two of P, B and A in the statement "P% of B is A" are known.

***Step* 2** Substitute the known values into the percent proportion, $\frac{P}{100} = \frac{A}{B}$.

***Step* 3** Solve the proportion.

EXAMPLE 1 Find 60% of 320.

Solution *Step* 1 60 is a percent so $P = 60$.

320 is the "of part" so $B = 320$

Step 2 $\frac{60}{100} = \frac{A}{320}$

Step 3 $100A = 19200$ Cross multiply

$A = 192$ Divide

Thus, 60% of 320 is 192.

EXAMPLE 2 35% of a number is 28. What is the number?

Solution *Step* 1 35 is a percent so $P = 35$.

28 is the "is part" so $A = 28$

Step 2 $\frac{35}{100} = \frac{28}{B}$

Step 3 $35B = 2800$ Cross multiply

$B = \frac{2800}{35} = 80$ Divide

Thus, the number is 80.

EXAMPLE 3 What percent of 60 is 25?

Solution *Step* 1 The "of part" is 60 so $B = 60$

The "is part" is 25 so $A = 25$

Step 2 $\frac{P}{100} = \frac{25}{60}$

Step 3 $60P = 2500$ Cross multiply

$P = \frac{2500}{60} = \frac{250}{6} = 41\frac{2}{3}$

Thus, the percent is $41\frac{2}{3}\%$.

WARM-UP

1. Find 22% of 85.

2. 72% of a number is 80. Find the number.

3. What percent of 220 is 140?

Answers:

1. 18.7 **2.** $111\frac{1}{9}$ **3.** $63\frac{7}{11}\%$

Verify Skill

Objective 6.3 B

14 is 25% of what number?

If your answer to this question is the same as given below then you may skip this objective.

Answer: 56

B. Application Problems

➡ **Solve problems using the percent formula**

Illustration

- 69 is what percent of 920?

  This translates to the percent formula:

  $$\frac{P}{100} \times 69 = 920$$

  $$\frac{69}{100} P = 920$$

  $$\frac{100}{69} \frac{69}{100} P = \frac{920}{1} \times \frac{100}{69}$$

  P = 7.5%

Discussion

- An alternative to using the percent proportion is to use the percent formula. Either will work. If your instructor does not have a preference, you may wish to try both and decide which you prefer.

> **Procedure** to solve percent problems using the percent formula.
>
> ***Step* 1** Determine which two of P, B and A in the statement "P% of B is A" are known.
>
> ***Step* 2** Substitute the known values into the percent equation, $\frac{P}{100} \cdot B = A$.
>
> ***Step* 3** Solve the resulting equation for the unknown.

Warm-Up

4. Compute $4\frac{2}{5}$% of 175.

EXAMPLE 4 Compute $10\frac{1}{2}$% of 250.

Solution

Step 1 $10\frac{1}{2}$ is the percent so $P = 10\frac{1}{2}$.

250 is the "of part" so $B = 250$.

Step 2 $$\frac{P}{100} \cdot B = A \quad \rightarrow \quad \frac{10\frac{1}{2}}{100} \cdot 250 = A$$

Step 3 $$\frac{10\frac{1}{2}}{100} \cdot 250 = A \quad \rightarrow \quad 10\frac{1}{2} \div 100 \cdot 250 = A$$

$$\frac{21}{2} \cdot \frac{1}{100} \cdot 250 = A$$

$$A = \frac{21}{200} \cdot \frac{250}{1}$$

$$= \frac{105}{4} = 26\frac{1}{4}.$$

So, $10\frac{1}{2}\%$ of 250 is $26\frac{1}{4}$.

EXAMPLE 5 $16\frac{2}{3}\%$ of a number is 50. What is the number?

Solution

Step 1 $16\frac{2}{3}$ is the percent so $P = 16\frac{2}{3} = \frac{50}{3}$

The "is part" is 50 so $A = 50$.

Step 2 Substitute the values of P and A in the percent formula $\frac{P}{100} \cdot B = A$

$$\frac{\frac{50}{3}}{100} \cdot B = 50$$

Step 3

$$\left(\frac{50}{3}\right)B = 100\,(50)$$

Multiply both sides of the equation by 100.

$$\left(\frac{50}{3}\right)B = 5000$$

$$B = 5000 \times \frac{3}{50}$$

Multiply both sides by the reciprocal.

$$B = 300$$

So, $16\frac{2}{3}\%$ of 300 is 50.

Check:

$$16\frac{2}{3}\% \text{ of } 300 = \frac{50}{3}\% \text{ of } 300$$

$$= \frac{50}{3}\left(\frac{1}{100}\right)(300) = \frac{50 \times 300}{3 \times 100} = 50,$$ which is **true**.

EXAMPLE 6 What percent of 75 is 8. Round to the nearest tenth of a percent.

Solution Here, $B = 75$, and $A = 8$

$$\frac{P}{100} \cdot B = A \rightarrow \frac{P}{100} \cdot 75 = 8 \rightarrow 75P = 100(8)$$

WARM-UP

5. 5% of a number is 24. Find the number.

6. What % of 120 is 30? Find the answer to the nearest whole number.

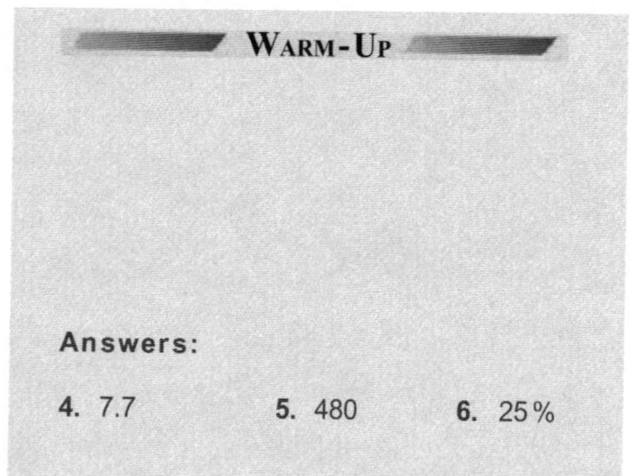

Warm-Up

Answers:

4. 7.7 5. 480 6. 25%

$$75P = 800 \rightarrow P = \frac{800}{75} = \frac{32}{3} \approx 10.67$$

$P \approx 10.67 \approx 10.7$ to the nearest tenth.

10.7% of 75 is 8.

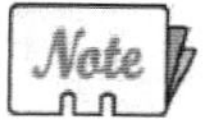

Since 10.7% is the rounded figure, 10.7% of 75 will be approximately equal to 8. Check that 10.7% of 75 = 8.025 ≈ 8.

C. Solve General Percent Applications

Discussion

- In daily life, it is often necessary to compute certain percents of a number or quantity.

  For example, if an article marked as \$750 is selling at a 15% discount, then computing the net price of the article requires computing the amount of the discount; that is 15% **of** \$750.

  Thus, 15 % of 750 means:

  $$15 \div 100 \times 750 = \frac{15}{100} \times 750 = 0.15 \times 750 = 112.5$$

  15% of \$750 = \$112.50, which is the total amount of the discount, so.

  the net price of the article is the Marked Price − Discount = \$750 − \$112.50 = \$637.50

- If we want to invest \$5000 at a rate of 11% per year, then to compute the interest for one year we need to compute 11% of \$5000.

  The income for one year = the amount of interest on \$5000 at the rate of 11%

  $$= 11\% \text{ of } \$5000 = \frac{11}{100} \times 5000 = \$550$$

- If 27% of the population of a certain country is rural, the *percentage* of people living in rural areas is 27%. This means that out of every 100 people, 27 live in rural areas. Obviously then, 100 – 27, or 73, people out of every 100 live in urban areas. Alternatively, the *percentage* of people living in urban areas is 73%. In this case, 73% is called the *complement* of 27 %. (Note that *rural* and *urban* are used as complementary terms.)

  The **complement** of a given percent is obtained by subtracting the given percent from 100%. Thus, the complement of 40% is 100% – 40% or 60%.

  In the following figure.

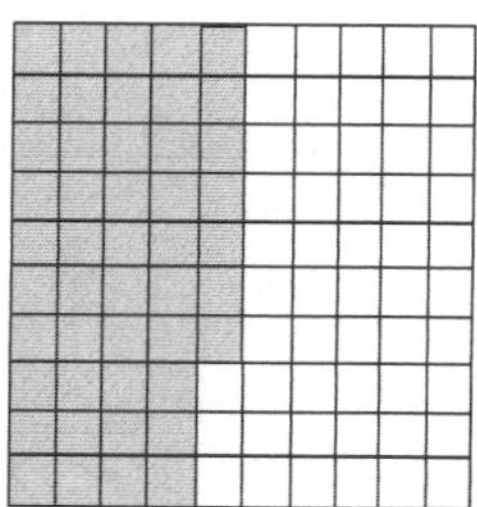

47% of the region is shaded. The percentage of the *unshaded* region is then 100 − 47 = 53%. Note that the shaded and the *unshaded* regions are complements of each other.

EXAMPLE 7 Mr. Smith earned \$15,000 last year. His total deductions amounted to 24% of his earnings. What was his take-home salary?

Solution

Deductions = 24% of \$15,000

= 24 ÷ 100 × 15,000

= \$3600

Therefore, his take-home salary = Total earnings − deductions

= \$15,000 − \$3,600

= **\$11,400.**

Alternatively,

The complement of 24% = (100 − 24)% = 76 %

Deductions and take home salary are complementary terms in this case.

The take home salary = 76 % of \$15,000

= 76 ÷ 100 × 15,000 = **\$11,400.**

EXAMPLE 8 A census determines that 20% of the residents of a certain city are age 50 or over, while $34\frac{1}{2}\%$ are age 25 or under. What is the percentage of the residents between the ages of 25 and 50?

Solution

Since the percentage of residents age 50 or over is 20%,

and the percentage of residents age 25 or under is $34\frac{1}{2}\%$,

the percentage of the residents not covered in the above categories is

WARM-UP

7. The listed price of a T.V. is \$575. If there is a 5% discount, how much does the T.V. cost?

8. If $17\frac{1}{2}\%$ of a region is shaded in blue, 52% in pink, and the remaining part in yellow, what percent of the region is shaded in yellow?

WARM-UP

Answers:

7. \$546.25 8. $30\frac{1}{2}\%$

$$\left(100-20-34\frac{1}{2}\right)\%$$

$$= 45\frac{1}{2}\%$$

$45\frac{1}{2}\%$ of the residents are between the ages of 25 and 50.

D. SOLVE VARIOUS KINDS OF BUSINESS-RELATED PERCENT PROBLEMS

Discussion

Most word problems can be translated into the simpler form, "**what percent of what is what?**", which can be solved using a percent proportion or formula. Among these are problems on profit and loss, interest rates, taxes *etc*. Below are some of the most common applications.

Percent increase – markups

In retailing, goods are purchased at a cost price (C) and sold at a higher figure (L), the list price. The difference, $L - C$, is called the **markup**. Percentage mark up is usually based on the *cost price*. For example, if the cost (C) of an article selling for 80 cents (L) is 50 cents, then the percentage mark up can be computed by solving the percent proportion $\frac{P}{100} = \frac{\text{mark up}}{\text{cost price}}$.

$$\frac{P}{100} = \frac{80-50}{50} \rightarrow \frac{P}{100} = \frac{3}{5} \rightarrow 5P = 300 \rightarrow P = 60$$

The percent mark up is **60**% of the cost price.

Other similar problems on percent increase include population increase and salary increase. (See examples 11 and 12).

Percent decrease - discounts

An article originally listed at a certain price may sell at a discounted price, that is the price may be lowered by a certain percentage. The *base* for calculation of *discount* is always the list price. For example, if the list price of a Honda Civic, selling at a discounted price of \$13,770, is \$16,200, then the percent of the discount can be computed by solving the following percent proportion:

$$\frac{P}{100} = \frac{A}{B} \rightarrow \frac{P}{100} = \frac{\text{discount}}{\text{list price}} = \frac{16{,}200-13{,}770}{16{,}200} = \frac{2{,}430}{16{,}200}$$

or

$$\frac{P}{100} = \frac{2{,}430}{16{,}200} \rightarrow 16200P = 243000 \rightarrow P = \frac{2{,}43000}{16{,}200} = 15$$

Thus, the rate of discount $= 15\%$

The concept of percent is frequently used in computing **simple interest** on bank deposits or on investments. Interest for one year can be computed by solving the following percent proportion:

$$\frac{P}{100} = \frac{A}{B} \rightarrow \frac{\text{rate}}{100} = \frac{\text{interest}}{\text{principal}}$$

For example, the interest on $2500 deposited in a bank for 2 years with an interest rate of 5% per year is computed as follows:

First solve for interest for one year ;

$$\frac{\text{rate}}{100} = \frac{\text{interest}}{\text{principal}} \rightarrow \frac{5}{100} = \frac{I}{2500} \rightarrow I = 125$$

So, in 2 years the interest would be $\$125 \times 2 = \$250$

Procedure to solve application problems involving percents using a percent proportion.

***Step* 1** Write the problem in the form "P% of B is A".

***Step* 2** Fill in the known values and find the unknown value using the proportion $\frac{P}{100} = \frac{A}{B}$.

EXAMPLE 9 Ms. Johnson deposited $8250 with a finance company which pays 14.5% simple interest per year. Find the total amount she will have after 3 years.

Solution

14.5% of $8250 is I. Here I denotes the interest per year.

$$\frac{14.5}{100} = \frac{I}{8250} \rightarrow 100I = 119625 \rightarrow I = 1196.25$$

The interest per year is $1196.25

Therefore, the interest for **3** years

$= \mathbf{3}(1196.25) = \$3588.75$

Multiply the amount of the interest per year by 3.

After three years, she has:

The amount she gets after 3 years = The amount deposited + the interest for 3 years.

$8250 + $3588.75 = **$11,838.75**

Alternative Method:

Solve this problem using the percent formula "$I = P \cdot r \cdot t$" where

$P = 8250$, $r = 14.5\% = 0.145$, and $t = 3$ years

Therefore, $I = 8250 \times 0.145 \times 3 = 3588.75$

The interest for three years $= \$3588.75$

WARM-UP

9. Mr. William deposits $7580 at a bank. The bank pays simple interest at a rate of 7.5% per year. Find the interest and the total amount he will have after $2\frac{1}{2}$ years.

WARM-UP

10. Mrs. Johnson deposited $850 in a bank that pays simple interest at a rate of 6.2% per year.

(a) Find the interest on this amount after 3 years.

(b) Find the total value of his deposit after 3 years.

11. Jack buys an old typewriter for $265 and spends $18 on its repairs. He sells it for $260. Find his loss percentage. Round to the nearest whole number percent.

EXAMPLE 10 Mr. Smith deposited $1250 in a bank that pays simple interest at a rate of 5.5% per year.

(a) Find the interest on this amount after $2\frac{1}{2}$ years rounded to the nearest cent.

(b) Find the total value of his account after $2\frac{1}{2}$ years.

Solutions

(a) Let I be the interest after one year.

then $\frac{5.5}{100} = \frac{I}{1250} \rightarrow 100I = 6875 \rightarrow I = 68.75$

So, the interest after $2\frac{1}{2}$ years is

$68.75 \times 2.5 = 171.875 \approx \$171.88$

(b) Total value of the account after $2\frac{1}{2}$ years.

= Principal + Interest

= $1250 + $171.88 = $1421.88

EXAMPLE 11 David buys a used car for $6650. He spends $1230 on its repairs and sells it for $8125. Find his profit percent. Round to the nearest hundredth of a percent, if necessary.

Solution

Cost price = $6650 + $1230 = $7880 (Cost price includes the cost of repairs.)

Selling price = $8125

Profit = $8125 – $7880 = $245 (Total profit = The selling price – the cost price.)

The problem now reduces to:

What percent of $7880 is $245? (Profit (or loss) percent is always computed on the cost price.)

$B = 7880, \; A = 245$

Using the percent proportion $\frac{P}{100} = \frac{A}{B}$ we get,

$$\frac{P}{100} = \frac{245}{7880} \rightarrow 7880P = 24500$$

$\rightarrow \quad P = \frac{24500}{7880} \approx 3.109$ Divide upto 3 decimal places.

$P \approx$ **3.11** to the nearest hundredth of a percent.

David's profit percent is approximately 3.11%.

Warm-Up

EXAMPLE 12 A new burning process used in the manufacturing of bricks increased the output of bricks from 1300 to 2200 bricks per cubic meter of furnace. What is the percent increase in the production of bricks? Round the percent to the nearest whole number.

Solution

The original number of bricks: 1300

The new number of bricks: 2200

The actual increase in the number of bricks: 2200 – 1300 = **900**

The problem reduces to:

What % of 1300 is 900? The increase or decrease is computed using the original number.

$B = 1300$, and

$A = 900$

Using the percent proportion $\frac{P}{100} = \frac{A}{B}$

$$\frac{P}{100} = \frac{900}{1300}$$

$$1300\,P = 100\,(900) \qquad \text{Cross multiply.}$$

$$P = \frac{90000}{1300} = \frac{900}{13} \approx 69.2 \qquad \text{Divide to one decimal place.}$$

$P \approx 69$ to the nearest whole number.

Brick production was increased by 69%

12. John's salary per month increased from \$2400 to \$2800. Find the percent increase of his salary rounded to a whole number.

EXAMPLE 13 Wage rates of \$4.50 per hour increased by 20%. What is the new rate?

Solution

The increase is 20 % of the original rate; so letting I be the increase, we get

$$\frac{20}{100} = \frac{I}{4.50} \rightarrow 100I = 90 \rightarrow I = 0.9$$

The new rate = Old rate + increase

= \$4.50 + \$0.90

The new rate = **\$5.40** per hour.

13. The monthly salary of an employee in a factory increases by 15%. If his salary increases by \$51.75, what was the original salary? Also find the new salary.

WARM-UP

14. An article, whose cost price is \$0.85 sells at \$1.19. Find the percent of the markup.

EXAMPLE 14 The cost of an article is \$6.40, and the selling price is \$10.24. What is the percent markup?

Solution

Markup is \$ 10.24 – \$ 6.40 = \$ 3.84.

The problem is "What percent of \$ 6.40 is \$ 3.84?"

Use the percent proportion $\frac{P}{100} = \frac{A}{B}$,

where $B = 6.40$, $A = 3.84$

$$\frac{P}{100} = \frac{3.84}{6.40} \rightarrow 6.40P = 384$$

$$\rightarrow P = \mathbf{60\%} \text{ Markup}$$

15. A departmental store declares a $33\frac{1}{3}$ % discount on the marked prices of all items. What is the sale price of a toaster that is marked \$28.96? (Round to the nearest hundredth)

EXAMPLE 15 A general store, during its annual inventory clearance sale, offered a 45% discount on the marked prices of all goods. What is the sale price of an item marked \$40?

Solution

45% of \$40 is the discount.

Use the percent proportion $\frac{P}{100} = \frac{A}{B}$,

$$\frac{45}{100} = \frac{A}{40} \rightarrow 100A = 1800 \rightarrow A = 18$$

Therefore, the discount is \$18.

The sale price = \$40 – \$18 (The sale price = Marked price – Discount)

= **\$22**

The sales price is \$22 for an item that is marked \$40.

16. For a single person, there is no tax on income up to \$15000, but all income in excess of \$15000 up to \$25,000 is taxed at 19%, and all above \$25,000 is taxed at 23%. What is the total tax paid by a single person whose income is \$42000?

EXAMPLE 16 A real estate commission is computed at 5% on the first \$5000, 3% on amounts above \$5000 up to \$100,000, 2% on the amount above \$100,000. What is the commission on a \$161,250 sale?

Solution

There are three slabs of commission.

(i) Commission on the *first* \$5000 at the rate of 5% is

$$5\% \text{ of } \$5000 = \frac{5}{100} \times 5000 = \mathbf{\$250}$$

(ii) Commission on the *next* \$95000 at the rate of 3% is (\$100,000 – \$5000 = \$95,000)

3% of $95,000

$$= \frac{3}{100} \times 95{,}000 = \mathbf{\$2850}$$

(iii) Commission on the remaining $61,250 at the rate of 2% is

$161,250 – $100,000 = $61,250

2% of $61,250

$$= \frac{2}{100} \times 61{,}250 = \mathbf{\$1225}$$

The total commission is

$$\$250 + \$2850 + \$1225 = \mathbf{\$4325}$$

EXAMPLE 17 The value of a new automobile depreciates 13% during the first year, and 14% during the second year. What is its depreciated value at the end of the second year, if its original cost was $11,500?

Solution

Let the amount of depreciation during the first year be D_1. Then.

$$\frac{13}{100} = \frac{D_1}{11500} \rightarrow 100D_1 = 149500$$

The *base* for the depreciation is the original cost.

$$\rightarrow D_1 = \mathbf{\$1495}$$

The depreciated value at the end of the first year is

The depreciated value is the original value minus the depreciation.

$$\$11{,}500 - \$1495 = \mathbf{\$10{,}005}$$

The depreciation during the second year is calculated by

The depreciated value at the end of the first year is considered the original cost at the beginning of the second year.

$$\frac{14}{100} = \frac{D_2}{10005} \rightarrow 100D_2 = 140070$$

$$\rightarrow D_2 = \mathbf{\$1400.70}$$

Therefore, the depreciated value of the automobile at the end of the second year is

$$\$10{,}005 - \$1400.70 = \mathbf{\$8604.30}$$

The value at the end of the second year is the value at the beginning of the second year the depreciation during the second year.

17. A refrigerator is selling at a discount of 12%. An additional discount of 3% is offered for cash payments only. How much is it if its market price is $380, and the payment is made in cash? Round to the nearest cent, if necessary.

(***Hint:*** *The second discount is computed on the price after the first discount)*

Answers:

9. $1421.25 ; $9001.25

10. **(a)** $158.1 **(b)** $1008.1

11. 8 % **12.** 17 %

13. $345 ; $396.75 **14.** 40 %

15. $19.31 **16.** $5810

17. $324.37

Exercise 6.7

In exercises 1-15, use the percent proportion or the percent formula to evaluate the expression.

1. 3.75% of 1000 **2.** 20% of 125 boys **3.** 40% of 280 horses **4.** $3\frac{1}{3}\%$ of 90 miles

5. 0.5% of 1000 **6.** 7.5% of $465 **7.** 6.25% of $1200 **8.** 125% of 200

9. 40% of 1365 **10.** 16% of 350 **11.** 5% of 720 **12.** 15% of 280 boxes

13. 12% of 435 **14.** $16\frac{2}{3}\%$ of 16 **15.** 37% of 60

In exercises 16-25, use the percent proportion or the percent formula to find the number.

16. 12.5 is 8% of what number? **17.** 150 is 150% of what number?

18. 42 is 6% of what number? **19.** $35 is 14% of what amount?

20. 1.03 is 4% of what number? Express the answer as a mixed number.

21. 150 chairs is 20% of how many chairs? **22.** 198 is 36% of what number?

23. 10 is 1% of what number? **24.** 27.5 is $2\frac{3}{4}\%$ of what number?

25. 11% of what number is 33.

In exercises 26-30, use the percent proportion or the percent formula to find the percent.

26. What % of 285 is 114?

27. What % of 22 is 7? Round to the nearest whole number percent.

28. What percent of $18.50 is $5.55?

29. What percent of $65,000 is $4875?

30. What percent of 1850 is 9.25?

31. Smith saves 15% of his monthly income. Find his monthly expenses if his income is $1250.

32. Johnson finished 73% of his homework. What percent of his homework is yet to be done?

33. If a contractor has completed 58% of a job, what percent remains to be completed?

34. 15% of a figure is shaded blue, and 24% of the same figure is shaded yellow. The remaining part is shaded red. What percent of the figure is shaded red?

35. In a gathering consisting of 160 men, women and children, 50% are men and 35% are women. Find the number of children.

36. Cynthia earned $120.50 in one week. The following week she earned 50% more. How much did she earn the second week?

37. The cost of a certain article increases from $50 to $60. What is the percentage increase?

38. The price of gasoline per gallon increased from 49 cents to $1.20 from 1971 to 1983. What was the percentage increase during this period?

39. In a "25%-off" sale, Jack saves $15 on an item. What was the original cost of the item?

40. Tax payments of $3862 represented 4.3% of a company's gross income. What was its gross income? Round to the nearest dollar.

41. An article costing $26.00 is given a markup of 32%. What is the selling price of that article?

42. A car salesman receives $12\frac{1}{2}$% commission for each car and 20% for all accessories sold. What commission is made on the sale of a car at $12,630 and accessories at $106.50? Round to the nearest cent.

43. The number of students admitted to a school increased from 360 to 432 in a year. Find the percent increase.

44. Mrs. Johnson invested $1,750 at 3% interest and $1,550 at 4% interest. What is the rate of interest on the total investment? Round the answer to the nearest tenth of a percent.

45. A firm buys a new car that costs $13,800. During the first year its value depreciates by $12\frac{1}{2}$% of its original value. What will its value be at the end of the year? If its value depreciates 13% during the second year, assess its value at the end of the second year.

46. A video camera is priced to sell for $560. If the markup is 40% of the cost price, what is the cost of the video camera?

47. Smith works with Fleet Jeweler. He receives a salary of $175 per week plus a commission of 1% of his total sales. He gets an additional commission of 0.5% on all sales above $25,000. What is his total income for the week if he sells $54,000 worth of jewelry?

48. An article that costs a shopkeeper $8.43 is to be marked up by $2.81. What is the percent of markup based on the cost?

49. Clark buys an old T.V. for $215 and spends $40 on repairs. He sells it at a loss of 15%. At what price is the T.V. sold?

50. Mrs. Johnson visits a department store and buys the following articles:

(i) One toaster for \$75, **(ii)** One shirt for \$15,

(iii) One pair of shoes for \$65, **(iv)** One pair of jeans for \$55,

Calculate the total amount of the bill including a 5% sales tax on the goods purchased.

51. A man makes a profit of \$378 by selling a carpet for \$2750. Find his profit percentage. Round to the nearest percent.

(***Hint***: Cost price = selling price   profit)

52. A store manager raises the prices of all the articles in his store by 20% and then declares "15% off" on each article. What will a customer pay for an article whose original price was \$1350.

53. Income Tax rates are as follow:

Income	Tax
Up to 12,000	0%
12,001 to 28,000	15%
28,001 to 38,000	18%
above 38,000	21%

Calculate the income tax payable by Mr. Brown if his annual income is \$75,000?

54. Compute the interest in the following cases using the formula $I = P \cdot r \cdot t$ for the interest.

(a) Principal, P = \$1750, rate of interests, r = 4% per year, and time, t = 2 years.

(b) P = \$1200, r = .05 per year, and t = 3 years. **(c)** P = 45, r = 3.5% per year, and t = 1.5 years.

55. Ms. Cynthia deposited \$1450 in a saving account that pays 8% annual simple interest. Find the value of the deposit after 3 years.

6.8 Rational Numbers: Identifying and Graphing

Vocabulary

Objectives

After completing this section you will be able to:

A. Identify rational numbers; and

B. Graph rational numbers on a number line.

1. A **fraction,** such as $\frac{3}{5}$ (read as **three-fifths**), is the name for a number.
2. A fraction has three components:

   (i) A horizontal line called the **fraction bar** ;

   (ii) A number above the fraction bar called the **numerator**; and

   (iii) A number below the fraction bar called the **denominator.**

   $$\text{Fraction bar} \longleftarrow \frac{\mathbf{2}}{\mathbf{7}} \begin{array}{l} \longrightarrow \text{Numerator} \\ \longrightarrow \text{Denominator} \end{array}$$

3. The term **rational number** is the technical term for a *fraction.*
4. A **rational number** is a number that can be written in the form $\frac{a}{b}$, where a and b are integers and $b \neq 0$.

A. Identify Rational Numbers

We have been working with the set of integers. We have seen that when we add, subtract, or multiply two integers, the answer is always an integer. This is not true for division of integers.

When we divide one integer by another integer, the result (quotient) may be an integer, or it may not be an integer.

For example, $12 \div (-3) = \frac{12}{-3} = -4$ is an integer;

but $(-3) \div 12 = \frac{-3}{12} = \frac{-1}{4}$ is not an integer.

This does not mean that we can not divide two integers. It simply means that when we divide two integers, we do not *always* get another integer.

$$\frac{1}{4}, \frac{2}{3}, \frac{-3}{4}, \frac{5}{-7}, \frac{-13}{-95}$$

These are just a few of the infinitely many numbers that we can obtain when we divide an integer by another integer. Such numbers are called **fractions** or **rational numbers.** Unless stated otherwise, we will use the terms *fraction* and *rational number* to mean the same thing. The word *rational* has the root word *ratio*. A rational number is a ratio or comparison of two integers, using division.

In chapters 1 and 2, we have emphasized that **division by 0 is not defined**. We reinforce the same thing here again: **We cannot divide by 0.**

Definition

A rational number is a number that can be written as a ratio $\frac{a}{b}$, where a and b are integers, and $b \neq 0$. $\frac{a}{b}$ ($a \longrightarrow$ Numerator, $b \longrightarrow$ Denominator)

- In previous chapters, we used the fraction form of a number to indicate division.

Examples: $\frac{-14}{2} = -7$; $\frac{25}{5} = 5$; $\frac{9}{-3} = -3$; $\frac{-12}{-4} = 3$

With this concept, a division represented in fraction form, every integer can be written in the form of a fraction with a denominator of 1.

$0 = \frac{0}{1}$, $1 = \frac{1}{1}$, $2 = \frac{2}{1}$, $3 = \frac{3}{1}$, ...

$-1 = \frac{-1}{1}$, $-2 = \frac{-2}{1}$, $-3 = \frac{-3}{1}$, ... and so on.

Every integer is a rational number.

We shall make no distinction between an integer n and the rational number $\frac{n}{1}$; thus, $n = \frac{n}{1}$ for each integer n.

WARM-UP

1. Which of the following numbers are rational numbers?

$14, 3, -\frac{7}{4}, \frac{9}{0}, -4$

Answer:

1. Except $\frac{9}{0}$, all are rational numbers.

EXAMPLE 1 Which of the following numbers are rational numbers?

$-5,\ \frac{-3}{5},\ 0,\ \frac{-5}{0},\ \frac{-12}{3},\ 4,\ \frac{0}{-2},\ \frac{3}{-1}$

Solution

Only $\frac{-5}{0}$ is not rational. In fact $\frac{-5}{0}$ is undefined. All other numbers are rational numbers. The number -5 can be written as $\frac{-5}{1}$.

The number 4 can be written as $\frac{4}{1}$.

The number 0 can be written as $\frac{0}{1}$.

- **Proper and Improper Fractions:** Non-negative fractions whose numerators are *less than* the denominators are called *proper fractions*. If the numerator is greater than or equal to the denominator then the fraction is called an improper fraction.

Examples: $\frac{1}{2}$, $\frac{3}{8}$, $\frac{7}{9}$, and $\frac{9}{11}$ are **proper** fractions.

4, $\frac{5}{2}$, $\frac{7}{5}$, $\frac{9}{9}$, and $\frac{21}{19}$ are **improper** fractions.

The value of an improper fraction in which the numerator is *equal* to the denominator is always 1, as reflected in the following examples:

$$\frac{8}{8}=1\,; \qquad \frac{25}{25}=1\,; \qquad \frac{4}{4}=1\,; \qquad \frac{-6}{-6}=1$$

- **Algebraic fractions** or rational expressions are fractions where the numerator or the denominator contains variable(s) instead of just integers.

  Some examples of algebraic fractions are given below:

  $$\frac{3x}{2y}\,; \qquad \frac{3ax^2}{5by}\,; \qquad \frac{12xy^2}{8x^2z}\,; \qquad -\frac{ab}{5a^2x}$$

- **Positive and Negative Rational Numbers:** Recall that the quotient of two integers with *like* signs is always positive $\left(\frac{45}{5}=9\ ;\ \frac{-24}{-6}=4\right)$ and the quotient of two integers with *unlike* signs is negative $\left(\frac{-35}{7}=-5\ ;\ \frac{18}{-3}=-6\right)$. Rational numbers like $\frac{1}{5}$, $\frac{3}{8}$, and $\frac{-4}{-9}$ are *positive rationals*; rational numbers like $\frac{-35}{7}$, $\frac{18}{-3}$, $\frac{-5}{3}$, and $\frac{2}{-7}$ are *negative rationals.*

  Let us observe the following three relationships:

  $$-\frac{15}{3} = -(15 \div 3)\,; \qquad \frac{-15}{3} = (-15) \div 3\,; \qquad \frac{15}{-3} = 15 \div (-3)\,;$$

  $$= \mathbf{-5} \qquad\qquad = \mathbf{-5} \qquad\qquad = \mathbf{-5}$$

  therefore, $-\frac{15}{3} = \frac{-15}{3} = \frac{15}{-3}$.

  We can conclude that a negative sign in a rational number can be placed in any one of the three positions without changing the meaning or the value of that number. Also, since $\frac{-18}{-6}=3$, and $\frac{18}{6}=3$, we observe that $\frac{-18}{-6} = \frac{18}{6}$; thus, we have the following rule:

Rule for the placement of Negative Signs

If a and b are two integers and $b \neq 0$, then

- $\frac{-a}{b} = \frac{a}{-b} = -\frac{\boldsymbol{a}}{\boldsymbol{b}}$
- $\frac{-\boldsymbol{a}}{-\boldsymbol{b}} = \frac{\boldsymbol{a}}{\boldsymbol{b}}$
- $-\frac{-a}{b} = \frac{-(-a)}{b} = \frac{\boldsymbol{a}}{\boldsymbol{b}}$, and
- $-\frac{a}{-b} = \frac{a}{-(-b)} = \frac{\boldsymbol{a}}{\boldsymbol{b}}$.

WARM-UP

2. Write one or more equivalent variations of each rational number that differs from the given number only in signs.

(a) $\frac{4}{3}$ **(b)** $-\frac{4}{5}$

(c) $\frac{-7}{-3}$ **(d)** $\frac{-5}{8}$

(e) $\frac{7}{-9}$

Answers:

2. (a) $\frac{-4}{-3}, -\frac{-4}{3}$ (b) $\frac{-4}{5}, \frac{4}{-5}$

(c) $\frac{7}{3}, -\frac{-7}{3}$ (d) $-\frac{5}{8}, \frac{5}{-8}$.

(e) $\frac{-7}{9}, -\frac{7}{9}$.

EXAMPLE 2 Write one or more equivalent variations of each rational number that differs from the given number only in signs.

(a) $-\frac{5}{6}$ **(b)** $\frac{15}{17}$ **(c)** $\frac{4}{-3}$ **(d)** $\frac{-8}{-9}$ **(e)** $\frac{-1}{2}$

Solutions

(a) $-\frac{5}{6}$ is equivalent to $\frac{-5}{6}$ and $\frac{5}{-6}$.

(b) $\frac{15}{17}$ is equivalent to $\frac{-15}{-17}$, $-\frac{15}{-17}$, and $-\frac{-15}{17}$.

(c) $\frac{4}{-3}$ is equivalent to $\frac{-4}{3}$ and $-\frac{4}{3}$.

(d) $\frac{-8}{-9}$ is equivalent to $-\frac{8}{-9}$ and $-\frac{-8}{9}$.

(e) $\frac{-1}{2}$ is equivalent to $-\frac{1}{2}$ and $\frac{1}{-2}$.

Now we can define *positive* and *negative* rational numbers:

- A rational number of the form $\frac{a}{b}$ is **positive** if either both a and b are positive integers or both a and b are negative integers.

  Example: $\frac{15}{3} = 15 \div 3 = \mathbf{5}$; $\frac{-15}{-3} = (-15) \div (-3) = \mathbf{5}$

  therefore, $\frac{-15}{-3} = \frac{15}{3}$.

- A rational number of the form $\frac{a}{b}$ is **negative** if a and b have opposite signs.

  Examples: $\frac{-15}{3} = (-15) \div 3 = -\mathbf{5}$;

  $\frac{15}{-3} = (15) \div (-3) = -\mathbf{5}$;

  therefore, $\frac{-15}{3} = \frac{15}{-3} = -5 = -\frac{15}{3}$.

B. Graph Rational Numbers on a Number Line

Just as we graphed integers on a number line, we can also graph the rational numbers (fractions) on a number line. To represent rational numbers on a number line, it is necessary to consider them as fractions (or parts) of a whole. We can interpret the numerator and the denominator of, say, $\frac{2}{3}$ in different ways.

$2 \longrightarrow$ The *numerator* counts the actual number of pieces of a unit.

$3 \longrightarrow$ The *denominator* describes the total number of pieces in a whole or a unit.

$\frac{2}{3}$ can be read "2 out of 3" equal parts in a unit or "two-thirds" of a unit.

To illustrate $\frac{7}{3}$ requires that several units be broken into thirds, so that we can count 7 thirds.

Consider the following number line:

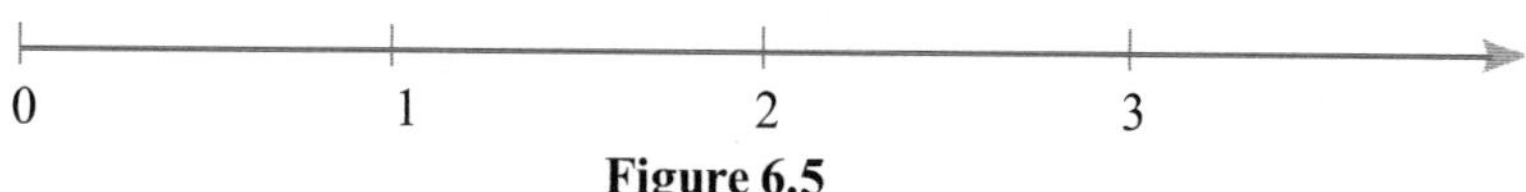

Figure 6.5

Divide each of these units into three equal parts as shown in Figure 6.6.

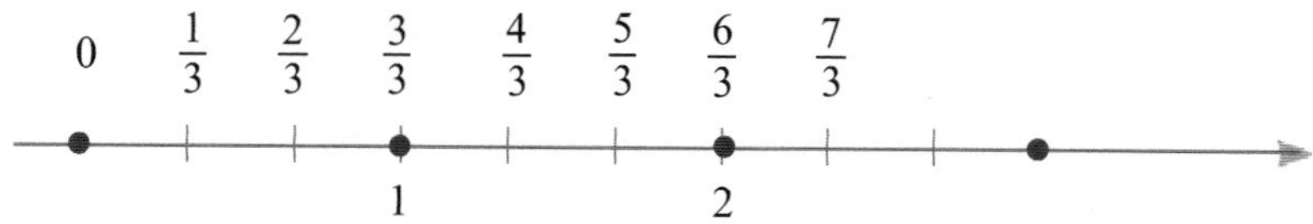

Figure 6.6

$\frac{1}{3}, \frac{2}{3}, \frac{3}{3}, \frac{7}{3}$ represent distances from zero (0).

In Figure 3.3, each unit is divided into 4 equal parts. Each segment is $\frac{1}{4}$ of a unit.

0 $\frac{1}{4}$ $\frac{2}{4}$ $\frac{3}{4}$ $\frac{4}{4}$ or 1 $\frac{10}{4}$

Figure 6.7

$\frac{1}{4}, \frac{2}{4}, \frac{3}{4}$, and $\frac{10}{4}$ represent distances from zero (0).

WARM-UP

3. Represent the fractions $\frac{1}{3}$ and $\frac{5}{3}$ on a number line.

EXAMPLE 3 Graph the fractions $\frac{2}{5}$ and $\frac{8}{5}$ on a number line.

Solution

Step 1 Draw a number line, indicating 0, 1, and 2.

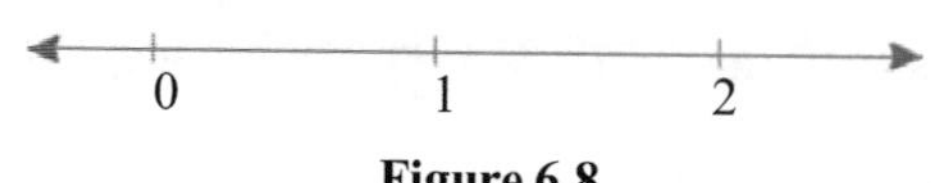

Figure 6.8

Step 2 Divide each of these units into five equal pieces because the denominator of both fractions is 5. Mark the ends of each piece with a tick mark (Figure 6.8a).

Step 3 **(i)** For $\frac{2}{5}$, count 2 pieces starting from the point 0, because the numerator is 2. Mark the point with a dot.

This dot is the graph of $\frac{2}{5}$.

Figure 6.8a

(ii) For $\frac{8}{5}$, count to the end of the 8th piece from 0, or 3 pieces from 1. Mark with a dot.

This dot is the graph of $\frac{8}{5}$.

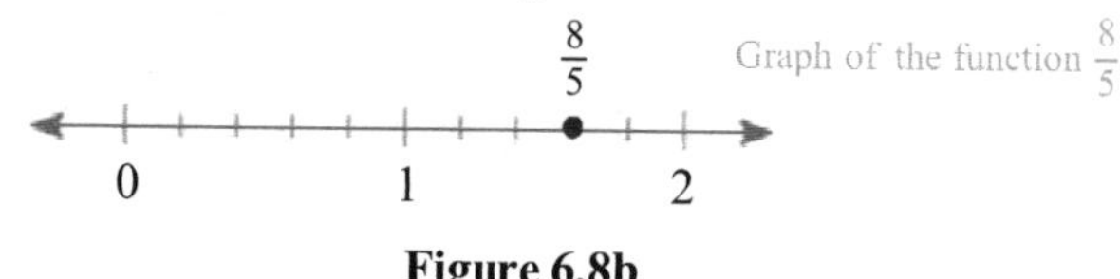

Figure 6.8b

The unit may also be shown on a ruler. The fraction $\frac{7}{10}$ represents the distance from 0 to the arrow in Figure 6.9:

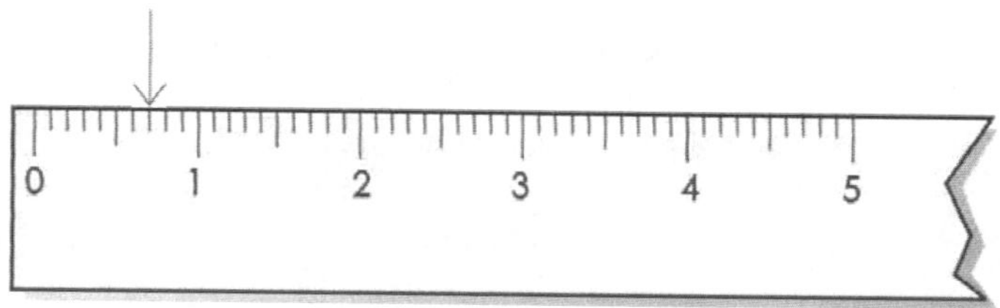

Figure 6.9

When using a ruler, representing the denominator correctly requires accurately counting the number of pieces in a whole.

EXAMPLE 4 Use a ruler to measure (in cm) the following objects. Express your answer as fractions.

(a) The diameter of a quarter

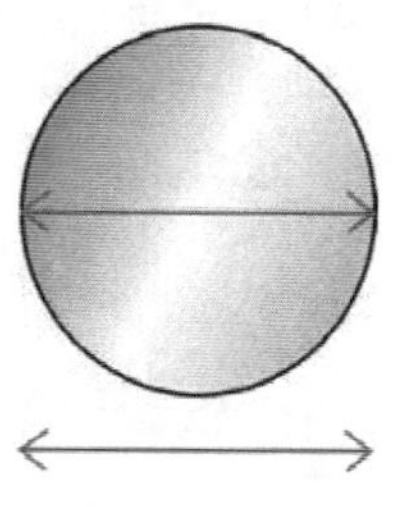

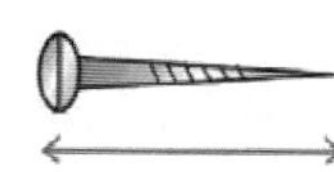

(b) The length of this nail

Solutions

(a) First count the pieces in 1 cm on your ruler. There are 10 pieces in 1 cm; so, the denominator for the length (in cm) of the diameter of a quarter must be $\frac{?}{10}$.

Next count the actual pieces in the length: $\frac{23}{10}$ cm.

(b) Similarly the length of the nail is $\frac{20}{10}$ cm.

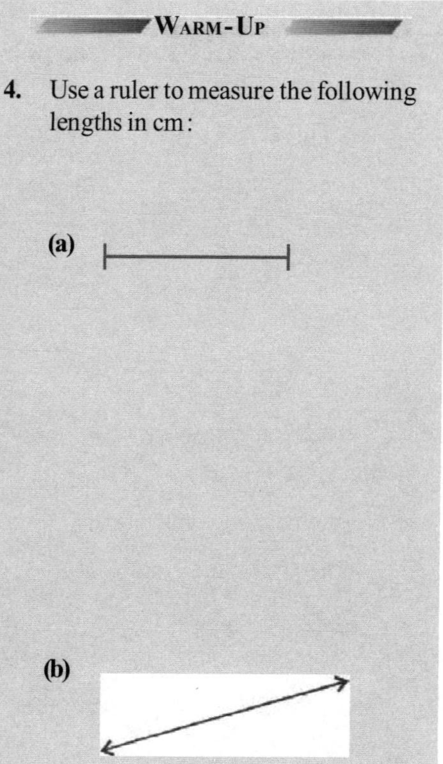

On the number line in Figure 6.10, the number $\frac{1}{2}$ lies one-half of the way between 0 and 1, while $\frac{3}{4}$ lies three-fourths of the way between 0 and 1.

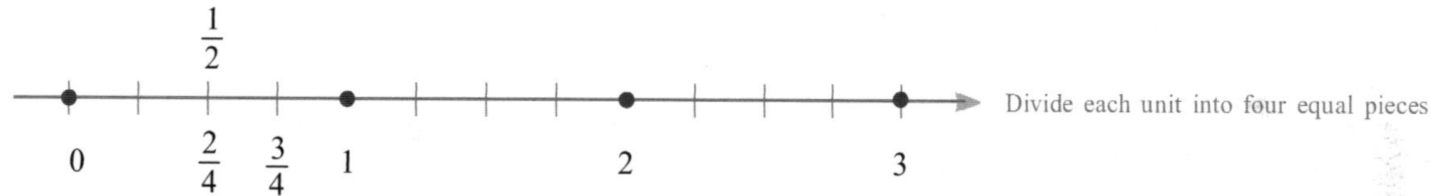

Figure 6.10

The fraction $\frac{3}{4}$ is three of the four equal pieces of a unit.

$3 \longrightarrow$ Number of pieces
4 Number of equal pieces in a unit

> **Note** The denominator gives the number of pieces in each unit. The numerator is the number of pieces.

- In order to graph a negative rational number, it is necessary to use the $-\frac{a}{b}$ form of the number.

The **negative rational number** $-\frac{3}{4}$ lies on the opposite side of 0 at a distance $\frac{3}{4}$ from 0.

Figure 6.11 shows the points on a number line representing the rational numbers $-\frac{3}{4}$, $-\frac{5}{4}$, and $-\frac{6}{4}$.

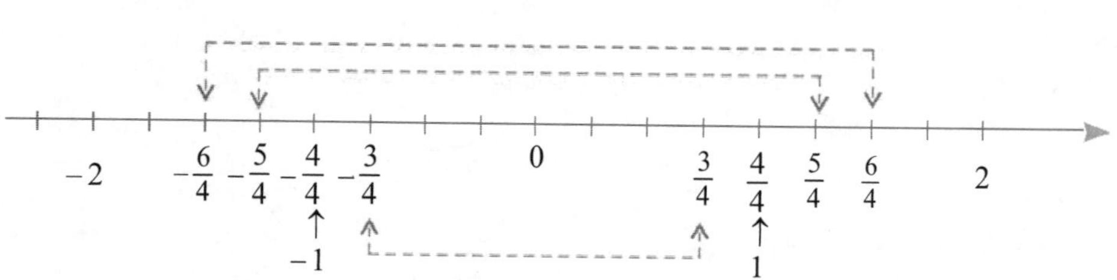

Figure 6.11

WARM-UP

5. Graph the fractions $\frac{-2}{5}$ and $\frac{-9}{5}$ on a number line.

EXAMPLE 5 Graph the fractions $\frac{-4}{7}$ and $\frac{-16}{7}$ on a number line.

Solution Since both fractions are negative, the points representing them are on the left of 0.

Step 1

−3 −2 −1 0

Draw a number line and mark the points representing −1, −2, −3, ... Since the fractions are negative, they will be represented by points on the negative side of 0.

Step 2

−3 −2 −1 0

Divide each of the units into 7 equal pieces because the common denominator is 7.

Step 3 For $-\frac{4}{7}$, count **four** pieces on the left of 0. Mark the point with a dot and label it $-\frac{4}{7}$.

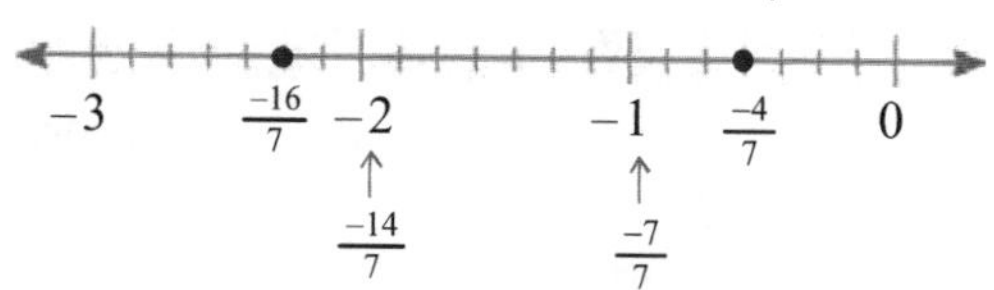

Figure 6.12

For $-\frac{16}{7}$, count 16 pieces from 0 (towards the left) or two pieces from −2 (towards the left). Mark the point with a dot and label it $-\frac{16}{7}$.

WARM-UP

6. Graph the fractions $-\frac{1}{2}$ and $\frac{5}{3}$ on the same number line.

EXAMPLE 6 Graph the fractions $\frac{3}{2}$ and $-\frac{4}{5}$ on the same number line.

Solution $\frac{3}{2}$ is positive; therefore, its graph will be on the right of 0.

$-\frac{4}{5}$ is negative; therefore, its graph will be on the left of 0.

Draw a number line and divide each unit to the right of 0 into two equal pieces and count three pieces from 0 or one piece from 1. Mark this point with a dot.

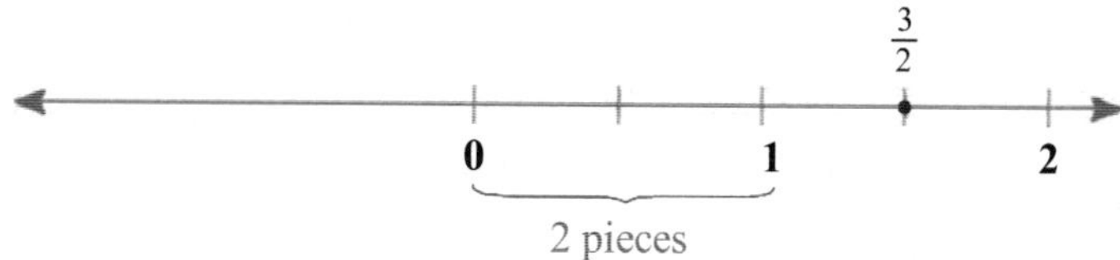

Divide each unit to the left of 0 into 5 equal pieces and count 4 pieces from 0 towards the left. Mark this point with a dot.

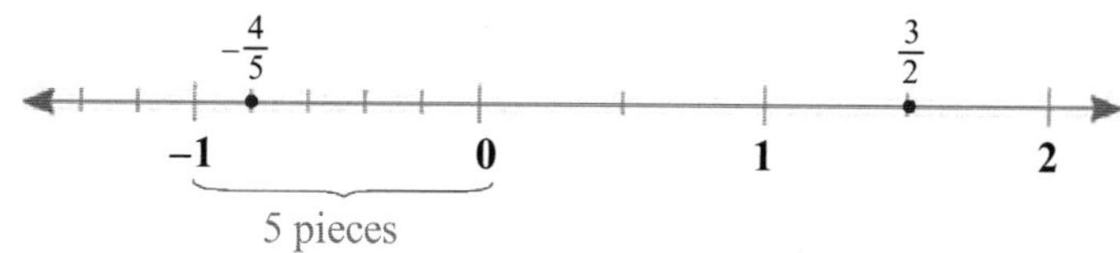

The graph of $\frac{3}{2}$ and $-\frac{4}{5}$ is shown below.

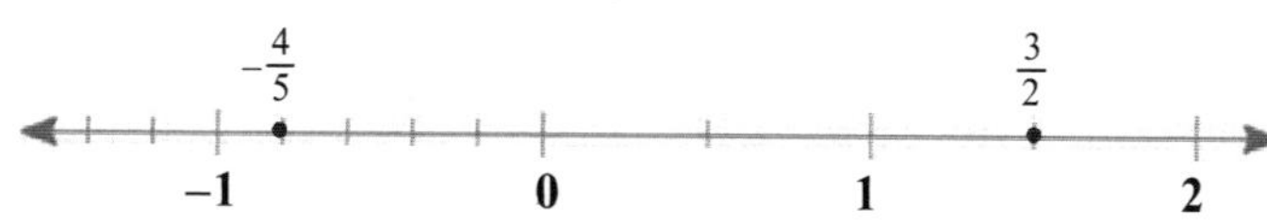

Answers:

3.

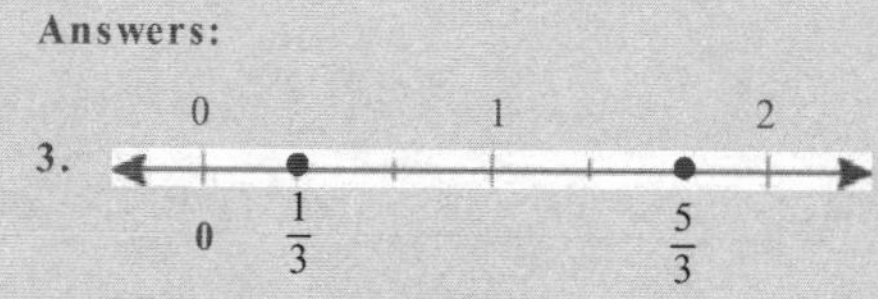

4. (a) $\frac{26}{10}$ cm (b) $\frac{34}{10}$ cm

5.

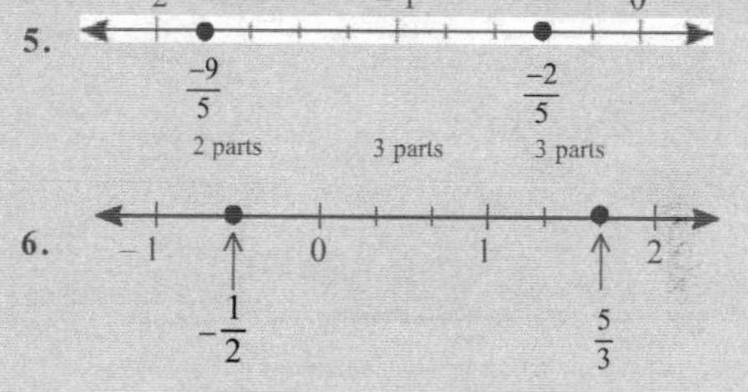

- **Absolute Values of Rational Numbers:** The absolute value of a rational number is its distance from 0 on the number line; thus, the absolute value of $\frac{-3}{4}$ is $\frac{3}{4}$ and the absolute value of $\frac{3}{4}$ is also $\frac{3}{4}$.

Both points have the same distance from zero on the number line in Figure 3.7.

Symbolically, we represent the absolute value of $\frac{a}{b}$ by $\left|\frac{a}{b}\right|$; thus, in Figure 3.7,

$$\left|\frac{-6}{4}\right| = \frac{6}{4}; \qquad \left|-\frac{5}{4}\right| = \frac{5}{4}; \qquad \left|\frac{6}{4}\right| = \frac{6}{4}.$$

The absolute value of 0 is 0, and the absolute value of a non-zero rational number is always positive. In general terms, we may define the absolute value of $\frac{a}{b}$ as follows:

$$\left|\frac{a}{b}\right| = \frac{|a|}{|b|}; \quad b \neq 0; \quad |0| = 0.$$

WARM-UP

7. Find the indicated absolute values.

(a) $\left|\frac{-7}{8}\right|$

(b) $\left|\frac{9}{-13}\right|$

(c) $\left|\frac{-4}{-11}\right|$

Answers:

7. (a) $\frac{7}{8}$ (b) $\frac{9}{13}$ (c) $\frac{4}{11}$

EXAMPLE 7 Find the indicated absolute values.

(a) $\left|\frac{-3}{7}\right|$ (b) $\left|\frac{11}{-15}\right|$ (c) $\left|\frac{-4}{-13}\right|$

Solution

(a) $\left|\frac{-3}{7}\right| = \frac{|-3|}{|7|}$ Using $\left|\frac{a}{b}\right| = \frac{|a|}{|b|}$ for $b \neq 0$.

$= \mathbf{\frac{3}{7}}$

(b) $\left|\frac{11}{-15}\right| = \frac{|11|}{|-15|}$ Using $\left|\frac{a}{b}\right| = \frac{|a|}{|b|}$ for $b \neq 0$.

$= \mathbf{\frac{11}{15}}$

(c) $\left|\frac{-4}{-13}\right| = \frac{|-4|}{|-13|}$ Using $\left|\frac{a}{b}\right| = \frac{|a|}{|b|}$ for $b \neq 0$.

$= \mathbf{\frac{4}{13}}$

EXERCISE 6.8

In exercises 1-12, identify the rational number.

1. $\frac{1}{2}$ 2. $\frac{-3}{4}$ 3. $\frac{7}{0}$ 4. 10 5. -8 6. $-\frac{9}{12}$

7. $\frac{7}{5-5}$ 8. $-\frac{0}{9}$ 9. $\frac{7-7}{4}$ 10. $-\frac{12}{0}$ 11. $\frac{9}{-7}$ 12. $\frac{-0}{-12}$

In exercises 13-16, write two equivalent variations of the rational number that differ from the given number only in signs.

13. $-\frac{4}{5}$ 14. $\frac{-5}{7}$ 15. $\frac{15}{-7}$ 16. $\frac{7}{5}$

In exercises 17-22, write the fraction represented by the shaded unit.

17. 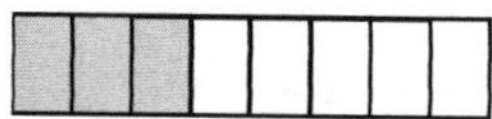

18. 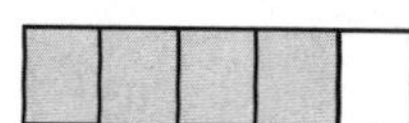

19. 

20. 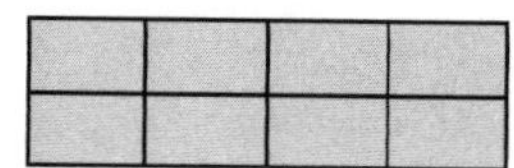

21. 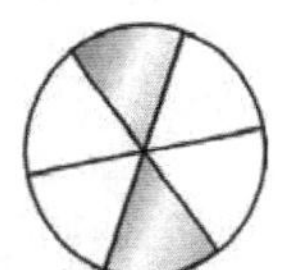

22. 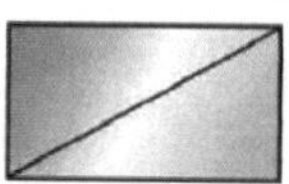 

In exercises 23-26, write the fraction represented by the point below the arrow in the given figure.

23. 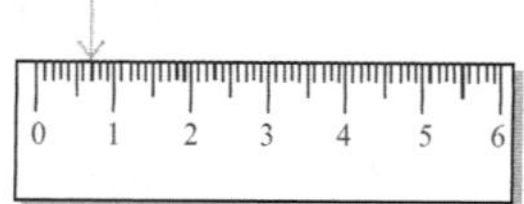

24. 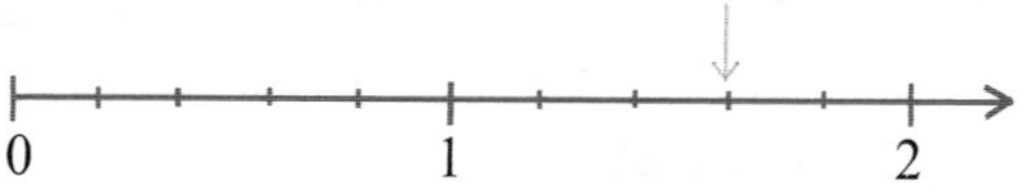

25. 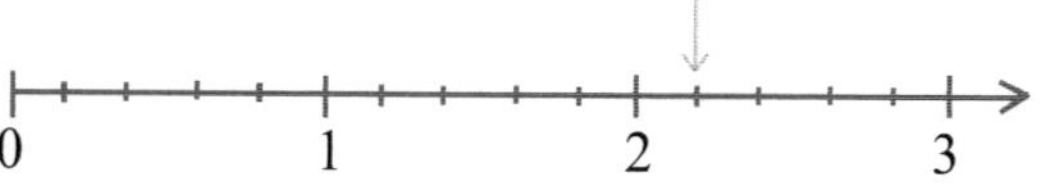

26. 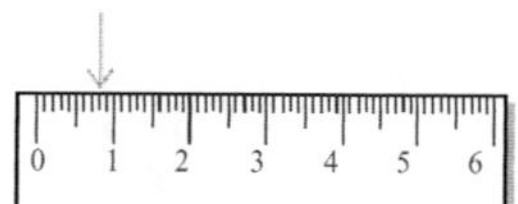

In exercises 27-39, represent the fraction on a number line.

27. $\frac{3}{4}$ 28. $\frac{5}{8}$ 29. $-\frac{4}{6}$ 30. $\frac{7}{5}$ 31. $-\frac{8}{3}$ 32. $\frac{5}{3}$ 33. $\frac{9}{4}$

34. $-\frac{7}{4}$ 35. $\frac{5}{7}$ 36. $-\frac{3}{7}$ 37. $-\frac{8}{10}$ 38. $\frac{3}{5}$ 39. $\frac{4}{10}$

In exercises 40-53, represent the pair of fractions on the same number line.

40. $-\frac{2}{3}$ and $\frac{1}{3}$ 41. $\frac{2}{5}$ and $\frac{7}{5}$ 42. $-\frac{4}{10}$ and $-\frac{7}{10}$ 43. $-\frac{3}{4}$ and $\frac{5}{4}$ 44. $-\frac{4}{5}$ and $\frac{3}{5}$

45. $\frac{2}{3}$ and $-\frac{2}{3}$ 46. $\frac{3}{6}$ and $-\frac{5}{6}$ 47. $\frac{7}{2}$ and $-\frac{4}{2}$ 48. $\frac{-3}{8}$ and $-\frac{9}{8}$ 49. $\frac{14}{5}$ and $-\frac{3}{5}$

50. $\frac{1}{4}$ and $\frac{9}{4}$ 51. $-\frac{5}{6}$ and $\frac{7}{6}$ 52. $\frac{1}{2}$ and $-\frac{3}{2}$ 53. $\frac{5}{8}$ and $-\frac{5}{8}$

In exercises 54-59, use the ruler to measure the length (l) in inches and centimeters.

54. 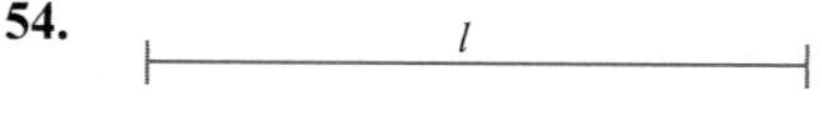

55. 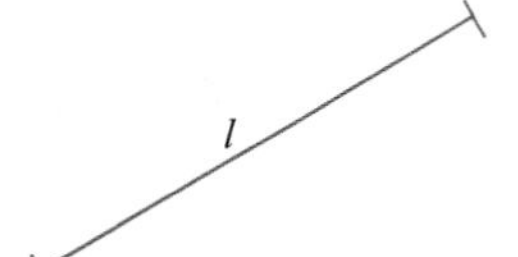

56. 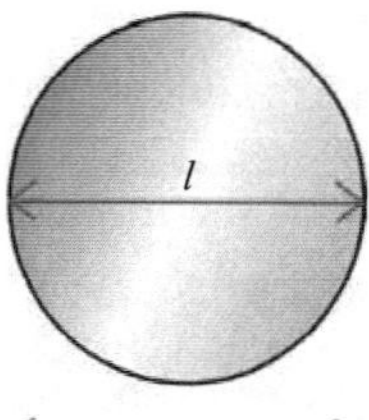

57. 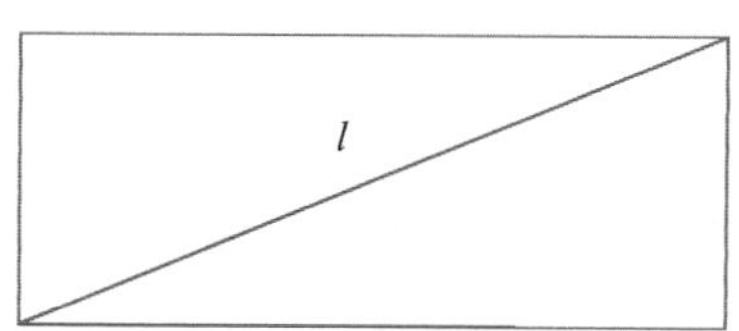

58. 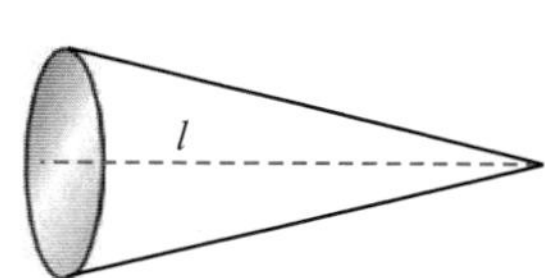

59. 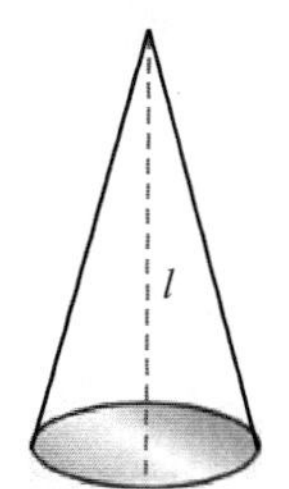

In exercises 60-70, find the indicated absolute value.

60. $\left|\frac{5}{9}\right|$ 61. $\left|\frac{-7}{3}\right|$ 62. $\left|\frac{8}{-3}\right|$ 63. $\left|\frac{0}{-4}\right|$ 64. $\left|-\frac{4}{5}\right|$ 65. $\left|\frac{-7}{-9}\right|$

66. $\left|\frac{129}{-130}\right|$ 67. $\left|\frac{-9}{-17}\right|$ 68. $\left|\frac{-13}{19}\right|$ 69. $\left|\frac{19}{-70}\right|$ 70. $\left|\frac{80}{-101}\right|$

6.9 Operations on Real Numbers

Objectives

After completing this section you will be able to:

A. Add and subtract real numbers;

B. Find the distance between two points;

C. Multiply and divide real numbers;

D. Use order of operations; and

E. Evaluate expressions for given values of variables.

Recall that there are four basic operations used for computing numerical expressions: addition, subtraction, multiplication, and division. We have been using these operations on whole numbers, decimal numbers and fractions. We revisit these operations and **discuss these using the number line**. We will also discuss these rules as applied to expressions involving exponents, and discuss how to evaluate algebraic expressions for specific values using these rules of operations.

A. Add and Subtract Real Numbers

• Add Two Numbers using the Number Line

To add two numbers a and b on a number line we proceed as follows.

***Step* 1** Mark the first point a.

***Step* 2** From the graph of the first number a, move b units to the right if b is positive, and $|b|$ units to the left if b is negative.

***Step* 3** Find the coordinate of the point in Step 2 and this is the sum of a and b.

Warm-Up

1. Use number line to compute the sum.

a) $4 + 2$

b) $(-3) + 2$

Answers:

1. a) 6 b) -1

EXAMPLE 1 Use number line to compute the sum.

a. $3 + 5$ **b.** $(-6) + 3$

c. $7 + (-3)$ **d.** $(-2) + (-3)$

Solutions:

a. **$3 + 5$:**

Here the second number is 5 (positive). We start from 3 and move 5 units to the right. We end up at 8.

$$3 + 5 = 8$$

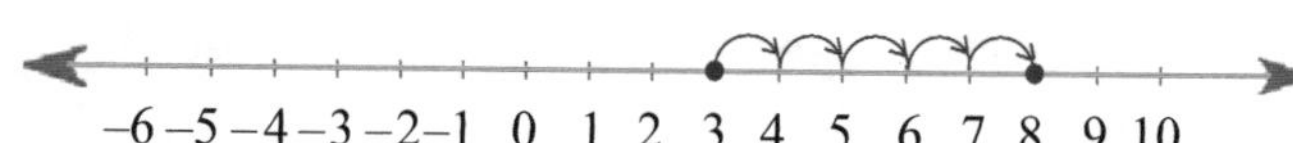

Figure 6.13

b. **$(-6) + 3$:**

The second number is 3 (positive). We start from -6 and move 3 units to the right. We end up at -3.

$$(-6) + 3 = -3$$

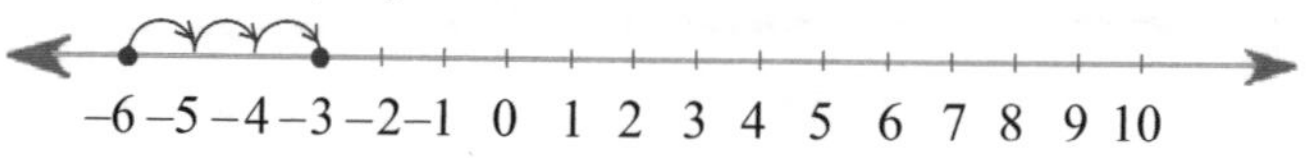

–6 –5 –4 –3 –2 –1 0 1 2 3 4 5 6 7 8 9 10

Figure 6.14

c. **7 + (–3):**

In this case the second number is -3 (negative), and $|-3| = 3$. We start from 7 and move 3 units to the left. We end up at 4.

$$7 + (-3) = 4$$

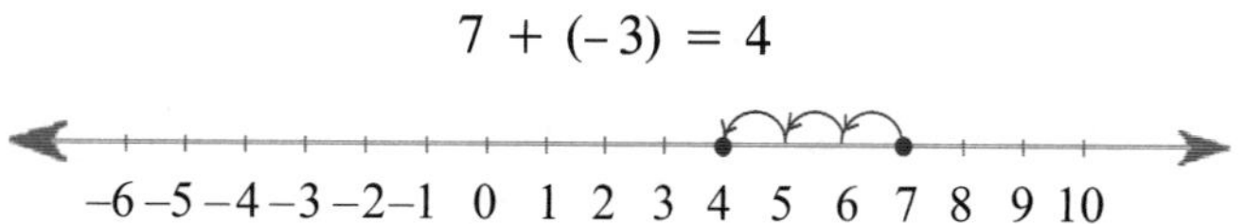

Figure 6.15

d. **(–2) + (–3):**

The second number is –3 (negative), and $|-3| = 3$. We start from -2 and move 3 units to the left. We end up at -5.

$$(-2) + (-3) = -5$$

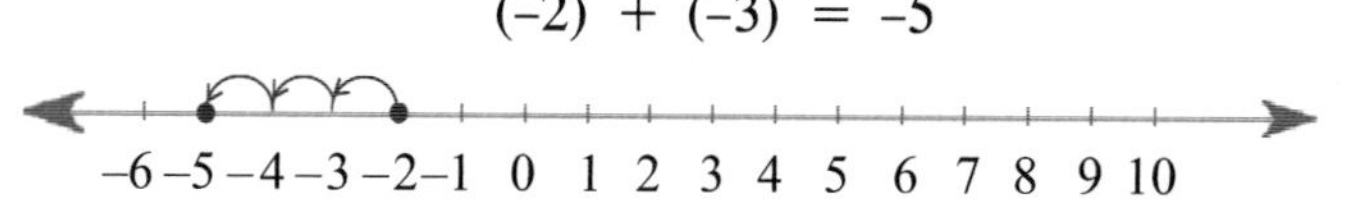

Figure 6.16

c) 5 + (–2)

d) (–1) + (–2)

Answers:

1. c) 3 d) –3

- To Add Two Numbers Algebraically (Both Numbers of the Same Sign)

If the two numbers are both positive or both negative, we can find the sum as follows.

***Step* 1** Find the absolute values of the two numbers.

***Step* 2** Add the absolute values.

***Step* 3** If both numbers are negative then assign a negative sign to the number in step 2.

EXAMPLE 2 Find the sum. **a.** 3 + 5 **b.** (–2) + (–3)

Solutions:

a. 3 + 5

Step 1 $|3| = 3$, $|5| = 5$

Step 2 $|3| + |5| = 3 + 5 = 8$

Therefore, 3 + 5 = 8. We do not need step 3 since both numbers are positive.

b. (–2) + (–3)

Step 1 $|-2| = 2$, $|-3| = 3$

Step 2 2 + 3 = 5

Step 3 Since both numbers are negative, we get (–2) + (–3) = –5

Warm-Up

2. Find the sum.

a) 7 + 4

b) (–5) + (–4)

Answers:

2. a) 11 b) –9

- To Add Two Numbers Algebraically when Numbers have Unlike Signs.

If the two numbers have unlike signs, that is one is **positive** and the other **negative**, then we find the sum as follows.

***Step* 1** Find the absolute values of the two numbers.

***Step* 2** Find the difference of the absolute values.

***Step* 3** Write the difference in Step 2 with the sign of the number having larger absolute value.

WARM-UP

3. Find the sum.

a) $(-2) + 5$

b) $6 + (-4)$

4. Find the sum.

a) $\frac{3}{4}+\frac{1}{6}$

b) $\left(-\frac{3}{4}\right)+\frac{1}{6}$

c) $\frac{3}{4}+\left(-\frac{1}{6}\right)$

Answers:

3. a) 3 b) 2

4. a) $\frac{11}{12}$ b) $\frac{-7}{12}$ c) $\frac{7}{12}$

EXAMPLE 3 Find the sum. **a.** $(-6) + 3$ **b.** $7 + (-3)$

Solutions:

a. **$(-6) + 3$:**

$|-6| = 6, \quad |3| = 3$

Difference is $6 - 3 = 3$

Since $|-6|$ is greater, therefore, $(-6) + 3 = -3$

b. **$7 + (-3)$:**

$|7| = 7, \quad |-3| = 3$

$7 - 3 = 4$

Since $|7|$ is greater, therefore, $7 + (-3) = 4$

EXAMPLE 4 Find the sum.

a. $\frac{5}{6}+\frac{2}{9}$ **b.** $\left(\frac{-5}{6}\right)+\frac{2}{9}$ **c.** $\frac{5}{6}+\left(\frac{-2}{9}\right)$

Solutions:

a. $$\mathbf{\frac{5}{6}+\frac{2}{9}} = \left(\left|\frac{5}{6}\right|+\left|\frac{2}{9}\right|\right) = \frac{5}{6}+\frac{2}{9} = \frac{15}{18}+\frac{4}{18} = \mathbf{\frac{19}{18}}$$

Both the numbers are positive.

b. $$\left(\mathbf{\frac{-5}{6}}\right)+\mathbf{\frac{2}{9}} = \left(\frac{-15}{18}\right)+\frac{4}{18} = -\left(\left|\frac{-15}{18}\right|-\left|\frac{4}{18}\right|\right)$$

The two numbers are of opposite signs.

$$= -\left(\frac{15}{18}-\frac{4}{18}\right) = \mathbf{\frac{-11}{18}}$$

c. $$\mathbf{\frac{5}{6}}+\left(\mathbf{\frac{-2}{9}}\right) = \frac{15}{18}+\left(\frac{-4}{18}\right) = +\left(\left|\frac{15}{18}\right|-\left|\frac{4}{18}\right|\right)$$

$$= \frac{15}{18}-\frac{4}{18} = \mathbf{\frac{11}{18}}$$

• SUBTRACTING REAL NUMBERS

To subtract real number $\boldsymbol{b}$ from a real number $\boldsymbol{a}$, we proceed as follows:

***Step* 1** Change the sign of the number to be subtracted $[b \to -b]$.

***Step* 2** Add a and $-b$. In other words, to subtract $\boldsymbol{b}$ from $\boldsymbol{a}$ we add the opposite of $\boldsymbol{b}$ to $\boldsymbol{a}$.

EXAMPLE 5 Simplify: **a.** $8 - 3$ **b.** $4 - (-3)$ **c.** $(-3) - 5$ **d.** $(-1) - (-9)$

Solutions:

a. $8 - \mathbf{3} = 8 + (\mathbf{-3}) = 5$

b. $4 - (\mathbf{-3}) = 4 + (-(\mathbf{-3})) = 4 + 3 = 7$

c. $(-3) - \mathbf{5} = (-3) + (\mathbf{-5}) = -8$

d. $(-1) - (\mathbf{-9}) = (-1) + (-(\mathbf{-9})) = -1 + 9 = 8$

WARM-UP

5. Simplify:

a) $9 - 4$

b) $8 - (-2)$

c) $(-4) -3$

d) $(-5) - (-6)$

Answers:

5. a) 5 b) 10 c) −7 d) 1

B. FINDING DISTANCE BETWEEN TWO POINTS

Consider points 2 and 4 on a number line.

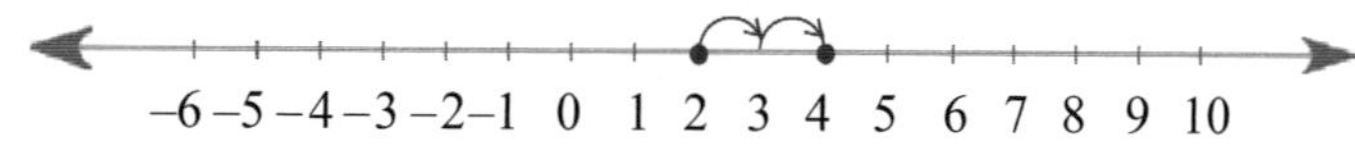

Figure 6.17

Observe that the distance between **2 and 4** is 2 units.

The distance between 4 and 2 is also 2 units.

Thus the distance between 2 and 4 is $|4-2| = 2$ or $|2-4| = 2$.

Now consider the points 3 and −4.

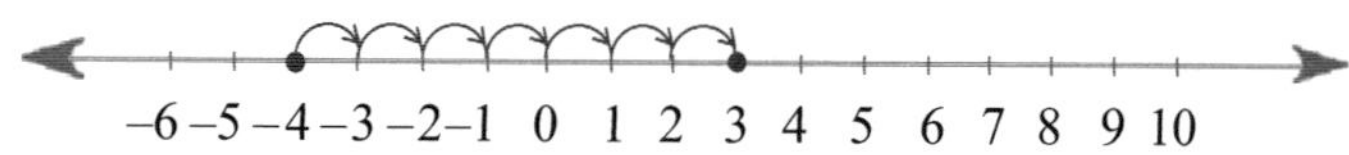

Figure 6.18

The distance between −4 and 3 is 7 units. Observe that $|3-(-4)| = 7$.

The distance between two points on a number line is the absolute value of the difference of their coordinates.

EXAMPLE 6 Find the distance between two points whose coordinates are given.

a. A(−4) and B(5) **b.** C(9) and D(−13)

Solutions:

a. The distance AB $= |5 -(-4)| = |5 + 4| = \mathbf{9}$

b. The distance CD $= |(-13) - 9| = |(-13) + (-9)|$
$= |-22| = \mathbf{22}$

WARM-UP

6. Find the distance between two points whose coordinates are given.

a) A(−3) and B(4)

b) C(2) and D(−10)

Answers:

6. a) AB = 7 b) CD = 12

(C.) MULTIPLY AND DIVIDE REAL NUMBERS

- **MULTIPLICATION OF REAL NUMBERS**

Recall that:

1. The result of multiplication of numbers is called the product.

2. The product of zero and any real number is zero. Thus
$$0 \cdot 3 = 0, \qquad (-5) \cdot 0 = 0, \qquad \text{and } 0 \cdot 0 = 0$$

3. To obtain the product of two real numbers with like signs, we multiply their absolute values. In this case, the product is always a positive number.
For example, $\quad 6 \cdot 4 = 24 \qquad (-5) \cdot (-7) = |-5| \cdot |-7| = 5 \cdot 7 = 35$

4. To obtain the product of two real numbers with unlike signs, multiply their absolute values and append a negative sign to the product. In this case, the product is always negative.
For example, $\quad \mathbf{(-6)\ 4} = -|-6| \cdot |4| = -(6 \cdot 4) = \mathbf{-24}$
$$\mathbf{5(-7)} = -|-5| \cdot |-7| = -(5 \cdot 7) = \mathbf{-35}$$

WARM-UP

7. Find the product.

a) $\left(\frac{-1}{3}\right)\left(\frac{-5}{7}\right)$

b) $\left(\frac{-2}{5}\right)\left(\frac{3}{4}\right)$

c) $\frac{4}{5}(-10)$

Answers:

7. a) $\frac{5}{21}$ b) $\frac{-3}{10}$ c) -8

EXAMPLE 7 Find the product.

a. $\left(-\frac{3}{7}\right)\left(-\frac{4}{5}\right)$ **b.** $\left(-\frac{2}{3}\right)\frac{6}{7}$ **c.** $\frac{3}{2}(-6)$

Solutions:

a. $\left(-\frac{\mathbf{3}}{\mathbf{7}}\right)\left(-\frac{\mathbf{4}}{\mathbf{5}}\right) = \left|\frac{-3}{7}\right|\left|\frac{-4}{5}\right| = \frac{3}{7} \cdot \frac{4}{5} = \frac{\mathbf{12}}{\mathbf{35}}$ Numbers have like signs

b. $\left(-\frac{\mathbf{2}}{\mathbf{3}}\right)\frac{\mathbf{6}}{\mathbf{7}} = -\left(\left|\frac{-2}{3}\right|\left|\frac{6}{7}\right|\right) = -\left(\frac{2}{3} \cdot \frac{6}{7}\right) = -\frac{\mathbf{4}}{\mathbf{7}}$ Numbers have unlike signs

c. $\frac{\mathbf{3}}{\mathbf{2}}\mathbf{(-6)} = -\left(\left|\frac{3}{2}\right| \cdot |-6|\right) = -\left(\frac{3}{2} \cdot 6\right) = \mathbf{-9}$ Numbers have unlike signs

- **DIVISION OF REAL NUMBERS**

Recall that subtraction was defined in terms of addition. Similarly, division is defined in terms of multiplication. Result of division is called quotient.

Recall that: **1.** Division by zero is not defined.

2. If $\boldsymbol{a}$ is a non-zero real number, then $\frac{\mathbf{1}}{\boldsymbol{a}}$ is called the **reciprocal** of a.

3. Dividing a real number ***a*** by a nonzero real numbers ***b*** is the same as multiplying ***a*** with the reciprocal of ***b***. $a \div b = a \cdot \frac{1}{b}$.

If a and b are real numbers, then $\frac{a}{b} = a \cdot \frac{1}{b}$

4. Since division is defined in terms of product, the rules for the sign of the quotient are the same as the rules for the sign of the product. If ***a*** and ***b*** are two real numbers, $b \neq 0$, then $\frac{-a}{b} = \frac{a}{-b} = -\frac{a}{b}$ and $\frac{-a}{-b} = \frac{a}{b}$

5. $a \div b$ or $\frac{a}{b}$ or $a \cdot \frac{1}{b}$ represent the same quotient.

EXAMPLE 8 Find the reciprocal of

a. 4 **b.** $\frac{13}{4}$ **c.** -3 **d.** $-\frac{4}{25}$

Solutions:

a. Reciprocal of 4 is $\frac{1}{4}$.

b. Reciprocal of $\frac{13}{4}$ is $\frac{4}{13}$.

c. Reciprocal of -3 is $-\frac{1}{3}$ or $\frac{-1}{3}$.

d. Reciprocal of $-\frac{4}{25}$ is $-\frac{25}{4}$

EXAMPLE 9 Find the following quotients

a. $-\frac{25}{5}$ **b.** $\frac{-4}{-12}$ **c.** $\frac{\frac{8}{5}}{-\frac{1}{10}}$

Solutions: **a.** $\frac{-25}{5} = (-25)\frac{1}{5} = -\left(25 \cdot \frac{1}{5}\right) = -5$ *a* and *b* are of opposite signs.

b. $\frac{-4}{-12} = \frac{4}{12} = \frac{1}{3}$ *a* and *b* are both negative.

c. $\frac{\frac{8}{5}}{-\frac{1}{10}} = -\left(\frac{\frac{8}{5}}{\frac{1}{10}}\right)$ *a* and *b* are of opposite signs.

$= -\left(\frac{8}{5} \div \frac{1}{10}\right) = -\left(\frac{8}{5} \cdot \frac{10}{1}\right) = -16$

WARM-UP

8. Find the reciprocal of

a) 8

b) $\frac{2}{7}$

c) -9

d) $-\frac{3}{4}$

9. Find the following quotients

a) $-\frac{24}{3}$

b) $\frac{-6}{-24}$

c) $\frac{-\frac{2}{3}}{\frac{7}{12}}$

Answers:

8. a) $\frac{1}{8}$ b) $\frac{7}{2}$ c) $-\frac{1}{9}$ d) $-\frac{4}{3}$

9. a) -8 b) $\frac{1}{4}$ c) $\frac{-8}{7}$

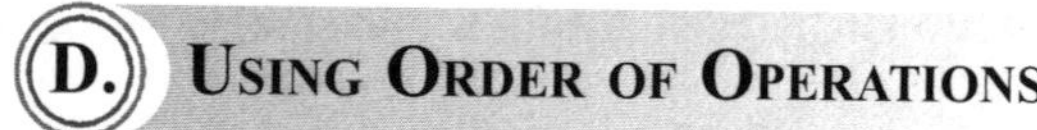

D. Using Order of Operations

Each of the four operations defined earlier in this section computes two numbers at a time. If expressions involving more than two numbers are to be simplified, then we may need more than one application of operations. This requires **rules for the order** in which operations should be performed. Different rules for order of operations can lead to different answers.

For example,

$3 + \mathbf{4 \cdot 5} = 3 + 20 = 23$, if addition is performed **after** multiplication.

$\mathbf{3 + 4} \cdot 5 = 7 \cdot 5 = 35$, if addition is performed **before** multiplication.

In some situations grouping symbols are used to indicate the order to be followed for simplification of expressions. The grouping symbols used are parentheses ( ), braces { }, brackets [ ], and the fraction bar —.

> **Procedure to simplify expressions (no grouping symbols)**
>
> ***Step* 1** Evaluate all exponents and radicals.
>
> ***Step* 2** Perform all multiplications and divisions from left to right.
>
> ***Step* 3** Perform all additions and subtractions from left to right.

EXAMPLE 10 Simplify:

a. $3^2 + 5^2 - 7$ **b.** $3 + 4 \cdot 6$

c. $3 + 5^2 - 7 \cdot 4$ **d.** $4 + 6 + 7 \cdot 6 \div 3$

Solutions: **a.** $\mathbf{3^2} + \mathbf{5^2} - 7 = \mathbf{9} + \mathbf{25} - 7$ *Step* 1

$= 34 - 7 = 27$ *Step* 3; *Step* 2 not needed

b. $3 + \mathbf{4 \cdot 6} = 3 + 24$ *Step* 2; *Step* 1 not needed

$= 27$ *Step* 3

c. $3 + \mathbf{5^2} - 7 \cdot 4 = 3 + 25 - \mathbf{7 \cdot 4}$ *Step* 1

$= \mathbf{3 + 25} - 28$ *Step* 2

$= 28 - 28 = 0$ *Step* 3

d. $4 + 6 + \mathbf{7 \cdot 6} \div 3 = 4 + 6 + \mathbf{42 \div 3}$ *Step* 2

$= \mathbf{4 + 6} + 14$ *Step* 2

$= 10 + 14 = 24$ *Step* 3

> **Warm-Up**
>
> **10.** Simplify:
>
> **a)** $4^2 + 6^2 - 10$
>
> **b)** $5 + 7 \cdot 9$
>
> **c)** $7 + 42 - 3 \cdot 4$
>
> **d)** $7 + 8 + 3 \cdot 8 \div 2$
>
> **Answers:**
>
> **10.** a) 42 b) 68 c) 37 d) 27

> **Procedure to simplify (grouping symbol)**
>
> ***Step* 1** Simplify within each grouping symbol starting from the innermost grouping symbol.
>
> ***Step* 2** If fraction bars are present then simplify the numerator and the denominator of each fraction separately.

WARM-UP

11. Simplify:

a) $4(7 + 3)$

b) $3(8 - 3 + 9)$

c) $5(4 + 2 \cdot 9)$

d) $5 + [7^2 + (19 - 3) \div 4]$

e) $8 + [9 + 3\{2 + 12 \div (3 + 1)\}]$

f) $20 - \left(10 - \frac{9 + 12}{3 \cdot 2 + 1}\right)$

g) $(7^2 - 24 \cdot 2)(8 + 9 \div 3)$

h) $\frac{7 - (-2)^3 (3)}{3\sqrt{4} + 5^2}$

Answers:

11. a) 40 b) 42 c) 110 d) 58
e) 32 f) 13 g) 11 h) 1

EXAMPLE 11 Simplify:

a. $3(5 + 11)$ **b.** $4(5 + 7 - 9)$

c. $3(8 + 5 \cdot 7)$ **d.** $2 + [5^2 + (8 - 2) \div 3]$

e. $4 + [10 + 2\{1 + 6 \div (1 + 1)\}]$

f. $4 + \left(3 + \frac{5+9}{2 \cdot 3 + 1}\right)$

g. $(4^2 + 3 \cdot 5)(7 - 4 \div 2)$ **h.** $\frac{3 - (-4)^2(5)}{2\sqrt{9} - 2^2 \cdot 5}$

Solutions:

a. $3(\mathbf{5} + \mathbf{11}) = 3(16) = 48$

b. $4(\mathbf{5} + \mathbf{7} - 9) = 4(\mathbf{12} - \mathbf{9}) = 4(3) = 12$

c. $3(8 + \mathbf{5} \cdot \mathbf{7}) = 3(\mathbf{8} + \mathbf{35}) = 3(43) = 129$

d.
$$\begin{aligned} 2 + [5^2 + (\mathbf{8} - \mathbf{2}) \div 3] &= 2 + [\mathbf{5}^2 + 6 \div 3] \\ &= 2 + [25 + \mathbf{6} \div \mathbf{3}] \\ &= 2 + [\mathbf{25} + \mathbf{2}] \\ &= 2 + 27 = 29 \end{aligned}$$

e.
$$\begin{aligned} &4 + [10 + 2\{1 + 6 \div (\mathbf{1} + \mathbf{1})\}] \\ &= 4 + [10 + 2\{1 + \mathbf{6} \div \mathbf{2}\}] \\ &= 4 + [10 + 2\{\mathbf{1} + \mathbf{3}\}] \\ &= 4 + [10 + \mathbf{2} \cdot \mathbf{4}] = 4 + [\mathbf{10} + \mathbf{8}] \\ &= 4 + 18 = 22 \end{aligned}$$

f.
$$\begin{aligned} 4 + \left(3 + \frac{\mathbf{5} + \mathbf{9}}{\mathbf{2} \cdot \mathbf{3} + \mathbf{1}}\right) &= 4 + \left(3 + \frac{\mathbf{14}}{\mathbf{7}}\right) \\ &= 4 + (\mathbf{3} + \mathbf{2}) = 4 + 5 = 9 \end{aligned}$$

g.
$$\begin{aligned} (\mathbf{4}^2 + \mathbf{3} \cdot \mathbf{5})(7 - \mathbf{4} \div \mathbf{2}) &= (16 + 15)(7 - 2) \\ &= (31)(5) = 155 \end{aligned}$$

h.
$$\begin{aligned} \frac{3 - (-\mathbf{4})^{\mathbf{2}}(5)}{2\sqrt{9} - \mathbf{2}^{\mathbf{2}} \cdot 5} &= \frac{3 - \mathbf{16} \cdot \mathbf{5}}{2 \cdot 3 - \mathbf{4} \cdot \mathbf{5}} \\ &= \frac{\mathbf{3} - \mathbf{80}}{\mathbf{6} - \mathbf{20}} = \frac{-77}{-14} = \frac{11}{2} \end{aligned}$$

(E.) EVALUATE EXPRESSIONS FOR GIVEN VALUE OF VARIABLE

Algebraic expressions usually involve variables or unknown quantities that can be assigned any permissible values. To find the value of an algebraic expression for any specific values of the variables, we simply substitute the values of the variables in the expression. When the values of the variables are negative we should enclose them in parentheses to avoid any possible error.

EXAMPLE 12 Evaluate the following expressions for the given values of the variables.

a. $3x - 5y$ for $x = 4, y = 2$

b. $5x^2 - 2yz + 8$ for $x = 3, y = 2$, and $z = 4$

c. $\dfrac{a^2 - 3b^2}{5b + a}$ for $a = 4, \quad b = -2$

Solutions:

a. $3x - 5y = 3 \cdot \mathbf{4} - 5 \cdot \mathbf{2}$
$= 12 - 10 = 2$

b. $5x^2 - 2yz + 8 = 5 \cdot \mathbf{3}^2 - 2 \cdot \mathbf{2} \cdot \mathbf{4} + 8$
$= 5 \cdot 9 - 16 + 8 = 45 - 16 + 8$
$= 29 + 8 = 37$

c. $\dfrac{a^2 - 3b^2}{5b + a} = \dfrac{\mathbf{4}^2 - 3(\mathbf{-2})^2}{5(\mathbf{-2}) + \mathbf{4}}$

$= \dfrac{16 - 3 \cdot 4}{-10 + 4} = \dfrac{16 - 12}{-6} = \dfrac{4}{-6} = -\dfrac{2}{3}$

WARM-UP

12. Evaluate the following expressions for the given values of the variables.

a) $7x + 2y$ for $x = 3, y = 4$

b) $2xy + 4z^2 - 9$ for $x = 2, y = 3$, and $z = 5$

c) $\dfrac{9a + 40b}{a^2 - b^2}$ for $a = 4, \; b = 3$

Answers:

12. a) 29 b) 103 c) $\frac{156}{7}$

EXERCISE 6.9

In exercises 1-26, simplify the numerical expression.

1. $(-6) + 7$

2. $-5 + (-4)$

3. $\left(-\frac{1}{4}\right) + \left(-\frac{2}{3}\right)$

4. $\frac{13}{5} - \frac{7}{5}$

5. $\left(-\frac{1}{2}\right) + \left(\frac{-5}{3}\right)$

6. $\frac{6}{5} - \frac{5}{6}$

7. $\frac{11}{5} - \left(\frac{-2}{3}\right)$

8. $\frac{5}{7} - \left(-\frac{3}{2}\right)$

9. $(-2 + 3 - 10) - (-3)$

10. $-(3 - 1 + 5) - (-7)$

11. $(5 - 3 - 12) - (-7)$

12. $-(4 - 5 - 6) + (-8)$

13. $\frac{1}{3} - \frac{1}{5} - 2$

14. $-\frac{1}{2} + \frac{1}{3} - 4$

15. $\frac{-1}{2} + \frac{1}{5} - 1$

16. $\frac{1}{3} - \frac{1}{4} - 2$

17. $(-3 - (-5)) + (-6 + 10)$

18. $-(-2 + (-4)) - (3 - 5)$

19. $\sqrt{9} - |-5| + \frac{1}{2}$

20. $-|-4| + \frac{1}{3} - \frac{1}{\sqrt{9}}$

21. $|-7| + |-4| - |3| + |-6|$

22. $|5|-|-3|+|-2|-|4|$

23. $3^2-|-3|+|-2^3|$

24. $-2^3-|-3^2|+2|2^2|$

25. $\sqrt{25}-\sqrt{16}-\sqrt{9}$

26. $-\sqrt{36}+\sqrt{4}+\sqrt{49}$

In exercises 27-40, simplify the numerical expression.

27. (-5) (13)

28. (-7) (-3)

29. (-54) ÷ 3

30. (54) ÷ (-9)

31. $\left(\frac{-4}{3}\right)\left(-\frac{6}{5}\right)$

32. $\left(-\frac{2}{3}\right)\left(-\frac{3}{4}\right)$

33. $\frac{6}{13}\div\left(-\frac{2}{15}\right)$

34. $-\frac{3}{11}\div\frac{9}{33}$

35. $\frac{3}{0}$

36. $\frac{0}{7}$

37. $\dfrac{\frac{8}{11}}{\frac{4}{33}}$

38. $\dfrac{\frac{7}{9}}{\frac{3}{18}}$

39. $\dfrac{-\frac{3}{5}}{0}$

40. $\dfrac{-\frac{4}{7}}{\frac{0}{3}}$

In exercises 41-64, simplify using rules for the order of operations.

41. 4 · 22 + 2 - (1 - 3)

42. 3 · 4 - 2 - (12 - 3)

43. $4^2\div 8-(3-5)$

44. $6^2\div 9-(5-1)$

45. $\frac{1}{2}\cdot 6+(6\div 3\cdot 7)$

46. $\frac{1}{4}\cdot 16+(18\div 2\cdot 3)$

47. $\frac{1}{3}\cdot 15-(8\div 2\cdot 9)$

48. $\frac{1}{4}\cdot 8-(2\div 4\cdot 4)$

49. $4\sqrt{81}+12\div 3$

50. $3\sqrt{49}+8\div 4$

51. (-3 + 9) · (-12 - 5)

52. (-5 + 4) · (-13 + 8)

53. 2 + 5 - 3(8 - 4 ÷ 2)

54. 3 + 1 - 2(4 - 4 ÷ 2)

55. $\dfrac{4^2+3\cdot 5-(8+2\cdot 6)\div 4}{5^2-\sqrt{16}}$

56. $\dfrac{2^3+2\cdot 4-(8+4\cdot 2)\div 2}{2^3-\sqrt{25}}$

57. $\dfrac{3+(-2)^3\cdot(4)}{2\cdot\sqrt{4}-3\cdot 2}$

58. $\dfrac{10+(-3)^2(-2)}{3\sqrt{9}-2^2}$

59. $\dfrac{|2(-5)|+(-4)(-3)^4}{5-7+\sqrt{4}}$

60. $\dfrac{|3(-2)|+(-2)(-4)^2}{9-4-\sqrt{16}}$

61. $3-5\left[\dfrac{42-5(2-4)}{|-13|}\right]$

62. $7-3\left[\dfrac{14-2(1-3)}{|-10|}\right]$

63. $\frac{3}{5}\left[4(-7)-8\div 2\cdot(6^2-5\cdot 4)\right]$

64. $\frac{2}{3}\left[2(-3)-4\div 2\cdot(4^2-3\cdot 2)\right]$

In exercises 65-74, evaluate the expression for the indicated values.

65. $3m+2k$ for $m=1$ and $k=-2$

66. $2m-3n$ for $m=2$ and $n=-1$

67. $4a(3b-2c)$ for $a=-2$, $b=4$, $c=6$

68. $a(2b+3c)$ for $a=4$, $b=3$, and $c=2$

69. $\dfrac{2m-1}{2p}$ for $p=\frac{1}{2}$, $m=4$

70. $\dfrac{2m+n}{m-n}$ for $m=3$ and $n=2$

71. $-2m^3+n^2-t$ for $m=-2$, $n=3$, and $t=-4$

72. $4x^3+3y^2-2z$ for $x=-1$, $y=2$, and $z=-3$

73. $\dfrac{3a-5b}{5a-2b+c}$ for $a=1$, $b=-2$, $c=1$

74. $\dfrac{2x+7y}{x-3y+z}$ for $x=2$, $y=1$, and $z=0$

In exercises 75-86, establish whether the statement is true or false for all real numbers by assigning different values to the real numbers a and b. Use sets of values with different signs as in exercise 75.

75. $|a+b| = |a| + |b|$

76. $|a+2b| = |a| + 2|b|$

77. $|a-b| \le |a| + |b|$

Let $a = 2,\ b = 5$; $|2+5| = |2| + |5|$ or $7 = 7$ True

Let $a = -2,\ b = 5$; $|-2+5| = |-2| + |5|$ or $3 = 7$ False

Let $a = -2,\ b = -5$; $|-2-5| = |-2| + |-5|$ or $7 = 7$ True

Let $a = 2,\ b = -5$; $|2-5| = |2| + |-5|$ or $3 = 7$ False

Therefore, the statement is not true for all real numbers, or the statement is false.

78. $|2a-3b| \le |2a| + |3b|$

79. $|a-b| = ||a| - |b||$

80. $|a-2b| = ||a| - |2b||$

81. $|a^2| = |a|^2$

82. $|a^3| = |a|^3$

83. $|ab| = |a||b|$

84. $|2ab| = 2|a||b|$

85. $\left|\frac{a}{b}\right| = \frac{|a|}{|b|}$

86. $\left|\frac{2a}{3b}\right| = \frac{2|a|}{3|b|}$

87. How will you express "10° below 0° " in mathematical symbols?

88. How will you express "25° above 0° " in mathematical symbols?

89. If we start measuring heights from a given surface, how will you express 32 ft below the surface in mathematical symbols?

90. If we start measuring heights from a given surface, how will you express 13 ft above the surface in mathematical symbols?

91. On a certain day the temperature at 2.00 a.m. was −8°C. By 12.00 noon the temperature increased by 27°. Find the temperature at noon.

92. On a certain day the temperature at 4.00 p.m. was 23°C. At 7.00 p.m. the temperature decreased by 7°C. Find the temperature at 7.00 p.m.

93. Telescope Peak has altitude 11,049 feet and is next to Death Valley which is 282 feet below the sea level. Find the difference between the two altitudes.

94. Two hilltops have altitudes 15,580 ft and 13,692 ft above sea level. Determine the difference between the altitudes of the two hills.

STATISTICS

The discussion in this chapter is divided into two sections.

7.1 Reading, Interpreting and Graphing Data

7.2 Sampling Methods

7.1 READING, INTERPRETING AND GRAPHING DATA

VOCABULARY

OBJECTIVES

After completing this section you will be able to:

A. Read data from a given table;

B. Read and interpret data from a bar graph and a line graph;

C. Read and interpret data from a pie chart (circle graph); and

D. Find the mean, median, mode and range of a set of data items.

1. A **table** is a systematic organization of data in **columns** and **rows**.

   Example:

   Time Spent Producing Skis

Type of production \ Type of ski	Trick ski	Slalom ski	production total (in hours)
Fabricate	6	4	10
Finish	1	2	3
Ski type total (in hours)	7	6	13

   Source: Summer SportsPress, Any Town, USA

2. **Rows** are horizontal arrangements of data.

   Example: The data in the second **row** are 1, 2, and 3.

3. **Columns** are vertical arrangements of data.

   Example: The data in the first column are 6, 1, and 7.

4. An **entry** or **cell** is the number which lies in a given row and column. It is the recorded value or observation. The entries constitute the **body** of the table.

   Example: The number in the second row and first column is 1.

5. A **title** indicates the type of data presented in the table,

6. **Sub-headings** consist of labels for the columns and rows for a table.

7. **A sub-total** of a row or column consists of the sum of the entries in the row or column.

8. A **unit indicator** explains the units of measurement used.

9. A **source note** indicates the source from where the data was supplied.

10. A **graph** is a visual presentation of numerical data.

11. A **bar graph** uses a number of disjoint rectangles, called bars, generally of equal width and different heights.

12. Bar graphs contain two axes, a **vertical axis** and a **horizontal axis**. The vertical axis represents one set of values, and the horizontal axis represents a second set of values.

13. In a **vertical bar graph**, bars are arranged vertically (Figure 7.1). In a **horizontal bar graph**, bars are arranged horizontally (Figure 7.2).

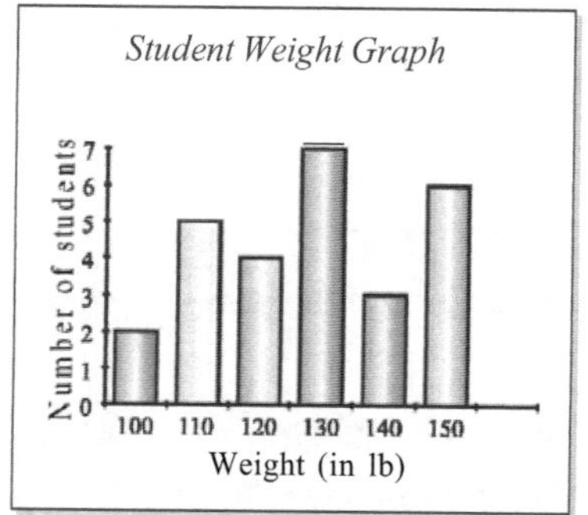

Figure 7.1

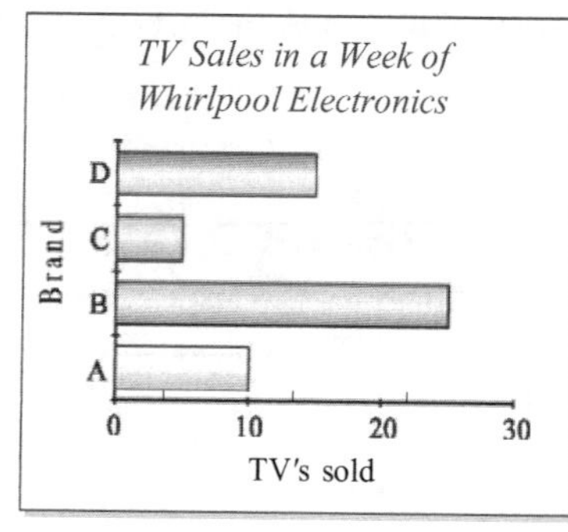

A : Black and White TV
B : Color TV with stereo
C : Color TV
D : Miniature TV

Figure 7.2

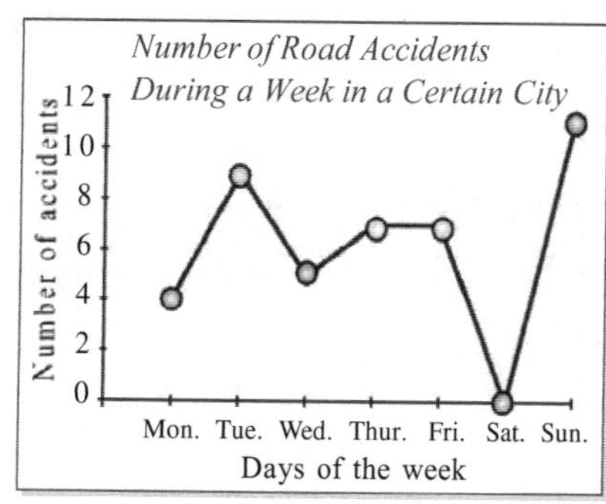

Figure 7.3

14. A **line graph** uses lines connecting points to show the variations in one set of values corresponding to the variations in another set of values. A line graph also has a horizontal and a vertical axis, like a bar graph. Figure 7.3 shows a line graph.

15. A **circle graph** or **pie chart** illustrates a whole unit divided into parts or percents. Each part is represented by a **sector** of a circle whose area is proportional to the percent of the part represented. The entire circle represents 100% (Figure 7.4).

Monthly Expenditure of a Certain family

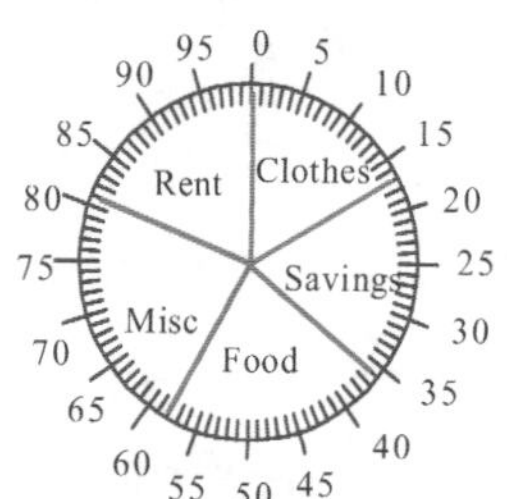

Figure 7.4

16. A **pictograph** uses symbol-pictures or drawings to represent numbers from a set. Each complete symbol represents a fixed (stated) number (Figure 7.5).

Number of Houses Built by a Housing Corporation

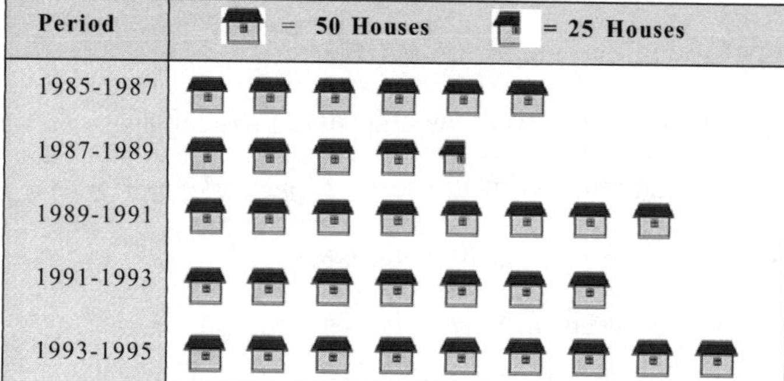

Figure 7.5

17. By **data** we mean collected information in the form of a set of numerical values.

18. The **mean** is the common arithmetic average of the data.

19. The **median** is a value that represents the 'middle' of the data after the data has been arranged in order (increasing or decreasing).

20. The **mode** is the single data item that appears most frequently.

21. A **statistic** is a single number (mean, median, or mode) describing some characteristic of the data.

22. The **range** is the difference between the largest and the smallest data items.

A. Reading and Interpreting Data from a Table

➡ **Read data from a given table.**

Discussion

Reading a table often involves finding the correct row and column, and then reading the entry at the intersection of that row and column. As an illustration, study table 7.1.

Table 7. 1

Transportation of coal (in tons) from three sources to four industries

Industries / Sources	Electric Works	Water Works	XX Railway	Hardware Company	Source total
Official Mining Corp.	9	4	12	8	33
Mines R Us	6	10	8	11	35
Coal 4 You	5	7	10	12	34
Industry Total (in tons)	20	21	30	31	**102**

Source: Pitts Ford Press, Any Town, USA

The **title** explains that the table contains information about transportation of coal from the three sources to four industries.

The short **sub-headings for the rows**, name the sources for the coal.

The **sub-headings for the columns** indicate the names of the industries.

There are 12 numerical **entries** in the **body** of the table. The first entry is 9 and the last entry is 12.

The **column sub-totals** are 20, 21, 30 and 31. They indicate the amount of coal shipped to each industry.

The **row sub-totals** are 33, 35 and 34. They indicate the amount of coal shipped from each source.

The **unit indicator** is tons indicating that the amount of coal was measured by the ton.

The **source note** indicates the source from which the information was supplied and is, in this case, ficticious.

The **total amounts** of coal received by four industries from all sources are given in the last row (20, 21, 30 and 31).

The **total amounts** of coal transported from the three sources to the industries are given in the last column (33, 35, and 34).

Use table 7.1 to fill in the blanks:

i) Electric Works received 9 tons of coal from Official Mining Corp., and _____ tons from Coal 4 You.

ii) XX Railway received 12 tons of coal from Official Mining Corp., and 8 tons from ____________.

iii) Mines R Us transported __________ tons of coal to four industries.

iv) Water Works recieved __________ tons of coal from three sources.

In order to find the amount of coal transported from Coal 4 You to Water Works, we find the entry at the intersection of row 3 and column 2.

Seven tons of coal were transported from Coal 4 You to Electric works.

Sources \ Industries	Electric Works	Water Works	XX Railway	Hardware Company	Sources Total
Official Mining Corp.	9	4	12	8	33
Mines R Us	6	10	**8**	11	35
Coal 4 You	5	7	10	12	34
Industry Total (in tons)	20	21	30	31	102

In order to find who transported 8 tons of

coal to XX Railway, we find the entry 8, in the 3rd column and trace it to the Mines R Us row, shown in the 1st table.

Mines R Us transported 35 tons of coal to four industries.

Sources \ Industries	Electric Works	Water Works	XX Railway	Hardware Company	Sources Total
Official Mining Corp.	9	4	12	8	33
Mines R Us	6	10	8	11	**35**
Coal 4 You	5	7	10	12	34
Industry Total (in tons)	20	21	30	31	102

Water Works received 21 tons of coal from the three sources.

Sources \ Industries	Electric Works	Water Works	XX Railway	Hardware Company	Sources Total
Official Mining Corp.	9	4	12	8	33
Mines R Us	6	10	8	11	35
Coal 4 You	5	7	10	12	34
Industry Total (in tons)	20	**21**	30	31	102

WARM-UP

1. Use Table 7.2 to answer he following questions:

EXAMPLE 1 Read the following table carefully and respond to the questions.

Table 7.2

Grade Distribution of Students in Mathematics Courses

Course \ Grades	A	B	C	D	F	Total
Pre-algebra	20	50	120	80	40	310
Algebra	10	40	60	40	50	200
Pre-calculus	4	10	30	10	5	59
Calculus I	2	5	10	10	4	31
Total	36	105	220	140	99	600

Source: University of Spodene

(a) How many students received a B in pre-calculus?

(b) What is the total number of students in algebra?

(c) What is the total number of students who earned an F?

(d) Find the total number of students enrolled in all four courses?

Solutions

(a) The number at the intersection of the **pre-calculus row** and the **B grade column** is 10.

Therefore, 10 students received a B in pre-calculus.

(b) The number at the intersection of the **algebra row** and the **total column** is 200.

Therefore, there are 200 students in algebra.

(c) The number at the intersection of the **F column** and the **total row** is 99.

Therefore, 99 students received an F.

(d) The total number of students is at the intersection of the **total row** and the **total column**. The entry is 600. There were 600 students in all four courses.

WARM-UP

(a) How many students received an A in algebra?

(b) What is the total number of students enrolled in pre-algebra?

(c) How many B's were awarded among all the courses?

(d) What is the course in which the total number of students enrolled is 31?

Answers:

1. (a) 10 (b) 310 (c) 105 (d) Calculus 1

B. Reading Data from Bar and Line Graphs

➡ **Read and interpret data from a bar graph and a line graph.**

Discussion

A bar graph contains two axes, a vertical axis and a horizontal axis, and a number of bars (rectangles) of equal width erected on one of the axes with equal spacing between them. Each rectangle or bar represents only one value of the numerical data, so there are as many bars as values in the numerical data. The height (or length) of each bar indicates, the corresponding value of the numerical data.

A line graph also has a horizontal and a vertical axis, like a bar graph. A line graph uses lines connecting points to show the variations in one set of values corresponding to the variations in the other set of values.

WARM-UP

2. Respond to the following questions using Figure 7.6.

(a) Find the total sales during the fourth (1-2) hour.

(b) Express the sales during the third hour as a percent of the total sales between 10 AM to 2 PM.

EXAMPLE 2 The total sale of goods in a general store between 10 AM to 2 PM is given in the following bar graph.

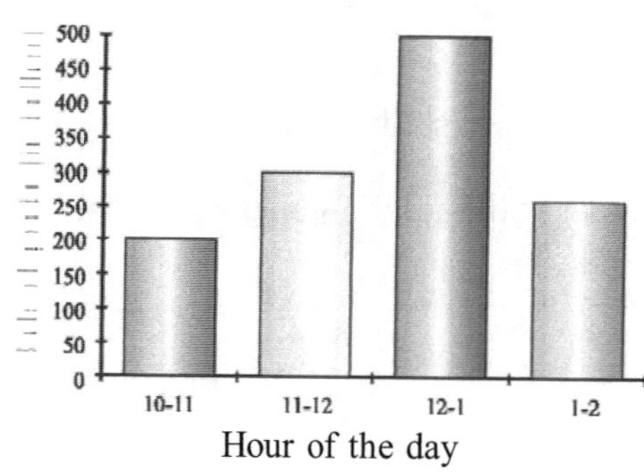

Figure 7.6

Answer the following questions using the bar graph in Figure 7.6.

(a) Find the total sales during the first hour.

(b) Find the percent increase in sales from the second to the third hour.

Solutions

(a) $200 — Read the vertical scale against the top of the bar in the 10-11 hour of the horizontal axis.

(b) Sales during the second (11-12) hour = $300

Sales during the third (12-1) hour = $500

The percent increase in sales between the second and the third hour

$$= \frac{200}{300} \times 100\ \%$$

The actual increase = 500 − 300 = 200; and the base value is 300.

$$= 66.\overline{6}\ \%$$

$\approx$ 67% to the nearest whole number percent.

EXAMPLE 3 Respond to questions (a) through (d) using the bar graph in Figure 7.7.

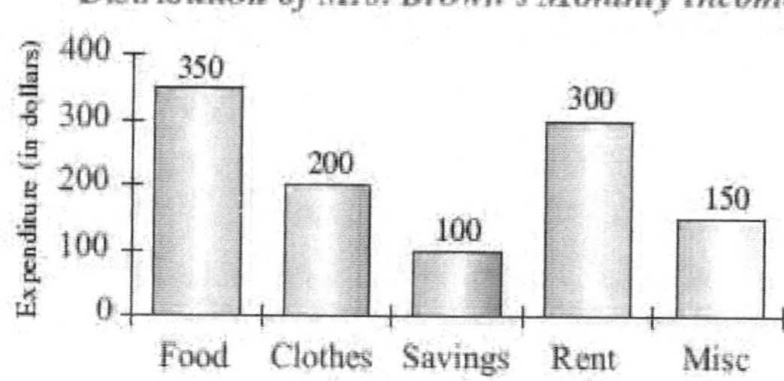

Figure 7.7

(a) What information is given by the bar graph?

(b) How much is spent on rent?

(c) What is the monthly income of Mrs. Brown?

(d) What percent of the income is spent on food?

Solutions

(a) The bar graph shows the distribution of Mrs. Brown's monthly income on various items. Suggested by the title of the bar graph.

(b) $300 are spent on rent. The height of the bar representing the item 'Rent' is 300.

(c) The monthly income of Mrs. Brown is $1100. The total monthly income = the total expenditure = the sum of the heights of all the 5 bars = 350 + 200 + 100 + 300 + 150 = 1100.

(d) The percentage of income spent on food:

$$\frac{350}{1100} \times 100\,\%$$

Percentage of income spent on food = $\frac{\text{Amount spent on food}}{\text{Total income}} \times 100$

$$= \frac{350}{11}\,\% \approx 31.82\,\%$$

EXAMPLE 4 Use the bar graph of Figure 7.2 to answer the following questions :

(a) What information is given by the bar graph?

(b) How many miniature TV sets are sold during the week?

(c) Which type of TV is most popular?

TV Sales in a Week of Whirlpool Electronics

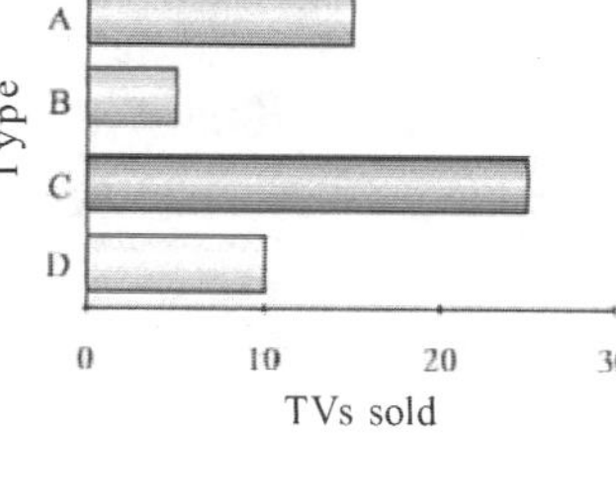

A: Flat screen TV
B: Big screen TV
C: Miniature TV
D: Color TV

WARM-UP

3. Use the bar graph of Figure 7.7 to answer the following questions:

(a) How much is spent on clothes?

(b) What percent of the monthly income is saved by Mrs. Brown? Round your answer to the nearest tenth of a percent.

(c) On which item does Mrs. Brown spend the most?

4. Use the bar graph of example 3 to answer the following questions:

(a) What is the total number of TV sets sold in the week?

WARM-UP

(b) What is the ratio of the number of Flat screen TV sets sold to that of color TV sets?

(c) Which is the least popular type of TV sold?

5. Use the graph of Figure 7.8 to answer the following questions.

(a) How many computers were sold in 2000?

(b) What is the decrease in sales in 2001 as compared to the sales in 2000?

(c) What is the percent decrease in sales in 2003 over the sales in 2002?

Answers:

2. (a) \$250 (b) 40%

3. (a) \$200 (b) 9.1% (c) Food

4. (a) 55 (b) $\frac{3}{2}$ (c) Big Screen TV's

5. (a) 3000 (b) 1000 (c) $33\frac{1}{3}\%$

Solutions

(a) The bar graph gives the details of the TV sales in a week at Whirlpool Electronics. Suggested by the title of the bar graph.

(b) 25. The length of the bar for C, representing the miniature TV sets is 25.

(c) Miniature TV's are the most popular type. The length of the bar for C, representing miniature TV sets is longest.

EXAMPLE 5 The number of computers sold by a company from 1999 to 2003 is shown in the following line graph.

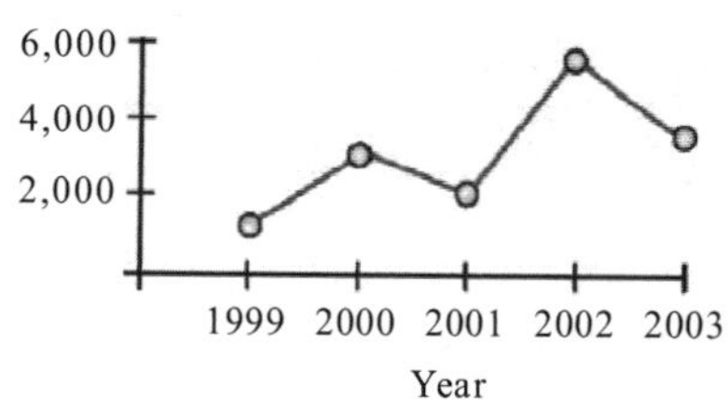

Figure 7.8

Use this line graph to answer the following questions.

(a) In which year did the company sell the most computers?

(b) What is the increase in sales in 2003 over the sales in 1999?

(c) What is the percentage increase in sales in 2003 over the sales in 1999?

Solutions

(a) From the graph it is evident that the company sold the most computers in the year 2002. The highest point on the graph is above 1994.

(b) The increase in sales in 2003 over those in 1999 is 3000.

Sales in 1995 = 4000
Sales in 1991 = 1000
Increase = 3000

(c) The percentage increase in sales in 2003 over the sales in 1999 is 300%.

Actual increase = 4000 − 1000 = 3000.

Percent increase (Sale in the base year) $= \frac{3000}{1000} \times 100\%$ $= 300\%$

C. READING DATA FROM PIE CHARTS AND PICTOGRAPHS

➔ **Read and interpret data from a pie-chart (circle graph)**

Discussion

In a *pie chart* or *circle graph* the whole unit (circle) is divided into parts. Each part or percent is represented by a sector of a circle whose size is proportional to the value of the data for that part.

To read data from a pie chart means finding a part of the whole as a *fraction* or as a *percent.* Often, the circumference of the circle is shown divided in hundredths (see Figure 7.9). In that case, to know the percentage of a particular part, simply count the number of hundredths falling on the arc of that sector.

If the division of the circumference into hundredths is not shown, the percentages are usually written along with the label for the parts. After having read data from a pie chart, it can be interpreted in a similar way as in the case of a bar chart or any other graph.

EXAMPLE 6 The following circle graph shows the distribution of sales at a Mini-Mart for three types of items: Sundries, Food, and Hardware.

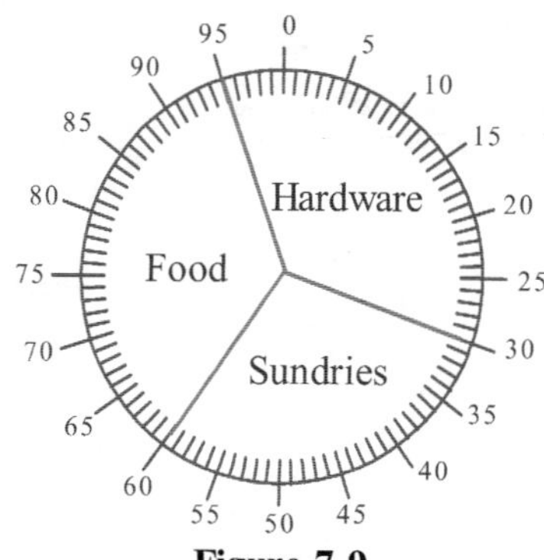

Figure 7.9

Respond to the following questions using this graph.

(a) Which of the three types of items produced the greatest sales?

(b) Find the sales from Sundries if the total sales are $1,500.

Solutions

(a) The sales from hardware and food were the largest, because they constituted 35% of the total sales while the percent of sundries was less than 35%.

(b) Thirty percent of the sales are from sundries so the sales from sundries are:

30% of $1500

$= \dfrac{30}{100} \times 1500$

$= \$450$

WARM-UP

6. Use the graph in Figure 7.9 to respond to the following questions:

(a) Which type of the items produced minimum sales?

(b) Find the sale for hardware if the total sale at the Mini-Mart is $2,000.

WARM-UP

7. Use the circle graph of Figure 7.10 to answer the following questions.

   (a) What percent of the funds are spent on library books?

   (b) On which item is the expenditure the greatest?

   (c) If the total funds available are $2,750,000, how much is spent on sports?

Answers:

6. (a) Sundries (b) $700

7. (a) 24% (b) Salaries (c) $440,000

EXAMPLE 7 The following circle graph shows different budget items in a school budget.

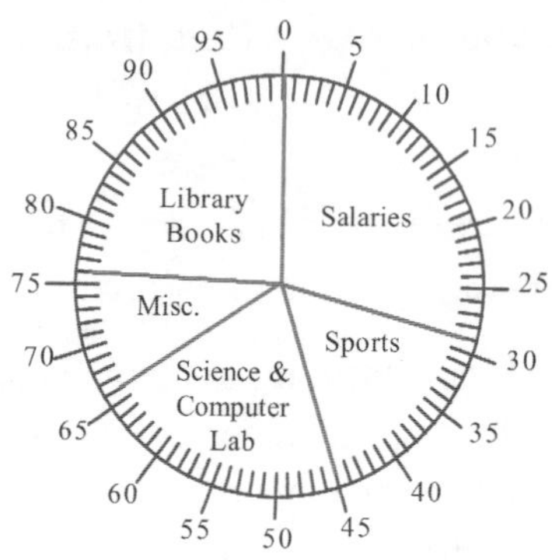

Figure 7.10

(a) What percent of the funds are spent on science and computer labs?

(b) On which item is the expenditure more, sports or library books?

(c) If the total funds available in the year 1996 are $3,570,000, how much will be spent on salaries, if the percentages for each expenditure item is the same?

Solutions

(a) 21%

Count the number of division lines between the markings 45 and 66: 66 − 45 = 21.

(b) Library books

The area of the sector representing 'Library books' is larger than the area of the sector representing 'Sports'.

(c) The amount spent on workers' salaries:

29% of $3570000

29 % of the funds are spent on workers salaries. The total funds available are $3,570,000

$$= \frac{29}{100} \times \$3{,}570{,}000$$

$$= \$1{,}035{,}300$$

D. FIND THE MEAN, MEDIAN, MODE, AND RANGE OF A DATA

- **Numerical representation of data:** The process of analyzing and interpreting data basically involves finding some **special numerical values** called **statistics.** Each statistic describes or measures a particular characteristic of the data. In this section we will study only four numerical statistics that are easily calculated: Mean, Median, Mode, and Range. Out of these, the first three, the mean, median, and mode are measures that describe the '**average**' or the '**middle**' of a set of data and are called the **measures of central tendency**. The fourth one, the range, is called the **measure of spread.**

- **The Mean**

The **mean** of a set of numbers (data) is the common arithmetic average or arithmetic mean. We calculate the mean of a set of observations by dividing the sum of the observations by the number of observations.

$$\text{Mean} = \frac{\text{sum of all the observations in the data}}{\text{number of observations in the data}}$$

For example, if the heights of six boys are:

162 cm, 176 cm, 180 cm, 182 cm, 178 cm, and 175 cm

then, ← Add all the numbers in the data.

the **mean** height $= \frac{162+176+180+182+178+175}{6}$ ← Divide the sum by 6 as there are 6 data items.

$= \frac{1{,}053}{6}$ (You may use a calculator for computations.)

$= 175.5$ cm

Note While giving the mean of a set of data, we must also mention the unit in which the observations have been measured/recorded. Thus, we say that the mean height is 175.5 cm. It is not proper to say that the mean height is 175.5.

- Following are two sets of data, Group I and Group II, that will be used in Examples 1-3.

Group I: Family incomes (weekly) in a survey of eleven workers are:
$350, $280, $450, $375, $470, $525, $450, $300, $500, $490, and $430.

Group II: The points scored by a basketball team in ten matches are:
28, 31, 27, 30, 55, 60, 65, 70, 100, and 84

EXAMPLE 8 **(a)** Find the mean weekly income for the 11 workers in Group I.

(b) Find the mean score of the basketball team from the data in Group II.

Solutions We know that mean $= \frac{\text{sum of the observations}}{\text{number of the observations}}$

(a) Refer to the data in Group I

WARM-UP

8. (a) Find the mean of the following data and identify whether or not it is a data-item:

54, 57, 61, 57, 62, 58, and 57

Step 1 Add the amounts of 11 salaries:

```
  350
  280
  450
  375
  470
  525
  450
  300
  500
  490
  430
-----
4,620   ← Sum
```

You may use a calculator for calculations. The solution in compact form is written as:

Sum of the observations = 350 + 280 + 450 + 375 + 470 + 525 + 450 + 300 + 500 + 490 + 430 = $4,620.

The number of observations = 11.

Step 2 Divide the sum by 11.

```
      4 2 0      ← mean salary
11 ) 4 6 2 0
     4 4
     ---
       2 2
       2 2
       ---
         0 0
         0 0
         ---
           0
```

The mean weekly salary is $420.

(b) Refer to the data in Group II.

Step 1 The sum of the data values

= 28 + 31 + 27 + 30 + 55 + 60 + 65 + 70 + 100 + 84

= 550

Step 2 The mean $= \frac{550}{10}$ ← The sum of observations. ← The number of observations.

= 55 points (Remember to mention the 'unit' of observations with the mean.)

The mean score of the basket ball team is 55 points.

(b) Find the mean for the following data:

45, 77, 69, 95, 50, 81, 32, and 70

(Round the answer to two decimal places)

Answers:

8. (a) 58 ; yes **(b)** 64.875 » 64.88

- **The Median**

In a set of data arranged in order, smallest to largest or largest to smallest, the **median** is the *middle* value.

For example, if the observed values are:

12, 14, 15, 17, **21**, 24, 26, 27, 30

then the median is equal to **21**. Observe that there are four values in the data that are less than 21, and exactly the same number of values greater than 21.

If the number of observations is even as in the following data set,

12, 14, 15, **17**, **21**, 24, 26, 27,

then there are two middle terms; namely, **17** and **21.** In such cases, the **average of the two middle terms** is taken as the median; thus, the median of the data under consideration is $\frac{17+21}{2} = \mathbf{19}$.

The determination of **median** depends on whether there is an odd or an even number of observations. The procedure to find the median is as follows:

> **Procedure** to find the median
>
> ***Step* 1** Arrange the data in order, either from smallest to largest or largest to smallest.
>
> ***Step* 2** **a.** If the number of items (n) is **odd**, the median is the middle term.
>
> **b.** If n is **even**, the median is the average of the two middle terms.

EXAMPLE 9 (a) Find the median weekly income for the 11 workers in Group I.

(b) Find the median score of the basketball team from the data in Group II.

Solutions To find the median we must express the data in descending or ascending order.

(a) Refer to the data in Group I.

Step 1 Rank the data in order from smallest to largest.

1.	2.	3.	4.	5.	6.	7.	8.	9.	10.	11.
280	300	350	375	430	**450**	450	470	490	500	525
					↑					

Step 2 Since there are 11 items (an **odd** number), of data, the median is the middle item (the sixth item);

Median weekly salary = \$450.

(b) Refer to the data in Group II

Step 1 Rank the data in order:

1.	2.	3.	4.	5.	6.	7.	8.	9.	10.
27	28	30	31	**55**	**60**	65	70	84	100
				↑	↑				

Step 2 Since there are 10 items (an **even** number) of data, there are two middle items, and the median is the average of these two.

$$\text{Median Score} = \frac{55+60}{2}$$

$$= 57.5 \text{ points}$$

The median score is 57.5 points.

WARM-UP

9. (a) Following are the ages (in years) of a group of seven friends. Find the median age.

54 , 57, 61, 57, 62, 58, 57

(b) Find the median for the following data:

45, 77, 69, 95, 50, 81, 32, 70

Answers:

9. (a) 57 yrs **(b)** 69.5

- **The Mode and Range**

The **mode** is also another measure of central tendency. It is that value of the data that occurs most frequently. For example, in the data

2 1 4 2 0 1 **3** 6 **3** 0 **3** 5 **3**

the value 3 occurs most frequently, so the mode of the data is 3.

Remark: A set of data may have more than one mode; however, the data sets that we use in this text will have either one mode or no mode. If each number in the data occurs only once then the data has no mode.

Range is a rough measure of 'spread' and is given by the difference of the largest and the smallest data values. For example, the range of the data

20 10 5 35 15 19 20

is the difference 35 – 5 = **30**, as 35 is the largest and 5 is the smallest data value.

Remark: We have called the range "a *rough* measure of spread"; 'rough', because it simply tells us the span in which the data values lie but does not convey any thing about the way they are spread. There are other measures of spread such as **standard deviation** and **variance** that describe how compact the data values are spread around the central value. Discussion of such measures is beyond the scope of this text.

WARM-UP

10. Find **(a)** the **mode** and **(b)** the **range** for the sets of data in Warm-Up 2 (a) and 2(b).

EXAMPLE 10 Find **(a)** the **mode** and **(b)** the **range** for both sets of data in Groups I and II.

Solutions Once the data has been ranked, as was done in Example 2, the mode and the range are easily determined. For both groups, refer to their ranked data in Example 2.

(a) **(i)** For Group I, the mode = **\$450.**

(ii) Data in Group II have **no mode** since each value occurs only once.

The value 450 appears the maximum number of times (twice in this case). Remember to use the unit in which the data items are measured.

(b) Range = (largest value) – (smallest value).

For Group I, range = 525 – 280
= **\$245;**

In Group I, from ranked data in Example 2, the largest value = 525; the smallest value = 280.

For Group II, range = 100 – 27
= 73 points.

Remember to mention the unit.

Answers:

10. **(a)** Mode of data in Warm-Up 2(a) = 57 yrs; No mode for data in 2(b).

(b) Range of data in Warm-Up 2(a) = 8 yrs; Range of data in Warm-Up 2(b) = 63.

EXERCISE 7.1

Use table 7.5 for exercises 1-4.

Table 7.5

The Expenditure of A School During the Year 2004.

Item	Amount spent in millions
Teachers Salaries	7.5
Library Books	2.5
Science Education	2.2
Music Education	1.3
Sports activities	1.5
Arts	1.1
Staff Salaries	2.0

Source : School Data Ware house

1. What was the total expenditure in 2004?
2. What percent of the total expenditure was spent on science education? Round to the nearest whole number percent.
3. What is the ratio of expenditure on teachers salaries to that on staff salaries?
4. What is the percentage of the excess expenditure on sports activities over that of the Arts? Round to the nearest tenth of a percent.

For exercises 5-9, use the information in Table 7.6 about the number of men and women workers in three factories A, B, and C.

Table 7.6

Factories	Men workers	Women workers
A	30	5
B	25	11
C	27	6

5. Which factory has the greatest number of workers? Which one has the least number of male workers?
6. Find the ratio of the total number of female workers to the total number of male workers.
7. What percent of the women employed work in Factory A?
8. What is the ratio of men to women in Factory C?
9. What percent of the men employed are working in Factory B? Round to the nearest tenth of a percent.

A firm has three plants I, II, and III, which make weekly despatches to four depots A, B, C, and D. The transport costs per crate of goods despatched along each route are shown below in Table 7.7. The table includes the quantities available from each plant and the requirements of each depot. Use this table for exercises 10-19.

Table 7.7
Transport Cost Per Crate From Three Plants to Four Depots

Plant / Depot	I	II	III	Quantities Required
A	$4	$1	$4	180
B	$7	$8	$6	370
C	$9	$3	$3	225
D	$2	$9	$5	245
Quantities Available	360	400	300	1020 / 1060

Source :

10. What is the requirement of depot B?

11. Which plant has the greatest availability?

12. Which depot do you think is at the greatest distance from Plant I? Why?

13. What percent of the total requirement is available with Plant I? Round to the nearest tenth of a percent.

14. Is there a sufficient quantity available with the three plants to meet the requirements of all the four depots? Why?

15. Which plant do you think is nearest to Depot A? Why?

16. Find the total transport cost of Depot B if it gets 125 crates from Plant I, 70 crates from Plant II, and 175 crates from Plant III.

17. What percent of the total quantity available is required by Depot D? Round to the nearest whole number percent.

18. What percent of the total requirement is required by Depot C? Round to the nearest whole number percent.

19. What is the ratio of the requirement of Depot A to the requirement of Depot B? Give the percent comparison also.

The following chart shows the total rainfall recorded in the years of 1999 through 2004 in a certain city. Use the graph for exercises 20-23.

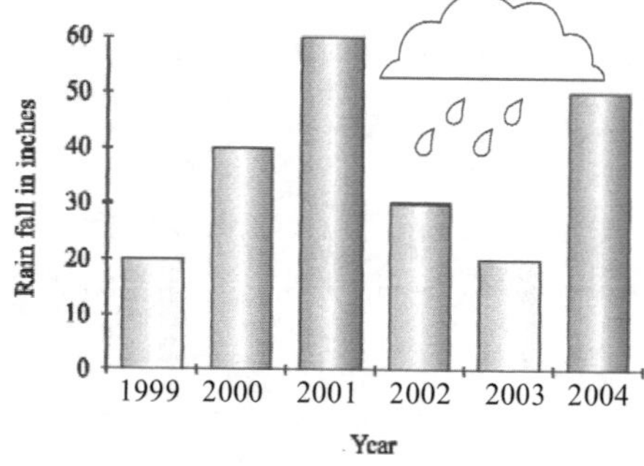

20. In which year(s) did the city have maximum rainfall?

21. In which year(s) did the city have minimum rainfall?

22. How much rainfall was recorded in the year 2002?

23. What is the average rainfall for the six years? Round to the nearest tenth of an inch.

The following bar graph shows the number of cars produced by a certain company during the period of 1998 through 2004. Use the graph for exercises 24-29.

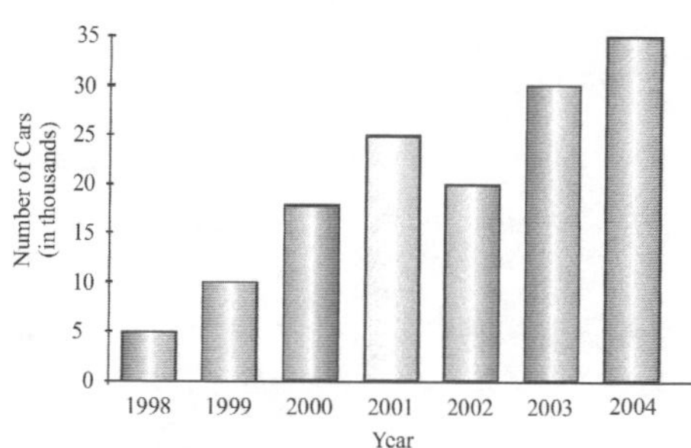

24. In which year did the company produce the most cars?

25. How many cars were produced in 2000?

26. In which year(s) did the production exceed 25 thousand cars?

27. In which year(s) was the production fewer than 10 thousand cars?

28. What was the total number of cars produced in the years 2002 to 2004?

29. Find the average car production per year during the period 1998 to 2004? Round to the nearest thousand.

The following graph shows the number of vehicles passing through a certain road crossing during normal business hours on a particular day. Use the graph for exercises 30-34.

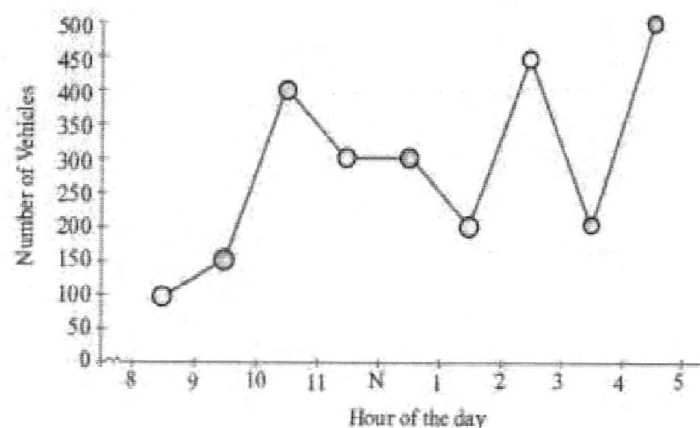

30. What type of the graph is this?

31. How many vehicles passed through the crossing between 10 and 11?

32. At what hour was the road the most busy?

33. How many cars passed through the crossing between 11 and 12?

34. At what hour of the day was the number of cars passing through the crossing the smallest?

The following graph displays the way funds in a school are allocated to different expenditure line items in a particular year. Use the graph for exercises 35-39.

0
Sports
Staff Salary
75
Misc.
25
Science Lab
Library
50

35. What kind of the graph is this?

36. What percent of the funds are allocated to sports?

37. What percent of the funds are spent on library books and miscellaneous items?

38. If the total funds available are $4,520,000, what amount is spent on science lab?

39. If the amount allocated to the library is $716,000, find the total amount of funds available.

In exercises 40-44, find the mean, median, mode (if any), and the range for the given set of numbers.

40. 60, 65, 55, 70, 90, 81, 76, 50, and 62 **41.** 5, 12, 2, 11, 8, 10, 7, 4, and 2 **42.** 85, 72, 70, 82, 72, 71, 84, and 75

43. 10, 5, 5, 2, 9, 8, 2, 3, 4, 6, 6, 5, and 9 **44.** 2.3, 3.5, 1.7, 1.9, 3.2, 2.3, and 2.4

In exercises 45-53, find the mean, median, mode (if there is one), and the range of the given data. Remember to use the unit of measurement in which the data items are measured.

45. The weekly salaries of six employees of Jack's establishment: $480, $210, $190, $185, $215, and $500

46. The ages (in years) of 16 boys selected at random from a class:

14 16 13 14 15 12 14 15

16 15 13 14 14 15 15 15

47. The weights (in kg) of 10 students surveyed in a chemistry class: 50 54 53 50 56 50 59 61 50 48

48. Earnings (in dollars) of a server/waiter in a restaurant from tips, for nine consecutive days:

20 21 24 24 23 28 28 24 36

49. The body temperatures (in Fahrenheit degrees) of 8 people:

99.2° 98.7° 96.4° 98.1° 100.2° 98.6° 99.8° 98.6°

50. The scores (out of 40) of 20 students surveyed in a Mathematics class:

24 17 26 35 36 23 19 21 20 19
20 18 20 21 18 22 23 23 23 18

51. The times, taken by 15 students to complete an experiment:

44 45 65 58 42 49 42 54

48 46 62 38 48 48 60

(Round the answers to the nearest second.)

52. The heights (in cm) of 10 students selected at random from Dr. Anderson's course in Business Mathematics:

150 148 147 146 145 143 153 139 141 142

53. The time of 11 movies:

99 min 105 min 110 min 88 min 90 min 100 min
93 min 90 min 155 min 90 min 113 min

In exercises 54-55, find the mean, median, and mode of the given series of observations.

54. 17, 8, 14, 12, 9, 3, 21, 5, 12, and 16

55. 26, 16, 14, 15, 17, 27, 26, 18, and 30

7.2 Sampling Methods

There are different sampling methods to select research participants whose responses will make up our data. We list a few for your review:

Objectives

After completing this section you will be able to define:

A. Random Sampling.
B. Convenience Sampling.
C. Systematic Sampling.
D. Stratified Sampling.
E. Cluster Sampling.

A. Random Sampling

The best and easiest method is called **Random Sampling**. This is where research participants are chosen from a specified population in such a way that each individual has an equal chance of being selected.

> ***Definition:***
>
> A random sampling is a technique in which each member of population has equal chances of being selected in the sample.

B. Convenience Sampling

Conveniences sampling is often used when the population is too large. This method is often used because the sample is readily available and the responses are easily accessed. As with the example of job satisfaction in a factory, an example of a convenient sample would be to survey only those employees who were in a particular room in the entire factory.

> ***Definition:***
>
> A **convenience sampling** is a technique in which a unit of sample is selected with convenience of persons. In other words, whatever sample is handy is chosen.

C. Systematic Sampling

The next method is called **Systematic Sampling**. This method consists of selecting any unit at random from the first k units numbered 1 to k and then selecting every k^{th} unit in succession subsequently.

> ***Definition:***
>
> A **systematic sampling** is a technique in which first unit of sample is selected at random and then each subsequent unit is picked at a fixed distance from the previous unit selected in the sample.

For example, the researcher has a population total of 100 individuals and needs 12 subjects. He first picks his starting number, 4. Then the researcher picks his interval, 8. The members of his sample will be individuals 4, 12, 20, 28, 36, 44, 52, 60, 68, 76, 84, 92.

Another example of systematic sampling would be checking the oxygen level in a river. The researcher stops every 10th mile to take a measurement.

D. Stratified Sampling

Another method is **Stratified Sampling**. We use stratified sampling when there are smaller sub-groups that are to be investigated. It begins with dividing the population into a set of smaller non-overlapping sub-groups (strata), and then randomly a sample is taken from each sub-group. Strata can be natural groupings, such as age ranges or ethnic origins.

> ***Definition:***
>
> A **statified sampling** is a technique in which the population is divided into a finite number of stratas (hetrogenous subgroups) and then units (proportional to size of strats) are picked randomly from each strator.

For example if a company employs more men than women but it is required to have each group equally represented, we would employ stratified sampling. Two strata are thus created, of men and women, with an equal number in each to sample from.

E. Cluster Sampling

The last method is called **Cluster Sampling**. Cluster sampling is a sampling technique in which the entire population of interest is divided into groups (clusters) and a random sample of these clusters is selected. Each cluster must be mutually exclusive, and the clusters all together must include the entire population. After clusters are selected, then all units within the clusters are selected. This method is widely used when the studied population is spread across a wide area and other sampling methods would be too difficult to implement.

> ***Definition:***
>
> A **cluster sampling** is one where the population is divided into sections and then one of the sections is selected with all members represented in it.

For example, in order to obtain the percentage of voters favoring a republican candidate for presidency, three suburbs are randomly selected from the entire region and all the qualified voters in these suburbs are questioned.

EXERCISE 7.2

1. **Use a search engine to find the definition of the following terms. If possible, use each term in an example demonstrating their use in the real world.**

- Statistics
- Variable
- Descriptive Statistics
- A Population
- A Sample
- Inferential Statistics
- Quantitative Variables
- Discrete Variables
- Continuous Variables
- Nominal Measurement
- Ordinal Measurement
- Random Sampling
- Systematic Sampling
- Stratified Sampling
- Cluster Sampling
- Independent Variable (explanatory variable)
- Dependent Variable (outcome variable)
- Qualitative Variables

2. **Answer each of the following questions in a sentence or two.**

   (a) Why do we use samples instead of the population in statistical studies?

   (b) What is the difference between ordinal and nominal measurements?

   (c) What is the difference between independent and dependent variables?

   (d) Use the internet, newspaper, or an article to find a statistical study, and determine if it's an observational or experimental study?

   (e) In the article dealt with in (d) above, identify the dependent and independent variables.

3. **Answer in short paragraphs.**

   (a) What is the difference between descriptive and inferential statistics?

   (b) How do sample and population differ?

   (c) What is the difference between a parameter and a statistic?

   (d) What are population variables called?

   (e) How do discrete data differ from continuous data?

   (f) How many levels of measurements are there?

   (g) What is the difference between a nominal level of measurement and an ordinal level of measurement?

   (h) What is the difference between the interval level of measurement and the ratio level of measurement?

   (i) What are the variables of interest called?

   (j) Why is it important to select the right method of sampling?

   (k) How many sampling techniques are there?

   (l) What is a random sample and how is it obtained?

   (m) How do you obtain a convenience sample?

   (n) How do random samples and convenience samples differ?

   (o) What is systematic sampling?

   (p) What is the difference between stratified sampling and cluster sampling?

   (q) When do we use cluster sampling?

   (r) How do we obtain a cluster sample?

4. **Determine whether the given statement is true or false.**

   (a) Descriptive statistics is a procedure used to describe a set of data.

   (b) A sample is a subset of the population.

   (c) A parameter is a numerical measurement describing a certain characteristic of a sample.

   (d) Data that represents values that correspond to some continuous scale without interruptions is called discrete data.

   (e) Data at ordinal level of measurement can be arranged in order but the difference in between is meaningless.

(f) Data at ratio level of measurement can be arranged in order and the difference in between entries is meaningful but it doesn't have a starting point zero.

(g) A systematic sample is one which uses results that are easy to obtain.

(h) Cluster Sampling is widely used when the studied population is spread across a wide area and other sampling methods would be difficult to implement in accessing the selected sample.

5. Identify the type of units (Sample or Population).

(a) At a university library there are 281 computers for use. In order to check the operating condition of computers a technician selects 23 for testing.

(b) A Gallup poll of 214 randomly surveyed students found that 7% are having difficulties with on-line testing.

(c) In a study of animal behavior, a researcher randomly selects 4 kangaroos from a zoo which has 32 kangaroos.

(d) During an investigation process of the parking citations issued by Officer Johnson, 57 cases were selected out of total 512 for a closer examination.

(e) A customer service manager in a call center at a bank randomly selects 19 out of 341 calls received in a day.

6. Identify the level of measurement.

(a) Temperature, year, account balance.

(b) IQ score, distance, speed.

(c) Color, blood type, gender.

(d) Weight, pressure, age.

(e) Rank, grade, size (small, large ...)

7. Identify the type of data (Qualitative or Quantitative).

(a) Year, weight, time.

(b) Zip code, religion, vehicle model.

(c) Alcohol concentration, height, voltage.

(d) Mood, fish type, nationality.

(e) Oxygen level, acceleration, amplitude

8. Identify the sampling method used.

(a) An insurance agent picks every 17th quote to respond.

(b) A medical researcher selects a group of students by selecting classrooms and selecting students from each class.

(c) A store manager surveys only those employees who showed up to work 15 minutes early.

(d) On a roulette table, in order to select 3 numbers to place a bet on, a gambler closes his eyes and points at 3 different numbers.

(e) On a street, every 5th pedestrian is being surveyed during a 2 hours period to obtain a group of responses for a research study on health care reform.

8

PROBABILITY

In previous classes, you learnt about experimental (or empirical) probability of an event which was based on the outcomes of an actual experiment. For example, if we toss a coin, say 800 times, and get heads and tails as :

Heads : 392 Tails : 408, then,

$$\text{experimental probability of getting a head} = \frac{392}{800}, \text{ and}$$

$$\text{experimental probability of getting a tail} = \frac{408}{800}$$

If we carry on this experiment say 10000 times, 50000 times, 1 million times, 10 million times, or more, you will see that as the number of tosses increases, the experimental probability of a head or a tail shall appear to be settling down around the fraction $\frac{1}{2}$ which is what we call the **theoretical probability** of getting a head (or getting a tail). In this chapter, we shall learn about theoretical probability of an event.

You are already familiar with terms like random experiment, outcome, event, *etc.* from earlier classes. Before studying the theoretical probability of an event, we shall be introducing some more terms which are basic to its study and will be frequently used in this chapter.

8.1 SINGLE AND MULTISTAGE EXPERIMENTS

A. SINGLE AND MULTISTAGE EXPERIMENTS

OBJECTIVES

Upon completion of this section you will study about:

A. Single and Multistage Experiments.

➜ **Sample Space**

The collection of all possible outcomes of an experiment is called the *sample space* for the experiment.

- When a coin is tossed, the sample space consists of outcomes Head (H) and Tail (T).

When we talk of a coin we mean a fair coin *i.e.*, it has no biasness *i.e.*, a head is as likely to occur as a tail.

- When a die is thrown, the sample space consists of outcomes :

usually denoted by 1, 2, 3, 4, 5 and 6 respectively.

The **plural of die is dice**. The sum of numbers on the opposite faces of a die is always 7. When we talk of throwing a die, we mean a fair die only.

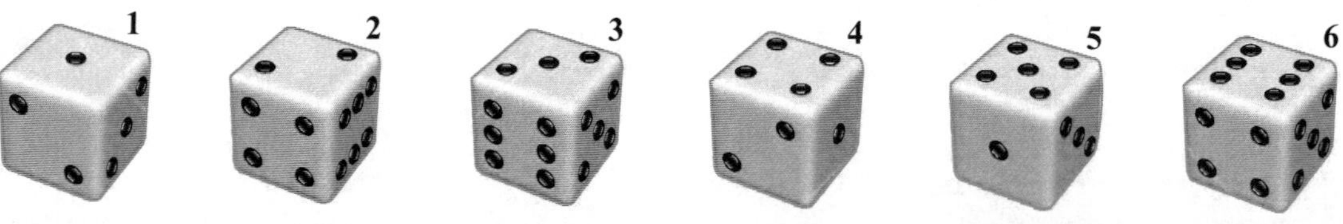

Figure 8.1

- When a coin is tossed twice, the sample space consists of outcomes HH, HT, TH, TT, where HH means head both times, HT means H first time and T second time *etc.*

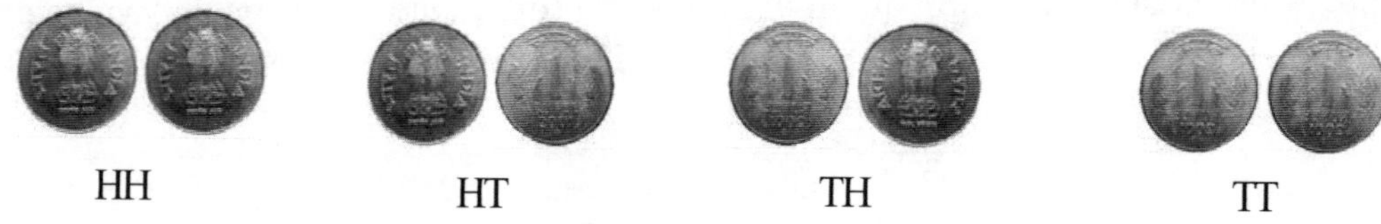

Figure 8.2

- When a card is drawn from a well shuffled deck of 52 playing cards and its suit is observed, the same space consists of 'hearts', 'clubs', 'diamonds' and 'spades'.

Cards

A deck of cards has 52 cards - 26 red and 26 black.

The 26 red cards contain 13 diamonds and 13 hearts

The 26 black cards contain 13 spades and 13 clubs

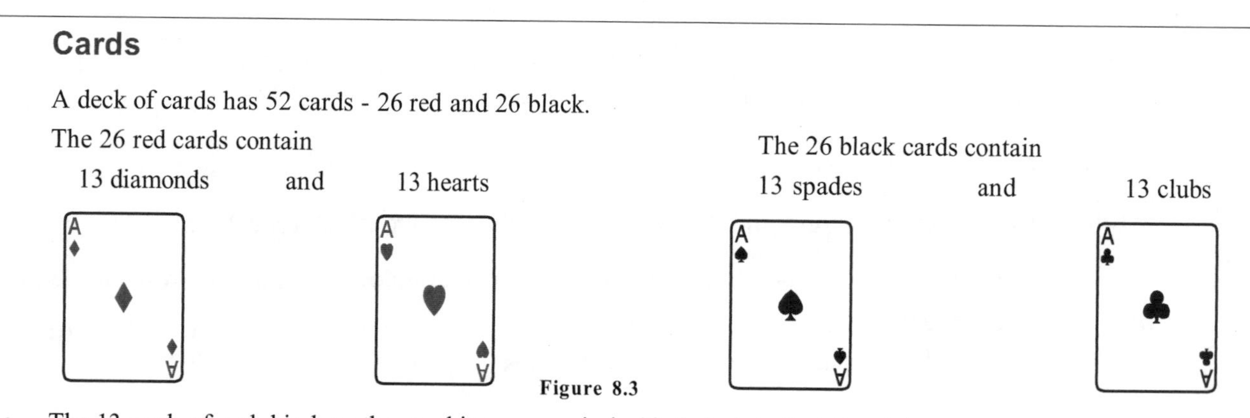

Figure 8.3

- The 13 cards of each kind are the ace, king, queen, jack, 10, 9, 8, 7, 6, 5, 4, 3 and 2.
- The king, queen and jack are known as face cards.

Thus, there are **12** face cards (**3** of each suit) in a pack of 52 playing cards.

In this chapter, when we speak of a coin or die, we mean a fair coin or fair die only. This means coin is symmetrical so that there is no reason for it to come down more often on one side than the other. Similar is the case with a die.

- A ball is drawn from a bag containing 3 red, 4 white and 2 blue balls. The outcomes of this experiment are 'red ball' 'white ball', 'blue ball'
- A customer selects a light-bulbs in a shop and the shopkeeper tests it for the customer. The outcomes are 'bulbs lights' 'bulb does not light'.

➜ Event

One or more outcomes of an experiment constitute an event. In a toss of a coin, 'getting an head', 'getting a tail' each is an event.

Similarly the outcomes favorable to the event "getting one head", when a coin is tossed two times, are HT and TH.

➜ Favourable Outcomes

Outcomes which ensure the occurence of an event are called outcomes favourable to that event. The favourable outcomes to the "occurence of an even number when a die is thrown" are "2, 4 and 6".

➜ Equally Likely Outcomes

The outcomes of a random experiment are called *equally likely*, if they all have the same chance of occurence.

- When a card is drawn from a well shuffled pack of cards, there are 52 **equally likely** outcomes as all cards have the same chance of being drawn.
- When a die is thrown, each of the faces bearing one, two, three, four, five or six dots is equally likely to appear on the top.

  (In case of equally likely outcomes, there is no reason to expect any one outcome in preference to others).

➜ Exhaustive Events

The total number of all the possible outcomes of an experiment or a trial are its exhaustive events.

If we toss a coin, two outcomes are possible. 'Head or Tail'. Head and Tail taken together are exhaustive events of this experiment, *i.e.*, either of the two occurs and nothing else occurs.

- When a single die is tossed, there are in all six exhaustive events (outcomes) namely, 1, 2, 3, 4, 5 and 6.

Similarly, when a single die is thrown, events "getting an even number" or "getting an odd number" are also **exhaustive**, the events "getting a number less than 4" and the event "getting a number greater than or equal to 4" are also exhaustive events.

➜ Mutually Exclusive Events

Two events in an experiment are *mutually exclusive*, if they can not occur together.

- When a coin is tossed, either a Head or Tail will appear. They cannot occur together.
- From a deck of 52 cards, if a card is drawn, either it will be a red card or a black card.

So, the events "getting a black card" and "getting a red card" are both *mutually exclusive* and *exhaustive*. But 'getting a spade card' and 'getting a heart card' are *mutually exclusive* but *not exhaustive events*.

➜ Theortical (or Classical) Probability

The probability of an event E, written as P(E), is defined as

$$P(E) = \frac{\text{Number of outcomes favourable to } E}{\text{Total number of possible outcomes of the experiment}}$$

provided the outcomes of the experiment are *equally likely* and mutually exclusive.

Thus $P(E) = \frac{m}{n}$, where m is the number of outcomes favourable to E and n is the total number of outcomes.

As $0 \leq m \leq n$, so, $0 \leq \frac{m}{n} \leq 1$.

Hence, $0 \leq P(E) \leq 1$.

Remark:

(i) On throwing a die, the event E "getting a number less than 7" is a **sure** event as every face of the die is marked with a number less than 7 and number of outcomes favourable to E is 6. So, its (theoretical) probability is $\frac{6}{6} = 1$.

(ii) On throwing a die, the event F "getting a number greater than 6" is an **impossible** event as no face of the die is marked with a number greater than 6 and the number of outcomes favourable to F is 0. So, its probability is $\frac{0}{6} = 0$.

(iii) In this chapter, by probability, we means theoretical probability only.

Just as real numbers can be represented on a line we can represent probability of an event on the interval [0, 1], *i.e.*, a number lying between 0 and 1 (0 and 1 both inclusive).

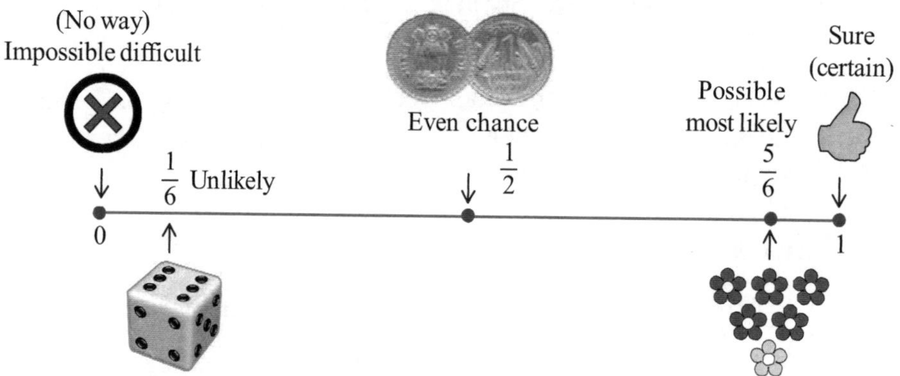

We can call this a *probability line*.

➜ Elementary and Compound Events

An event which has one (favourable) outcome from the sample space is called an **elementary event**.

An event which has more than one (favourable) outcome from the sample space is called a ***compound event***.

On throwing a die, the event of getting the number **5**, is an *elementary event*, but the event of getting an even number (**2**, **4** or **6**) is a *compound event*. Similarly, in a toss of a coin 'getting a head' is an **elementary event**.

Note that: $P(\text{Head}) = \frac{1}{2}, \quad P(\text{Tail}) = \frac{1}{2}$

$$P(\text{Head}) + P(\text{Tail}) = \frac{1}{2} + \frac{1}{2} = 1 \qquad \ldots(i)$$

Similarly, if a die is thrown once, then

$$P(\text{getting 1 on its top}) = \frac{1}{6}, \quad P(2) = \frac{1}{6}, \quad P(3) = \frac{1}{6}$$

$$P(4) = \frac{1}{6}, \quad P(5) = \frac{1}{6}, \quad P(6) = \frac{1}{6}$$

We have $P(1) + P(2) + P(3) + P(4) + P(5) + P(6) = \frac{1}{6} + \frac{1}{6} + \frac{1}{6} + \frac{1}{6} + \frac{1}{6} + \frac{1}{6} = 1 \ldots(ii)$

From the above examples, we see that the *sum of probabilities of all possible outcomes of an experiment* is 1.

➔ Complementary Events

If E is an event, then the event "not E", denoted by $\overline{E}$, is called **complementary event** of E.

On tossing a coin once, if E is the event "getting a head", then the event $\overline{E}$ (not E) "getting no head" (or "getting a tail") is complementary event of E.

As $P(E) = \frac{m}{n}, \quad P(\overline{E}) = \frac{n-m}{n}$ (from definition)

$$= 1 - \frac{m}{n}$$

$$= 1 - P(E) \qquad \left(\text{Since } P(E) = \frac{m}{n}\right)$$

$$\mathbf{P(E) + P(\overline{E}) = 1}$$

Illustration 1 On tossing a coin once, it can land up in one of two possible ways - either head (H) or tail (T) up.

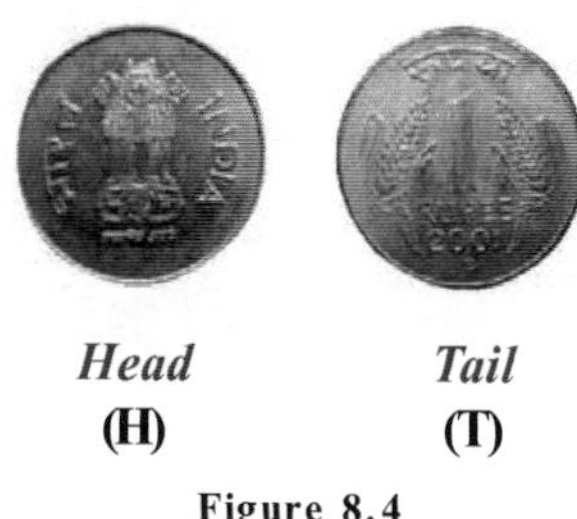

Figure 8.4

So, the number of possible outcomes of the experiment = 2

Each outcome H or T is as likely to occur as the other, *i.e.*, the outcomes H or T are **equally likely**.

Let E be the event "getting a head". Then

$$P(E) = \frac{\text{Number of outcomes favourable to E}}{\text{Total number of possible outcomes}} = 2$$

Similarly, P(getting a tail) = P(F) = $\frac{1}{2}$

Note that, P(E) + P(F) = $\frac{1}{2} + \frac{1}{2} = 1$

i.e., the sum of probabilities of events "getting a head" and "getting a tail" is 1.

Illustration 2 A die is thrown once. In this case, total number of possible outcomes = 6 (*i.e.*, 1, 2, 3, 4, 5, 6)

Let K be the event "getting a prime number *i.e.*, 2, 3, 5".

Number of outcomes favourable to K = 3.

So, $P(K) = \frac{3}{6} = \frac{1}{2}$.

EXAMPLE 1 A die is thrown once. Find the probability of getting an odd number.

Solution : When a die is thrown, its outcomes are (1, 2, 3, 4, 5 or 6). Let E be the event "getting an odd number".

Number of favourable outcomes to E = 3

Total number of possible outcomes = 6

Probability of getting an odd number = *P(E)* =

$$\frac{\text{Number of favourable outcomes to E}}{\text{Total number of possible outcomes of the experiment}}$$

$$= \frac{3}{6} = \frac{1}{2}$$

EXAMPLE 2 A die is thrown once. Find the probability of getting 3 or 4.

Solution : Let E be the event "getting 3 or 4".

Number of possible outcomes on throwing a die = 6

Number of outcomes favourable to E = 2

$$P(E) = \frac{2}{6} = \frac{1}{3}$$

EXAMPLE 3 A bag contains 7 white, 4 red and 3 green balls. A ball is drawn at random from the bag. Find the probablity that it is a red ball.

Solution : Total number of balls in the bag = 7 + 4 + 3 = 14

So, there are 14 possible outcomes.

Let E be the event "getting a red ball".

Number of outcomes favourable to E = 4 (as there are 4 red balls)

So, $P(E) = \frac{4}{14} = \frac{2}{7}$.

EXAMPLE 4 Out of 19 boys and 21 girls of a class, one student is to be selected at random. Find the probability of selecting a girl.

Solution : Total number of students in the class $= 19 + 21 = 40$

As 1 student is to be selected, so the total number of possible outcomes $= 40$

Let A be the event "selecting a girl".

Number of outcomes favourable to A $= 21$

So, $P(A) = \dfrac{21}{40}$.

Selection process involves writing name of each student on a slip and put in a box and then the bag is stirred well. In case of there are two or more same names then they are written in such a way on the steps to distinguish one from the other. One slip is drawn at random from the bag.

EXAMPLE 5 Find the probability that a leap year selected at random will contain 53 wednesday.

Solution : In a leap year there are 366 days. There are 7 days in a week.

As 366 days = 52 complete weeks + 2 'extra' days

The extra days can be Wednesday and Thursday; Thursday and Friday; Friday and Saturday; Saturday and Sunday, Sunday and Monday; Monday and Tuesday; Tuesday and Wednesday.

Therefore, total outcomes $= 7$

Number of outcomes favourable to the event 'day is wednesday' $= 2$

Probability that leap year has 53 wednesday $= \dfrac{2}{7}$

EXAMPLE 6 Out of 500 lottery tickets, 10 are prize winning tickets. A person buys a ticket. Find the probability of his getting a prize winning ticket.

Solution : Number of total outcomes = 500

Number of favourable outcomes, *i.e.*, prize winning ticket $= 10$

Probability of getting a prize winning ticket $= \dfrac{10}{500} = \dfrac{1}{50}$

EXAMPLE 7 A letter is chosen from the letters of English alphabet. Find the probability that it is a consonant.

Solution : There are 26 letters in English alphabets. Out of these, 5 are vowels and 21 are consonants.

Let E be the event "getting a consonant".

(a, e, i, o, u are vowels remaining are consonants)

Number of total outcomes $= 26$

Number of outcomes favourable to event E $= 21$

$$P(E) = \frac{21}{26}$$

EXAMPLE 8 A box contains 90 discs which are numbered from 1 to 90. If one disc is drawn at random from the box, find the probability that the disc has a two digit number.

Solution : Total outcomes = 90

Outcomes favourable to the event E "getting a two digit number" are 10, 11, 12..., 89, 90.

Number of outcomes favourable to E = 90 – 9 = 81

Probability of the disc having a two digit number $= \frac{81}{90} = \frac{9}{10}$

EXAMPLE 9 A game of chance consists of spinning an arrow which comes to rest pointing at one of the numbers 1, 2, 3, 4, 5, 6, 7, 8 and these are equally likely outcomes. What is the probability that it will point at 8?

Solution : The number of total possible outcomes = 8

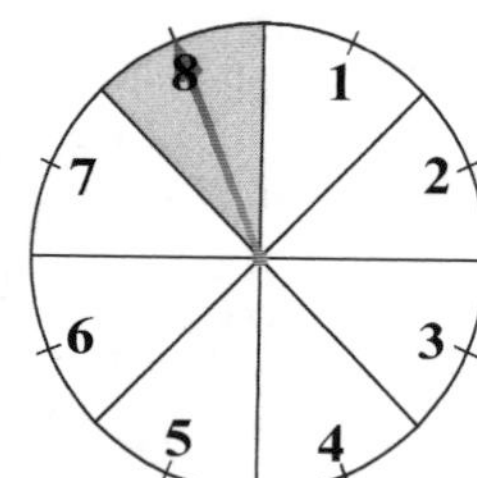

Let E be the event that arrow points at 8.

The number of outcomes favorable to E = 1

$$P(E) = \frac{1}{8}$$

EXAMPLE 10 If the probability that it will rain tonight is 0.17, find the probability that it will not rain tonight.

Solution : If the probability that an outcome (event) E occurs is $P(E)$, then the probability that the outcome event (E) does not occur is given as

$$P(\text{not } E) = 1 - P(E)$$

Thus, we get

$$P(\text{not rain}) = 1 - P(\text{rain}) = 1 - 0.17 = 0.83$$

EXAMPLE 11 A piggy bank contains one hundred $50p$ coins, fifty ₹1 coins, twenty ₹2 coins and ten ₹5 coins. If it is equally likely that one of the coins will fall out when the piggy bank is turned upside down, what is the probability that the coin fell out :

(i) will be a $50p$ coin? **(ii)** will not be a ₹5 coin?

Solution : Total number of coins in the piggy bank = 100 + 50 + 20 + 10 = 180

So, total number of possible outcomes = 180

(i) Number of $50p$ coins = 100

Therefore, P ($50p$ coin) $= \frac{100}{180} = \frac{5}{9}$

(ii) There are (100 + 50 + 20 = 170) coins other than ₹5 coin

Therefore, P (₹5 coin) $= \frac{170}{180} = \frac{17}{18}$

EXAMPLE 12 One card is drawn from a well shuffled deck of 52 playing cards. Determine the probability that the card drawn is a face card.

Solution : Total number of cards = 52.

Number of face cards = 3 + 3 + 3 + 3 = 12 [Face cards are king, queen and jack]

$$P(\text{face card}) = \frac{12}{52} = \frac{3}{13}.$$

EXAMPLE 13 The King, Queen and Jack of clubs are removed from a pack of 52 cards and then remaining cards are well shuffled. A card is selected from the remaining cards. Find the probability of getting a card of

(*i*) heart (*ii*) king (*iii*) club

Solution : 49 cards are left in the pack after removing the 3 cards (King, Queen and Jack of clubs).

(*i*) There are 13 cards of hearts in 49 cards

$$\text{Therefore, P (a card of heart)} = \frac{13}{49}$$

(*ii*) There are 3 kings left in 49 cards as king of clubs has been removed

$$\text{Therefore, P (a card of king)} = \frac{3}{49}$$

Well shuffling ensures equally likely.

(*iii*) 10 club cards are left as 3 cards of club have been removed

$$\text{Therefore, P (a card of club)} = \frac{10}{49}$$

EXAMPLE 14 If E is an event such that $P(E) = \frac{2}{7}$, find $1 - P(\overline{E})$.

Solution : For an event E, the event 'not E' is complementary event of E, denoted by $\overline{E}$.

Also, $P(E) = 1 - P(\overline{E})$

Therefore, $1 - P(\overline{E}) = P(E) = \frac{2}{7}$

EXAMPLE 15 12 nuts are defective in a box containing 600 nuts. One nut is drawn at random from the box. Find the probability that the nut drawn is non defective.

Solution : Total nuts = 600. Number of defective nuts = 12

Number of non defective nuts P (E)

= Total nuts – Number of defective nuts

= 600 – 12 = 588

$$P(\text{non defective nut}) = \frac{588}{600} = \frac{49}{50}.$$

$$P(\text{defective nut}) = \frac{12}{600}$$

$$P(\text{non-defective nut}) = 1 - \frac{12}{600} = \frac{588}{600} = \frac{49}{50}$$

EXAMPLE 16 A lot of 20 bulbs contains 4 defective ones. One bulb is drawn from the lot. Suppose the bulb drawn is not defective and is not replaced. Again, a bulb is drawn from the rest. Find the probability that this bulb is not defective.

Solution : Total number of bulbs $= 20$

Total number of defective bulbs $= 4$

Total number of non-defective bulbs $= 20 - 4 = 16$

A non-defective bulb is drawn out and is not replaced.

Therefore, number of bulbs left $= 19$

Number of non-defective bulbs $= 19 - 4 = 15$

$$\mathbf{P}\text{ (not defective bulb)} = \frac{15}{19}$$

EXAMPLE 17 A coin is tossed two times, find the probability of getting (i) two heads, (ii) no head.

Solution: When a coin is tossed two times, the possible outcomes are

HH, HT, TH, TT [HH means head on first toss and head on second toss *etc*]

Number of possible outcomes = 4

Number of outcomes favorably to the event "getting 2 head" = 1(HH)

(i) So, $P\text{ (getting 2 heads)} = \frac{1}{4}$, **(ii)** $P\text{ (no head)} = P(TT) = \frac{1}{4}$

EXAMPLE 18 Three coins are tossed at the same time. What is the probability of getting two heads?

Solution : Three coins are tossed.

So, the possible outcomes are HHH, HHT, HTH, HTT, THH, THT, TTH, TTT, which are 8 in number. Let E be the event "getting two heads".

Outcomes favourable to E are HHT, HTH, THH.

So, the number of outcomes favourable to E $= 3$. Hence, $P(E) = \frac{3}{8}$

EXAMPLE 19 Two dice, one blue and one grey, are thrown at the same time. Write down all the possible outcomes. What is the probability that the sum of the two numbers appearing on the top of the dice is 3?

Solution : On throwing two dice simultaneously, the possible outcomes are :

(1, 1), (1, 2), (1, 3), (1, 4), (1, 5), (1, 6)
(2, 1), (2, 2), (2, 3), (2, 4), (2, 5), (2, 6)
(3, 1), (3, 2), (3, 3), (3, 4), (3, 5), (3, 6)
(4, 1), (4, 2), (4, 3), (4, 4), (4, 5), (4, 6)
(5, 1), (5, 2), (5, 3), (5, 4), (5, 5), (5, 6)
(6, 1), (6, 2), (6, 3), (6, 4), (6, 5), (6, 6)

Therefore, total number of possible outcomes $= (6 \times 6) = 36$

Let A be the event of getting the sum as 3.

Outcomes favourable to A are (1, 2) and (2, 1).

i.e., number of favourable outcomes $= 2$

$$\text{Therefore, P(A)} = \text{P(3 as sum)} = \frac{2}{36} = \frac{1}{18}$$

EXAMPLE 20 A die is numbered in such a way that its faces show the numbers 1, 2, 2, 3, 3, 6. It is thrown twice and the total score in two throws is noted. What is the probability that the total score is even ?

Solution :

Number in first throw (columns); *Number in second throw* (rows)

+	1	2	2	3	3	6
1	2	3	3	4	4	7
2	3	4	4	5	5	8
2	3	4	4	5	5	8
3	4	5	5	6	6	9
3	4	5	5	6	6	9
6	7	8	8	9	9	12

Values of total score on the two throws

Total number of outcomes $= 6 \times 6 = 36$

Favourable outcomes for total score is even are :

2, 4, 4, 4, 4, 8, 4, 4, 8, 4, 6, 6, 4, 6, 6, 8, 8 and 12.

Number of favourable outcomes $= 18$

$$\text{Therefore, P (total score is even)} = \frac{18}{36} = \frac{1}{2}.$$

EXAMPLE 21 A die is thrown twice. What is the probability that

(i) 5 will come up at least once?

(ii) 5 will not come up either time?

Solution : *(i)* Number of possible outcomes on two throws of a single die $= 6 \times 6 = 36$

Favourable outcomes, *i.e.*, 5 will come up at least once are :

(5, 1), (5, 2), (5, 3), (5, 4), (5, 5), (5, 6),

(1, 5), (2, 5), (3, 5), (4, 5), (6, 5)

Number of favourable outcomes $= 11$

$$\text{P (5 will come up at least once)} = \frac{11}{36}$$

(ii) P (5 will not come up either time) $= 1 - $ P (5 will come up at least once)

$$= 1 - \frac{11}{36} = \frac{36-11}{36} = \frac{25}{36}.$$

EXAMPLE 22 A bag contains 5 red balls and some blue balls. If the probability of drawing a blue ball from the bag is 4 times that of a red ball. Find the number of blue balls in the bag.

Solution :

Number of red balls in the bag = 5

Let the number of blue balls in the bag = x

Total number of balls in the bag = $x + 5$

Probability of getting blue ball = $\dfrac{x}{x+5}$

Probability of getting red ball = $\dfrac{5}{x+5}$

Probability of getting blue ball = 4 (Probability of getting red ball)

$$\frac{x}{x+5} = 4\left(\frac{5}{x+5}\right) \qquad [x + 5 \neq 0]$$

$$x = 4 \times 5 = 20$$

Therefore, number of blue balls in the bag = 20.

EXAMPLE 23 A die is dropped randomly on the rectangular region as shown in the figure. What is the probability of some portion of the die landing inside the circle of diameter 1m (lying inside the rectangle). (in term of π)

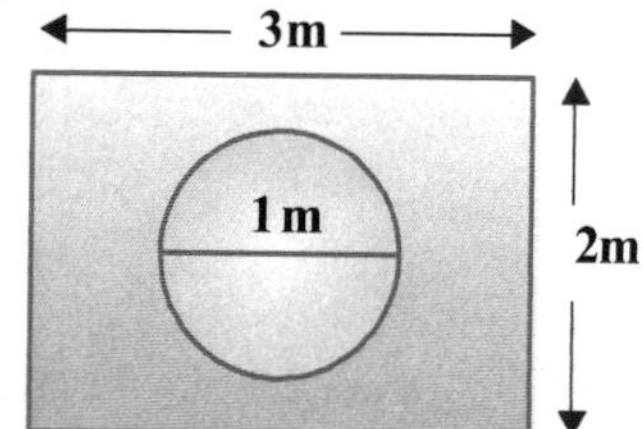

Solution : Total area in which outcomes lie = Area of rectangle

$= l \times b = 3 \times 2 = 6\text{m}^2$

The die is **equally likely** to land anywhere on the rectangular region.

$$\text{Area of circle} = \pi r^2 = \pi\left(\frac{1}{2}\right)^2 \text{m}^2 = \frac{\pi}{4}\text{m}^2$$

Probability that some portion of the die will land inside the circle $= \dfrac{\frac{\pi}{4}}{6} = \dfrac{\pi}{24}$

Note: The probability determined in Example 23 is known as 'geometric probability'

EXAMPLE 24 What is the probability that a family of these children will contain atleast two boys ?

Solution : If B stands for a boy and G for a girl, then the possible outcomes are BBB, BBG, BGB, GBB, BGG, GBG, GGB, GGG.

Total number of possible outcomes = 8

Let E be the event "at least two boys".

So, outcomes favourable to E are BBB, BBG, BGB, GBB

Number of outcomes favourable to E = 4

So, P(E) $= \dfrac{4}{8} = \dfrac{1}{2}$.

EXAMPLE 25 Two customers Ankit and Babita are visiting a particular shop in the same week (Tuesday to Saturday). Each is likely to visit the shop on any day as on another day. What is the probability that both will visit the shop on the same day ?

Solution : Let (x, y) represent the outcome that during the week Ankit visited the shop on day x and Babita on day y.

The possible outcomes are :

(T, T),	(T, W),	(T, Th),	(T, F),	(T, S)
(W, T),	(W, W),	(W, Th),	(W, F),	(W, S)
(Th, T),	(Th, W),	(Th, Th),	(Th, F),	(Th, S)
(F, T),	(F, W),	(F, Th),	(F, F),	(F, S)
(S, T),	(S, W),	(S, Th),	(S, F),	(S, S)

T = Tuesday
W = Wednesday
Th = Thursday
F = Friday
S = Saturday

Therefore, total number of possible outcomes $= 5 \times 5 = 25$

The favourable outcomes of both visiting the shop on the same day are

(T, T), (W, W), (Th, Th), (F, F), (S, S).

Number of favourable outcomes $= 5$

Therefore, P (both visit the shop on same day) $= \frac{5}{25} = \frac{1}{5}$.

EXAMPLE 26 A jar contains 24 marbles, some are green and others are blue. If a marble is drawn at random from the jar, the probability that it is green is $\frac{2}{3}$. Find the number of blue marbles in the jar.

Solution :

Total number of marbles $= 24$

Let number of green marbles $= x$

then P (green marble), *i.e.*, P (G) $= \frac{x}{24}$

but P (G) $= \frac{2}{3}$ (given)

i.e. $\frac{x}{24} = \frac{2}{3}$ or $x = \frac{2}{3} \times 24$ (8) or $x = 16$

Number of green marbles $= 16$

Therefore, number of blue marbles $= 24 - 16 = 8$

EXAMPLE 27 A bag contains 12 balls out of which x are white. If addition of 6 more white balls to the bag, doubles the probability of drawing a white ball from the bag, find the number of original white balls in the bag.

Solution :

Initially, total number of balls $= 12$

Number of white balls $= x$

So, probability of getting a white ball $= \dfrac{x}{12}$

On adding 6 white balls, total number of balls $= 12 + 6 = 18$

and the number of white balls $= x + 6$

Now, the probability of getting a white ball $= \dfrac{x+6}{18}$

According to the question,

$$\frac{x+6}{18} = 2 \times \frac{x}{12} \quad \text{or} \quad \frac{x+6}{3} = \frac{x}{1} \quad \text{or} \quad x + 6 = 3x$$

or $2x = 6$, *i.e.,* $x = 3$

Hence, the number of white balls originally in the bag = 3.

EXERCISE 8.1

In exercises 1-3, a die is thrown once. Find the probability of getting

1. a number less than 5. **2.** a number greater than 3. **3.** an even number.

In exercises 4-7, a die is thrown once. Find the probability of getting

4. 1 or 4. **5.** 2 or 5. **6.** 4 or 5. **7.** 3 or 5.

In exercises 8-11, a bag contains 7 white, 4 reds and 3 green balls. A ball is drawn from the bag. Find the probablity that it is

8. a green ball **9.** a white ball **10.** a red ball **11.** a non-white ball

In exercises 12-13, find the probability of selecting a boy at random out of

12. 20 boys and 15 girls of a class if one student is to be selected.

13. 18 boys and 20 girls of a class if one student is to be selected.

In exercises 14-15, find the probability that a leap year selected at random, will contain 53

14. Thursdays. **15.** Tuesdays.

In exercises 16-17, find the probability that a non-leap year selected at random will contain

16. Fridays. **17.** Sundays.

18. Out of 1000 lottery tickets, there are 50 prize winning tickets. A ticket is bought at random. Find the probability of its being a prize-winning ticket.

In exercises 19-20, a letter is chosen at random from the letters of English alphabet. Find the probability that it is a

19. letter of word 'BASIC'. **20.** *vowel.*

In exercises 21-24, a box contains 90 discs which are numbered from 1 to 90. If one disc is drawn at random from the box, find the probability that the disc has a

21. number divisible by 7. **22.** number divisible by 6. **23.** perfect square number. **24.** number divisible by 5.

In exercises 25-28, a game of chance consists of spinning an arrow which comes to rest pointing at one of the numbers 1, 2, 3, 4, 5, 6, 7, 8 and these are equally likely outcomes. What is the probability that it will point at

25. a number less than 9? **26.** an even number? **27.** an odd number? **28.** a number greater than 2?

29. A roulette wheel has 38 compartments numbered 0, 00, 1, 2, 3, ..., 36. Half of 1 through 36 are coloured red and the other half are coloured black. The remaining two compartments, numbered 0, and 00 are coloured green. A ball is spun and lands in one of the compartments. Find the probability that the ball lands on a red compartment.

In exercises 30-31, find the probability that it will not rain tonight, if the probability that it will rain tonight is

30. 0.82. **31.** 0.93.

32. A piggy bank contains eighty 50p coins, sixty ₹1 coins, ten ₹2 coins and twenty ₹5 coins. If it is equally likely that one of the coins will fall out when the bank is turned upside down, what is the probability that the coin fell out :

(*i*) will be a ₹1 coin? ; (*ii*) will not be a ₹2 coin?

33. A piggy bank contains sixty 50p coins, hundred ₹1 coins, ten ₹2 coins and ten ₹5 coins. If it is equally likely that one of the coins will fall out when the bank is turned upside down, what is the probability that the coin fell out :

(*i*) will be a ₹2 coin? ; (*ii*) will not be a 50p coin?

34. Gopi buys a fish from a shop for his aquarium. The shopkeeper takes out one fish at random from a tank containing 5 male fish and 8 female fish. What is the probability that the fish taken out is a male fish?

35. A bag contains 5 white, 7 red , 4 black and 2 blue balls. A ball is taken from the bag at random, find the probability that the ball taken out is not white.

In exercises 36-39, one card is drawn from a well shuffled deck of 52 cards. Calculate the probability that the card drawn is

36. a face card. **37.** a red face card. **38.** a black face card. **39.** not a face card.

40. A card is drawn from a pack of 52 playing cards. What is the probability that it is an ace?

In exercises 41-43, a card is drawn from a pack of 52 cards playing cards. What is the probability that it is

41. a jack? **42.** a queen? **43.** a king?

In exercises 44-46, the King, Queen & Jack of spades are removed from a pack of 52 cards and then remaining are well shuffled. A card is selected from the remaining cards. Find the probability of getting a card of :

44. (*i*) diamond (*ii*) queen (*iii*) spade **45.** (*i*) king (*ii*) club

46. (*i*) ace (*ii*) jack of heart

In exercises 47-48, find $1 - P(\overline{E})$, if E is an event such that

47. $P(E) = \frac{5}{11}$. **48.** $P(E) = \frac{5}{9}$.

In exercises 49-50, find the the probability that a nut drawn at random from the box is non defective, if

49. 16 nuts are defective in a box containing 500 nuts. **50.** 15 nuts are defective in a box containing 500 nuts.

In exercises 51-52, find the probability that the bulb drawn is not defective, if

51. a lot of 30 bulbs contains 5 defective ones. One bulb is drawn from the lot. Suppose the bulb drawn is not defective and is not replaced. Again a bulb is drawn from the rest.

52. a lot of 19 bulbs contains 3 defective ones. One bulb is drawn from the lot. Suppose the bulb drawn is not defective and is not replaced. Again a bulb is drawn from the rest.

53. A coin is tossed two times. Find the probability of getting

(i) two tails **(ii)** at least one head **(iii)** no tail

54. Two coins are tossed simultaneously. Find the probability of getting at most one head.

In exercises 55-58, three unbiased coins are tossed. What is the probability of getting

55. at most two heads? 56. at least two heads? 57. two tails? 58. at least two tails?

59. A coin is tossed three times, find the probability of getting at least one head.

60. Three coins are tossed simultaneously. Find the probability of getting exactly two heads.

In exercises 61-62, three unbiased coins are tossed simultaneously. Find the probability of getting

61. at least one tail. 62. at most one tail.

In exercises 63-66, two dice, one blue and one grey, are thrown at the same time. Write down all the possible outcomes. What is the probability that the sum of the two numbers appearing on the top of the dice is

63. 6? 64. 7? 65. 8? 66. 4?

In exercises 67-70, a die is numbered in such a way that its faces show the numbers 1, 2, 2, 3, 3, 6. It is thrown two times and the total score in two throws is noted. What is the probability that the total score is

67. 6? 68. atleast 6? 69. odd? 70. 4?

In exercises 71-74, a die is thrown twice. What is the probability that

71. (*i*) 4 will come up at least once? (*ii*) 4 will not come up either time?

72. (*i*) 1 will come up at least once? (*ii*) 1 will not come up either time?

73. (*i*) 3 will come up at least once? (*ii*) 3 will not come up either time?

74. (*i*) 6 will come up at least once? (*ii*) 6 will not come up either time?

In exercises 75-76, find the number of blue balls in the bag :

75. A bag contains 5 red balls and some blue balls. If the probability of drawing a blue ball from the bag is 3 times that of a red ball.

76. A bag contains 6 red balls and some blue balls. If the probability of drawing a blue ball from the bag is 4 times that of a red ball.

In exercises 77-78, on droping a die randomly on the rectangular region as shown in the figure, what is the probability some of its portion landing inside the circle with diameter (in term of π)

77. 4m?

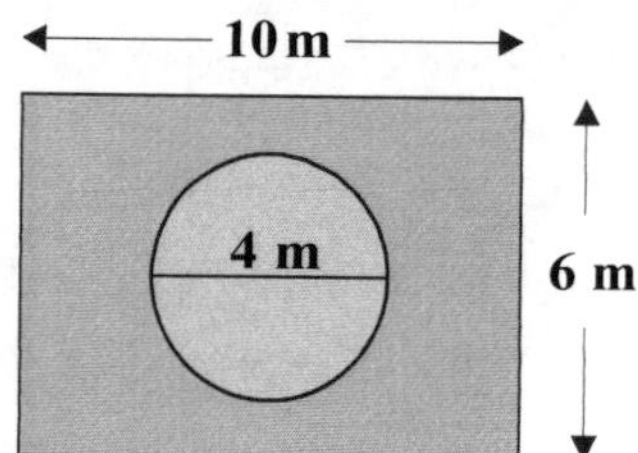

78. 5m?

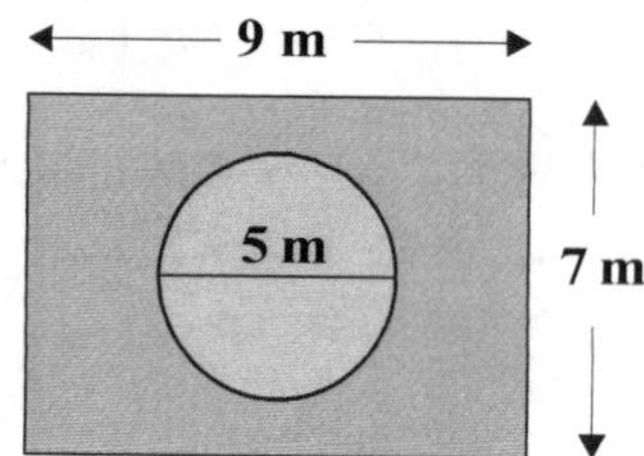

In exercises 79-80, find the probability of the desired outcome of the following statements:

79. In a two-child family, find the probability of at least one girl.

80. In the three-child family, find the probability of at least two girls.

In exercises 81-82, two customers Shyam and Ekta are visiting a particular shop in the same week (Tuesday to Saturday). Each is likely to visit the shop on any day as on another day. What is the probability that both will visit the shop on the

81. consecutive days?

82. different days?

In exercises 83-84, find the number of blue marbles in the jar, if a jar contains

83. 32 marbles, some are green and others are blue. A marble is drawn at random from the jar, the probability that it is green is $\frac{3}{4}$.

84. 45 marbles, some are green and others are blue. A marble is drawn at random from the jar, the probability that it is green is $\frac{3}{5}$.

In exercises 85-86, find the value of x.

85. A bag contains 30 balls out of which x are white. On adding 10 more white balls, probability of drawing a white ball will become double.

86. A bag contains 20 balls out of which x are white. On adding 10 more white balls, probability of drawing a white ball will become double.

87. A and B are two friends. What is the probability that both have the

(*i*) different birthdays (*ii*) the same birthday (ignoring a leap year).

88. In a musical game, the person playing the music has been advised to stop playing the music at any time within 2 minutes after she starts playing. What is the probability that the music will stop within the first half minute after starting ?

89. A number a is randomly selected from the numbers 1, 2 and 3, and then a second number b is randomly selected from the number 1, 4 and 9. What is the probability that the product ab will be less than 9 ?

90. Which of the following arguments are correct and which are not correct. Give reasons for your answer.

(i) If a die is thrown, there are two possible outcomes - an odd number or an even number. So, the probability of getting an odd number is $\frac{1}{2}$.

(ii) If two coins are tossed at the same time, the possible outcomes are - two heads, two tails or one of each. So, for each of these outcomes, the probability is $\frac{1}{3}$.

(iii) Two dice are thrown simultaneously and the sum of numbers appearing on them is noted. The sums are 2, 3, 4, 5, 6, 7, 8, 9, 10, 11 and 12. So, the probability of each of the sum is $\frac{1}{11}$.

GEOMETRIC MEASUREMENTS

This chapter is divided into three sections:

9.1 *Plane Figures Polygons and Tessellations ;*

9.2 *Space figures ; and*

9.3 *Symmetric Figures.*

9.1 SINGLE AND MULTISTAGE EXPERIMENTS

Once we know some basic concepts and terms in geometry like point, line, plane, *etc.*, our next step is to use them in understanding different geometrical shapes such as curves, angles, polygons, circles *etc*. In this section, we shall learn these basic geometrical shapes.

GEOMETRICAL SHAPES

Curves

Any drawing on a paper done with a pencil or pen without lifting, it is **curves**.

Curves in everyday usage means 'not straight', but in mathematics curve can be straight too.

The curve that does not cross itself is called a **simple curve**.

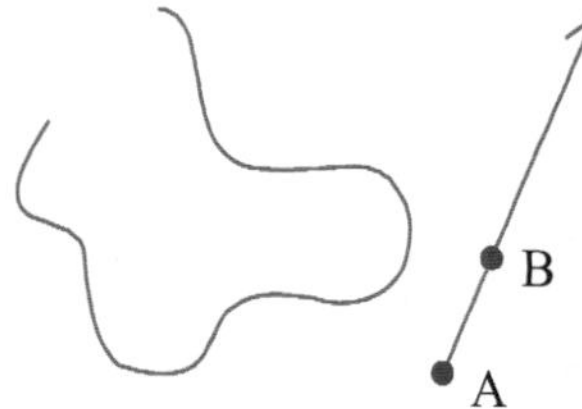

Figure 9.1 (a)

Figure 9.1 (b)

Figure 9.1 (c)

Simple Curves

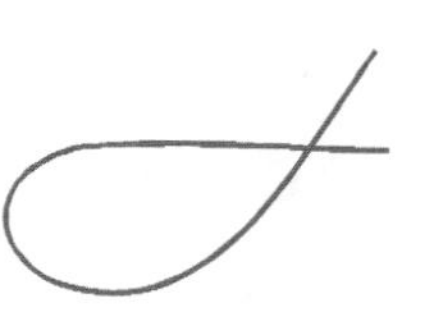

Figure 9.1 (d)

Figure 9.1 (e)

Not Simple Curves (They cross themselves)

A curve that has no end point and which completely encloses a certain area is called a **closed curve**. (Figure 9.2 (a), (b)).

A curve that is not closed is called an **open curve**.

A curve that is **simple** as well as **closed** is called a **simple closed curve**. (Figure 9.3 (a) to (c)).

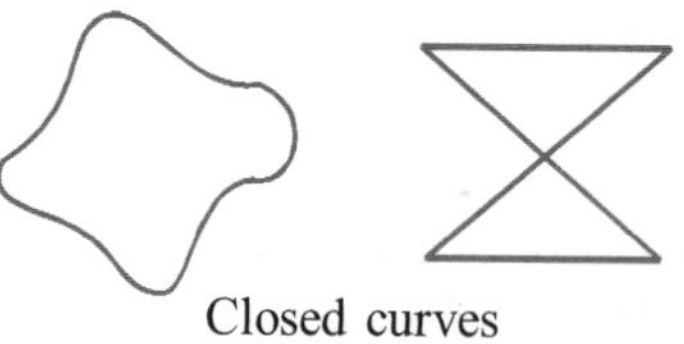

Closed curves

Figure 9.2 (a) **Figure 9.2 (b)**

Open curve

Figure 9.2 (c)

Figure 9.3 (a)

Figure 9.3 (b) Figure 9.3 (c)

Simple closed curves

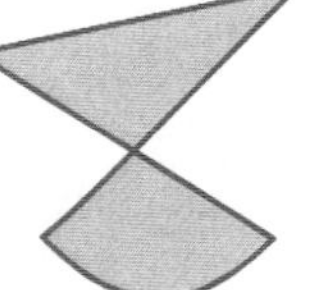

Figure 9.3 (d) Figure 9.3 (e) Figure 9.3 (f)

Not Simple closed curve

Regions : A simple closed curve has three regions associated with it.

(i) Interior (inside) region: The part of the plane which consists of all points such as E, F is called the **interior region** of the curve. (Figure 9.4 (a))

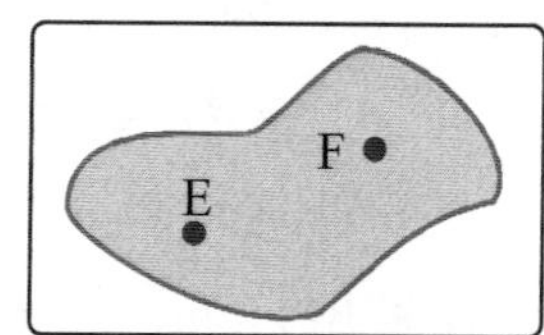

Figure 9.4 (a)

(ii) Boundary ('on') region: The part of the plane which consists of points such as E, F (Figure 9.4 (b)) which lie on the simple closed curve forms the **boundary** of the curve. The interior of a curve together with its boundary is called its ***region***.

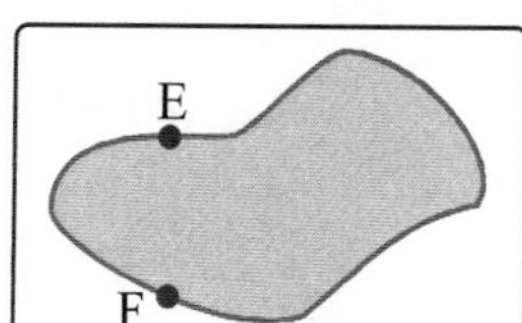

Figure 9.4 (b)

(iii) Exterior (outside) region: Points E and F are in the exterior of the curve. (Figure 9.4 (c))

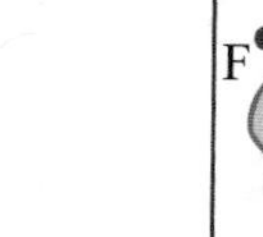

The part of the plane which consists of all points such as E, F (Figure 9.4 (c)) is called the **exterior region** of the curve.

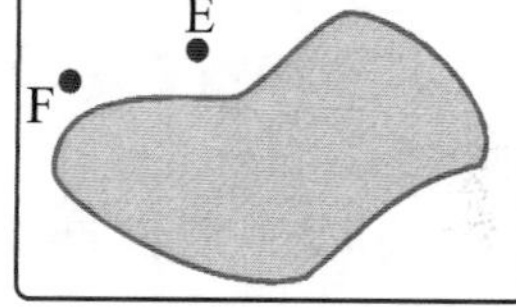

Figure 9.4 (c)

➜ Polygons

A polygon is a "simple closed curve" formed by three or more **line segments** only.

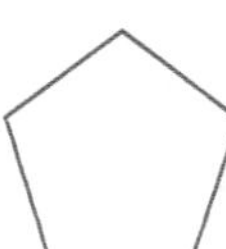

Simple closed curves formed by line segments

Polygons

Figure 9.5 (a)

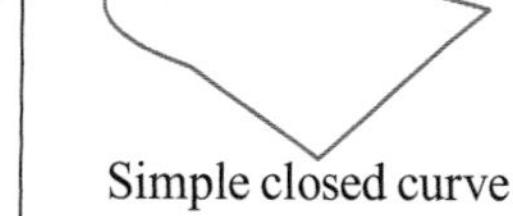

Simple closed curve not a line segment.

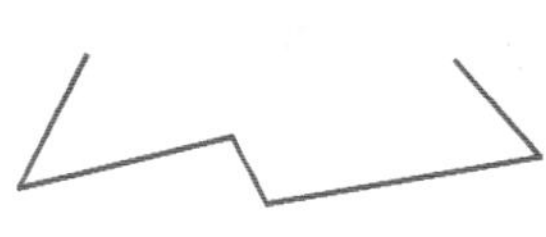

Open curve, not closed.

Not Polygons

Figure 9.5 (b)

(i) Side and vertex

- The line segments forming the polygon are called the **sides** of the polygon. The point of intersection of the sides is called its **vertex**.
- In the Figure 9.6, points A, B, C, D, E and F are **vertices** (plural of vertex) of the polygon ABCDEF, while AB is a side. Similarly, AF, FE, ED, DC, and CB are also sides.

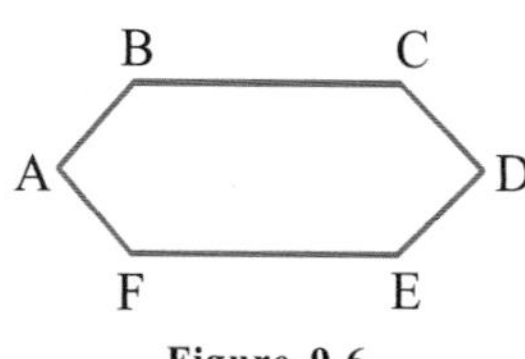

Figure 9.6

- Any two sides of a polygon having a common end point are called its **adjacent sides**.

In Figure 9.6, AB and BC is a pair of adjacent sides whereas AB and CD are **not** adjacent sides. The end points of the same side of a polygon are called the **adjacent vertices**.

The vertices E and D are adjacent, whereas vertices E and C are not adjacent vertices.

- A polygon can be named by listing its vertices in consecutive order, either clock-wise or anticlock-wise.

(ii) Diagonal

A diagonal of a polygon is a line segment whose end points are two non-adjacent vertices.

In Figure 9.7 (a), AC is a diagonal of polygon ABCD.

In Figure 9.7 (b), EC is a diagonal of polygon ABCDE. Similarly, AD is also a diagonal. What about AC? Is it also a diagonal?

BD and BE are also diagonals.

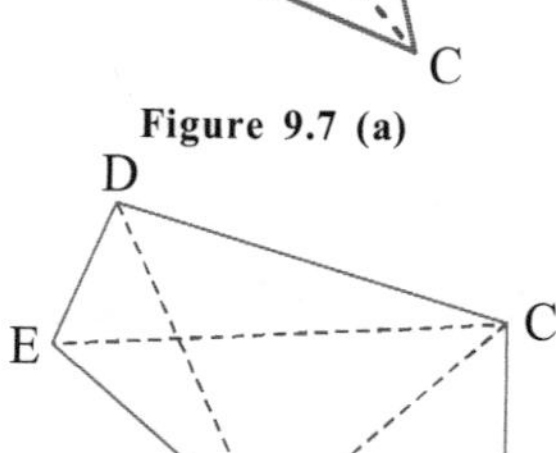

Figure 9.7 (a)

Figure 9.7 (b)

(iii) Convex polygon

A polygon is said to be convex if the line segment joining any two points in its interior lies entirely in the interior.

Unless stated otherwise, by a 'polygon' we shall always mean a convex polygon.

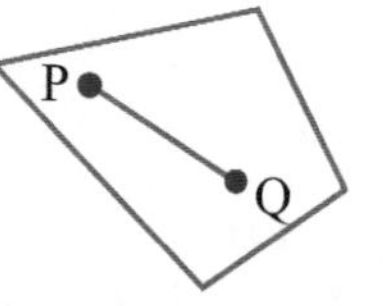

Convex polygon
Figure 9.8 (a)

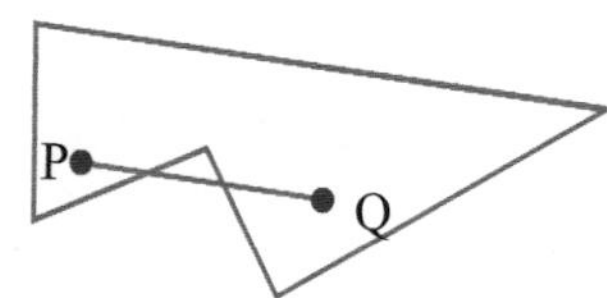

Not Convex polygon
Figure 9.8 (b)

Angles

(i) Angle

An angle (symbol: $\angle$) is formed by two rays having a common initial point, called the **vertex** (Figure 9.9 (a)). The rays forming the angle are called its **arms** or **sides**.

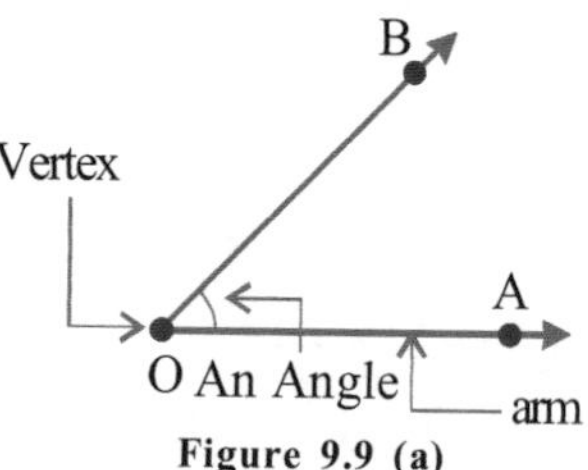

Figure 9.9 (a)

(ii) Naming an Angle

Any two points, one on each of the two rays of the angle, along with the vertex can be used to name an angle.

The angle shown in Figure 9.9 (b) is written as $\angle$AOB and read as angle AOB, or $\angle$AOB.

It should be noted that the common initial point, the vertex, is written in the middle.

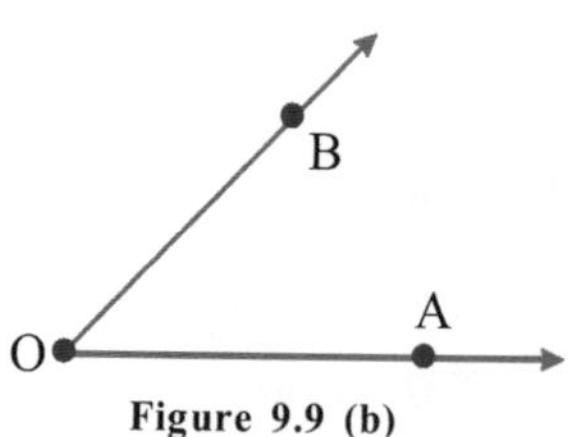

Figure 9.9 (b)

(iii) Alternative ways of naming an angle

An angle may also be denoted by the single letter as its vertex, or by some different letter or symbol designated for this purpose. For example, $\angle$QOP; $\angle$POQ; $\angle$O; $\angle x$ are different names of the angle shown in Figure 9.9 (c).

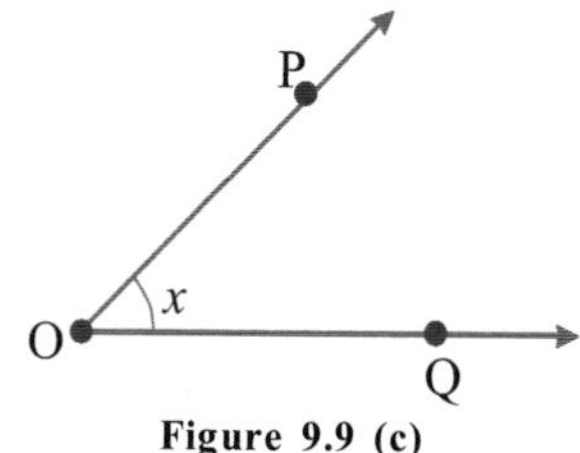

Figure 9.9 (c)

Regions:

An angle has three regions associated with it.

(i) Interior ('inside') region

Points E and F are in the interior of the angle ABC.

The part of the plane which is within the arms of an angle, produced indefinitely, is called the **interior** of the angle.

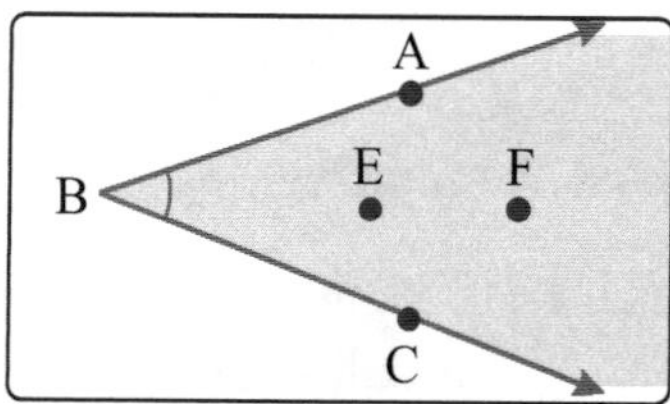

Figure 9.10 (a)

(ii) Boundary ('on') region

Points E and F are on the **angle** (boundary) itself.

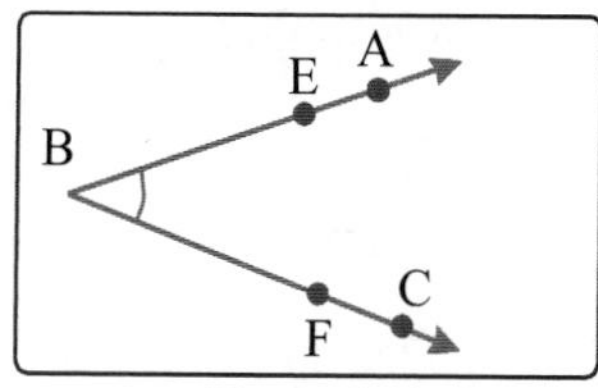

Figure 9.10 (b)

(iii) Exterior ('outside') region

Points E and F are in the exterior of the angle.

The points in the plane which are neither in the interior nor lie on the arms, are called exterior points and those points consitute the **exterior region** of the angle.

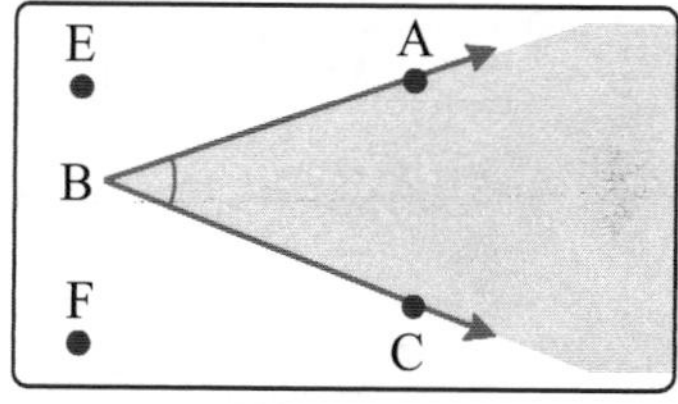

Figure 9.10 (c)

➔ **Triangles**

A triangle is a polygon having three sides. It is usually named by its vertices, taken in clockwise and anticlockwise order.

Symbol Δ is used to denote the word triangle. ΔABC is read as triangle ABC.

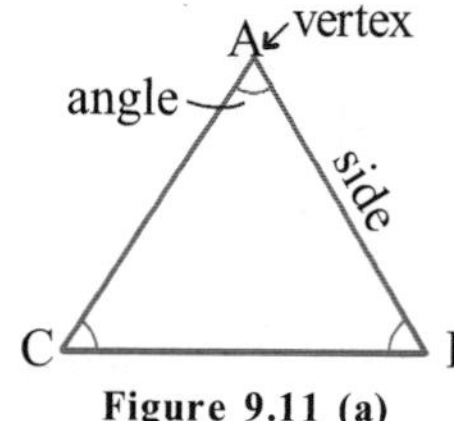

Figure 9.11 (a)

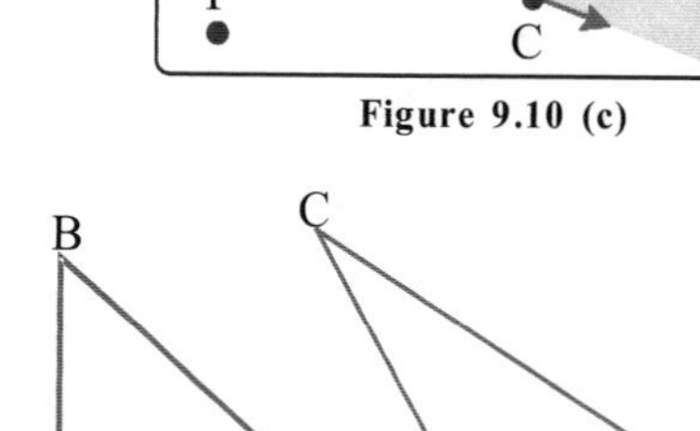

Figure 9.11 (b) Figure 9.11 (c)

The three points A, B and C are called **vertices** of the triangle. AB, BC and CA are its three **sides**. $\angle$ BAC, $\angle$ BCA and $\angle$ ABC are three **angles** of the triangle.

Three angles and three sides of a triangle taken together are called **six elements (or parts)** of the triangle.

Regions:

A triangle has three regions associated with it.

(i) Interior region

The part of the plane which consists of all points such as P and Q, is called the **interior** of the triangle.

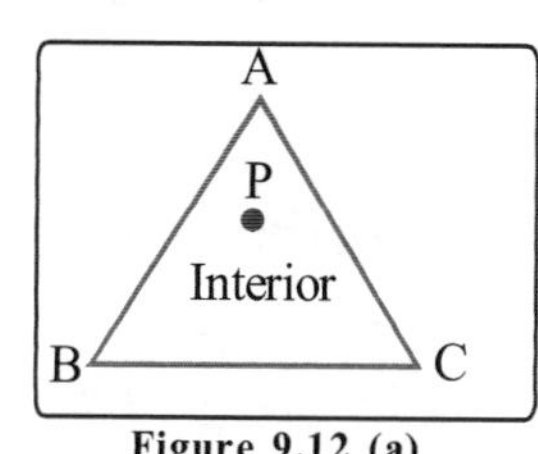

Figure 9.12 (a)

(ii) Boundary ('on') region

The part of the plane which consists of all points such as P and Q, forms the **triangle** (boundary) itself.

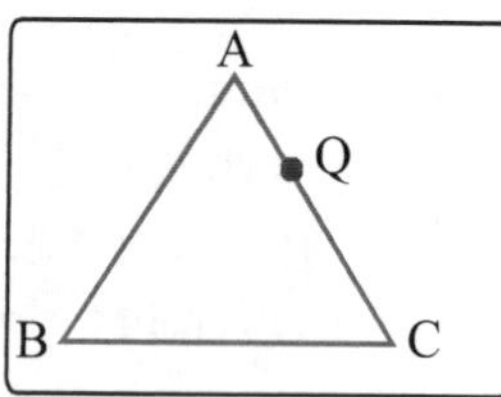

Figure 9.12 (b)

(iii) Exterior region

The part of the plane which consists of all points such as P and R, is called the **exterior** of the triangle.

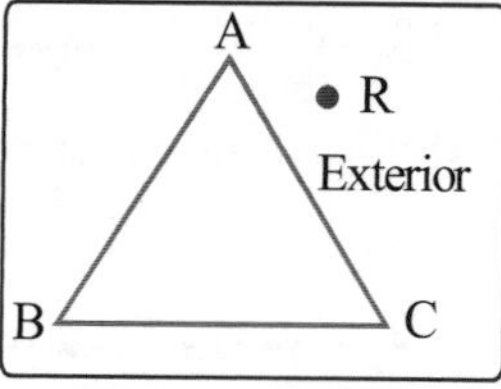

Figure 9.12 (c)

(iv) Triangular region

The interior of the triangle ABC together with the triangle itself, is called the **triangular region ABC**.

➜ Quadrilaterals

A quadrilateral is a polygon having four sides and is usually named by its vertices taken in clockwise or counterclockwise order.

The quadrilateral in the given figure is named as ADCB or ABCD. (Figure 9.13)

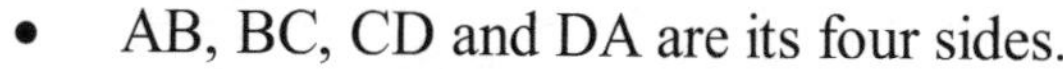

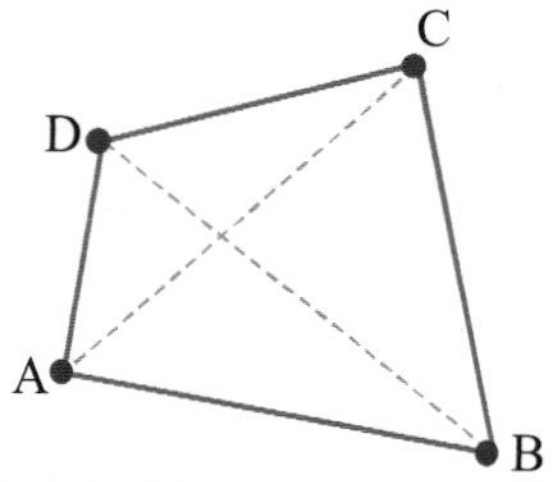

- AB, BC, CD and DA are its four sides.
- $\angle A$, $\angle B$, $\angle C$ and $\angle D$ are its four angles.
- AC and BD are its two diagonals.

C D A B

Figure 9.13

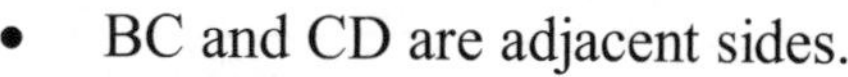
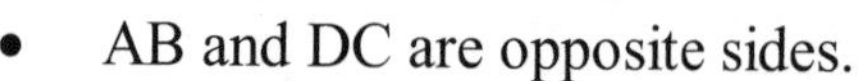
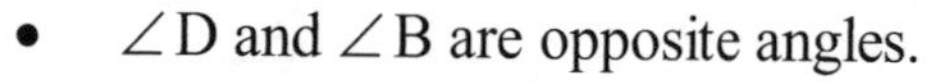

- BC and CD are adjacent sides.
- AB and BC are adjacent sides.
- AB and DC are opposite sides.
- $\angle A$ and $\angle C$ are opposite angles.
- $\angle D$ and $\angle B$ are opposite angles.
- $\angle A$ and $\angle B$ are adjacent angles.

Other pairs of adjacent angles are $\angle B$ and $\angle C$; $\angle C$ and $\angle D$; $\angle D$ and $\angle A$.

➜ Circles

A circle is also a simple closed curve (Figure 9.14). It is the set (collection) of all points in a plane equidistant from a given point called its **centre** (C).

- P, Q, R are three points on a circle.
- CQ = CR = CP, *i.e.*, $r_1 = r_2 = r_3$.

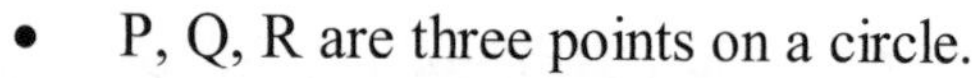

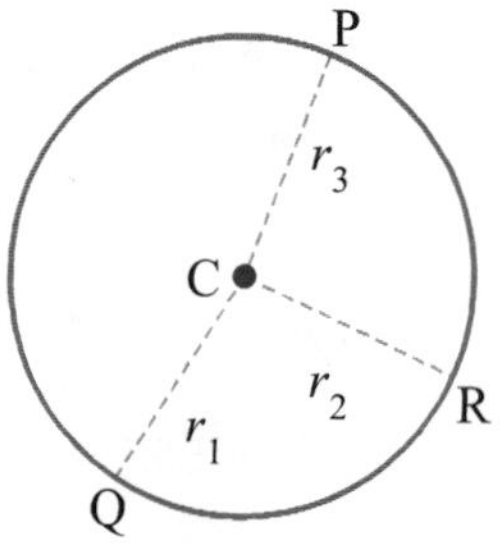

P C r_3 r_2 r_1 R Q

Figure 9.14

Radius

A **radius** of a circle is a line segment joining the centre of the circle to a point on the circle. It is also the length of this line segment. In Figure 9.15,

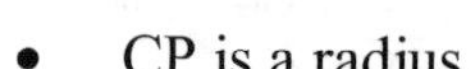

- CP is a radius.
- r is the length of this radius since CP = r.
- CP = CQ = CR = r.
- CP, CQ and CR are radii **(plural of radius)** of the given circle.

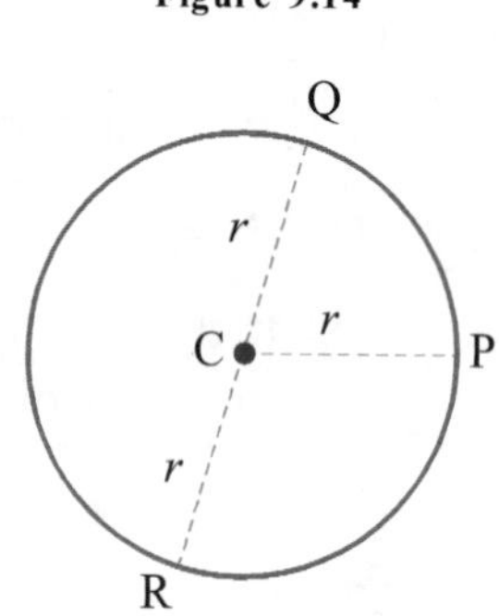

Figure 9.15

Diameter

A diameter of a circle is a line segment joining two points on the circle and also passing through the centre.

Diameter is double the size of a radius

Diameter = 2 × radius

The end points of a diameter divide the circle into two equal parts. Each part is called a "**semi-circle**". Thus, a semi-circle is half of a circle.

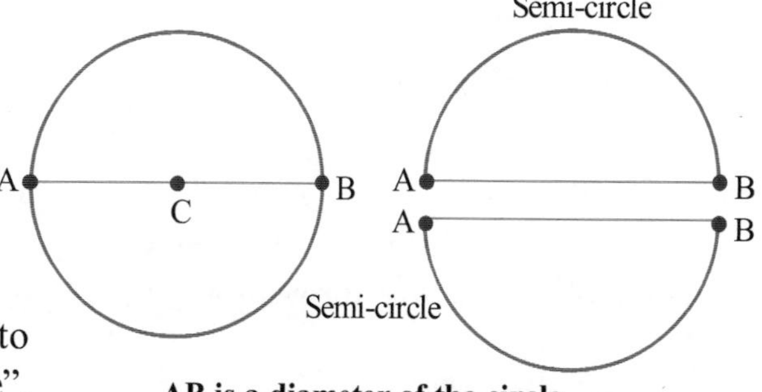

AB is a diameter of the circle.

Figure 9.16

Circumference

The distance moved around a circle once is called its perimeter or **circumference**.

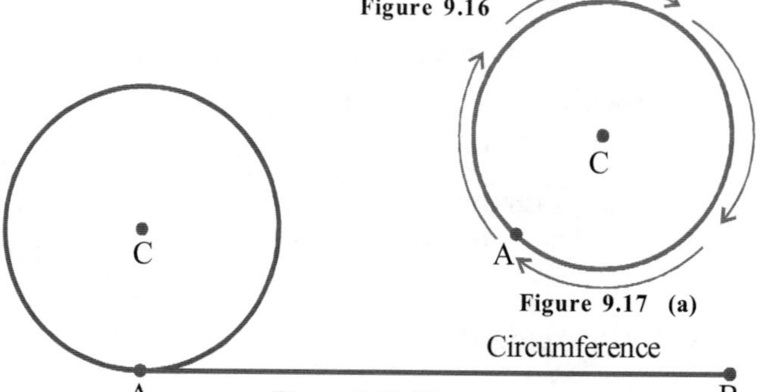

Figure 9.17 (a)

Figure 9.17 (b)

> **Note** Circumference, diameter, and radii are measured in linear units such as inches and centimetres. A circle has many radii and many diameters, each passing through the centre.

Example of a radius is the spoke of a bicycle wheel. A 9-inch pizza is an example of a diameter. When a round pizza pie is cut in half, this cut is the diameter of the pizza. So, a 9-inch pizza has 9-inch diameter.

Figure 9.18 (a)

Figure 9.18 (b)

Chord and arc

A chord of a circle is a line segment joining any two points on it.

AB is a chord of the circle. (Figure 9.19 (a))

If the chord passes through the centre of the circle, it is called its **diameter**. (Figure 9.19 (a))

AB is a diameter.

The diameter is the longest chord of a circle.

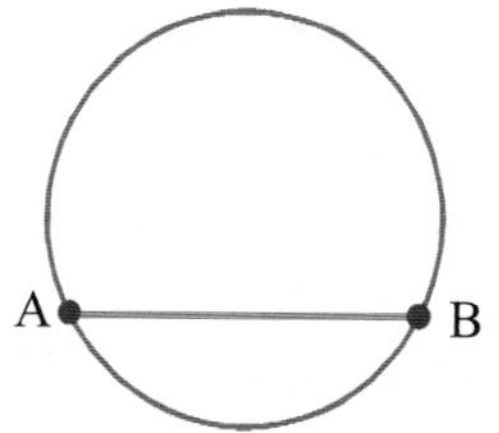

Figure 9.19 (a)

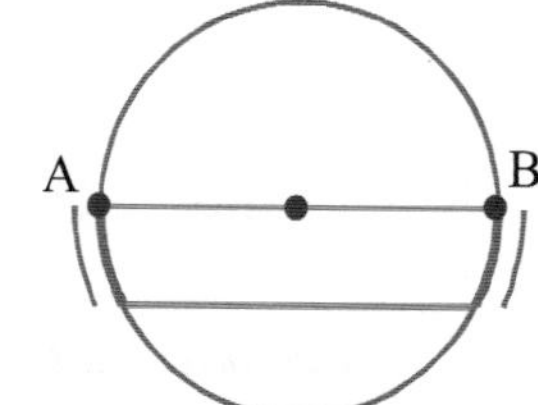

Figure 9.19 (b)

If A and B are two points on the circle, then we get an arc AB, written as $\widehat{AB}$. (Figure 9.19 (c))

In fact, any two points A and B of a circle divide it into two parts called **arcs** of the circle. Generally, the two parts are unequal (Figure 9.19 (c)). The smaller part is called **minor arc** and the other one is called the **major arc**. In Figure 9.19 (c), APB is minor arc and ASB is the major arc.

Note that points A and B are common to both the arcs.

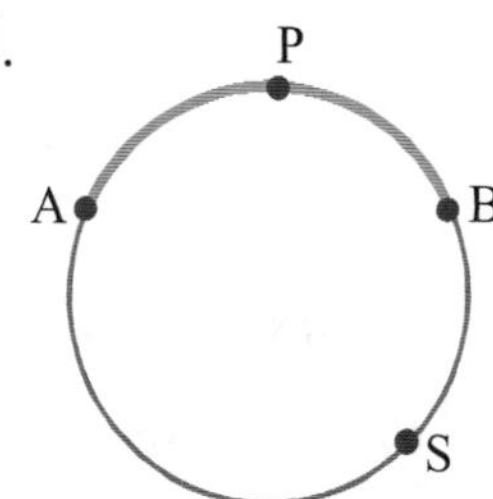

Figure 9.19 (c)

Circular Region :

Like other simple closed curves, a circle also divides the plane into three regions (parts) as follows:

(i) Interior region

The part of the plane which consists of all points such as E, F is called the **interior region** of the circle. (Figure 9.20 (a))

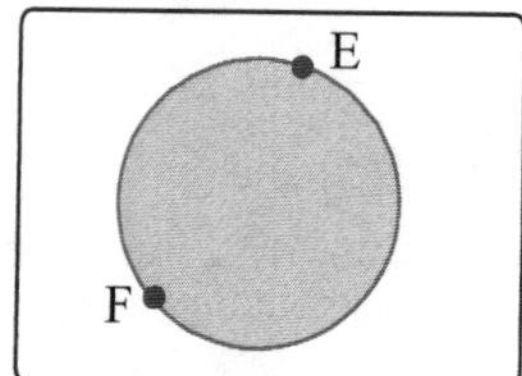

Figure 9.20 (a)

(ii) Boundary region

The part of the plane which consists of all points such as E, F (Figure 9.20 (b)), lying on the circle forms the **boundary** of the circle.

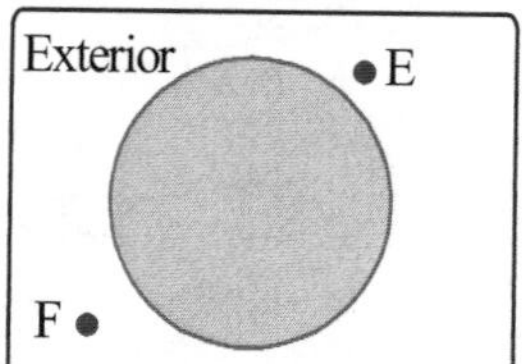

Figure 9.20 (b)

The interior of the circle along with its boundary (*i.e.*, circle itself) is called the **circular region**.

(iii) Exterior region:

The part of the plane which consists of all points such as E, F (Figure 9.20 (c)) is called the **exterior region** of the circle.

Figure 9.20 (c)

(iv) Semi-circular region:

Recall that the end points of a diameter of a circle divide the circle into two equal parts called *semi-circles*. Each of the region enclosed by the diameter and the semi-circle is called the semi-circular region.

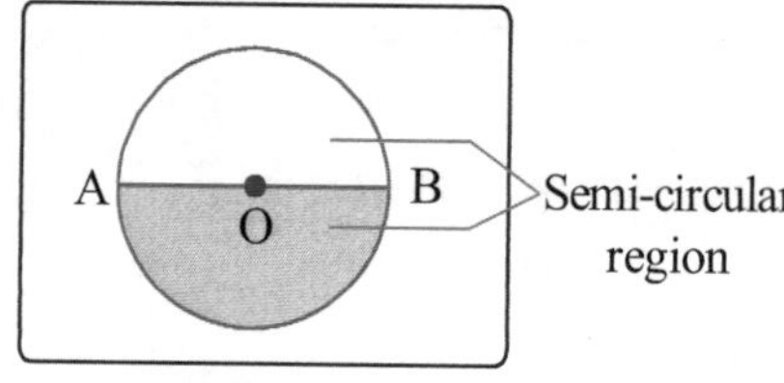

Figure 9.20 (d)

Sector of a circle:

A region that is bounded by arc AB and radii, with end points at A and B respectively is called a **sector**.

If the region is bounded by a minor arc, then it is called a **minor sector** and if it is bounded by a major arc, it is called a **major sector**.

A region that is bounded by a chord AB, and an arc is called a **segment**. If the arc AB is minor, we have **minor segment** otherwise **major segment**.

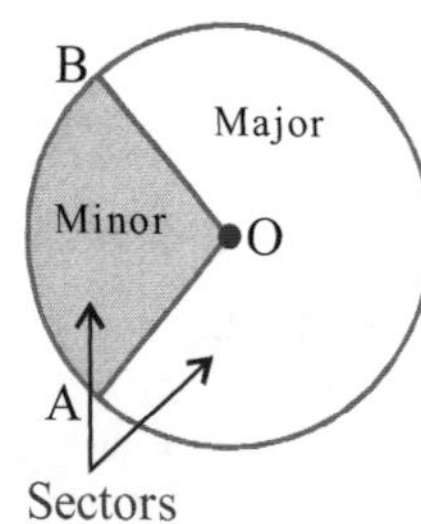

Figure 9.21 (a)

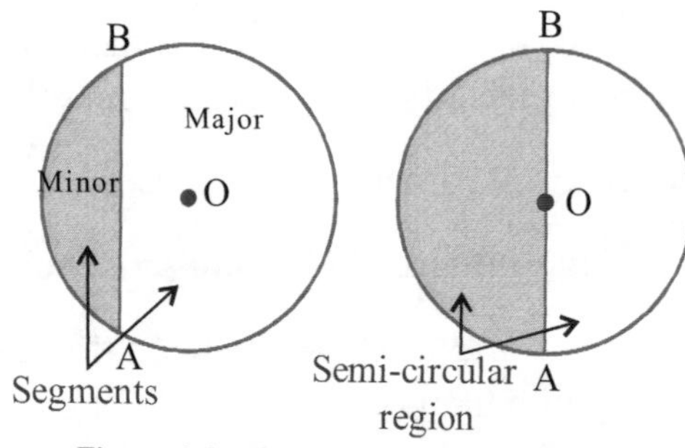

Figure 9.21 (b) Figure 9.21 (c)

Sectors and **segments** are in the interior of a circle.

We now consider some examples.

EXAMPLE 1 Determine, whether the given curve is open or closed.

Solution : The curve has two end points. Therefore, it is an open curve.

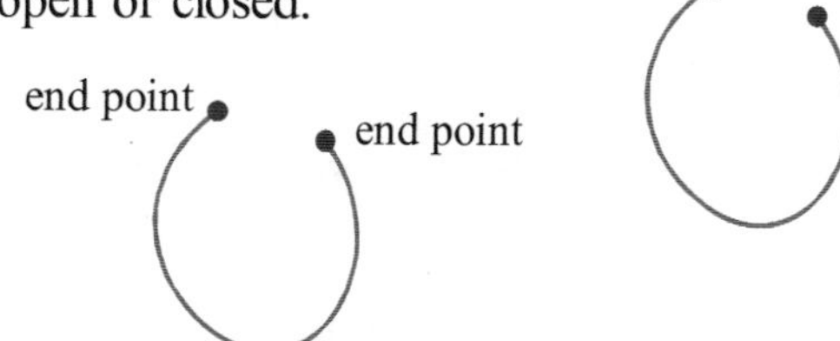

EXAMPLE 2 Identify all the line segments and all the angles in the adjoining figure:

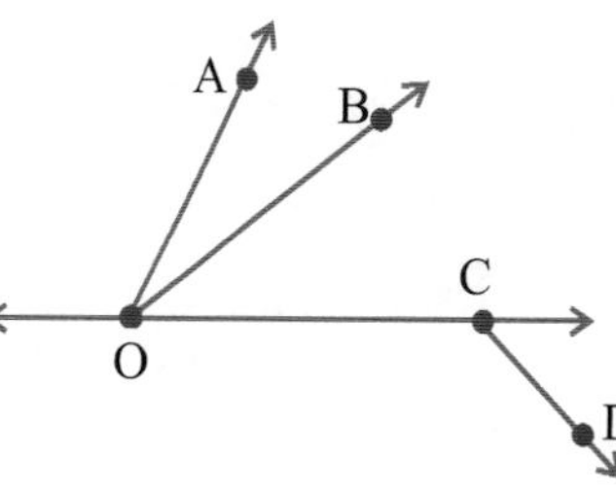

Solution : There are four line segments in the given figure : OA, OB, OC, CD

There are four angles in the figure:

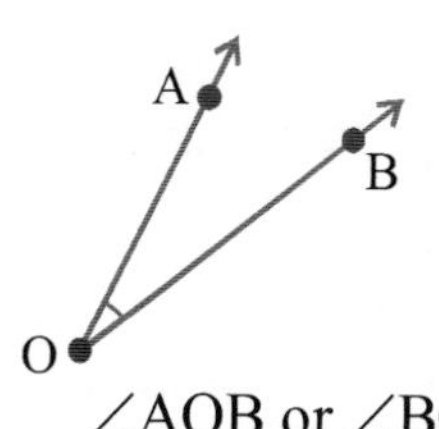

∠AOB or ∠BOA,

(a)

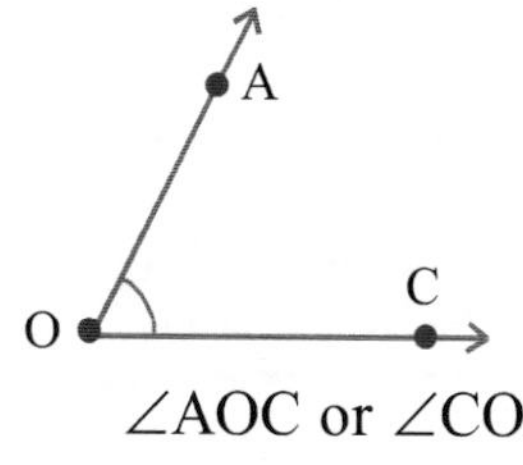

∠AOC or ∠COA,

(b)

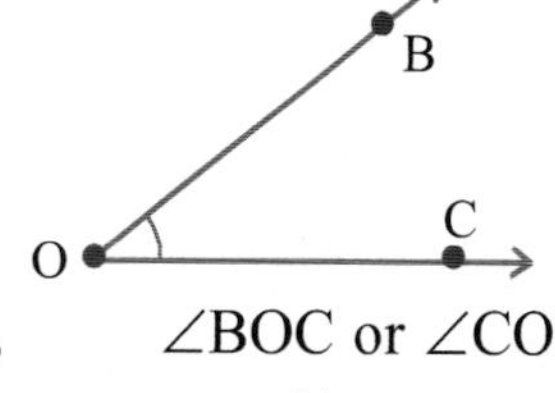

∠BOC or ∠COB,

(c)

O C D

∠OCD or ∠DCO

(d)

EXAMPLE 3 In the given figure, name the point (s) :

(a) In the interior of ∠EOB.

(b) In the exterior of ∠COE.

(c) On ∠COB.

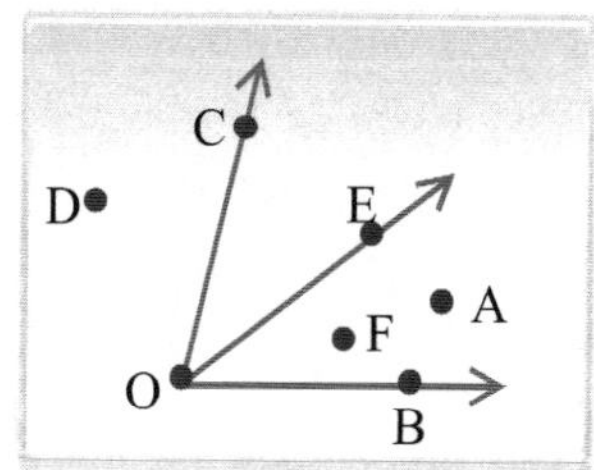

Solution : **(a)** The points in the interior of ∠EOB are A and F.

(b) The points in the exterior of ∠COE are A, B, D and F.

(c) The points on ∠COB are B, C and O.

EXAMPLE 4 In the given circle, identify the name of : Shaded region

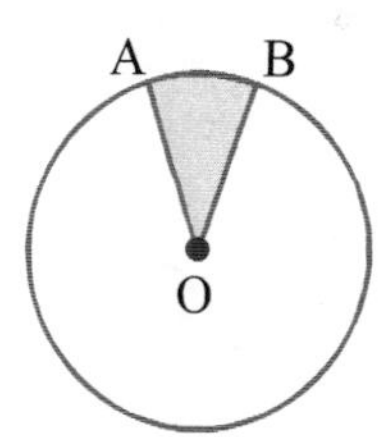

Solution : The shaded region is bounded by $\overset{\frown}{AB}$ and two radii OB and OA. Therefore, it is a **sector**.

EXAMPLE 5 In the given circle, identify the name of : OA and OB

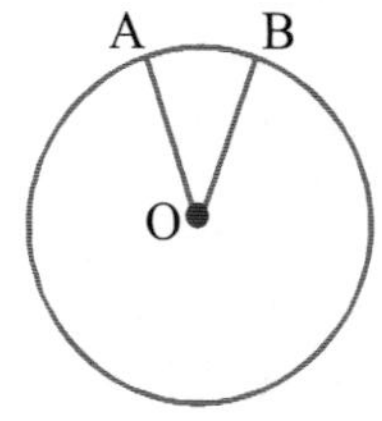

Solution : OA and OB are the line segments joining the centre of the circle O to the points A and B on the circle. Therefore OA and OB are the **radii** of the circle.

EXAMPLE 6 Count the number of quadrilaterals in the given figure.

Solution : We know, that a quadrilateral is a four sided polygon.

Number of quadrilaterals in the given figure = **3**

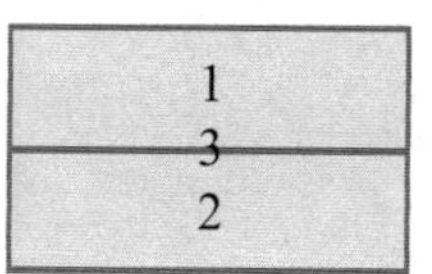

EXAMPLE 7 Count the number of triangles in the given figure.

Solution : We know that a triangle is a three sided closed figure.

There are **six triangles** in the given figure.

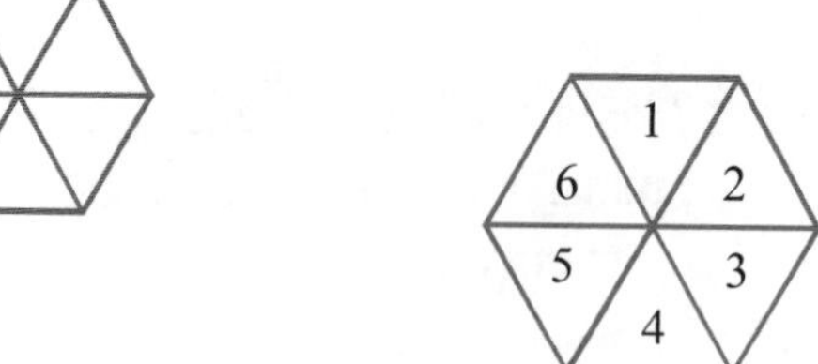

EXAMPLE 8 Name the vertex and the arms of the given angle :

Solution : The vertex of the given angle is C.

Its arms are CA and CB.

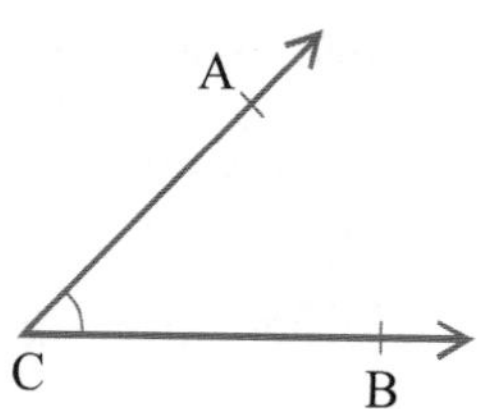

EXAMPLE 9 Fill in the blanks :

A ______ of a circle is a line segment joining any two points on the circle.

Solution : A **chord** of a circle is a line segment joining any two points on the circle.

EXERCISE 9.1

In questions 1-9, determine whether the given curve is open or closed.

1. 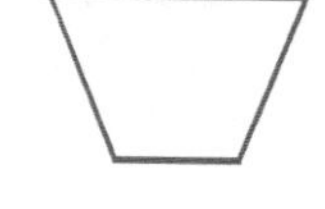

2. 

3. 

4. 

5. 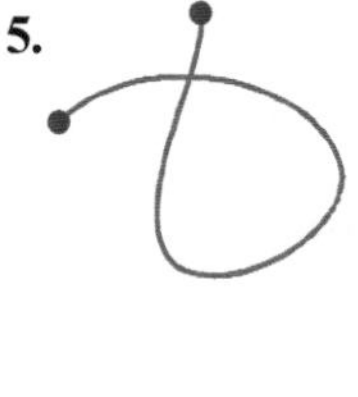

6.

7.

8.

9.

In questions 10-13, identify all the line segments and all the angles in the given figure.

10. 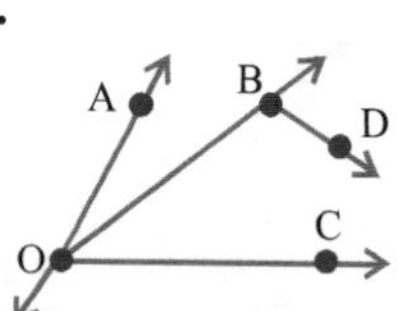

11. 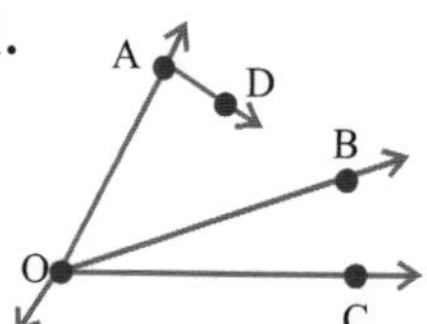

12. 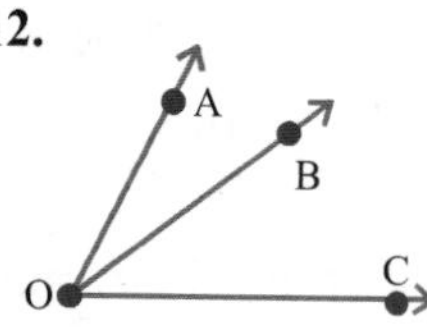

13. 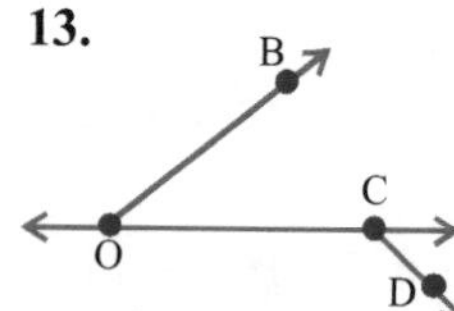

In questions 14-19, look at the figure and name the points.

14. **(a)** In the interior of ΔABC.
(b) In the exterior of ΔABC.
(c) On ΔABC.

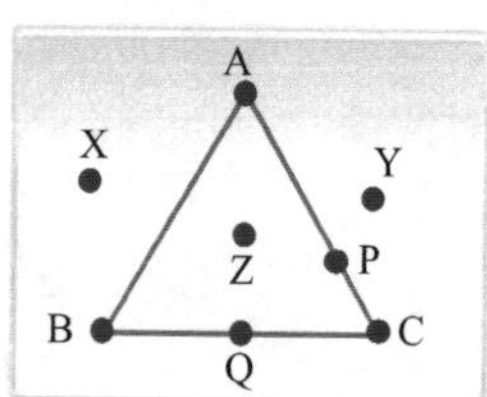

15. **(a)** In the interior of $\angle PQR$.
(b) In the exterior of $\angle PQR$.
(c) On $\angle PQR$.

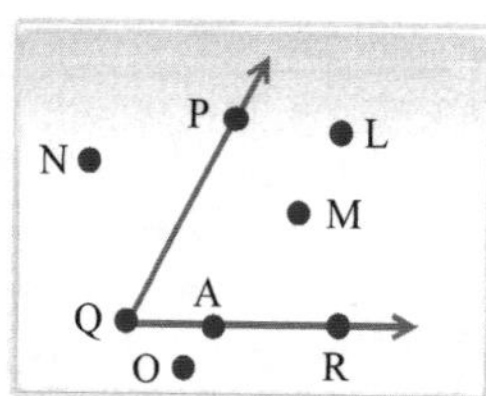

16. **(a)** In the interior region.
(b) In the exterior region.
(c) On the boundary region.

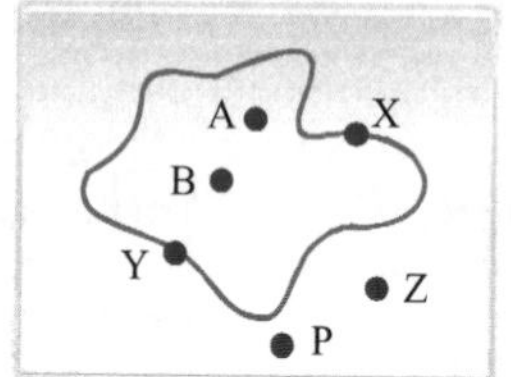

17. **(a)** In the interior region.
(b) In the exterior region.
(c) On the boundary region.

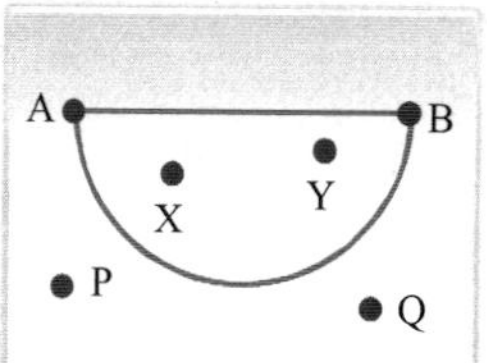

18. **(a)** In the interior region.
(b) In the exterior region.
(c) On the boundary region.

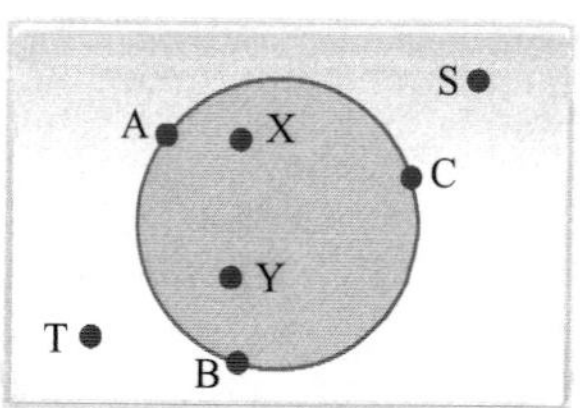

19. **(a)** In the interior region.
(b) In the exterior region.
(c) On the boundary region.

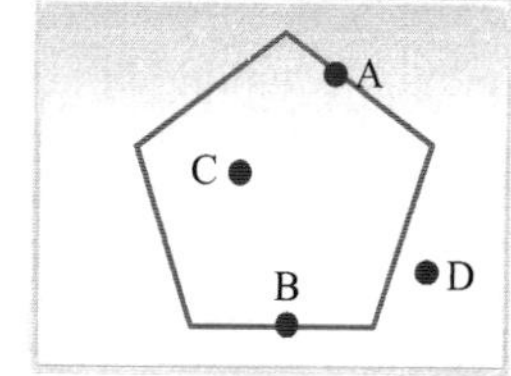

20. In each of the following circles what is the shaded region called?

(a)

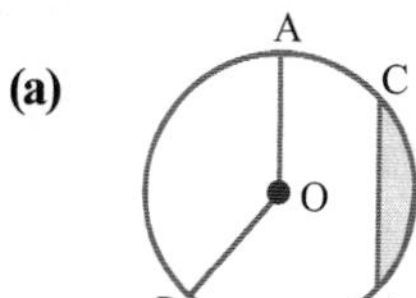

(b)

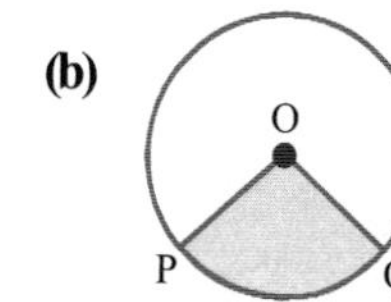

(c)

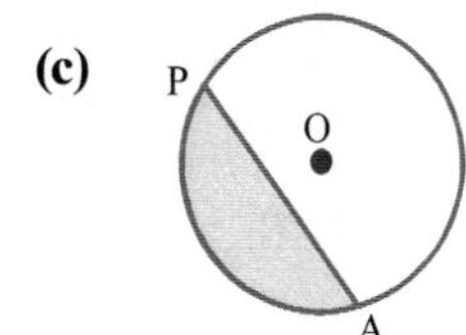

(d)

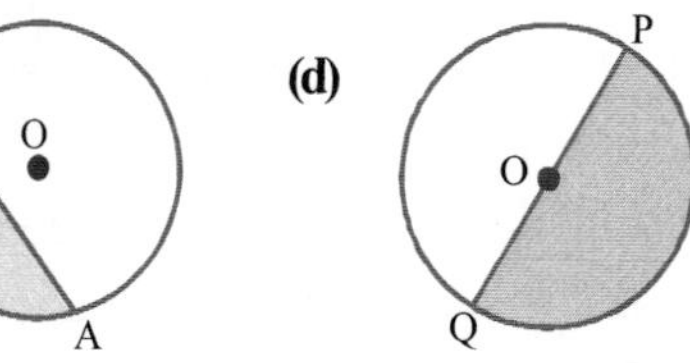

21. In the given circle with centre O, identify the name of AB.

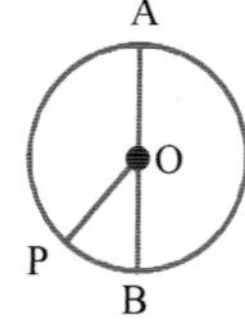

22. In the given circle with centre O, identify the name of $\overset{\frown}{PQ}$.

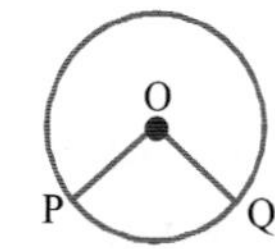

23. In the given circle with centre O, identify the name of AP.

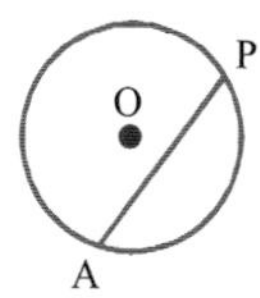

24. In the given circle with centre O, identify the name of OP and OA.

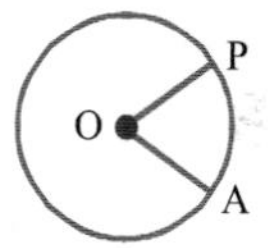

In questions 25-27, count the number of quadrilaterals in the given figure.

25.

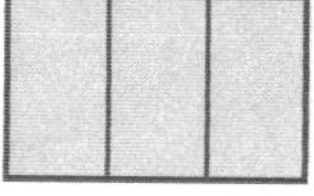

26.

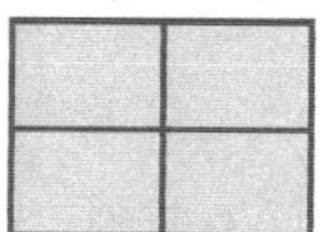

27.

In questions 28-30, count the number of triangles in the given figure.

28.

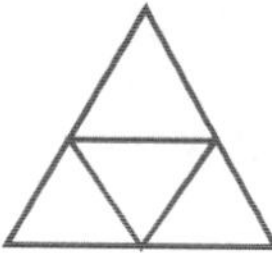

29.

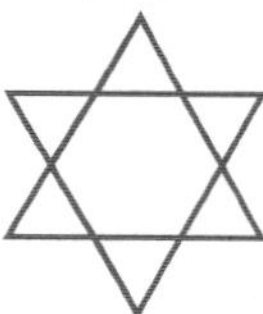

30.

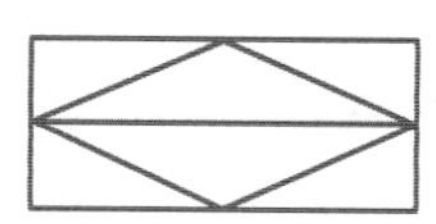

In questions 31-33, name the vertex and the arms of the given angle :

31.

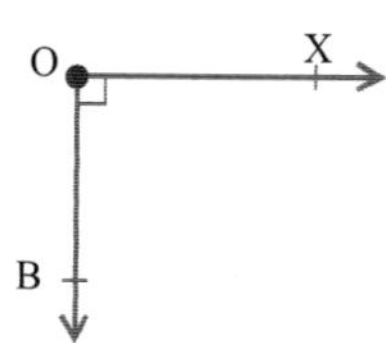

32.

33.

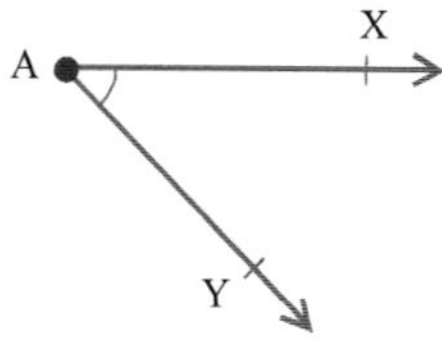

In questions 34-38, fill in the blanks:

34. A ________ is a chord passing through the centre of the circle.

35. End points of the ________ of a circle divides it into two semi-circles.

36. ________ is the total length of a circle.

37. A ________ is a region in the interior of the circle enclosed by its arc and a chord.

38. A ________ is a region in the interior of the circle enclosed by an arc and a pair of radii on the other two sides.

9.2 SPACE FIGURES

A. THREE DIMENSION SHAPES

So far, you have learnt about plane figures such as polygons,circles *etc.* These are called two dimensional (or 2D) shapes. You can draw such figures on your notebooks.

Following are some shapes (Figure 9.22) which we see in our day to day life. Each shape is a solid shape and not flat like surface of a blackboard, top of the table *etc.* These are called **three diamensional shapes** or 3D shapes.

A ball is a sphere

Figure 9.22 (a)

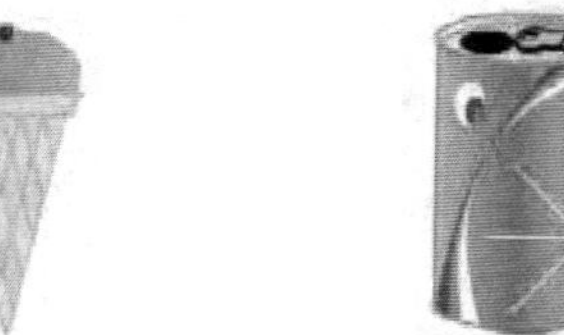

An ice cream cone

Figure 9.22 (b)

A can is a cylinder

Figure 9.22 (c)

If you put each of these shapes on a plane, only a part of it touches the plane.

We now discuss some other 3D shapes one by one.

A box is a cuboid

Figure 9.23 (d)

A playing die is a cube

Figure 9.23 (e)

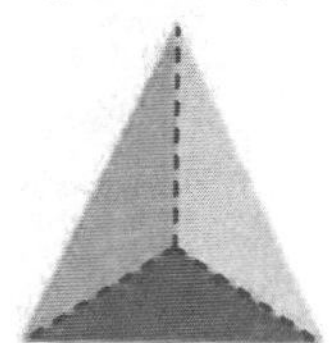

This is the shape of a pyramid

Figure 9.23 (f)

➜ **Cuboid and Cube**

Cuboid : A cuboid is a 3-dimensional figure bounded by six rectangular surfaces or **faces**.

Illustration 1: Shoe box, brick, an almirah *etc.* are examples of the shape of a cuboid.

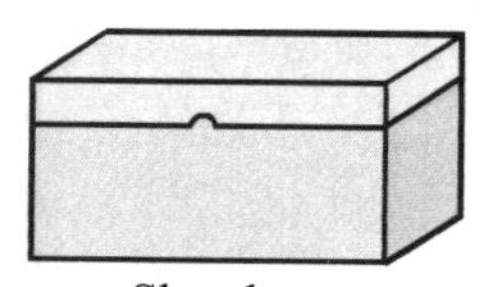

Shoe box

Figure 9.24 (a)

A brick

Figure 9.24 (b)

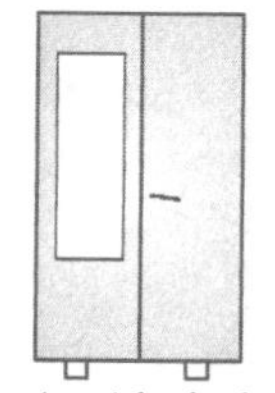

An Almirah

Figure 9.24 (c)

A cuboid has 6 faces. Any two adjacent faces of a cuboid meet in a line segment, called **edge** of the cuboid. There are 12 edges in a cuboid.

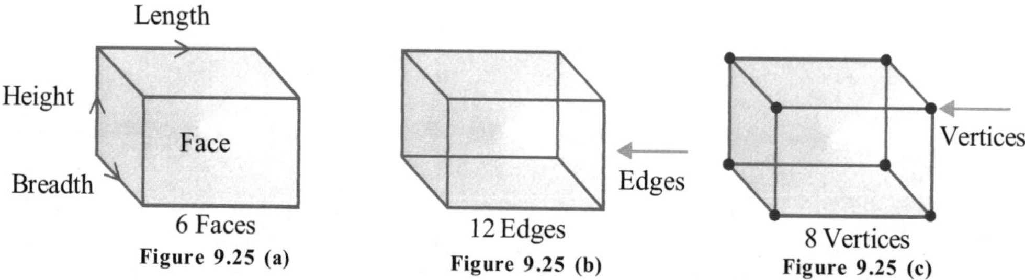

6 Faces

Figure 9.25 (a)

12 Edges

Figure 9.25 (b)

8 Vertices

Figure 9.25 (c)

The point of intersection of three edges of a cuboid is called **vertex**. There are 8 vertices in a cuboid.

A cuboid has three distinct dimensions known as length, breadth and height.

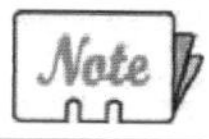

Each face of a cuboid has 4 edges. Each face of a cuboid has 4 vertices or corners.

Cube: A cuboid in which length, breadth and height are equal is called a **cube**.

Illustration 2: A die, a sugar cube *etc.* are examples of the shape of a cube.

The playing die
Figure 9.26 (a)

The sugar cube
Figure 9.26 (b)

Breadth
Height
Length
Figure 9.26 (c)

A cube has 6 square faces, 12 edges and 8 vertices.

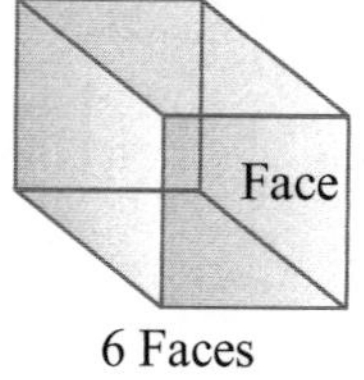

6 Faces
Figure 9.27 (d)

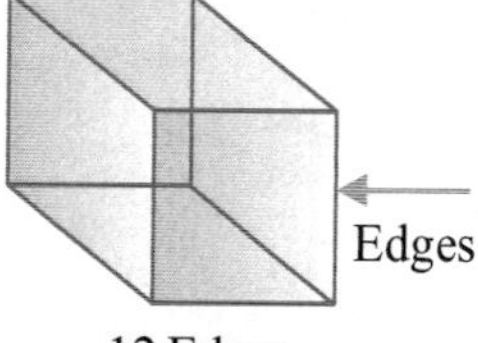

12 Edges
Figure 9.27 (e)

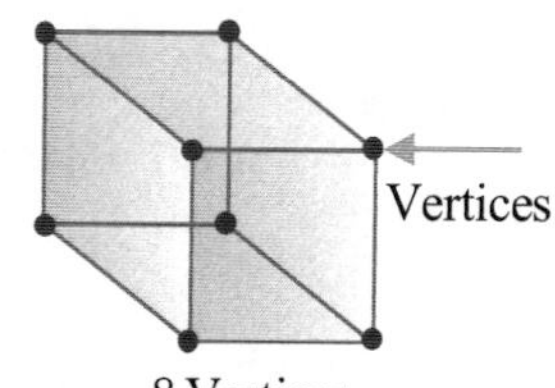

8 Vertices
Figure 9.27 (f)

➜ Cylinder

A solid having curved surface with circular ends is called a cylinder.

Illustration 3: Circular pipe, gas cylinder, measuring jar, garden roller *etc.*

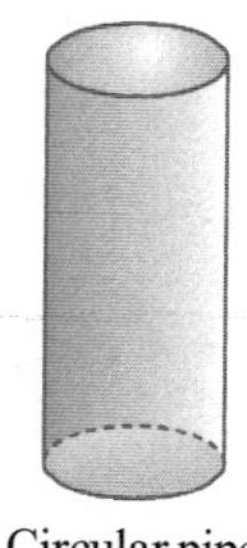

Circular pipe
Figure 9.28 (a)

Gas cylinder
Figure 9.28 (b)

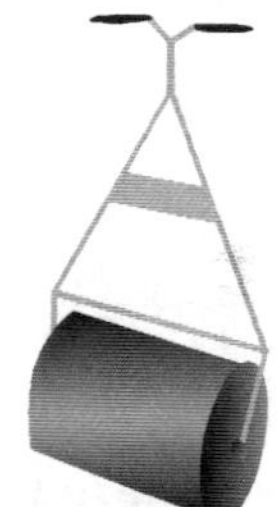

Garden roller
Figure 9.28 (c)

A cylinder has **curved surface** and **two circular faces.**

It has no vertex. It has two circular edges and no straight edge.

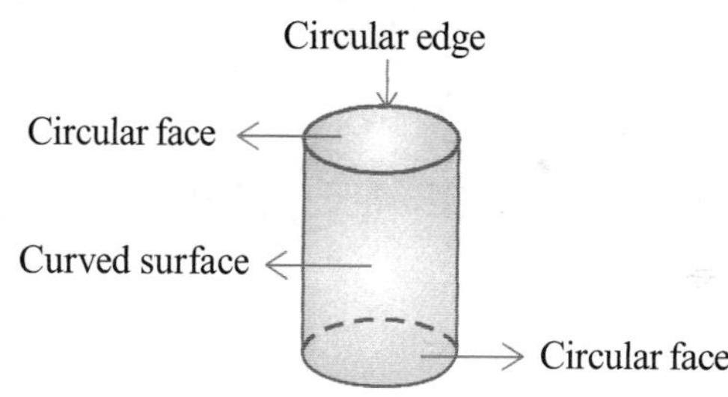

Figure 9.28 (d)

➜ Cone

A cone looks like the cap of a circus clown. It has **curved surface** and **one circular face**.

Illustration 4: It has **one vertex** and **one circular edge** (no straight edge).

An ice cream cone, a conical tent, tapered end of a pencil are in the shape of a cone.

Clown cap
Figure 9.29 (a)

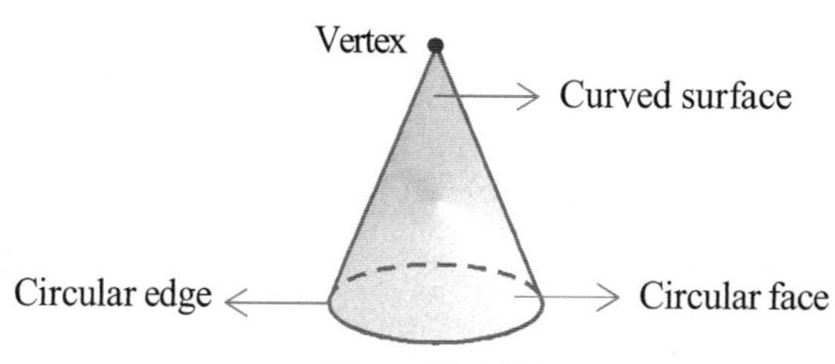

Figure 9.29 (b)

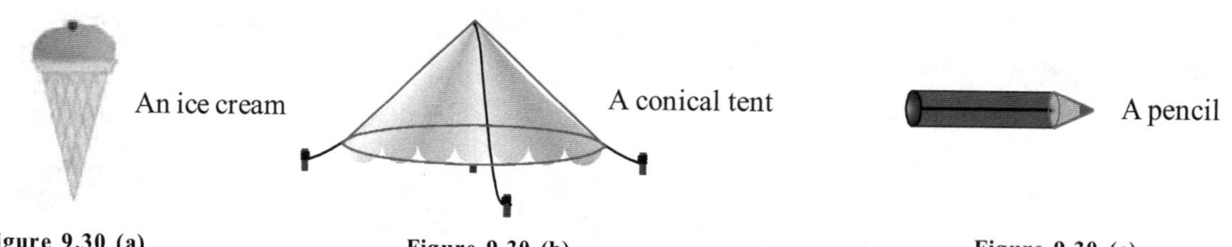

Figure 9.30 (a) Figure 9.30 (b) Figure 9.30 (c)

➜ Sphere

A sphere has curved surface.
It has no faces and no vertex. It has no edges.

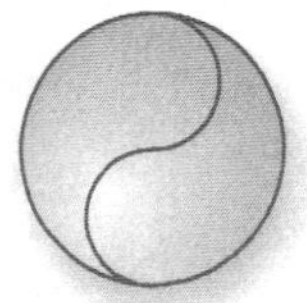

Figure 9.31

Illustration 5: A football, round marble, *etc.* are in the shape of a sphere.

A Football
Figure 9.32 (a)

Round marble
Figure 9.32 (b)

➜ Prism and Pyramid

Prism :

A prism is a solid with two identical polygonal bases and rectangular lateral faces.

A prism in which the two bases are triangles is called a **triangular prism**.

Illustration 6:

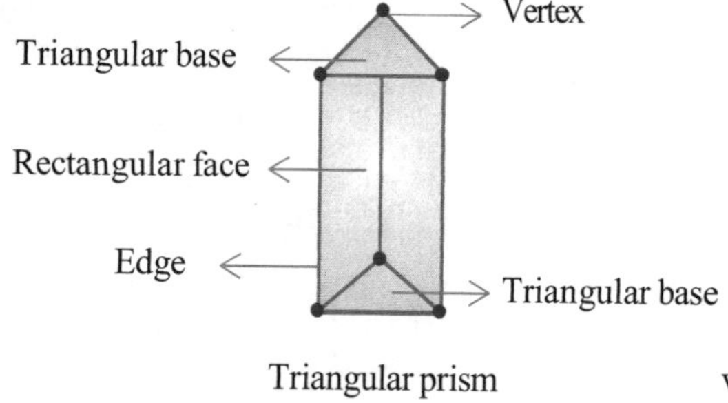

Triangular prism
Figure 6.33 (a)

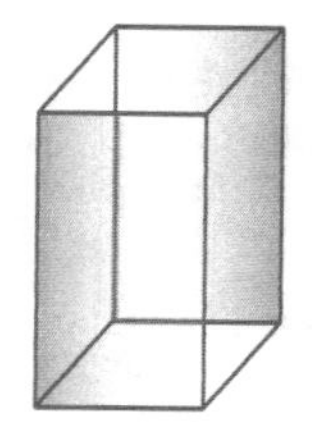

Cuboid is also a prism with base as a rectangle.
vertices : 8, Faces : 6, Edges : 12
Figure 9.33 (b)

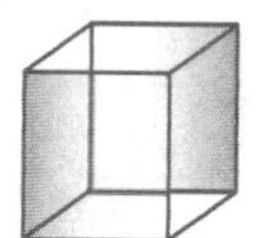

Cube is also a prism with base a square.
vertices : 8, Faces : 6, Edges : 12
Figure 9.33 (c)

A triangular prism has 6 vertices, 3 rectangular faces, 2 triangular faces (bases) and 9 edges.

Pyramid :

- A ***pyramid*** is a solid geometric figure that has a single polygonal base and whose side or lateral faces are triangles having a common vertex, called the ***vertex of the pyramid***.
- The side faces of a pyramid are called its ***lateral faces***.
- The pyramid whose base is a triangle is called a ***triangular pyramid***.
- The pyramid whose base is a square is called a ***square pyramid***.
- The pyramid whose base is a pentagon is called a ***pentagonal pyramid***.

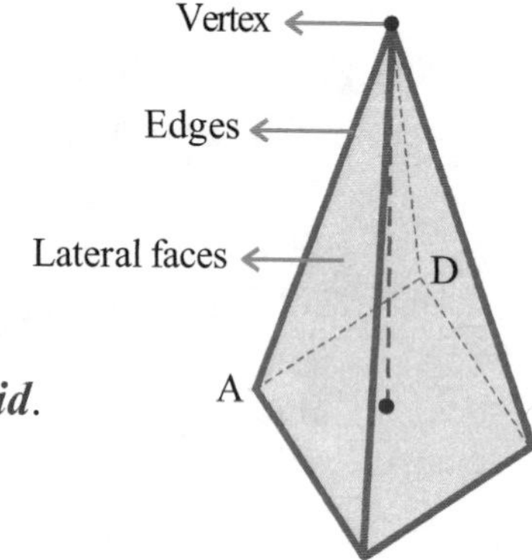

Figure 9.34

Illustration 7:

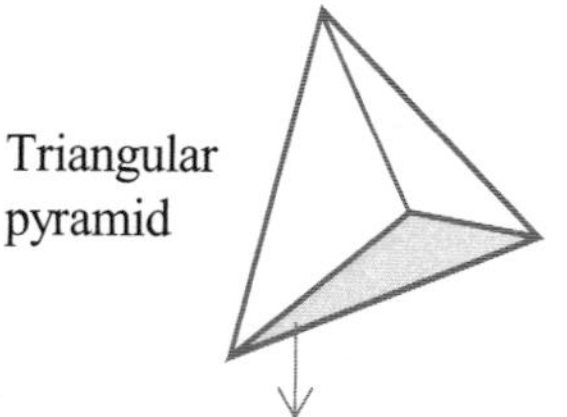

Vertices : 4, Faces : 4, Edges : 6

Figure 9.35 (a)

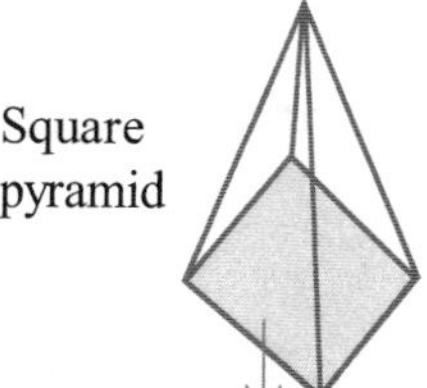

Vertices : 5, Faces : 5, Edges : 8

Figure 9.35 (b)

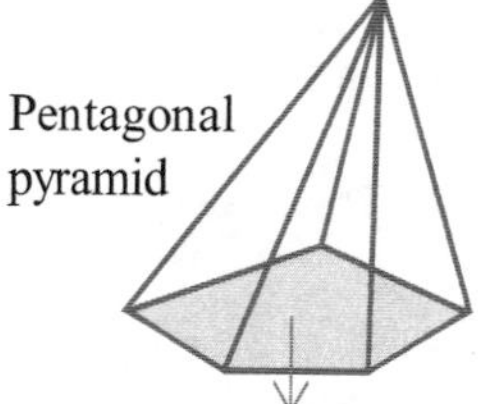

Vertices : 6, Faces : 6, Edges : 10

Figure 9.35 (c)

EXAMPLE 1 Count the number of visible faces in the given diagram:

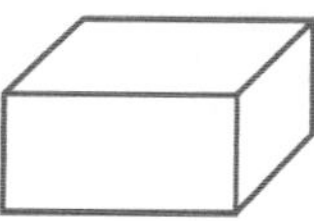

Solution : See the given figure.

The given figure has three visible faces.

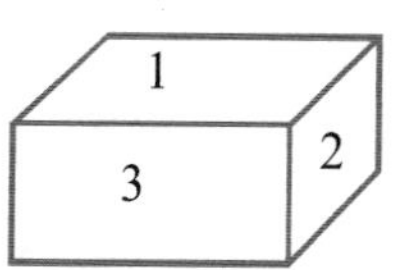

EXAMPLE 2 In the given shape, find the number of:

(a) Faces

(b) Edges

(c) Vertices

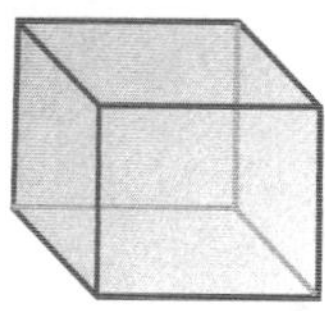

Solution :

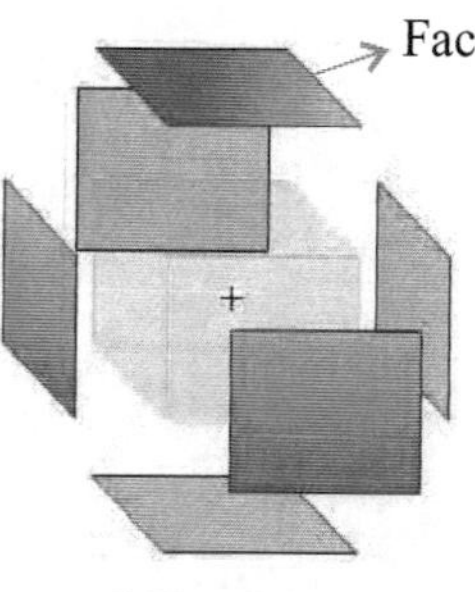

6 Faces

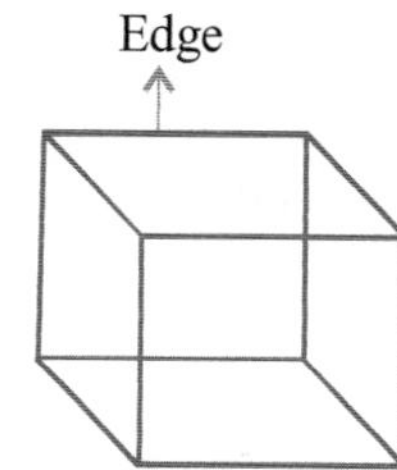

12 Edges

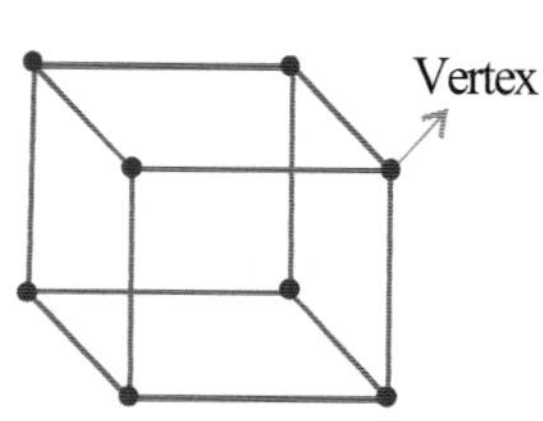

8 Vertices

Exercise 9.2

1. Count the number of visible faces in the given figure.

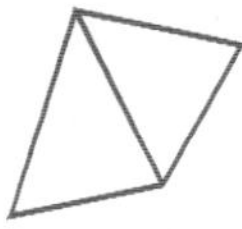

2. Count the number of visible vertices in the given figure.

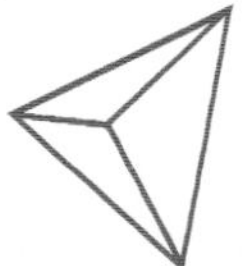

3. Count the number of visible edges in the given figure.

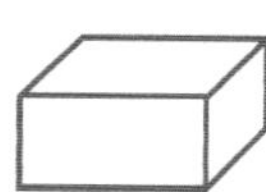

4. Find the number of: **(i)** Faces, **(ii)** Edges, and **(iii)** Vertices in the following:

(a)

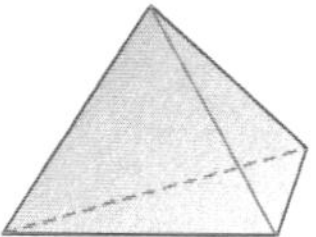

(b)

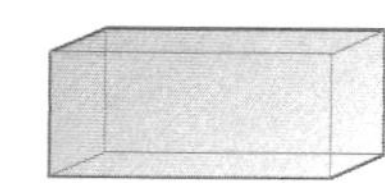

(c)

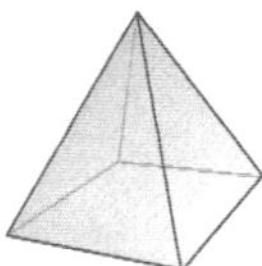

9.3 SYMMETRIC FIGURES

A. UNDERSTANDING SYMMETRY

- If we fold a picture (figure) in halves such that the two halves match exactly, then the picture is said to have **line symmetry**. The line from where we fold the picture is called its line (or axis) of symmetry.

  You can see *line symmetry* in butterflies, tree leaves, human faces, *etc*. (Figure 9.36)

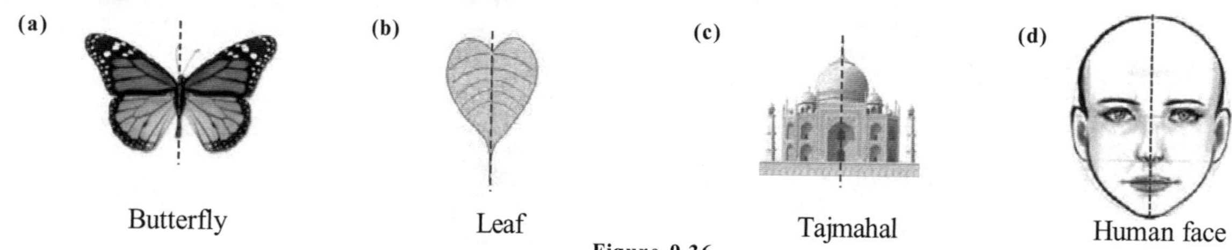

Figure 9.36

Dotted lines represent the lines of symmetry. Thus, we may also say that **a figure has line symmetry, if it is symmetrical (or symmetric) about a line (called its line of symmetry).**

Look at these shapes. They are also *symmetrical* about a line. That is, they have line symmetry.

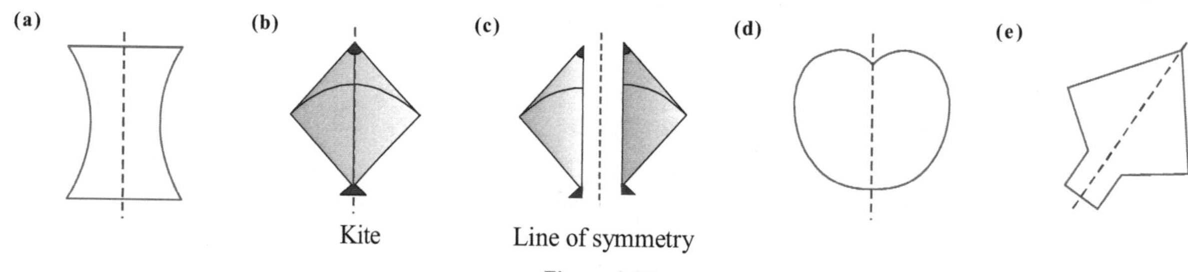

Figure 9.37

B. NUMBER OF LINES OF SYMMETRY

Recall that different figures have different number of lines of symmetry. A figure may have no line of symmetry, one line of symmetry, two lines of symmetry and so on.

No line of Symmetry:

Following figures have no line of symmetry :

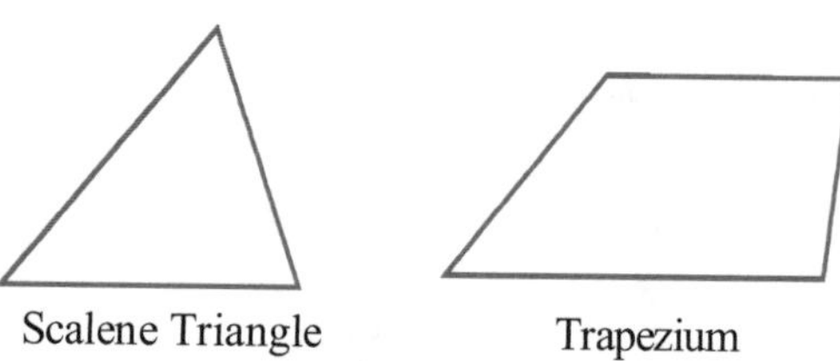

Figure 9.38

One line of Symmetry:

Look at the following pictures (figures) :

These figures have only **one** line of symmetry.
Dotted line shows the line of symmetry.

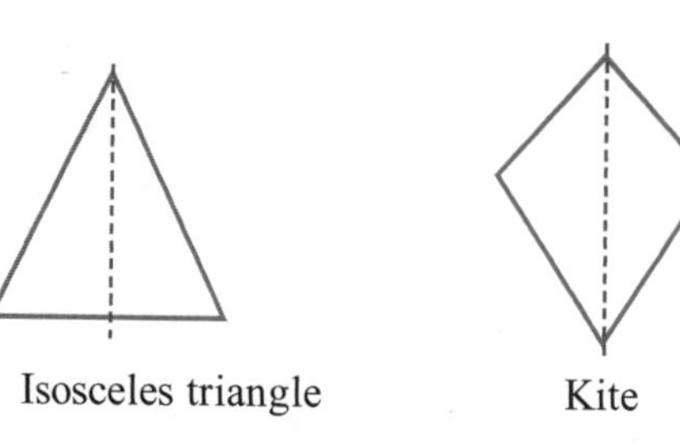

Figure 9.39

Two line of Symmetry:

Look at the following pictures (figures) :

These figures have **two** lines of symmetry. Dotted lines show the lines of symmetry.

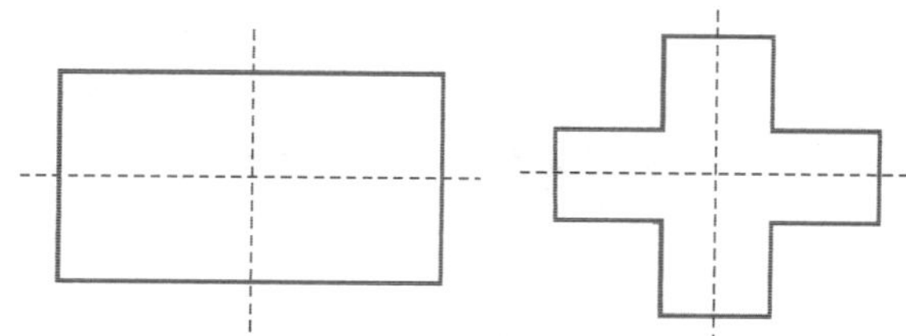
Figure 9.40

Multiple lines of Symmetry:

The objects which have more than two lines of symmetry are said to have multiple lines of symmetry.

For example, an equilateral triangle has *three lines of symmetry*.

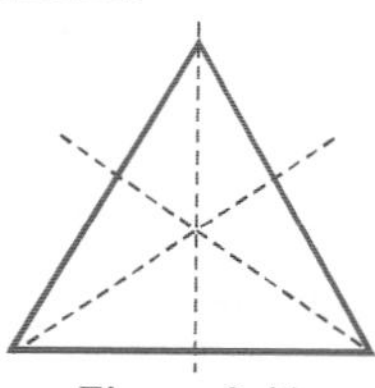
Figure 9.41

A circle has *countless (infinite number of) lines of symmetry*. Every line that passes through the centre of the circle is a line of symmetry.

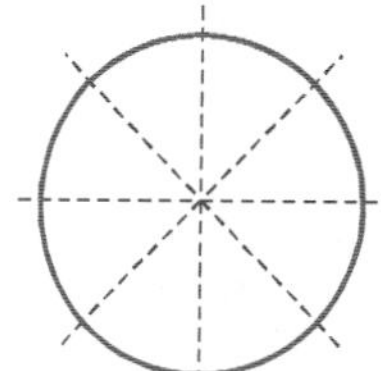
Figure 9.42

Reflection and Symmetry:

Mirror reflection and line symmetry are closely related to each other.

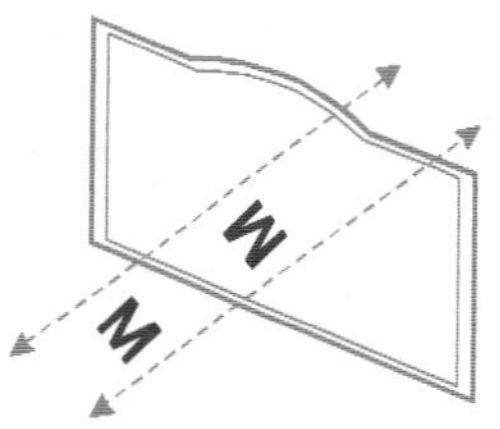
Figure 9.43

The picture shows the reflection of letter **M** in a mirror. Imagine that the mirror is placed along the dotted line. See the letter and its image again.

On folding the picture along the dotted line, we see that the object and its image are ***symmetrical*** (or symmetric) with reference to the mirror (dotted) line.

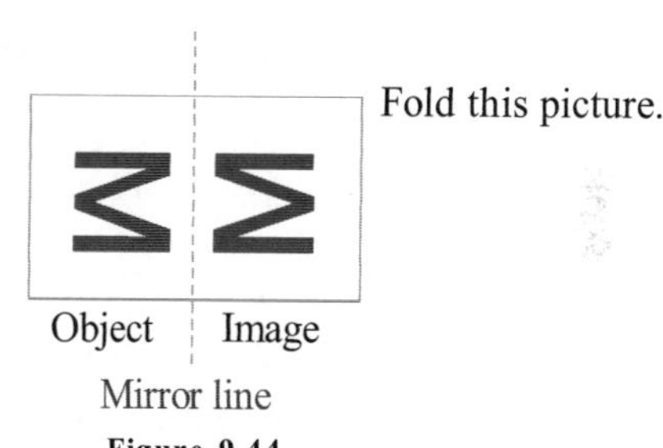

Figure 9.44

You may recall that **distance of an object from a mirror (object distance) is equal to the distance of its image from the mirror (image distance).**

- Using the above fact, to make (draw) a **point A' symmetric** to a given **point A** with reference to a line l, we draw **AP** $\perp$ l and take point A' on AP produced such that AP = A' P (Figure 9.45). If a point, say B lies on l, then its symmetric point B' will lie on line l itself.

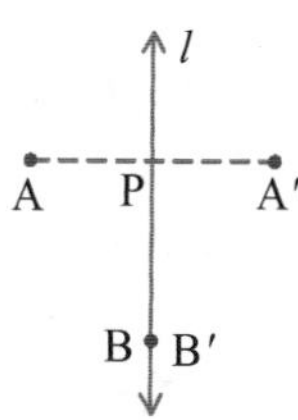

Figure 9.45

This knowledge of locating point A' symmetric to a given point A with respect to a given line l can be used to **complete a figure so that it becomes symmetric to a line or to draw a figure symmetric to a given figure with respect to a given line l.**

Illustration 1: In the Figure 9.46 (ii), has been obtained by completing figure (i). Here, A' is symmetric to A, B' is symmetric to B, C' is symmetric to C, D is symmetric to itself and E is symmetric to itself with respect to line l.

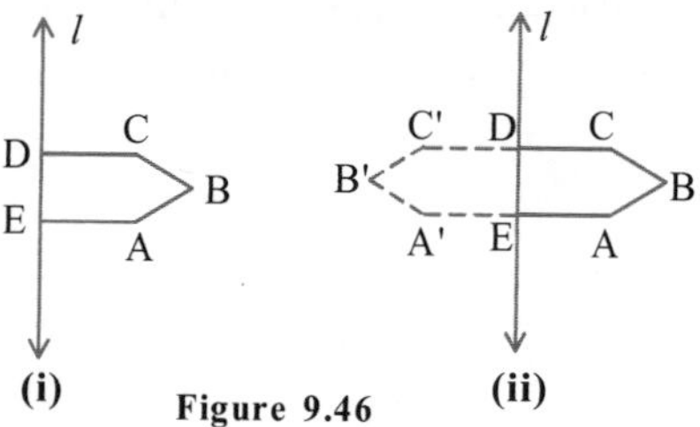

Figure 9.46

Illustration 2: In the Figure 9.47, triangle A'B'C' has been drawn symmetric to triangle ABC with respect to line m by locating points A', B' and C' respectively symmetric to the vertices A, B and C of the given triangle ABC, with respect to the line l.

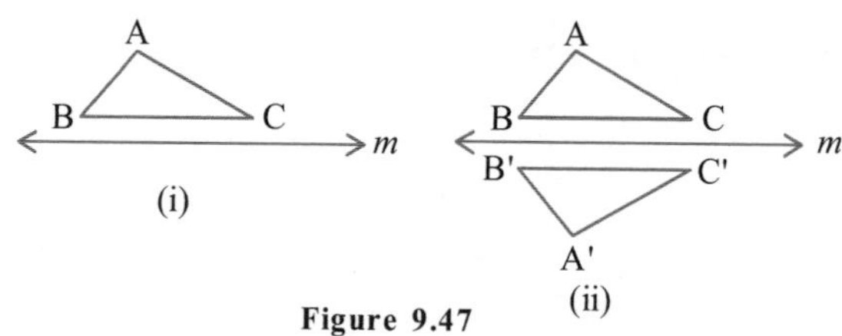

Figure 9.47

Note: The lengths and angles of two symmetric figures are the same, but they have different orientations (from left to right or from anticlockwise to clockwise.)

C. Lines of Symmetry for Regular Polygons

➜ Polygon

Recall that a polygon is a simple closed curve made of line segments only.

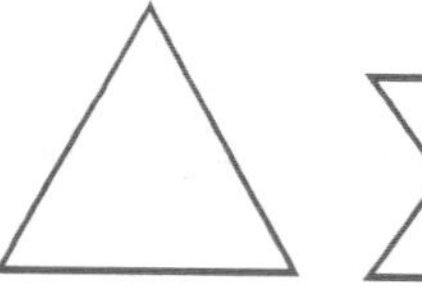

Figure 9.48

A polygon is a regular polygon, if all its sides are of equal length and all its angles are of equal measure. An equilateral triangle and a square are examples of regular polygons (Figure 9.49)

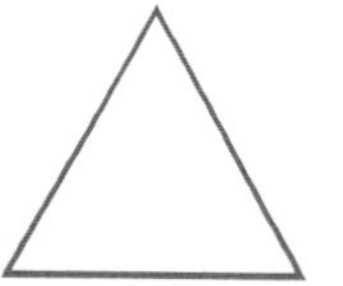

Figure 9.49

➜ Equilateral Triangle

An equilateral triangle is a regular polygon of three sides. Each of its side has same length and each of its angle measures 60°.

You know that an equilateral triangle has three lines of symmetry (Figure 9.50).

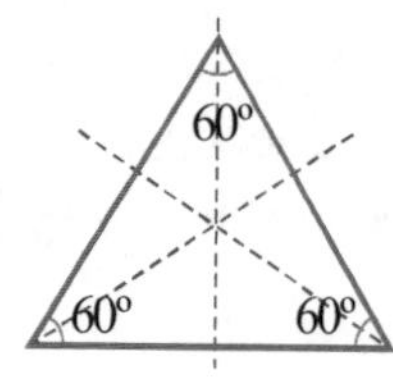

3 sides
3 lines of symmetry

Figure 9.50

➜ Square

A square is a regular polygon of four sides as each of its sides is of same length and each of its angles is a right angle (90°).

You know that a square has four lines of symmetry (Figure 9.51).

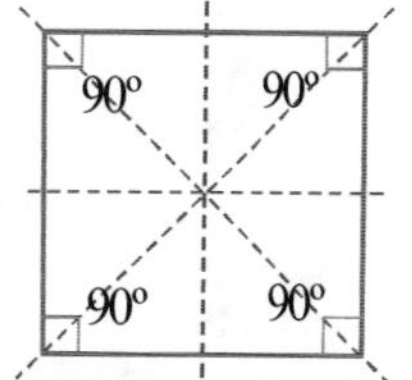

Figure 9.51

4 sides
4 lines of symmetry

➜ Regular Pentagon

A regular pentagon is a regular polygon of five sides. Each of its side has same length and each of its angle is of same measure (108°). (Figure 9.52)

From the figure, you can see that a regular pentagon has five lines of symmetry. You can verify this fact by cutting the figure out and folding it along the five dotted lines.

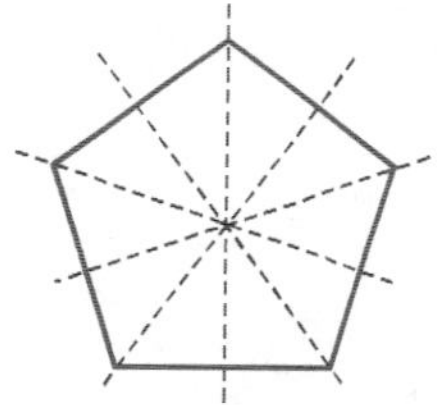
Figure 9.52

5 sides
5 lines of symmetry

➜ Hexagon

A regular hexagon is a regular polygon of six sides. Each of its side has same length and each of its angle measures 120°. (Figure 9.53)

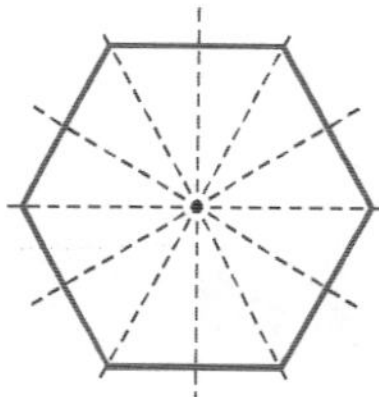
Figure 9.53

6 sides
6 lines of symmetry

From the figure, you can see that a regular hexagon has six lines of symmetry. Observing the above pattern, we may say that : A regular polygon has as many lines of symmetry as the number of its sides.

EXAMPLE 1 State the number of lines of symmetry for an equilateral triangle. Also, identify these lines.

Solution: Each regular polygon has as many lines of symmetry as the number of its sides.

An equilateral triangle is a regular polygon of three sides.

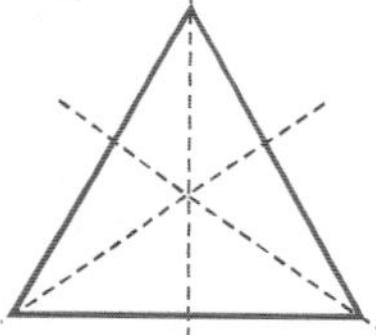

3 sides
3 lines of symmetry

Therefore, an equilateral triangle has **three lines of symmetry**. They are along the **three medians** or the **three altitudes** of the triangles.

EXERCISE 9.3

In questions 1-10, identify the line(s) of symmetry in the given figures :

1. 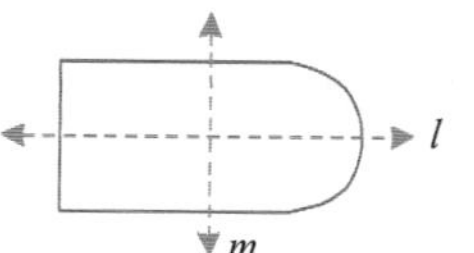

2. 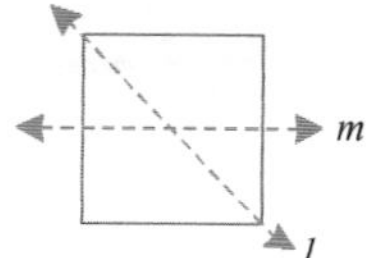

3. 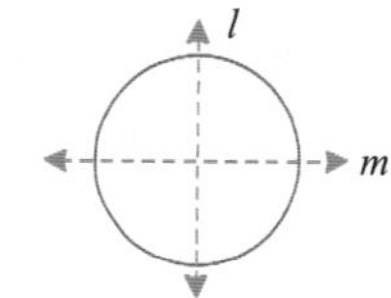

4.

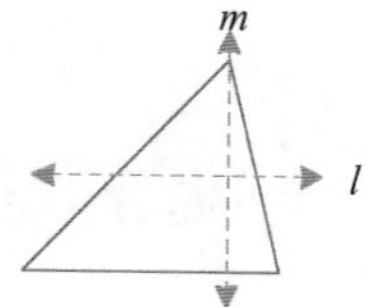

5.

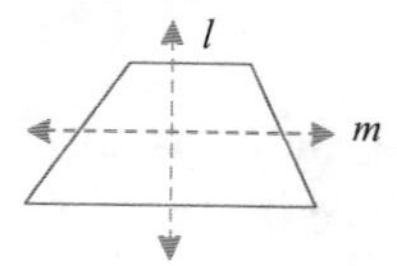

6.

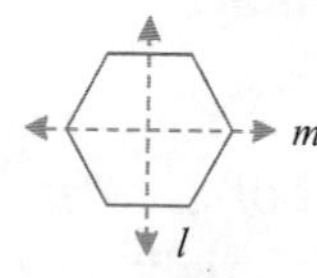

7.

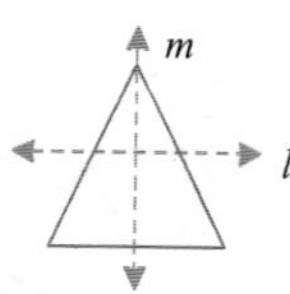

8.

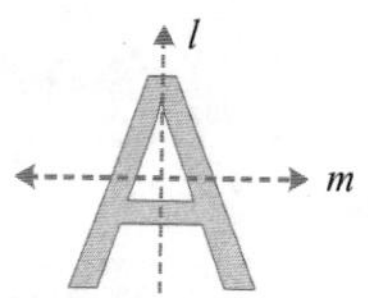

9.

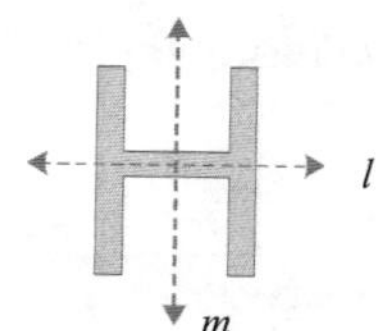

10.

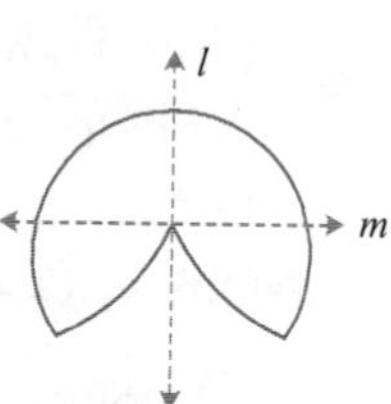

In questions 11-16, find the number of lines of symmetry for the following letter of the English alphabet :

11. B **12.** H **13.** S **14.** E **15.** I **16.** Z

17. Complete the figure so that the completed figure is symmetric to the line n :

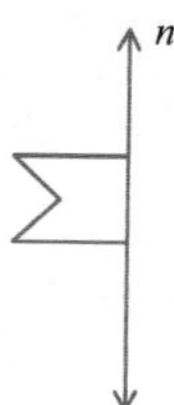

18. Complete the figure so that lines l and m become the lines of symmetry for the completed figure :

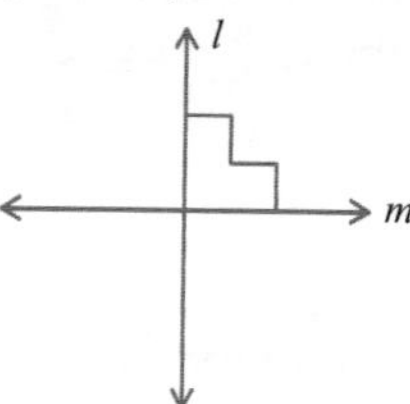

19. Draw a line segment A'B' symmetric to the line segment AB of the given figure with respect to line m.

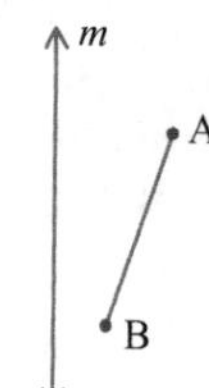

20. Draw an angle A'B'C' symmetric to angle ABC with respect to line n in the given figure :

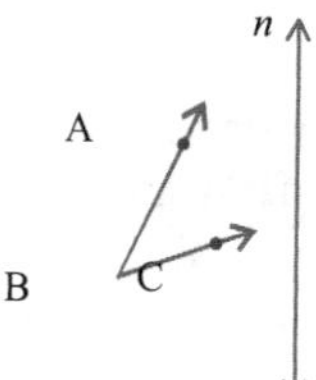

In questions 21-25, state the number of lines of symmetry for the figure. Also, mark these lines of symmetry.

21. square

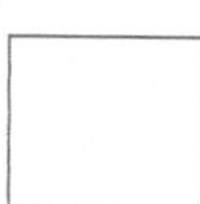

22. regular pentagon

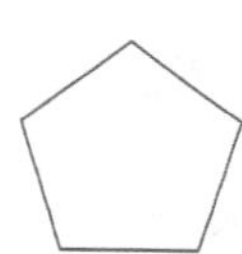

23. regular hexagon.

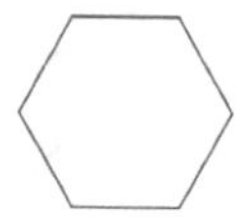

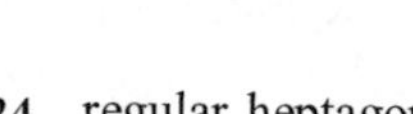

24. regular heptagon.

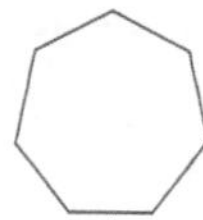

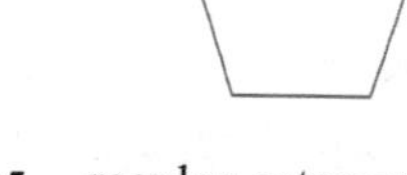

25. regular octagon.

MEASUREMENTS

This chapter is divided into three sections:

10.1 *Systems of Measurement;*

10.2 *Area and Perimeter; and*

10.3 *Volume and Surface Area.*

10.1 SYSTEMS OF MEASUREMENT

VOCABULARY

OBJECTIVES

After completing this section you will be able to:

A. Multiply or divide any measurement by a number;

B. Add or subtract two measurements with common units;

C. Convert units in the English system;

D. Convert units in the Metric system;

E. Convert units of measurement from English to Metric and from Metric to English; and

F. Estimate measurements of common objects in the Metric system.

1. A **measurement** is written with a number and a unit of measure. It shows "how many" or "how much".

25 *lb*, 1.5 *m*, 10 *l* are examples of measurements.

2. Some units of the **English System** of measurement are:

(a) **Length:** **inch** (in), **foot** (ft), **yard** (yd), **mile** (mi).

(b) **Mass:** **ounce** (oz), **pound** (lb), **ton**.

(c) **Volume:** **teaspoon** (tsp), **tablespoon** (tbs), **cup** (c), **pint** (pt), **quart** (qt), **gallon** (gal).

3. The basic units of the **Metric System** are:

(a) **Length:** **meter** (m), **centimeter** (cm).

(b) **Mass:** **kilogram** (kg), **gram** (g).

(c) **Volume:** **liter** (*l*), **cubic centimeter** (cc).

4. **Equivalent measures** are measures of the same thing using different units. For example,

1 pound (1 *lb*) = 16 ounces (16 *oz*).

4 quarts (4 *qt*) = 1 gallon (1 *gal*).

5. A **conversion ratio** is used to convert measurements and is equivalent to 1.

$\frac{12\text{ in}}{1\text{ ft}}$ is a conversion ratio.

$$3\text{ ft} = 3\text{ ft} \times 1 = 3\text{ ft} \times \frac{12\text{ in}}{1\text{ ft}} = 36\text{ in}$$

6. The metric prefixes are:

Kilo = 1000, **Hecto** = 100, **Deka** = 10

Deci = $\frac{1}{10}$, **Centi** = $\frac{1}{100}$, **Milli** = $\frac{1}{1000}$

A. Multiply or divide any measurement by a number.

Discussion

- To determine size or quantity, a unit of measurement can be chosen arbitrarily. Then, multiples of this unit may be used to measure objects. For example, to measure length, one may choose "hand-span" or "pace" or "rod" as a basic unit of measurement.

  Such units are non-standard units of length. If two people measure the length of an object using their own footsteps, their answers may differ. However, if they measure the length of an object by using a fixed scale, such as sticks of equal lengths, they will get the same answer. For consistency, there must be standard units of measure.

- **The English System** of measurement uses 1 foot (1 ft) as a *standard unit of length*, while in the **metric system** a standard unit of length is 1 meter (1 m). For most purposes, these standard units along with their multiples are sufficient. For measuring the lengths of shorter objects, the English system uses a smaller unit of length called an **inch**. If a length of 1 foot is divided into 12 equal parts, then the length of each part is 1 inch. That is, 1 inch = $\frac{1}{12}$ of a foot. The length measuring 1 inch is shown below:

  1 inch

  To measure a larger object, count how many of these inches are needed to measure the length. In Figure 10.1, we need three 1 - inch units to measure the given line segment.

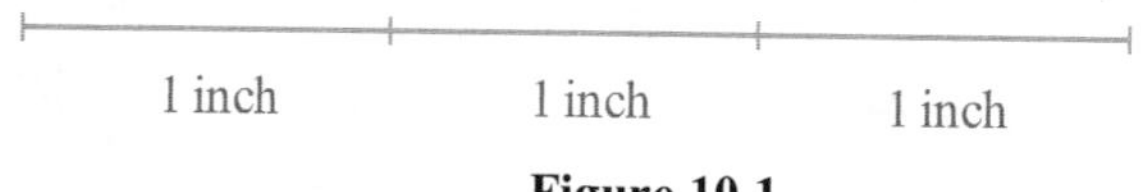

Figure 10.1

  The length of the line is 3 times 1 inch, that is, 3 · (1 inch) or just 3 inches.

- In the **metric system**, the standard unit of length is a **meter**. For measuring lengths of shorter objects, the system uses a smaller unit called **centimeter** abbreviated by **cm**. 1 meter = 100 centimeters. In Figure 10.2 below, eight 1- centimeter units are used to measure the length of the line segment.

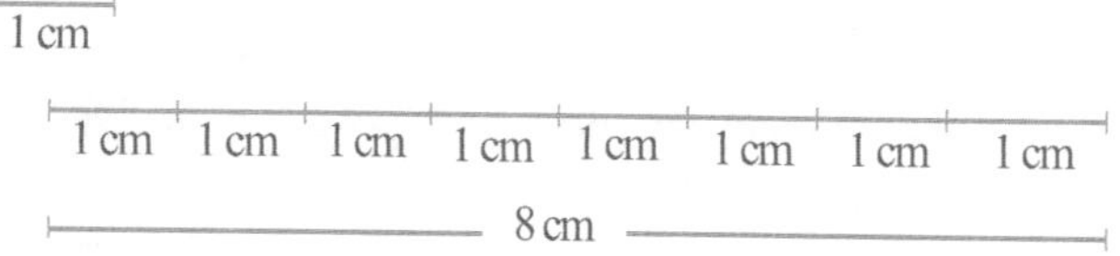

Figure 10.2

  The length of the line segment is 8 times 1 cm, that is, 8 · (1 cm) or just 8 cm.

- The expressions "3 · (1 in) = 3 in" and "8 · (1 cm) = 8 cm" show that a measurement can be written as a number times the unit. Thus,

4 hand-spans	=	4 · (1 hand span) ;
2.5 miles	=	(2.5) · (1 mile) ;
14 gallons	=	14 · (1 gallon).

- This way of writing measurements is used to multiply or divide any measurement by a number. Consider three jars, each containing 1 liter of water.

  If the water is poured from these three jars into a bigger jar, what quantity of water is in the bigger jar? Surely, 3 liters. So, $3 \text{ liters} = 3 \cdot (1 \text{ liter})$

  If there are 4 containers, each holding 3 liters of water, how many liters of water are in the 4 containers? Obviously, 12 liters.

  $4 \cdot (3 \text{ liters}) = (4 \cdot 3) \text{ liters} = 12 \text{ liters}.$

- Dividing a mesurement by a number is similar to multiplying. If a rod of length 5 inches is divided into two equal parts, as in Figure 10.3, what will be the length of each part?

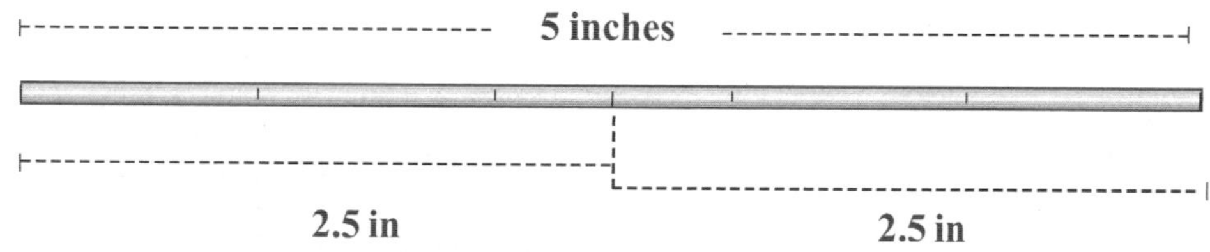

Figure 10.3

The length of each part $= 5 \text{ inches} \div 2 = (5 \div 2) \text{ inches} = 2.5 \text{ inches}.$

Thus, to multiply or divide a measurement by a number, multiply or divide the two numbers and write the unit of measure.

$4 \cdot (3 \text{ liters}) = (4 \cdot 3) \text{ liters} = 12 \text{ liters}, \qquad 5 \text{ in} \div 2 = (5 \div 2) \text{ in} = \frac{5}{2} \text{ in} = 2.5 \text{ in}$

Procedure to multiply or divide a measurement by a number.

***Step* 1** Multiply or divide the two numbers.

***Step* 2** Write the product or the quotient followed by the unit of measure.

EXAMPLE 1 Multiply or divide as indicated.

(a) Multiply 35 gallons by 6.

(b) Divide 43.7 yards into 19 equal lengths.

Solutions:

(a) $(35 \text{ gallons}) \cdot 6 = (35 \cdot 6) \text{ gallons}$
$= 210 \text{ gallons}$

- Multiply the numbers: $35 \cdot 6 = 210$
- Write the product followed by the unit of measure.

(b) $(43.7 \text{ yards}) \div 19 = (43.7 \div 19) \text{ yards}$
$= 2.3 \text{ yards}$

- Divide the numbers: $43.7 \div 19 = 2.3$
- Write the quotient, 2.3, followed by the unit of measure, yards.

EXAMPLE 2 Perform the indicated operation.

(a) $(8 \text{ hours}) \cdot (7)$ **(b)** $(45.6 \text{ dm}) \div 3$

Solutions:

WARM-UP

1.(a) Multiply: 16.5 ounces by 7.

(b) Divide 127 kg into 8 equal weights.

2. Perform the indicated operation.

(a) (4 miles) (16)

WARM-UP

(b) (57 pounds) ÷ 4

3. If 3qt of milk are poured equally in 4 glasses, what is the quantity of milk in each glass?

4. There are 24 hours in a day. How many hours are there in 13 days?

Answers:

1.	(a) 115.5 ounces	(b) 15.875 kg
2.	(a) 64 miles	(b) 14.25 pounds
3.	0.75 qt	4. 312 hours

(a) $(8 \text{ hours}) \cdot (7) = (8 \cdot 7) \text{ hours}$ • Multiply the numbers.

$= 56 \text{ hours}$ • Simplify.

(b) $(45.6 \text{ dm}) \div 3 = (45.6 \div 3) \text{ dm}$ • Divide the numbers.

$= 15.2 \text{ dm}.$ • Simplify.

EXAMPLE 3 If 1.5 lb of peanuts are distributed equally among 3 students, how much does each student get?

Solution: To find the share of each student, divide the total weight by the number of students.

$1.5 \text{ lb} \div 3 = (1.5 \div 3) \text{ lb}$ • Divide the numbers.

$= 0.5 \text{ lb}$ • Write the quotient followed by the unit of measure.

Each student gets 0.5 lb of peanuts.

EXAMPLE 4 If a can contains 275 grams of soup, how many grams are contained in seven cans?

Solution:

To find the total quantity of soup in seven cans, multiply the quantity in one can by seven.

$(275 \text{ grams}) \cdot 7 = (275 \cdot 7) \text{ grams}$ • Multiply the numbers.

$= 1925 \text{ grams}.$ • Write the product, followed by grams.

Seven cans contain 1925 grams of soup.

B. ADDING AND SUBTRACTING MEASUREMENTS

➜ **Add or subtract two measurements with common units.**

Application

Laura buys three pieces of rope measuring 5 ft. 4 in., 7 ft. 9 in., and 10 ft. 6 in. What is the total length of all the pieces she bought? If she cuts and uses a length measuring 8 ft. 9 in. from the piece measuring 10 ft. 6 in., what is the total measure of the remaining lengths of rope?

Discussion

- Two or more measurements with **common units** can be added just by adding the number of measures. For example,

$3 \text{ g} + 7.5 \text{ g} = (3 + 7.5) \text{ g}$ Group the numbers.

$= 10.5 \text{ g}$ Add the numbers.

$14 \text{ cm} + 10 \text{ cm} + 3 \text{ cm} = (14 + 10 + 3) \text{ cm}$ Group the numbers.

$= 27 \text{ cm}$ Simplify.

- Similarly, to subtract two measurements with **common units**, subtract the numbers of measures. For example,

$$\begin{aligned} 25 \text{ gal} - 17 \text{ gal} &= (25 - 17) \text{ gal} && \text{Group the numbers.} \\ &= 8 \text{ gal} && \text{Subtract the numbers.} \end{aligned}$$

- It is possible to add or subtract measurements which are expressed in two or more units. For example, to add 26 m 25 cm and 12 m 70 cm, add the number of meters and the number of centimeters in both the measures:

$$\begin{array}{rrl} & 26 \text{ m} & 25 \text{ cm} \\ + & 12 \text{ m} & 70 \text{ cm} \\ \hline & 38 \text{ m} & 95 \text{ cm} \end{array}$$

Arrange the meters (m) and the centimeters (cm) in columns.

Add centimeters, and then add meters.

Thus, the sum of 26 m 25 cm and 12 m 70 cm is 38 m 95 cm.

Similarly, subtract 14 min 29 sec from 21 min 47 sec.

$$\begin{array}{rrl} & 21 \text{ min} & 47 \text{ sec} \\ - & 14 \text{ min} & 29 \text{ sec} \\ \hline & 7 \text{ min} & 18 \text{ sec} \end{array}$$

Arrange the minutes (min) and the seconds (sec) in columns.

Subtract 29 sec from 47 sec, and 14 min from 21 min.

The difference is 7 min 18 sec.

- While adding or subtracting measurements that are expressed in two (or more) units, it is often necessary to know the equivalent measures. For example, to buy two articles, one costing 4 dollars 65 cents, and the other costing 12 dollars 47 cents, how much money is needed? The total cost is the sum of 4 dollars 65 cents and 12 dollars 47 cents.

$$\begin{array}{rrl} & 4 \text{ dollars} & 65 \text{ cents} \\ + & 12 \text{ dollars} & 47 \text{ cents} \\ \hline & 16 \text{ dollars} & 112 \text{ cents} \end{array}$$

Arrange the dollars and cents in columns.

Add cents, and then add dollars.

Since

$$\begin{aligned} 112 \text{ cents} &= 100 \text{ cents} + 12 \text{ cents} && \text{Recall: } 100¢ = \$1. \\ &= 1 \text{ dollar} + 12 \text{ cents.} \end{aligned}$$

$$\begin{aligned} \textbf{16 dollars 112 cents} &= 16 \text{ dollars} + (1 \text{ dollar} + 12 \text{ cents}) \\ &= (16 \text{ dollars} + 1 \text{ dollar}) + 12 \text{ cents} \\ &= 17 \text{ dollars} + 12 \text{ cents} \\ &= 17 \text{ dollars } 12 \text{ cents.} \end{aligned}$$

This shows that it costs 17 dollars 12 cents for the two articles.

Another example which illustrates the need of knowing equivalent measures can be seen if we subtract 2 ft 7 in from 6 ft 5 in. As in the case of addition, arrange the two measurements in columns and subtract.

$$\begin{array}{rrl} & 6 \text{ ft} & 5 \text{ in} \\ - & 2 \text{ ft} & 7 \text{ in} \\ \hline \end{array}$$

Recall: 1 ft = 12 in.

Now, 7 in cannot be subtracted from 5 in, so regroup 1 ft from the 6 ft and add it to the 5 in. Add 12 in to 5 in, and then subtract 7 in from the sum obtained.

$$\begin{array}{rr} 6\text{ ft} & 5\text{ in} \\ -\ 2\text{ ft} & 7\text{ in} \\ \hline \end{array} \rightarrow \begin{array}{rr} 5\text{ ft} & 1\text{ ft } 5\text{ in} \\ -\ 2\text{ ft} & 7\text{ in} \\ \hline \end{array} \rightarrow \begin{array}{rr} 5\text{ ft} & 17\text{ in} \\ -\ 2\text{ ft} & 7\text{ in} \\ \hline 3\text{ ft} & 10\text{ in} \end{array}$$

A shortened form is shown as:

$$\begin{array}{rr} 5\text{ft} & 17\text{in} \\ \not{6}\text{ ft} & \not{5}\text{ in} \\ -\ 2\text{ ft} & 7\text{ in} \\ \hline 3\text{ ft} & 10\text{ in} \end{array}$$

- English and metric measures and their equivalents are listed in Tables 10.1 and 10.2.

TABLE 10.1 ENGLISH MEASUREMENTS AND EQUIVALENTS

Length	Time
12 inches (in.) = 1 foot (ft)	60 seconds (sec) = 1 minute (min)
3 feet (ft) = 1 yard (yd)	60 minutes (min) = 1 hour (hr)
5,280 feet (ft) = 1 mile (mi)	24 hours (hr) = 1 day
	7 days = 1 week
Liquid Volume	**Weight**
3 teaspoons (tsp) = 1 tablespoon (tbs)	4 quarts (qt) = 1 gallon (gal)
2 table spoons = 1 fluid ounce (fl oz)	16 ounces (oz) = 1 pound (lb)
8 fluid ounces (fl oz) = 1 cup (c)	2,000 pounds (lb) = 1 ton
2 cups (c) = 1 pint (pt)	
2 pints (pt) = 1 quart (qt)	

TABLE 10.2 METRIC MEASUREMENTS AND EQUIVALENTS

Length (Basic Unit is 1 Meter)				
1 millimeter	(mm)		=	0.001 m
1 centimeter	(cm)	= 10 millimeters	=	0.01 m
1 decimeter	(dm)	= 10 centimeter	=	0.1 m
1 METER	(m)	= 10 decimeters	=	1 m
1 dekameter	(dam)	= 10 meters	=	10 m
1 hectometer	(hm)	= 10 dekameters	=	100 m
1 kilometer	(km)	= 10 hectometers	=	1,000 m

Weight (Basic Unit is 1 Gram)				
1 milligram	(mg)		=	**0.001 g**
1 centigram	(cg)	= 10 milligrams	=	**0.01 g**
1 decigram	(dg)	= 10 centigrams	=	0.1 g
1 GRAM	(g)	= 10 decigrams	=	1 g
1 dekagram	(dag)	= 10 grams	=	10 g
1 hectogram	(hg)	= 10 dekagrams	=	100 g
1 kilogram	(kg)	= 10 hectograms	=	**1,000 g**
1 metric ton		= **1,000 kilograms**	=	**1,000,000 g**

Liquid Measurements (Basic Unit is 1 Liter)					
1 milliliter	(ml)			=	**0.001 l**
1 centiliter	(cl)	=	10 milliliters	=	0.01 l
1 deciliter	(dl)	=	10 centiliters	=	0.1 l
1 LITER	(l)	=	10 deciliters	=	1 l
1 dekaliter	(dal)	=	10 liters	=	10 l
1 hectoliter	(hl)	=	10 dekaliters	=	100 l
1 kiloliter	(kl)	=	10 hectoliters	=	1,000 l

TABLE 10.3 MONETARY SYSTEM

		1 cent	=	**0.01 dollar**
5 cents	=	1 nickel	=	0.05 dollar
10 cents	=	1 dime	=	0.1 dollar
100 cents = 10 dimes	=	1 dollar	=	1 dollar

Procedure to add or subtract two measurements in a common unit, or in two or more common units:

***Step* 1** Arrange the measurements in columns lining up the place values and units.

***Step* 2** Add or subtract as required and use the common unit.
Use equivalent measures, if necessary.

EXAMPLE 5 Add or subtract as indicated.

(a) $45.6\ l + 39.8\ l$ **(b)** 26.5 yd − 17.8 yd.

Solutions:

(a)

$$\begin{array}{r} \overset{1}{45}.6\ l \\ +\ 39.8\ l \\ \hline 85.4\ l \end{array}$$

- Arrange the measurements in columns lining up the place values and the common unit.
- Add the numbers and use the common unit with the sum.

(b)

$$\begin{array}{r} 26.5 \text{ yd} \\ -\ 17.8 \text{ yd} \\ \hline 8.7 \text{ yd} \end{array}$$

- Arrange the measurements in columns lining up the place values and the common unit.
- Subtract the number and use the common unit with the difference.

EXAMPLE 6 Perform the indicated operations.

(a) 25 lb 5 oz + 7 lb 9 oz + 13 lb 6 oz.

(b) 7 gal 2 qt − 4 gal 3 qt 1 pt.

Solutions:

(a)

$$\begin{array}{rr} 25 \text{ lb} & 5 \text{ oz} \\ 7 \text{ lb} & 9 \text{ oz} \\ +\ 13 \text{ lb} & 6 \text{ oz} \\ \hline 45 \text{ lb} & 20 \text{ oz} \end{array} = 45 \text{ lb} + (1 \text{ lb} + 4 \text{ oz}) = 46 \text{ lb } 4 \text{ oz}$$

- Write in columns lining up the place values and units.
- Add.

Since 20 oz is more than 1 lb (16 oz = 1 lb from table 9.1). Change 20 oz to 1 lb 4 oz and add the pounds.

The sum is 46 lb 4 oz

WARM-UP

5. Add or subtract as indicated.

(a) 19.2 lb + 23.9 lb

(b) 123 ft − 72.7 ft

6. Perform the indicated operations.

(a) 8 min 43 sec + 3 min 12 sec + 7 min + 25 sec

(b) 4 yd 1 ft 10 in
– 2 yds 2 ft 11 in

Answers:

5. (a) 43.1 lb **(b)** 50.3 ft

6. (a) 19 min 20 sec **(b)** 1 yd 1 ft 11 in

(b)

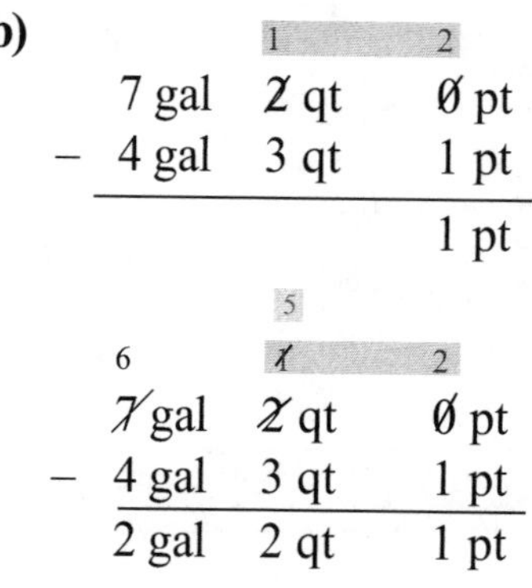

		1	2
	7 gal	~~2~~ qt	~~0~~ pt
–	4 gal	3 qt	1 pt
			1 pt

- Write in columns, lining up the place value and units.
- Subtract pints (pt). Since 1 pt cannot be subtracted from 0 pt, regroup 1 qt from the 2 qt and use 1 qt = 2 pt.

	6	5 ~~1~~	2
	~~7~~ gal	~~2~~ qt	~~0~~ pt
–	4 gal	3 qt	1 pt
	2 gal	2 qt	1 pt

- 3 qt cannot be subtracted from the remaining 1 qt, so regroup 1 gal (=4 qt) from the 7 gal and add it to the 1 qt.

The difference is 2 gal 2 qt 1 pt.

- Subtract gallons.

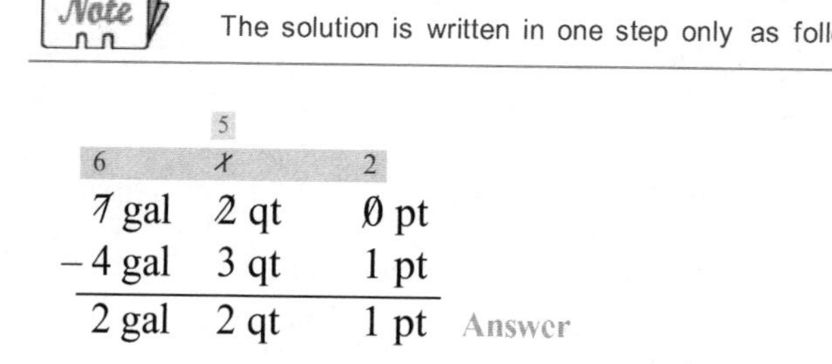

Note In practice, do not write the solution in steps as shown above. The solution is written in one step only as follows.

	6	5 ~~1~~	2	
	~~7~~ gal	~~2~~ qt	~~0~~ pt	
–	4 gal	3 qt	1 pt	
	2 gal	2 qt	1 pt	Answer

Note Although the word weight is commonly used in place of mass because the English unit pound refers to both weight and mass, the metric unit kilogram is only used for mass. However, mass is commonly and incorrectly used for weight.

Solution to the Application:

Laura buys three pieces of rope measuring 5 ft 4 in, 7 ft 9 in, and 10 ft 6 in. What is the total length of all the pieces she bought? If she cuts and uses a length measuring 8 ft 9 in from the piece measuring 10 ft 6 in, what is the total measure of the remaining lengths of rope?

To find the total length of all the pieces of rope bought, add the lengths of the three pieces.

	5 ft	4 in
	7 ft	9 in
+	10 ft	6 in
	22 ft	19 in

- Write measurements of the three pieces in columns lining up the place-values and the units.
- Add in columns.

= (22 ft) + (1 ft + 7 in)
= 23 ft 7 in

- Since 19 in is more than 1 ft (1 ft = 12 in), split up 19 in into 1 ft and 7 in.

The total length of all the three pieces of rope bought is 23 ft 7 in.

Laura uses a length measuring 8 ft 9 in. To find the measure of the remaining lengths of rope, subtract 8 ft 9 in from the total length.

22	19
~~23~~ ft	~~7~~ in
– 8 ft	9 in
14 ft	10 in

- Subtract inches. Since 9 cannot be subtracted from 7 in, regroup 1 ft (=12 in) from 23 ft, and add it to 7 in to get 19 in.
- Subtract 8 ft from the remaining 22 ft.

The length of the remaining rope is 14 ft 10 in.

C. Converting Units in the English System

Application

Mr. Lemandowski measured the perimeter of an office for baseboard. The perimeter was 55 ft. If baseboard comes in 1-yd sections, how many sections are needed?

Discussion

- 12 inches and 1 foot are equivalent measurements:

  $$12 \text{ inches} = 1 \text{ foot}$$

  This equation shows that the ratio of 12 inches to 1 foot, or 1 foot to 12 inches is 1,

  $$\frac{12 \text{ inches}}{1 \text{ foot}} = \frac{1 \text{ foot}}{1 \text{ foot}} = 1 \quad \text{and} \quad \frac{1 \text{ foot}}{12 \text{ inches}} = \frac{12 \text{ inches}}{12 \text{ inches}} = 1$$

  The ratio $\frac{12 \text{ inches}}{1 \text{ foot}}$ along with the property of 1 is used to convert a measurement in feet to a measurement in inches. Similarly, the ratio $\frac{1 \text{ foot}}{12 \text{ inches}}$ along with the property of 1 is used to convert a measurement in inches to a measurement in feet. These ratios $\frac{12 \text{ inches}}{1 \text{ foot}}$ or $\frac{1 \text{ foot}}{12 \text{ inches}}$ are referred to as **conversion ratios.**

  For example, to convert 5 feet to inches, use the conversion unit $\frac{12 \text{ inches}}{1 \text{ foot}}$.

  $$5 \text{ feet} = (5 \text{ feet}) \cdot 1$$

  Multiply by 1.

  $$= \frac{5 \cancel{\text{feet}}}{1} \cdot \frac{12 \text{ inches}}{1 \cancel{\text{foot}}}$$

  Substitute $\frac{12 \text{ inches}}{1 \text{ foot}}$ for 1. Divide out the common unit as a common factor. Simplify.

  $$= (5 \cdot 12) \text{ inches} = 60 \text{ inches.}$$

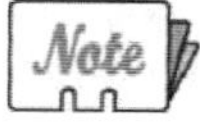

Although there are two conversion ratios to choose from when comparing inches and feet, it is clear when the appropriate ratio has been chosen because the units that we are trying to eliminate, cancel from the numerator and denominator.

- The above discussion was about length, but it would apply to any other types of measurement.
- In some cases, it may be necessary to multiply by several different conversion ratios. For example, convert 96 pints to gallons using conversion units.

$$96 \text{ pints} = (96 \text{ pints}) \cdot 1 \cdot 1$$

$$= \frac{96 \text{ pints}}{1} \cdot \frac{1 \text{ quart}}{2 \text{ pints}} \cdot \frac{1 \text{ gallon}}{4 \text{ quarts}}$$

Use the equivalent measure relations: 2 pints = 1 quart, 4 quarts = 1 gallon.

$$= \frac{96}{8} \text{ gallons.}$$

Divide out the common units from the numerator and the denominator.

$$= 12 \text{ gallons.}$$

Simplify.

Thus, in converting units in the same system, the units of measure are treated like factors. They are cancelled out before multiplying or dividing the numbers. Table 8.1 and 8.2 provided in section 8.1 will prove to be useful in making conversions of units.

Procedure to convert the units of a measurement in the English system.

***Step* 1** Multiply the given measurement by the appropriate conversion ratio(s).

***Step* 2** Cancel the common units.

***Step* 3** Simplify.

EXAMPLE 7 Convert the units of measurement

(a) 7 pounds to ounces. **(b)** 27456 feet to miles.

(c) 3 days to minutes.

Solutions

(a)

$$7 \text{ pounds} = 7 \text{ lb} = (7 \text{ lb}) \cdot 1$$

- Multiply by 1.

$$= \frac{7 \text{ lb}}{1} \cdot \frac{16 \text{ oz}}{1 \text{ lb}}$$

- 1 lb = 16 oz, $1 = \frac{16 \text{ oz}}{1 \text{ lb}}$.

$$= 112 \text{ oz}$$

- Cancel lb from the numerator and the denominator and simplify.

So, 7 pounds is equivalent to 112 ounces.

(b)

$$27456 \text{ ft} = (27456 \text{ ft}) \cdot 1$$

- Multiply by 1.

$$= \frac{27456 \text{ ft}}{1} \cdot \frac{1 \text{ mi}}{5280 \text{ ft}}$$

- Replace 1 by $\frac{1 \text{ mi}}{5280 \text{ ft}}$, since 5280 ft = 1 mi and cancel the common units

$$= \frac{27456}{5280} \text{ mi}$$

- Simplify.

$$= 5.2 \text{ mi.}$$

27456 ft is equal to 5.2 miles.

WARM-UP

7. Convert the units of measurement.

(a) 15 yards to feet

(b) 800 pounds to tons

(c) $3 \text{ days} = (3 \text{ days}) \cdot 1 \cdot 1$

For days to hours.

For hours to minutes.

$$= \frac{3 \text{ days}}{1} \cdot \frac{24 \text{ hr}}{1 \text{ day}} \cdot \frac{60 \text{ min}}{1 \text{ hr.}}$$

Since 24 hr = 1 day, and 60 min = 1 hr.

$$= (3 \cdot 24 \cdot 60) \text{ min}$$

$$= 4320 \text{ min.}$$

3 days are equal to 4320 minutes.

(c) 3 miles to yards.

EXAMPLE 8 Convert the units of measurement as indicated.

(a) 72 ft^2 to yd^2 (b) $\frac{\$36}{\text{ft}^2} = \frac{? \text{ cents}}{\text{in}^2}$

Solution

(a) Recall that the exponent 2 means to use the base as a factor twice, so

$$72 \text{ ft}^2 = 72 \text{ ft}^2 \cdot 1 = 72 \text{ ft}^2 \left(\frac{1 \text{yd}}{3 \text{ft}}\right)^2$$

$$= \frac{72 \text{ft}^2}{1} \cdot \frac{1 \text{yd}^2}{9 \text{ft}^2}$$

$$= \frac{72}{9} \text{yd}^2 = 8 \text{yd}^2$$

(b) First convert 36 dollars to cents, and next convert 1 ft^2 to 1 in^2.

$$\frac{\$36}{1 \text{ ft}^2} = \frac{\$36}{1 \text{ ft}^2} \cdot 1$$

$$= \frac{\$36}{1 \text{ ft}^2} \cdot \frac{100¢}{\$1} = \frac{3600¢}{1 \text{ft}^2}$$

$$= \frac{3600¢}{1 \text{ft}^2} \left(\frac{1 \text{ ft}}{12 \text{in}}\right)^2$$

Use 1 ft = 12 in.

$$= \frac{3600¢}{1 \text{ft}^2} \left(\frac{1 \text{ft}^2}{144 \text{in}^2}\right)$$

$$= 25 ¢/\text{in}^2$$

8. Convert as indicated.

(a) 432 in^2 to ft^2.

(b) $\frac{81 \text{ lb}}{\text{ft}^2} = \frac{? \text{ oz}}{\text{in}^2}$

Answers:

7. (a) 45 ft (b) .4 tons (c) 5280 yds.

8. (a) 3 ft^2 (b) $\frac{9 \text{oz}}{\text{in}^2}$

Solution to the Application:

Mr. Lemandowski measured the perimeter of an office for baseboard. The perimeter was 55 ft. If baseboard comes in 1-yd sections, how many sections are needed?

Solution: To find the number of sections needed, convert 55 ft to yards.

$$55 \text{ ft} = 55 \text{ ft} \times 1 = 55\text{ft} \times \left(\frac{1\,\text{yd}}{3\,\text{ft}}\right) = \frac{55}{3}\text{yd} = 18\frac{1}{3}\text{yd}$$

Therefore, $18\frac{1}{3}$ pieces are needed. Since part of a piece is not sold, Mr. Lemandowski will need to purchase 19 pieces.

D. Converting Units in the Metric System

Application

Nurse Maria sees that the doctor has ordered 0.9 g of Tetracyn for his patient. If the available capsules contain 150 mg of Tetracyn, how many capsules will she write on the prescription?

Discussion

- The procedure explained in objective 10.2 A can be used for converting units of measurement in any system of measurement. For equivalent measurements in the metric system, we can use Table 10.2.

  For example, convert 5 km to meters (m):

$$\begin{aligned} 5 \text{ km} &= (5 \text{ km}) \cdot 1 && \text{From km to meter.} \\ &= \frac{5 \cancel{\text{km}}}{1} \cdot \frac{1000 \text{ m}}{1 \cancel{\text{km}}} && 1 \text{ km} = 1000 \text{ m} \\ &= 5000 \text{ m.} \end{aligned}$$

  Observe that to change km to m, the number representing the magnitude of measurement in km (in this case, 5) is multiplied by 10^3.

- As another example, let us convert 7000 millimeter (mm) to dekameter (dam):

$$7000 \text{ mm} = (7000 \text{ mm}) \cdot 1 \cdot 1 \cdot 1 \cdot 1$$

  For mm to centimeter (cm). For cm to decimeter (dm). For dm to meter (m). For m to dam.

$$\begin{aligned} &= \frac{7000 \cancel{\text{mm}}}{1} \cdot \frac{1 \cancel{\text{cm}}}{10 \cancel{\text{mm}}} \cdot \frac{1 \cancel{\text{dm}}}{10 \cancel{\text{cm}}} \cdot \frac{1 \cancel{\text{m}}}{10 \cancel{\text{dm}}} \cdot \frac{1 \text{ dam}}{10 \cancel{\text{m}}} \\ &= 7000 \left(\frac{1}{10^4}\right) \text{dam} \\ &= 0.7 \text{ dam.} \end{aligned}$$

  1 cm = 10 mm; 1 dm = 10 cm; 1 m = 10 dm; 1 dam = 10m.

Changing millimeter to dekameter is equivalent to dividing the number 7000 (the magnitude of the given measurement) by 10^4.

- Conversions within the metric system involve multiplying or dividing by powers of 10 (moving the decimal point).

  Studying Table 8.2 carefully shows that the metric system of measurement is very similar to our base-ten place value system of numbers. Each unit of measure is *named* by using a prefix (generally called a "metric prefix") together with the basic unit, and can be obtained by multiplying or dividing the basic unit by powers of ten. Look at the common metric prefixes; they tell how each unit of measure relates to the basic unit:

Kilo means 1,000	**Deci** means $\frac{1}{10}$
Hecto means 100	**Centi** means $\frac{1}{100}$
Deka means 10	**Milli** means $\frac{1}{1000}$

- To convert measurements from one unit to another, identify the metric prefixes, and their relative positions with respect to one another. Figure 10.4 shows the relation of the metric units for length.

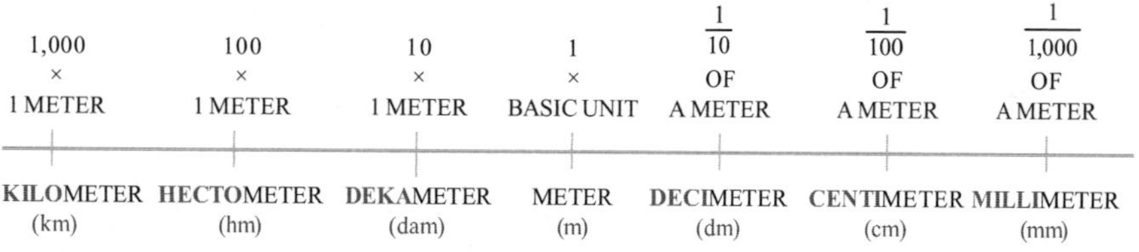

Figure 10.4

With the help of this figure, conversions of units become relatively easy and fast. To illustrate how to use this figure simply reconsider the examples discussed above.

- Look at Figure 10.5 to convert 3 kilometers to meters.

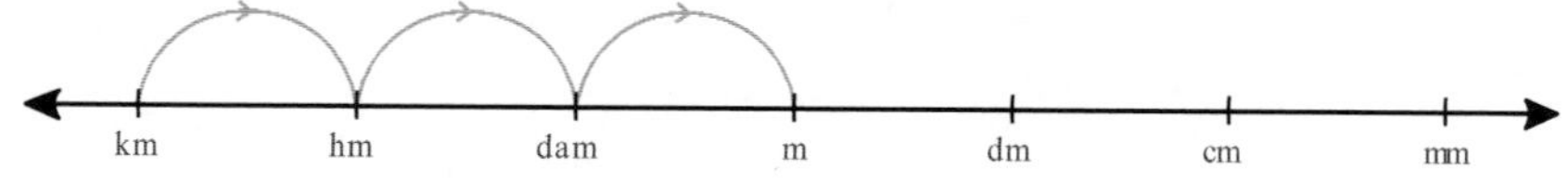

Figure 10.5

Meter is 3 places to the *right* of kilometer. To change kilometers to meters, move the decimal point three places to the *right*, or multiply by 10^3.

Therefore, 3 km = 3.000 km = 3000 m or 3 km = 3×10^3 m = 3000 *m*

Also, to convert 4000 millimeters to decameters look at Figure 10.6.

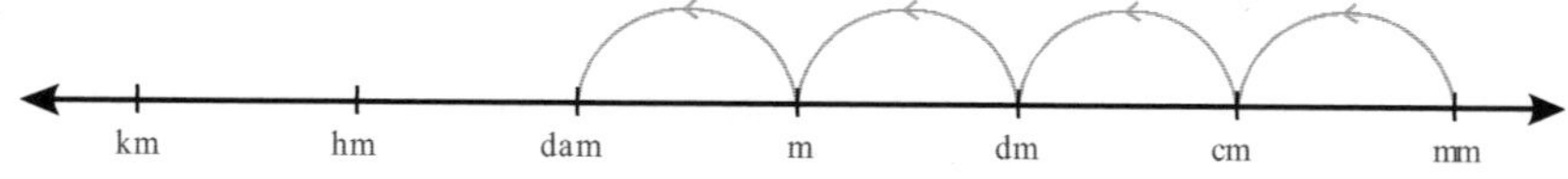

Figure 10.6

From the figure, there are 4 places to the *left* from millimeter to decameter. To change millimeter to decameter, move the decimal point 4 places to left. 4000.0 mm = .4000. dam = .4 dam

4000 mm = 0.4 dam.

- Although the above discussion is concerned only with length, it also applies to any other basic measurements in the metric system.
- Figures 10.7 and 10.8 below are similar to Figure 8.4, and show the relation of the metric units for weight and volume (or capacity).

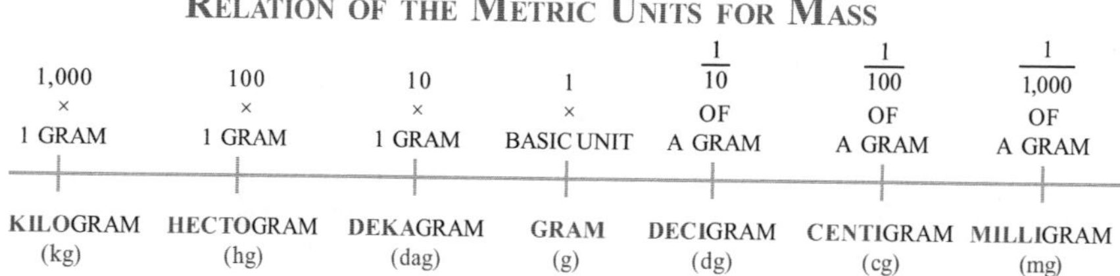

Figure 10.7

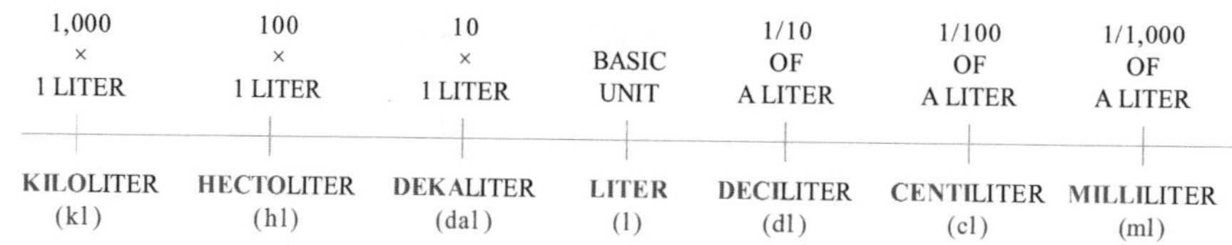

Figure 10.8

Procedure to Convert from one metric unit of measure to another metric unit.

***Step* 1** Write the number in the given measurement as a decimal number.

***Step* 2** Draw or visualize a line showing the positions of the metric prefixes.

***Step* 3** Move the decimal point the same number of places and in the same direction as you do from the original prefix to the new one.

WARM-UP

9. Convert the units of measurement.

(a) 0.087 kg to g.

EXAMPLE 9 Convert the units of measurement.

(a) 7.3 liters to millimeters (ml).

(b) 6500 centigrams (cg) to dekagrams (dag).

Solution

(a) 7.3 liters = 7.3 *l* — *Step* 1 Not needed.

= 7.3 0 0 ml — *Step* 2 (dal, *l*, dl, cl, ml)

= 7300. ml — *Step* 3 Move the decimal point to the right through 3 place.

So, 7.3 liters = 7300 ml.

(b) 6500 cg = 6500. cg   *Step 1* Write 6500 = 6500.

= 6 5 0 0. dag   *Step 2* Kilo hecto deka (g) deci centi milli

= 6.5 dag   *Step 3* Move the decimal point to the left through 3 place.

So, 6500 centigrams = 6.5 dekagrams.

WARM-UP

(b) 32 centiliters to dekaliters.

EXAMPLE 10 Convert:

(a) 18.7 meter per liter to kilometer per centiliter

(b) 2750 cm^2 to m^2.

Solution

(a) 18.7 meter per liter $= \dfrac{18.7 \text{ m}}{1 l}$ 18.7 m = 0.0 1 8 . 7 km and 1. l = 1 0 0 . cl

$= \dfrac{0.0187 \text{ km}}{100 \text{ cl}}$ $\dfrac{0.018}{100} = 0.00018$

$= \dfrac{0.000187 \text{ km}}{\text{cl}} = \dfrac{0.0187}{100} = 0.000187$

= 0.000187 km per centiliter.

(b) $2750 \text{ cm}^2 = 2750\ (1 \text{ cm})^2$

$= 2750\ (0.01 \text{ m})^2$

$= 2750\ (0.0001 \text{ m}^2)$

$= 0.275 \text{ m}^2$

10. Convert:

(a) 480 grams per liter to milligram per kiloliter.

(b) 2.5 m^2 to cm^2.

Answers:

9. **(a)** 87 g **(b)** 0.032 dal

10. **(a)** 480,000,000 mg/kl **(b)** 25,000 cm^2

Solution to the Application:

Nurse Maria sees that the doctor has ordered 0.9 g of Tetracyn for his patient. If the available capsules contain 150 mg of Tetracyn, how many capsules will she write on the prescription?

Solution: The dose prescribed is in grams whereas the quantity of tetracyn per capsule is in milligrams. To find the total number of capsules required, divide the dose prescribed by the quantity per capsule.

Number of capsules $= \dfrac{0.9 \text{ g}}{150 \text{ mg}}$ To cancel out the factors of units, change 0.9 grams to milligrams by shifting the decimal point to the right 3 places, as

$= \dfrac{900 \text{ mg}}{150 \text{ mg}}$ g ⟶ dg ⟶ cg ⟶ mg, means 3 places. Divide out the common units and simplify.

$= \dfrac{900}{150} = 6.$

The nurse will write 6 capsules on the prescription.

(E.) Converting Units Between the English and Metric System

➡ **Converting units of measure from English to Metric and Metric to English**

Application

An Australian runner has recently run 1500 m in 3 min 43 sec. Find his average rate in miles per hour. Round the answer to the nearest mile per hour.

Discussion

- Conversion of units from one system to another can be done in the same manner as it is done within the same system, provided the conversion relationship between the basic units in the two systems is known. This discussion covers some conversions between the English and Metric systems. Table 10.4 facilitates conversion from English units to Metric units, while Table 10.5 can be used for conversion from Metric units to English units.

	Table 10.4 English-Metric Conversions		Table 10.5 Metric-English Conversions
Length	1 inch = 2.54 centimeters		1 centimeter = 0.3937 inch
	1 foot = 0.3048 meter		1 meter = 3.281 feet
	1 yard = 0.9144 meter		1 meter = 1.094 yards
	1 mile = 1.609 kilometers		1 kilometer = 0.6214 mile
Mass	1 ounce = 28.35 grams		1 gram = 0.0353 ounce
	1 pound = 453.59 grams		1 gram = 0.0022 pound
Liquid	1 quart = 0.946 liter		1 liter = 1.057 quarts
Volume	1 gallon = 3.785 liters		1 liter = 0.2642 gallon

Use the conversion unit $\frac{1 \text{ in}}{2.54 \text{ cm}}$.

$$5 \text{ cm} = \frac{5 \cancel{\text{cm}}}{1} \cdot \frac{\mathbf{1\ in}}{\mathbf{2.54\ \cancel{cm}}}$$

- "Multiply by 1" in the form $\frac{1 \text{in}}{2.54 \text{ cm}}$.

$$= \left(\frac{5}{2.54}\right) \text{in} \approx 1.9685 \text{ in}$$

- Quite often, it is necessary to use more than one conversion units. For example, to convert 2,450 inches to meters, proceed as follows.

$$2450 \text{ in} = \frac{2450 \text{ in}}{1} \cdot 1 \cdot 1$$

For converting in to cm. (first 1)

For converting cm to m. (second 1)

$$= \frac{2450 \cancel{\text{in}}}{1} \cdot \frac{\mathbf{2.54\ \cancel{cm}}}{\mathbf{1\ \cancel{in}}} \cdot \frac{1 \text{ m}}{100 \cancel{\text{cm}}}$$

1 in = 2.54 cm.
1 m = 100 cm.

$$= \frac{2450\,(2.54)}{100}\text{ m} \quad = \quad 62.23\text{ m}$$

2450 in ≈ 62.23 m.

- Conversions of measurements for weights and volumes can be done in a similar way.
- It should be noted that converting units from one system to another, gives approximate measurements. This is because the systems were developed independently; there are no exact comparisons. The conversion relations in Tables 10.4 and 10.5 are approximate.

Remark: Results in the examples and exercises are rounded to two decimal places, unless otherwise specified.

Procedure to make conversions between the English and Metric systems.

***Step* 1** Multiply the given unit(s) of measure by appropriate conversion ratios using information in tables 10.4 or 10.5.

***Step* 2** Simplify.

EXAMPLE 11 Convert the units of measurement as indicated.

(a) 25 quarts to liters **(b)** 3 kiloliter to gallons.

Solutions

(a) $25\text{ quarts} = \frac{25\,\cancel{\text{quarts}}}{l} \cdot \frac{1\,l}{1.057\,\cancel{\text{quarts}}}$

- Multiply by conversion unit. $\frac{1\,l}{1.057\text{ qt}}$ 1 *l* = 1.057 qt.

$= \frac{25}{1.057}\,l \approx 23.651844\,l$

- Simplify.

25 quarts ≈ 23.65 liters

(b) $3\text{ kiloliters} = 3\text{ kl} \cdot 1 \cdot 1$

For kl to *l*; For *l* to gal

Use: 1 kl = 1000 *l*, and 1 *l* ≈ 0.2642 gal.

$\approx \frac{3\,\cancel{\text{kl}}}{1} \cdot \frac{1000\,\cancel{l}}{1\,\cancel{\text{kl}}} \cdot \frac{0.2642\text{ gal}}{1\,\cancel{l}}$

$= 3(1000)\,(0.2642)\text{ gal} = 792.6\text{ gal}$

3 kiloliters = 792.6 gal

EXAMPLE 12 Convert 35 centigrams per centimeter to ounces per inch.

Solution

35 centigrams per centimeter

WARM-UP

11. Convert the units of measurement as indicated.

(a) 79 inches to centimeters.

(b) 3 kilograms to pounds.

12. Convert 55 pounds per foot to grams per meter.

$$= \frac{35\text{ cg}}{1\text{ cm}} \cdot 1 \cdot 1 \cdot 1$$

For cg to g.
For g to oz.
For cm to in.

$$\approx \frac{35\text{ cg}}{1\text{ cm}} \cdot \frac{1\text{ g}}{100\text{ cg}} \cdot \frac{0.0353\text{ oz}}{1\text{ g}} \cdot \frac{1\text{ cm}}{0.3937\text{ in}}$$

Use 1 g = 100 cg; 1 g ≈ 0.0353 oz; and 1 cm ≈ 0.3937 in for conversion factors.

$$= \frac{35\,(0.0353)\text{ oz}}{100\,(0.3937)\text{ in}} \approx \frac{0.0313817\text{ oz}}{1\text{ in}}$$

Simplify.

35 centigrams per centimeter ≈ 0.03 ounces per inch.

13. Convert

(a) 475 cm^2 to square inches.

(b) 8.3 lb/ft^2 to g per cm^2

EXAMPLE 13 Convert:

(a) 378 square inches to square meters.

(b) 12 g/cm^2 to pounds per square foot.

Solution

(a) $378\text{ in}^2 = (378\text{ in}^2) \cdot 1 \cdot 1$

For in^2 to cm^2.
For cm^2 to m^2.

$$\approx \frac{378\text{ in}^2}{1} \cdot \frac{(2.54)^2\text{ cm}^2}{1\text{ in}^2} \cdot \frac{1\text{ m}^2}{(100)^2\text{ cm}^2}$$

Since 1 in ≈ 2.54 cm, therefore $1\text{ in}^2 \approx (2.54\text{ cm})(2.54\text{ cm}) = (2.54)^2\text{cm}^2$, *etc.*

$$= \frac{378\,(2.54)^2}{(100)^2}\text{ m}^2$$

Group the numbers and simplify - use a calculator.

$$= \frac{378\,(6.4516)}{10000}\text{ m}^2 \approx 0.2438704\text{ m}^2$$

378 square inches is approximately 0.24 square meters.

(b) $$\frac{12\text{ g}}{\text{cm}^2} = \frac{12\text{ g}}{\text{cm}^2} \cdot \frac{0.0022\text{ lb}}{1\text{ g}} \cdot \frac{(2.54)^2\text{ cm}^2}{1\text{ in}^2} \cdot \frac{(12)^2\text{ in}^2}{1\text{ ft}^2}$$

$$= \frac{12\,(0.0022)\,(6.4516)\,(144)\text{ lb}}{1\text{ ft}^2}$$

Use 1 g = 0.0022 lb; 1 in ≈ 2.54 cm; and 1 ft = 12 in.

$$= \frac{24.526402\text{ lb}}{1\text{ ft}^2} \approx 24.53\text{ lb/ft}^2$$

12 g/cm^2 is approximately equal to 24.53 lb/ft^2.

Answers:

11. (a) 200.66 cm (b) 6.6 lb

12. 81830.54 g/m

13. (a) 73.62 in^2 (b) $4.05\ \frac{g}{cm^2}$

Solution to the Application:

An Australian runner has recently run 1500 m in 3 min 43 sec. Find his average rate in miles per hour. Round the answer to the nearest mile per hour.

Since the runner has run 1500 m in 3 min 43 sec,

his average rate is $\dfrac{1500 \text{ m}}{3 \text{ min } 43 \text{ sec}}$

$= \dfrac{1500 \text{ m}}{223 \text{ sec}}$

Change $\dfrac{1500 \text{ m}}{223 \text{ sec}}$ to miles per hour.

$$\frac{1500 \text{ m}}{223 \text{ sec}} = \frac{1500 \cancel{\text{m}}}{223 \cancel{\text{sec}}} \cdot \frac{3.281 \cancel{\text{ft}}}{1 \cancel{\text{m}}} \cdot \frac{1 \text{ mi}}{5280 \cancel{\text{ft}}} \cdot \frac{60 \cancel{\text{sec}}}{1 \cancel{\text{min}}} \cdot \frac{60 \cancel{\text{min}}}{1 \text{ hr}}$$ Multiply by the conversion factors.

$$= \frac{1500\,(3.281)\,(60)\,(60) \text{ mi}}{223\,(5280) \text{ hr}}$$ Simplify.

$$\approx 15.04739 \text{ mi per hr.}$$

The average rate of the runner is approximately 15 miles per hour.

F. Estimating Measurements in the Metric System

➡ Estimating measurements of common objects in the Metric system

Application

If a person using the metric system says his height is 1.72, what unit can you assume he left out?

Discussion

As observed in Section 10.2, the Metric system is very similar to our base-ten place-value system of numbers. This is why all but two countries in the world use the Metric system as their official system of measurement. We need to understand it and be able to "think metric". The objective of this section is to think metric rather than make conversions between the English and Metric systems.

- **Estimating lengths, distances or heights**

1. To measure **very small lengths**, use millimeter (mm) or centimeter (cm). For example,

Rainfall on a particular day in a city : 8 mm

Length of a pencil : 12 cm

Height of a doll : 25 cm

2. To measure **common life-size objects**, use meters (m).
For example,
The height of a horse is about 1.3 m.
The height of a telephone pole is about 25 m.
The height of a person is about 1.9 m.

3. To measure **large lengths and long distances**, use kilometers (km). For example,
The distance travelled by a motorist in one hour may be 56 km.
The distance between two cities may be 75 km.

- **Estimating masses:** Normally, the mass of an object or quantity is measured in kilograms or grams. To express mass of various components in pharmaceutical formulations, use milligrams (mg).

  A patient takes three 0.25 mg tablets of reserpine.
  The mass of a candy bar is 40 g.
  The average mass of a newborn baby is 3.8 kg.
  The mass of a medium sized bag of wheat is 298 kg.

- **Estimating Volumes (quantities of liquids and capacities of containers):** Measure the quantity of liquids and the capacity of containers in liters and milliliters. Generally, water, milk, oil, gasoline, *etc.* are measured in liters, while dosages of medication are measured in milliliters

WARM-UP

14. Fill in the blanks with suitable Metric System.
   (a) A bucket can hold about 8 _____ of water.
   (b) The weight of one bag of wheat flour is about 25 ____.
   (c) Your height is about 165 ____.
   (d) A family consumes about 30 ____ of wheat and 2 ____ of sugar every month.
   (e) A 7 month old child drinks about 1 ____ of milk everyday.

Answers:

14. (a) Liter (*l*) (b) Kilogram (kg)
   (c) 165 cm
   (d) 30 kg of wheat and 2 kg of sugar
   (e) Liter(*l*)

EXAMPLE 14 Fill in the blanks with suitable Metric units.

(a) A bucket can hold about 5 ________ of water.

(b) The mass of one bag of rice is about 25 ________.

(c) Your height is about 1 ________ 60 ________.

(d) A family consumes about 22 ________ of wheat and 900 ________ of sugar every month.

(e) A 7–month old child drinks about 450 ________ of milk everyday.

Solution

(a) Liters (*l*) — The commonly used units of volume are liter and milliliter. Milliliter is used for very small quantities.

(b) Kilograms (kg) — Mass is normally measured in kg or g. The weight of a bag of rice cannot be 25 g since it is too small for a bag. It would be measured in kg.

(c) 1 m 60 cm. — A person's height is usually measured in meters and centimeters.

(d) 22 kg of wheat and 900 g of sugar. — 22 g would be a very small measurement for wheat; a family cannot consume 900 kg of sugar in a month.

(e) milliliters (ml) — 450 liters would be a very large quantity.

Solution to the Application:

If a person using the Metric system says his height is 1.72, what unit can you assume he left out?

The commonly used units for length measurements are km, m, and cm.

1.72 km = 1720 meters is too large for the height of a person.

1.72 cm is very small measurement so it cannot represent the height of a person.

1.72 m may represent the height of a person.
The correct unit should be meters. A person may be 1.72 m tall.

EXERCISE 10.1

In exercises 1-10, multiply or divide the measurement by the number as indicated.

1. Multiply 27 ounces by 8 **2.** Multiply 32 meters by 5 **3.** Divide 486 lb by 54 **4.** Divide 42 g by 7

5. Multiply 35 cm by 6 **6.** Divide 17 miles by 5 **7.** Divide 15 gallon by 6 **8.** Divide 18.9 oz by 14

9. Multiply 4.25 kg by 16 **10.** Divide 35 liters by 8

In exercises 11-20, perform the indicated operation.

11. $\left(2\frac{3}{4}\right)$ (8g) **12.** (8.95 cg)(4) **13.** $(3.6 \text{ feet}) \div \left(3\frac{1}{3}\right)$ **14.** $(17.5 \text{ ounces}) \div \left(3\frac{1}{2}\right)$ **15.** (15.5 m)(6)

16. $(288 \text{ quarts}) \div 48$ **17.** $40 \text{ kg} \div \left(1\frac{1}{2}\right)$ **18.** (16.5 mg)(13) **19.** $3.44\ l \div 2.5$ **20.** $256 \text{ gallons} \div 8$

In exercises 21-30, add or subtract as indicated.

21. 54 m + 78 m + 12 m **22.** 3 g + 89 g + 32 g **23.** 38 kl + 21 kl + 43 kl

24. 96 cm − 48 cm **25.** 89 min − 48 min **26.** 56 lb − 29 lb

27. 104 ml − 52.6 ml **28.** 2.56 ounces + 9.3 ounces − 3.8 ounces

29. 190 yd − 63.7 yd + 24.5 yd − 78 yd **30.** 9.82 kg − 7.728 kg

In exercises 31-35 add the given measurements.

31.

3 ft	8 in
7 ft	4 in
20 ft	8 in
+ 12 ft	10 in

32.

6 hr	20 min
3 hr	10 min
+ 5 hr	15 min

33.

5 gal	3 qt	1 pt
+ 9 gal	1 qt	1 pt

34.

6 yd	2 ft	8 in
+ 10 yd		4 in

35.

23 lb	15 oz
+ 31 lb	8 oz

In exercises 36-40, subtract the given measurements.

36.
8 kg 235 g
2 kg 839 g

37.
18 kl 5 hl
– 6 kl 9 hl

38.
25 hr 37 min 9 sec
– 12 hr 43 min 20 sec

39.
14 ft 5 in
– 6 ft 9 in

40.
6 yd 1 ft 2 in
– 2 yd 2 ft 6 in

Applications

41. A boy weighed 73 lb, but lost 2.5 lb due to illness. Find his weight after the weight loss.

42. From a 75-yd roll of ribbon, Linda used three pieces of ribbon measuring 19 yd 2 ft, 20 yd 1 ft, and 28 yd 1 ft 6 in. Find the length of ribbon remaining in the roll.

43. The sides of a rectangle are 7 ft 7 inches, 5 ft 1 inch, 7 ft 7 inches and 5 ft 1 inch. Find the perimeter of this rectangle.

44. The weights of four laboratory samples were: 4.961 g, 5.006 g, 4.752 g, and 4.819 g. Find the average weight of these four samples.

In exercise 45-64, convert the units of measurement.

45. 84 inches = ___________ feet

46. 6 gallons = ___________ pints

47. 5 pounds = ___________ ounces

48. 27 feet = ___________ yards

49. 2.5 yards = ___________ inches

50. 112 ounces = ___________ pounds

51. 1 mile = ___________ inches

52. 7920 yards = ___________ miles

53. 9.65 tons = ___________ pounds

54. 30 miles = ___________ feet

55. 264 yards = ___________ mile

56. 2.7 gallons = ___________ pints

57. 3798 inches = ___________ feet

58. 540 hours = ___________ days

59. 75 teaspoons = ___________ tablespoons

60. 4.5 gallons = ___________ cups

61. 2 weeks = ___________ hours

62. 7 days = ___________ minutes

63. 18,828 seconds = ___________ hours

64. 82 feet = ___________ yards

In exercise 65-74, convert the units of measurement as indicated.

65. 88 feet per second to miles per hours.

66. 10 pounds per inch to pounds per foot.

67. $255 per hour to dollars per minute.

68. 8 ounces per inch to pounds per foot.

69. 3 quarts per minute to gallons per hour.

70. 14 ft^2 to in^2.

71. 45 dollars per ft^2 to cents per in^2.

72. 12 cents per in^2 to dollars per yd^2.

73. 25 pounds per ft^2 to tons per yd^2.

74. 8.1 pounds per yd^2 to pounds per ft^2.

In exercises 75-82, use the information given in Figure 10.9:

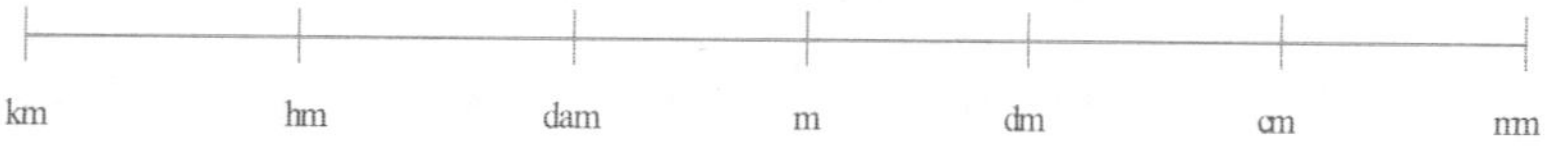

km hm dam m dm cm mm

Figure 10.9

75. 60 m = ____________ cm

76. 76.6 mm = ____________ m

77. 0.87 hm = ____________ dm

78. 27cm = ____________ dm

79. 3 mm = ____________ km

80. 1.50 m = ____________ km

81. 40 dm = ____________ mm

82. 5 mm = ____________ km

Fill in the blanks in Figure 10.10 with the units for metric mass and then use this information to complete exercises 84-91.

83.

kg ___ ___ ___ ___ ___ ___

Figure 10.10

84. 12 dag = ____________ cg

85. 8 g = ____________ cg

86. 6400 cg = ____________ hg

87. 232.4 dag = ____________ dg

88. 5 mg = ____________ kg

89. 0.4 g = ____________ mg

90. 42 dg = ____________ kg

91. 4.33 g = ____________ hg

Fill in the blanks in Figure 10.11 with the units for metric liquid measure and then use this information to complete exercises 93-101.

92.

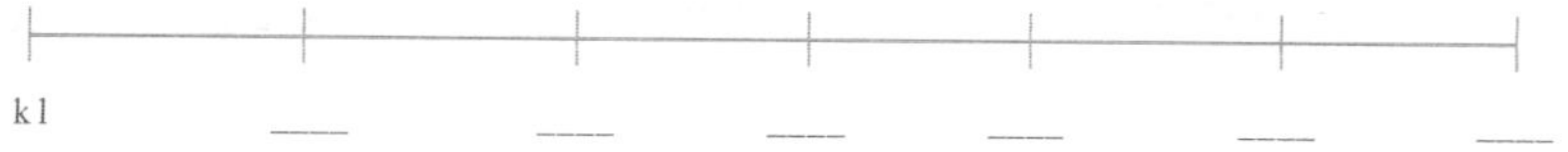

kl ___ ___ ___ ___ ___ ___

Figure 10.11

93. 204 *l* = ____________ hl

94. 15 ml = ____________ *l*

95. 0.06 kl = ____________ cl

96. 57 dl = ____________ ml

97. 0.0768 kl = ____________ *l*

98. 200 dal = ____________ dl

99. 7.61 = ____________ kl

100. 496,533 cl = ____________ hl

101. 4,385 cg = ____________ g

102. Convert 40 meters per second to kilometers per hour.

103. Convert 17 kilometers per liter to meter per milliliter.

104. Convert 24,000 kg per km^2 to gram per m^2.

Applications

105. The mass of one pineapple is 1 kg 800 g while another has a mass of 1850 g. Which one has more mass?

106. Maria walks at 3 km per hr while her brother walks 45 m per min. Who walks faster, Maria or her brother?

107. A physician prescribes a dose of 1.6 g of Steptomycine for his patient. If the drug is available in 100 mg tablets, how many tablets are needed for the prescribed dose?

108. Carpet is sold by the square foot. Lakeisha has measured her room and finds she needs 12 square yards of carpet. How many square feet does she need?

In exercises 109-128, convert the given measures as indicated.

109. 3,450 inches to meters.

110. 625 gallons to liters.

111. 5.64 kilometers to miles.

112. 6.76 kilometers to miles.

113. 5.62 feet to meters.

114. 3,760 ounces to pounds.

115. 378 inches to meters.

116. 0.064 kilometers to feet.

117. 3.15 miles to kilometers

118. 628 inches to centimeters.

119. 21.6 feet per second to centimeters per second.

120. 10.3 feet per second to centimeters per second.

121. 30 miles per hour to kilometer per hour.

122. 66 miles per hour to feet per second.

123. 1534 ounces to kilograms.

124. 3720 grams to pounds.

125. 180 miles per hour to kilometers per hour.

126. 62 kilometers per second to miles per hour.

127. The shipping mass of a radio set is 12 pounds. What is this in kilograms?

128. An imported transistor radio has dimensions 7cm × 5cm × 4.5cm. Find its dimensions in inches.

Applications

129. A patient is to take 15 ml of medication. How many 5-ml teaspoons should a nurse direct the patient to take to get the proper dosage?

130. A patient is to receive one pint of blood. How many milliliters of blood should be administered?

131. A quarter-inch wrench is to be used on a fitting. What size wrench does the fitting take in centimeters?

132. The rainiest spot on earth is Mount Waialeale, Hawaii, with an average annual rainfall of 11,648 millimeters (11648 mm / yr). How many inches per month is this?

133. The diameter of No. 10 wire is 0.102 inches. What is its radius in centimeters?

134. If 1000 cycles = 1 kilocycle, then 1,500 kilocycles per second equals how many cycles per minute?

In exercises 135-159, choose the best estimate for the measurement of the object named.

135. The length of a standard paper clip.

(a) 3.2 mm **(b)** 3.2 cm **(c)** 3.2 m **(d)** 3.2 km

136. The length of a yardstick.

(a) 5 m **(b)** 1 m **(c)** 10 cm **(d)** 1 km

137. The amount of liquid in a can of soda pop.

(a) 355 ml **(b)** 355 *l* **(c)** 355 kl

138. The amount of oil in a railroad tanker car.

(a) 43 *l* **(b)** 43 ml **(c)** 70 kl

139. The amount of liquid in a quart of milk.

(a) 4 *l* **(b)** 100 ml **(c)** .95 *l* **(d)** 4 ml

140. The amount of liquid in a bottle of wine.

(a) 1 *l* **(b)** 10 *l* **(c)** 3.8 *l* **(d)** 20.7 *l*

141. The height of a tree.

(a) 2.1 mm **(b)** 10 cm **(c)** 10 m **(d)** 10 km

142. The height of a standard house door.

(a) 2.1 mm **(b)** 2.1 cm **(c)** 2.1 m **(d)** 2.1 km

143. The height of an average man.

(a) 1.7 km **(b)** 1.7 mm **(c)** 1.7 cm **(d)** 1.7 m

144. The height of a three-floor building.

(a) 12 m **(b)** 5 m **(c)** 500 m **(d)** 50 cm

145. The distance from New York to California.

(a) 50 km **(b)** 4800 km **(c)** 5000 m **(d)** 5000 cm

146. The diameter of a dime.

(a) 1.7 cm **(b)** 1.7 m **(c)** 1.7 mm **(d)** 1.7 km

147. The mass of a package of six hot dogs.

(a) 300 mg **(b)** 300 g **(c)** 300 kg **(d)** 300 dag

148. The volume of a can of paint

(a) 4 ml **(b)** 4 *l* **(c)** 4 kl

149. The mass of a bird feather.

(a) 50 mg **(b)** 50 g **(c)** 50 kg

150. The altitude of a plane flying above ground.

(a) 10 mm **(b)** 10 cm **(c)** 10 m **(d)** 10 km

151. The volume of a small bottle of perfume.

(a) 7 ml **(b)** 7 *l* **(c)** 7 kl

152. The length of this page.

(a) 28 cm **(b)** 28 mm **(c)** 28 m **(d)** 3 cm

153. The diameter of a large pizza.

(a) 0.5 m **(b)** 20 cm **(c)** 15 m **(d)** 0.5 km

154. The amount of coffee in a 20-cup coffee pot.

(a) 200 ml **(b)** 1 *l* **(c)** 4.8 *l* **(d)** 16 *l*

155. The mass of a dinner steak.

(a) 4 kg **(b)** 14 kg **(c)** 16 mg **(d)** 280 g

156. The mass of a candy bar.

(a) 40 mg **(b)** 40 g **(c)** 4 g **(d)** 4 kg

157. One drop from an eye dropper.

(a) 0.2 ml **(b)** 200 ml **(c)** 2 *l* **(d)** 0.2 kl

158. The mass of horse.

(a) 100 mg **(b)** 500 g **(c)** 100 kg **(d)** 1000 kg

159. The capacity of a car gas tank.

(a) 70 ml **(b)** 200 *l* **(c)** 70 *l* **(d)** 1 kl

10.2 AREA AND PERIMETER

FINDING PERIMETERS

Perimeter

OBJECTIVES

After completing this section you will be able to:

A. Find the perimeter of a polygon;

B. Find the area of a rectangle and square; and

C. Find the area of a triangle, parallelogram, and trapezoid.

Discussion

The **perimeter** of a geometric figure is the length of the boundary or the *distance* along the boundary.

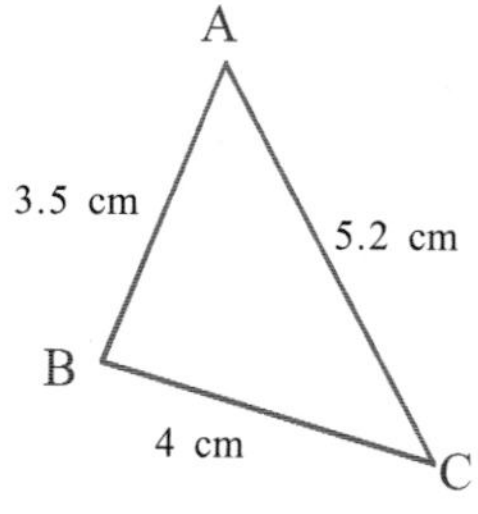

Figure 10.9

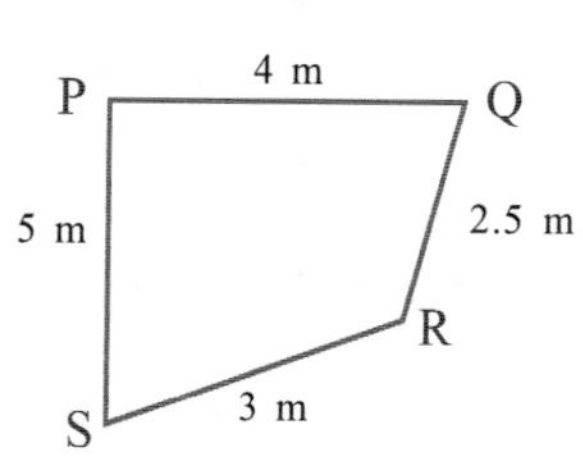

Figure 10.10

The perimeter of a polygon is the sum of the lengths of all its sides, and is generally denoted by the letter P. For example, the perimeter of a triangle whose sides measure 4 cm, 5.2 cm, and 3.5 cm (Figure 10.9) is

$$\begin{aligned} P &= 4 \text{ cm} + 5.2 \text{ cm} + 3.5 \text{ cm} \\ &= 12.7 \text{ cm}. \end{aligned}$$

The perimeter of the quadrilateral PQRS (Figure 10.10) is

$$\begin{aligned} P &= \text{PQ} + \text{QR} + \text{RS} + \text{SP} \\ &= 4 \text{ m} + 2.5 \text{ m} + 3 \text{ m} + 5 \text{ m} \\ &= 14.5 \text{ m} \end{aligned}$$

The lengths of the sides of a rectangle are generally called the **length** (symbol: l) and the **width** (symbol: w) of the rectangle. Thus, the perimeter of a rectangle is:

Perimeter of a rectangle = $2(l + w)$ or $2l + 2w$

In the case of a square, all the four sides are equal. If the length of each side of the square is a, then by the definition of perimeter:

Perimeter of a square = $a + a + a + a = 4a$

FINDING THE PERIMETER OF POLYGONS

EXAMPLE 1 Find the perimeter of the polygon in Figure 10.11.

Solution

$$\begin{aligned} P &= 9 \text{ m} + 9 \text{ m} + 9 \text{ m} + 8.2 \text{ m} + 8.2 \text{ m} \\ &= (9 + 9 + 9 + 8.2 + 8.2) \text{ m} \\ &= 43.4 \text{ m} \end{aligned}$$

8.2 m　8.2 m
9 m　9 m
9 m

Figure 10.11

WARM-UP

1. Find the perimeter of the following trapezoid:

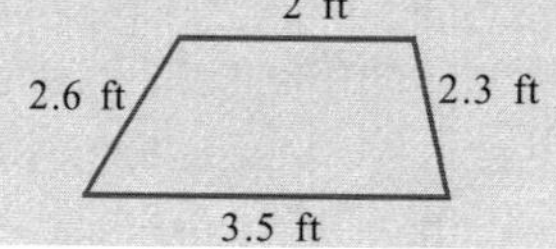

WARM-UP

2. Find the perimeter of a rectangle with 9 in and 6 in as two adjacent sides.

EXAMPLE 2 Find the perimeter of the rectangle with length 4 in and width 3 in.

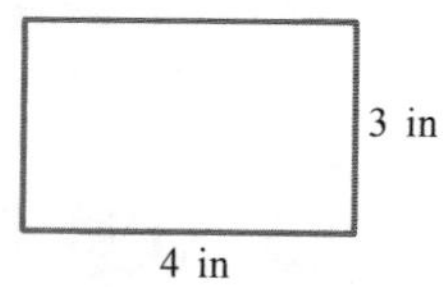

Figure 10.12

Solution

$$\text{Perimeter} = 2(4 \text{ in}) + 2(3 \text{ in}) = 8 \text{ in} + 6 \text{ in} = 14 \text{ in.}$$

$$\text{or Perimeter} = 2(l + w) = 2(4 \text{ in} + 3 \text{ in}) = 2 \cdot 7 \text{ in} = 14 \text{ in.}$$

3. Find the perimeter of a square with sides of length 12 cm.

EXAMPLE 3 Find the perimeter of a square whose side is 5 cm.

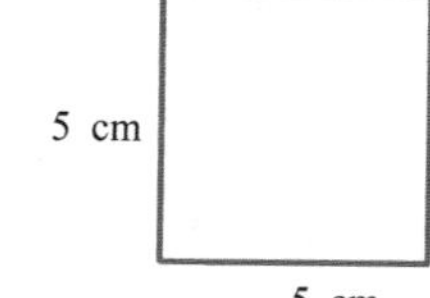

Figure 10.13

Solution

Note that Perimeter of a square

$$= 4\,(\text{length of its side}) = 4\,(5 \text{ cm}) = 20 \text{ cm}$$

4. Repeat example 4 for a playground which is 45 m long and 30 m wide.

EXAMPLE 4 A rectangular field is 130 m long and 80 m wide. Find the length of fencing needed to fence the field. Also find the cost of the fence if fencing sells for \$3.05 per meter.

Solution The length of wire needed to fence all around the field is the perimeter of the field.

$$P = 2(130 \text{ m}) + 2(80 \text{ m}) = 420 \text{ m.}$$

80m

130m

Figure 10.14

For the total cost:

The cost of 1 m of fencing is \$3.05

Therefore, the cost of 420 m of fencing = 420 × \$3.05 = \$1,281.00.

Answers:

1.	10.4 ft	2.	30 in
3.	48 cm	4.	150 m, \$457.50

B. FINDING AREAS OF RECTANGLES AND SQUARES

➡ **The area of a rectangle and a square.**

Discussion

- The **area** of a geometric figure is the measure of the region enclosed by the boundary of the figure. The measure of the perimeter cannot be used to find the area. For example, the rectangles in Figure 10.15 have the *same* perimeter (check), but they do not have the same area. The rectangles in Figure 10.16 have *unequal* perimeters (check), but they have the same area.

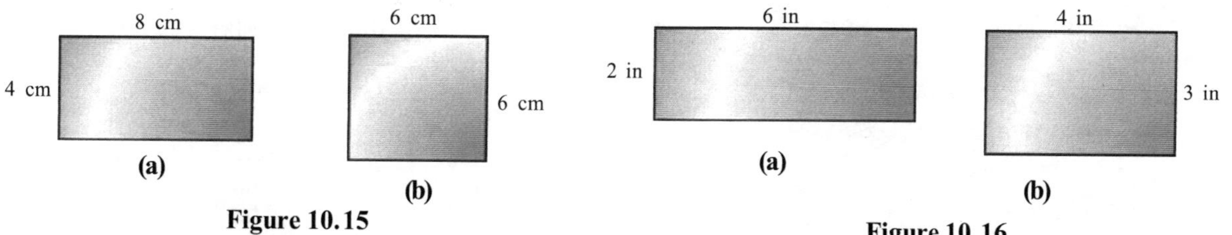

Figure 10.15

Figure 10.16

- **Unit of area:** To measure the area of a plane region, use square units. *The area of a region is the number of square units in the region.*

Consider the rectangular region that is 8 cm by 4 cm and complete the region with unit squares as in Figure 10.17. Observe that there are 32 square units .

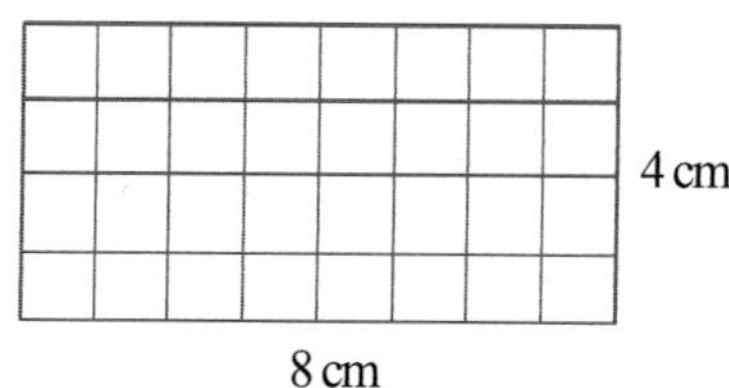

Figure 10.17

The number of square units $= 8 \times 4 = 32$

Area $= 32 \text{ cm}^2$

Area of a rectangle = length × width

Caution: To find the area of a plane surface using a formula, all of its dimensions should be expressed in the same units of measure.

The Area of a Rectangle or Square Region.

EXAMPLE 5 Find the area of a rectangle with length 3 ft and width 5 ft.

Solution

$$\begin{aligned} \text{Area} &= \text{length} \times \text{width} \\ &= 3 \text{ ft} \times 5 \text{ ft} \\ &= 15 \text{ ft} \times \text{ft} \\ &= 15 \text{ ft}^2 \end{aligned}$$

EXAMPLE 6 Find the area of a square with sides which measure 2.5 cm.

Solution

$$\begin{aligned} \text{Area} &= 2.5 \text{ cm} \times 2.5 \text{ cm} \\ &= 6.25 \text{ cm} \times \text{cm} \\ &= 6.25 \text{ cm}^2 \end{aligned}$$

Warm-Up

5. Find the area (in m^2) of a rectangle with length 4 m and width 95 cm (95 cm = 0.95 m).

6. Find the area of a square with sides of length 3.5 cm.

WARM-UP

7. Find the area of the region shown in the following figure.

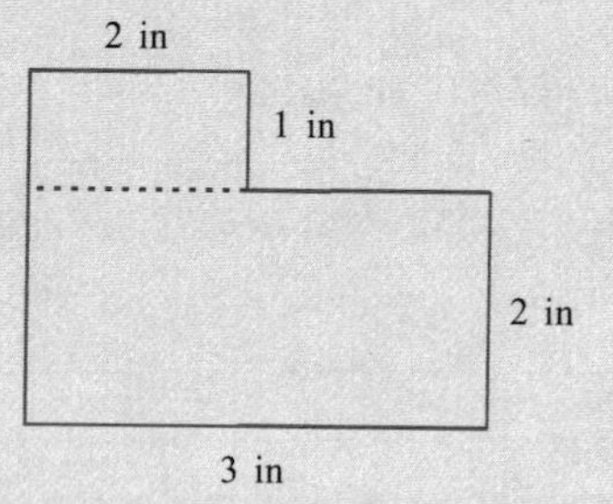

8. Find the cost of plowing a field with area 1170 m^2 at 70 cent per square meter. Also, find the cost of fencing it if the fencing material costs at $2.70 per meter, and the length of the field is 45 m.

Answers:

5. 3.8 m^2 6. 12.25 cm^2 7. 8 in^2
8. $819, $383.40

EXAMPLE 7 Find the area of the region shown in Figure 10.18.

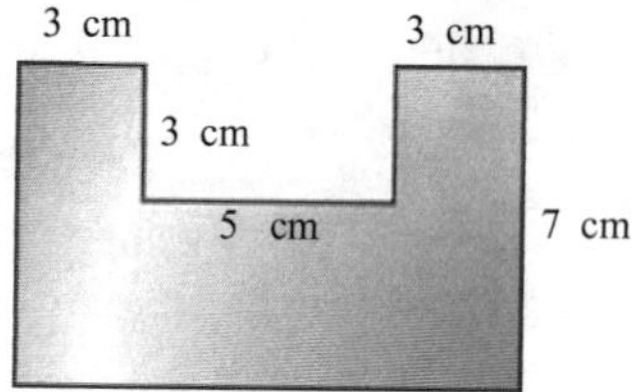

Figure 10.18

Solution

The given area is composed of rectangular and square regions as shown in Figure 10.19.

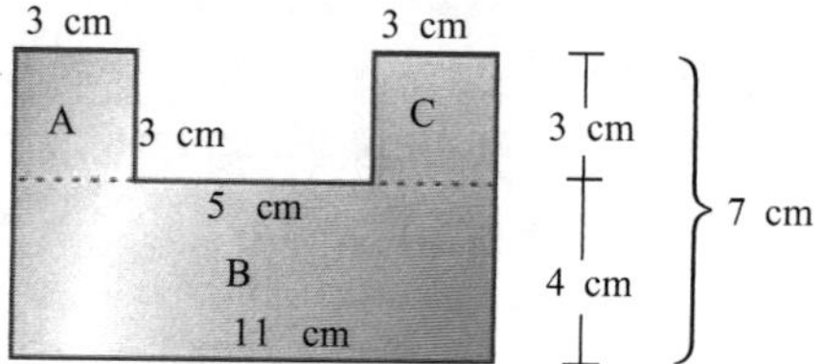

Figure 10.19

The total area = area of a square A + area of rectangle B + area of square C

$= (3 \text{ cm})(3 \text{ cm}) + (11 \text{ cm})(4 \text{ cm}) + (3 \text{ cm})(3 \text{ cm})$

$= 9 \text{ cm}^2 + 44 \text{ cm}^2 + 9 \text{ cm}^2$

$= 62 \text{ cm}^2$

EXAMPLE 8 Find the cost of levelling a 1560 yd^2 rectangular park at the rate of 50¢ per square yard. Also, find the cost to fence it if fencing costs $2.50 per yd, and the dimensions of the playground are 32 yd by 48.75 yd.

Solution **Cost of levelling:** 1 yd^2 = 50 cents, So the cost of levelling 1560 yd^2 is (1560) · 50¢ = 78000¢ = $780.00

Cost of fence:

The fence will be placed along the perimeter of the playground.

Perimeter = 2 (48.75 yd) + 2(32 yd)

= 161.5 yd

1 yd of fencing costs $2.50

Thus, the total cost of fencing is (161.5) ($2.50) = $403.75

The cost of fencing the playground is $403.75

C. FINDING AREAS OF TRIANGLES, PARALLELOGRAMS AND TRAPEZOIDS

➡ **Find the area of triangles, parallelograms, and trapezoids.**

Discussion

Formulae for the perimeter of polygons are not needed. It is only necessary to recall that the perimeter of a polygon can be found by adding the lengths of the sides. Formulae for the area of some polygons are listed in Table 10.6.

Table 10.6

Formulas for the Perimeter and Area of Some Polygons

Polygon	Area (A)
1. Triangle (sides a, b, c; height h)	(i) $A = \frac{1}{2} b h$ $= \frac{1}{2}$ (base)(height)
Right Triangle (sides a, b, c)	$A = \frac{1}{2} a b$
2. Square (side a)	$A = a^2$ $=$ (side)^2
3. Rectangle (sides l, w)	$A = l \times w$ $=$ (length) (width)
4. Parallelogram (sides a, b; height h)	$A = b \times h$ $=$ (base) (height)
5. Trapezoid (sides b, c, d; height h)	$A = \frac{1}{2}(b + d) h$ $=$ half the sum of the parallel sides multiplied by the distance between them.

WARM-UP

9. Find the area of each of the following triangles:

(a) 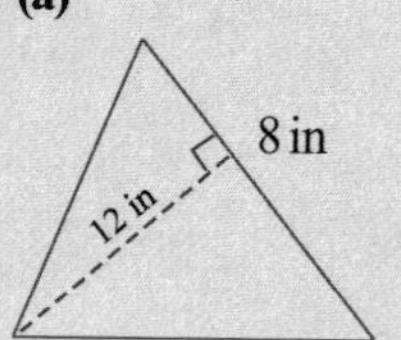

(b) 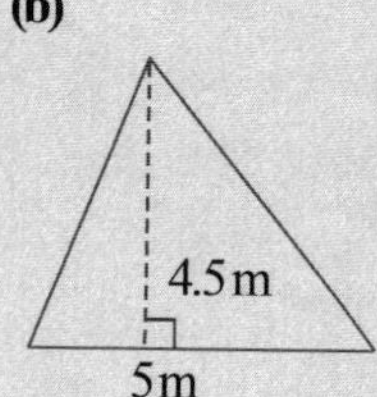

10. Find the area of the parallelogram.

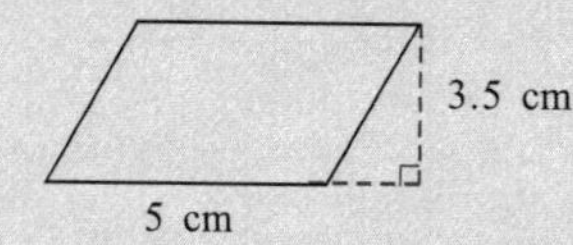

Answers:

9. (a) 48 in^2 (b) 11.25 m^2

10. 17.5 cm^2

EXAMPLE 9 Find the area enclosed by each of the following triangles.

(a)

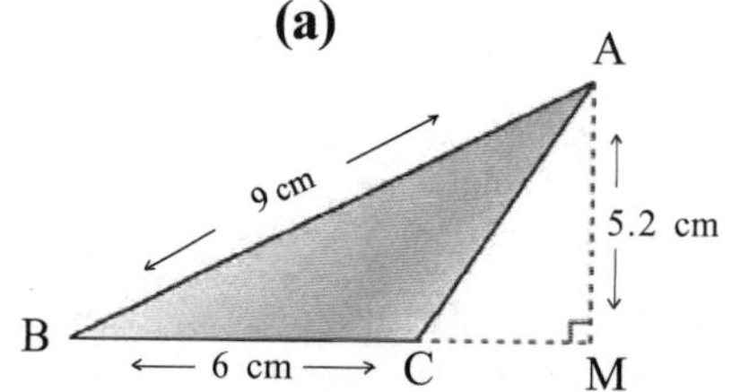

(b)

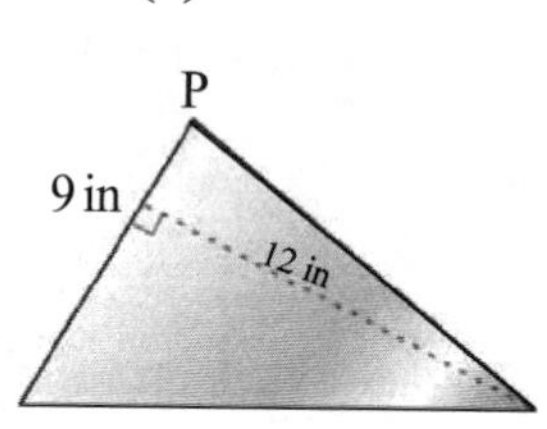

Solutions

(a) Using the side BC for the base and AM for the height, the area is given by

$$A = \frac{1}{2}\text{ (base) (height)}$$

$$= \frac{1}{2}\text{ (6 cm) (5.2 cm)}$$

$$= 15.6 \text{ cm} \times \text{ cm}$$

$$= 15.6 \text{ cm}^2$$

(b) Take 9 in as the base and 12 in as the height.

$$A = \frac{1}{2}\text{ (9 in) (12 in)}$$

$$= 54 \text{ in}^2$$

EXAMPLE 10 Find the area of the following parallelogram.

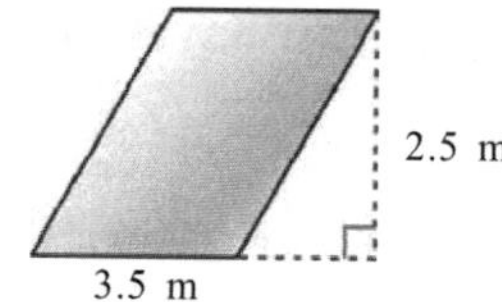

Solution

The base and height are given.

The area = base × height

$$= (3.5 \text{ m})(2.5 \text{ m}) = (3.5)(2.5)\text{ m}^2$$

$$= 8.75 \text{ m}^2$$

EXERCISE 10.2

In exercises 1-5, find the perimeter.

1. 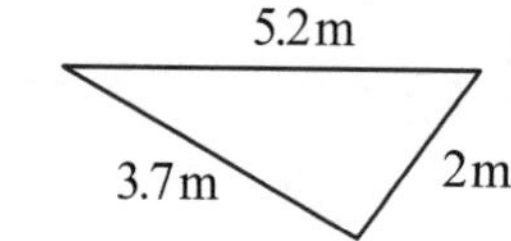

2. 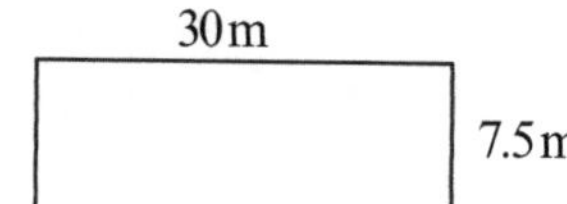

3. 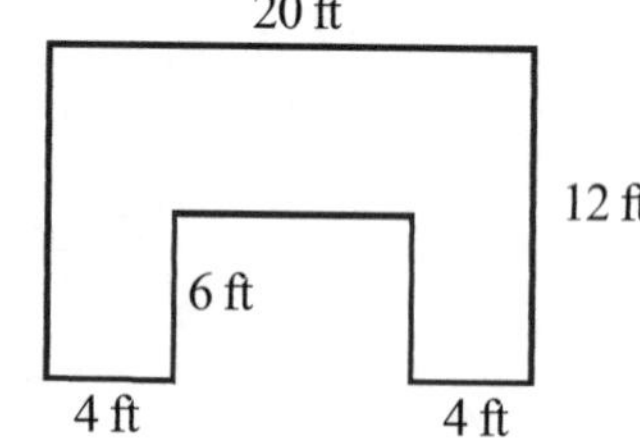

4.

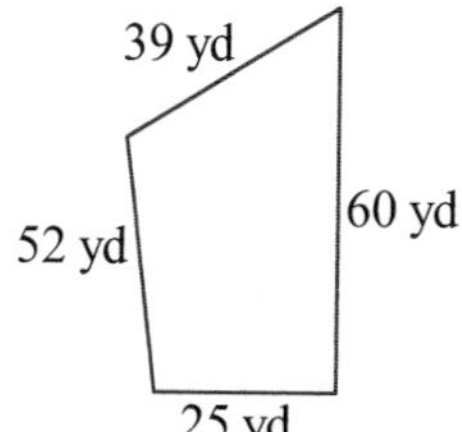

5.

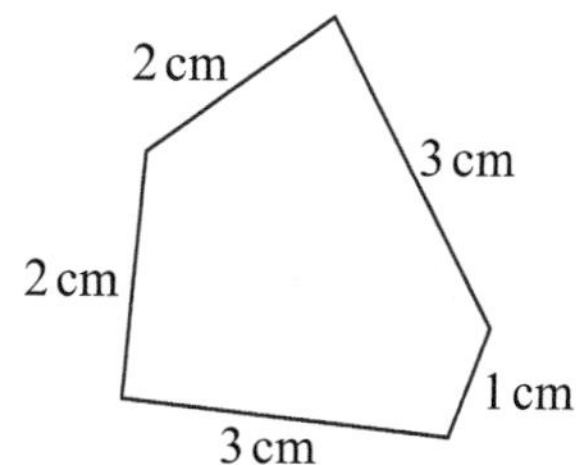

In exercises 6-14, find the area.

6.

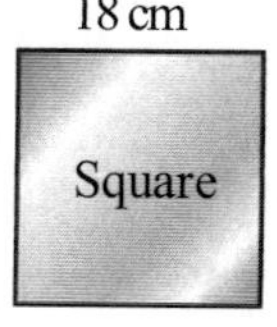

7.

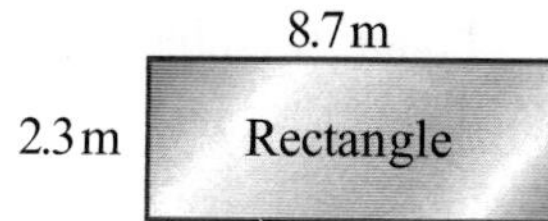

8.

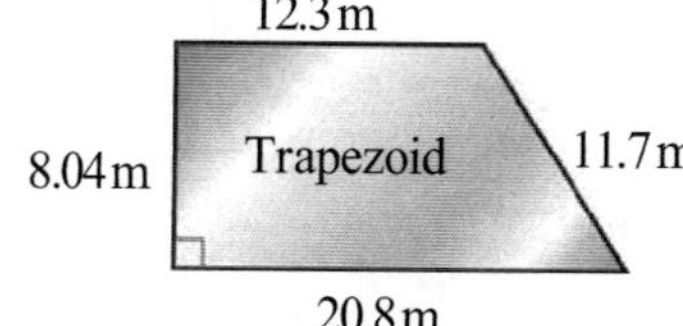

9.

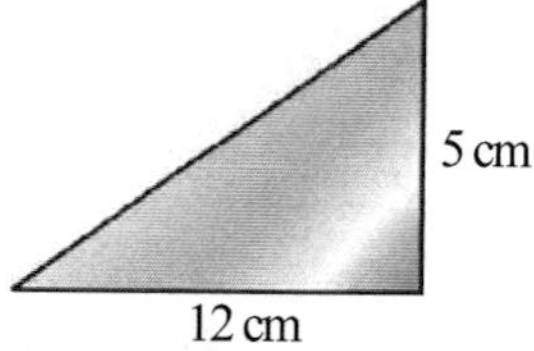

10.

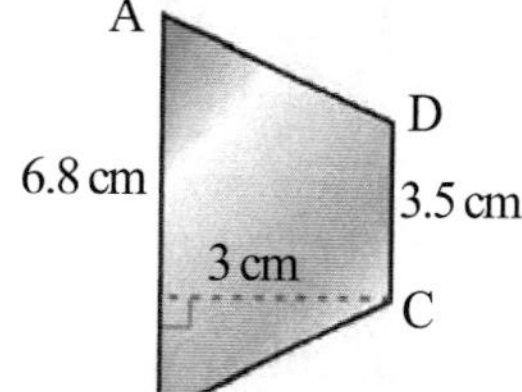

11.

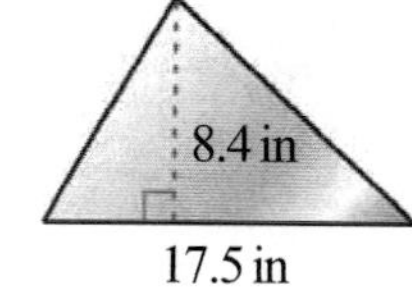

12.

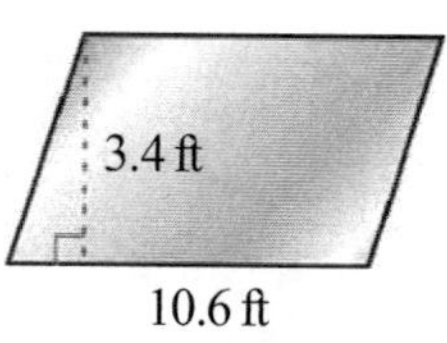

13.

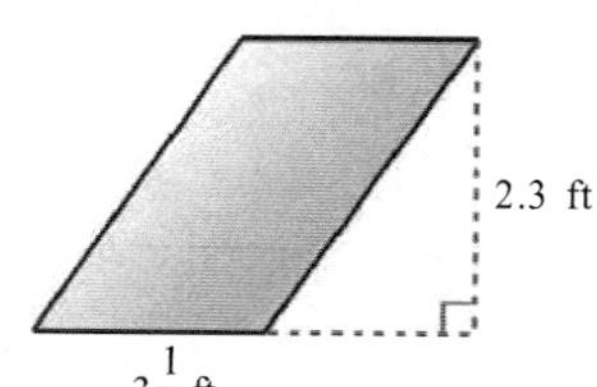

14.

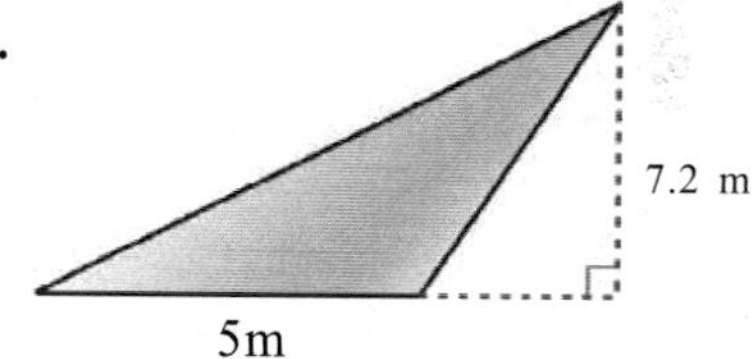

In exercises 15-18, find the area of the shaded region.

15.

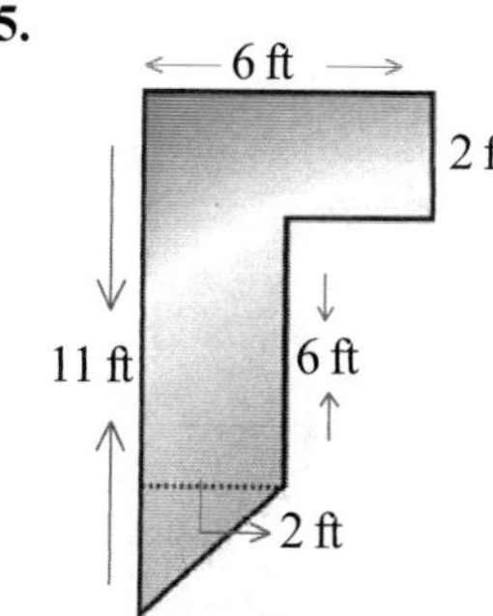

16.

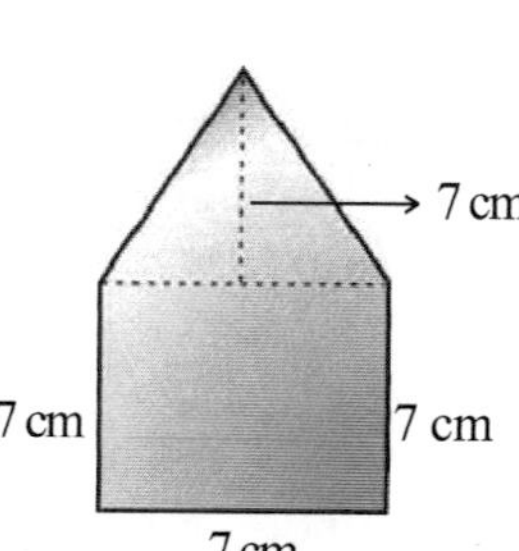

17.

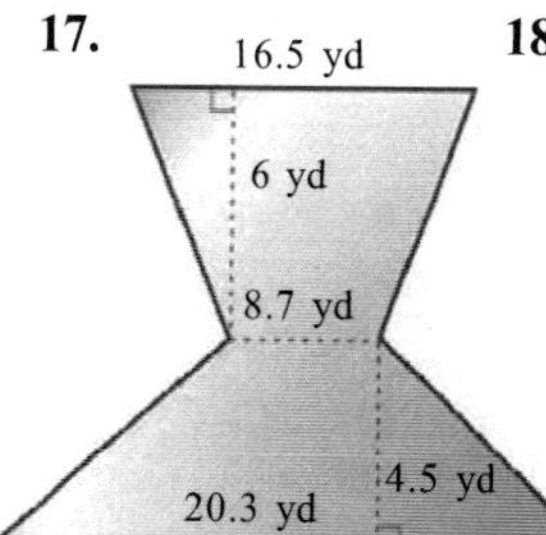

18.

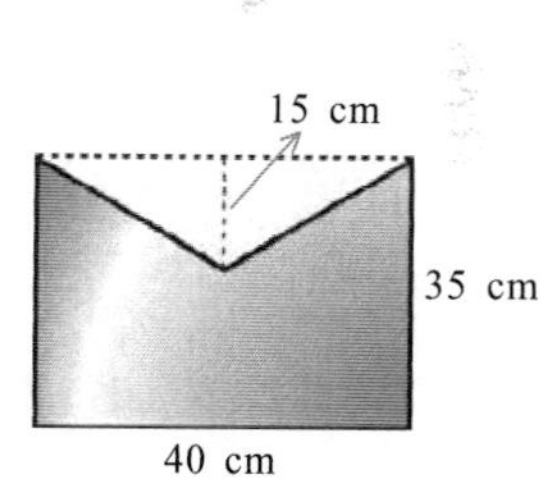

Applications

19. The length and width of a rectangular field are 75 yd and 45 yd respectively. Find the cost of running two lengths of wire around the field if the wire costs $2.75 per yd. Also find the cost of plowing it at the rate of 65 cents per square yard.

20. Which parking lot has larger area, the one measuring 85 m by 54 m, or the one measuring 80 m by 59 m?

10.3 Volume and Surface Area

Identifying 3-D Figures and Finding Volumes

Discussion

> **Objectives**
>
> After completing this section you will be able to:
>
> Identify specific three dimensional figures by name and find their volume.

Solid : A solid is a three dimensional figure bounded by surfaces which may be plane or curved. These surfaces are called **faces** or **curved surfaces** of the solid. The line (or curve) of the intersection of any two faces or surfaces of a solid is called an **edge** of the solid.

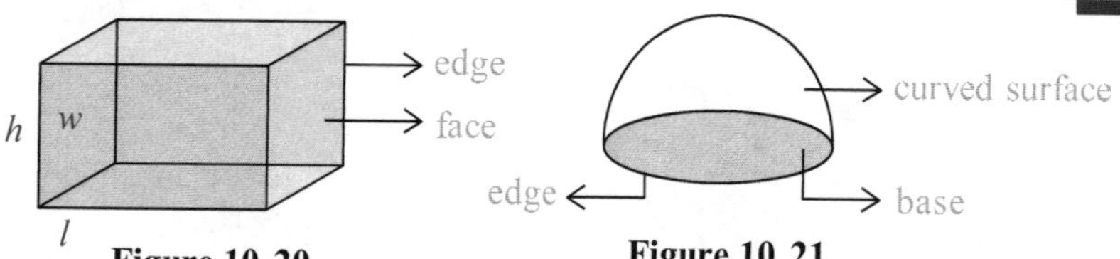

Figure 10.20 **Figure 10.21**

The **volume** of any solid is the amount of space enclosed within its boundaries. The volume of a solid is a *measure of its capacity*. To say that a Coca Cola bottle contains 300 *ml* of soda, means the volume of the bottle is 300 ml.

Unit of volume:

Since the term 'volume' is related to three-dimensional figures, it is often expressed in cubic units: cubic centimeters (cm^3), cubic meters (m^3), cubic inches (in^3), *etc*. In each of the formulae for the volume of a solid, three measures are multiplied. Since the measures are expressed in centimeters, meters, inches, *etc*., in computing the volume, these units get multiplied three times, giving a cubic-unit.

Types of solids and their volumes:

Three-dimensional figures (solids) are classified into different types according to their shapes. This discussion will review only six common types of solids: (1) rectangular solids, (2) cubes, (3) spheres, (4) cylinders, (5) cones, and (6) pyramids.

1. **Volume of a Rectangular Solid**

A **rectangular solid** (Figure 10.22) is a solid bounded by six rectangular faces. Two of the parallel faces are called **bases**, and the other four faces are called **sides**. The length (l), width (w), and height (h) of a rectangular solid are shown in Figure 10.23

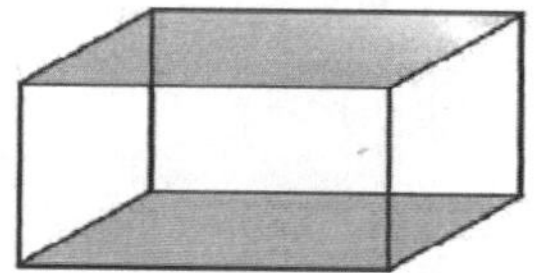

Figure 10.22

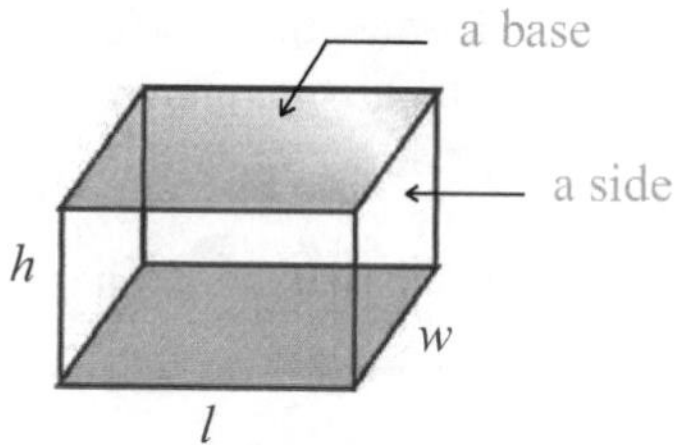

Figure 10.23

The volume, V, of a rectangular solid is given by the formula

$$V = \text{(Area of the base)} \cdot \text{(height)}$$
$$= (l \cdot w) \cdot h = l \cdot w \cdot h$$

2. **Volume of a Cube**

A **cube** is a special rectangular solid whose length, width, and height are all equal. All six faces of a cube are squares of the same size (Figure 10.24). All the edges of a cube are equal. The volume (V) of a cube is given by the formula:

$$V = \text{(area of the base)} \cdot \text{height}$$
$$= (a \cdot a) \cdot a = a \cdot a \cdot a = a^3$$

where a is the length of one of its edges

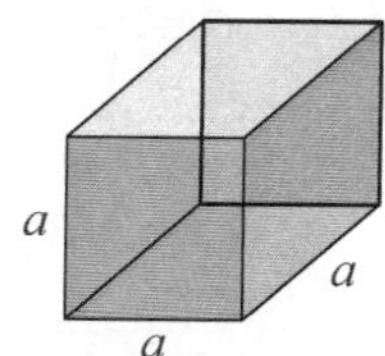

Figure 10.24

3. **Volume of a right circular Cylinder**

A right circular cylinder is a three-dimensional figure similar in shape to a soup can (Figure 10.25). It has two circular bases with the same radii which are parallel to each other, and the line joining their centers is perpendicular to the bases. A right circular cylinder is identified by the radius of the base and the distance between the two bases is called the **height** of the cylinder. The term **cylinder** will be used to mean a **right circular cylinder**.

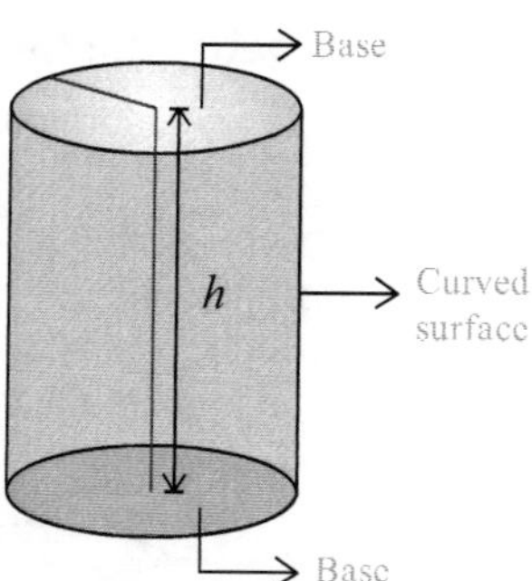

Figure 10.25

The volume (V) of a cylinder is given by formula

$$V = \text{(area of the base)} \cdot \text{height} = \pi r^2 \cdot h\ ,$$

where r is the radius of the base and h is the height of the cylinder.

4. **Volume of a Right Circular Cone**

A **right circular cone** is a three-dimensional figure similar in shape to an ice-cream cone (Figure 10.26). It has a circular base, a curved surface, and a vertex. The line joining the vertex to the center of the base is perpendicular to the base. In the discussion, the term **cone** will always mean a **right circular cone**. Like a cylinder, a cone is also identified by the radius of its base and the height. The formula for the volume (V) of a cone is

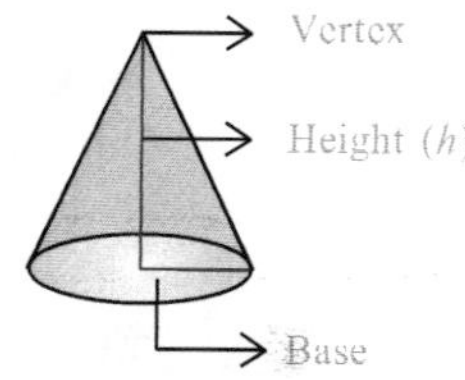

Figure 10.26

$$V = \frac{1}{3}\text{ (area of the base)} \cdot \text{(height)} = \frac{1}{3}\pi r^2 \cdot h\ ,$$

where r is the radius of the base and h the height of the cone.

5. **Volume of a Sphere**

A **sphere** is a solid geometric figure like a ball. It has a curved surface where each point is at the same distance from the center. The constant distance is called the **radius** of the sphere. The formula for the volume of a sphere is $V = \frac{4}{3}\pi r^3$, where r is the radius of the sphere.

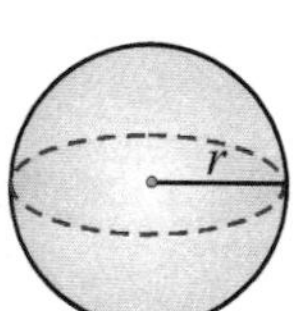

Figure 10.27

6. Volume of a Pyramid

A **pyramid** (Figure 10.28) is a solid geometric figure that has a polygon **base** and triangular lateral sides that meet in a common **vertex**. The lines that join the vertex to the base are called **lateral edges**. The volume of a pyramid is given by the formula,

$$V = \frac{1}{3} B \cdot h \ ,$$

where B is the area of the base polygon and h is the height.

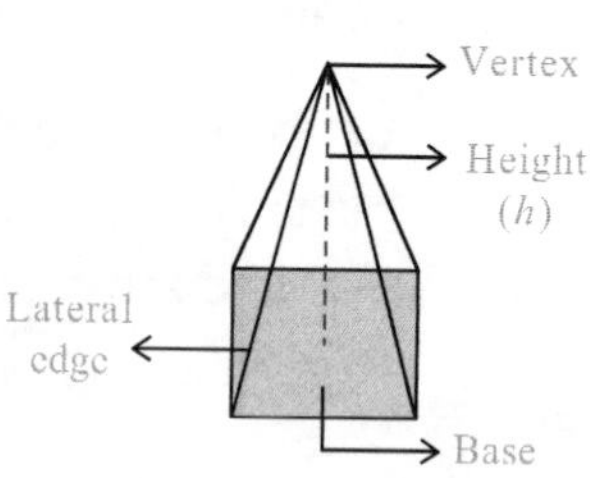

Figure 10.28

EXAMPLE 1 Find the volume V of a rectangular solid with length 4 inches, width 3 inches, and height 2 inches.

Solution

$$\begin{aligned} \text{Volume } V &= l \cdot w \cdot h \\ &= (4 \text{ in})\,(3 \text{ in})\,(2 \text{ in}) \\ &= \mathbf{24\ in^3}. \end{aligned}$$

EXAMPLE 2 Find the volume of a cube whose sides measure 1.7 meters each. Round the answer to the nearest units.

Solution

$$\begin{aligned} V &= S^3 = (1.7 \text{ m})\,(1.7 \text{ m})\,(1.7 \text{ m}) \\ &\approx \mathbf{5\ m^3}. \end{aligned}$$

EXAMPLE 3 Find the volume of a cylinder with radius 2.1 cm and height 12 cm. Round to the nearest unit.

Solution

$$V = \pi\ r^2 \cdot h$$

$$\begin{aligned} V &= (\pi)(2.1 \text{ cm})^2\,(12 \text{ cm}) \\ &\approx (3.14)\,(4.41 \text{ cm}^2)\,(12 \text{ cm}) \\ &\approx \mathbf{166\ cm^3} \end{aligned}$$

EXAMPLE 4 Find the volume of a cone of radius 5 ft and the height 8 ft. Round to the units.

Solution

$$V = \frac{1}{3}\ \pi \cdot r^2 \cdot h$$

WARM-UP

1. Find the volume of a rectangular solid with length 15 cm, width 9 cm, and height 7 cm.

2. Find the volume of cube 4 inches on each side.

3. Find the volume of a cylinder of radius 1.5 cm and height 4 cm. Round to the nearest tenth.

4. Find the volume of cone of height 10 in and diameter of the base 8 in. Round to the nearest units.

WARM-UP

$$\approx \frac{1}{3}\ (3.14)\ (5\text{ ft})^2\ (8\text{ ft})$$

$$= \frac{1}{3}\ (3.14)\ (200\text{ ft}^3)$$

$$= \frac{628\text{ ft}^3}{3} \approx \mathbf{209\ ft^3}$$

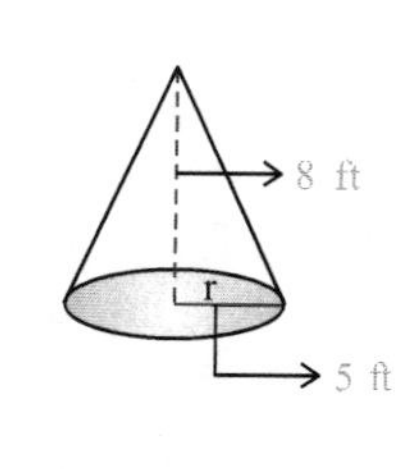

5. Find the volume of a sphere of radius 3.5 cm Use p $\approx \frac{22}{7}$. Round to the units.

EXAMPLE 5 Find the volume of a sphere of radius 20 in. Round to the hundreds.

Solution

$$V = \frac{4}{3}\pi r^3$$

$$V \approx \frac{4}{3}(3.14)\ (20\text{ in})^3$$

$$= \frac{4}{3}(3.14)\ (8000\text{ in}^3)$$

$$= \frac{32000}{3} \cdot 3.14\text{ in}^3 = \frac{100480}{3}\text{ in}^3$$

$$\approx 33{,}500\text{ in}^3$$

6. Find the volume of a pyramid with square base of side 40 ft and a height of 27 ft. Round to the nearest cubic feet.

EXAMPLE 6 Find the volume of a pyramid with a rectangular base 20 ft by 10 ft and a height of 20 ft. Round to the nearest cubic feet.

Solution Since the base polygon is a rectangle, its area $B = l \times w$

$$= (20\text{ ft})\ (10\text{ ft}) = 200\text{ ft}^2$$

$$V = \frac{1}{3}\ B \cdot h$$

$$= \frac{1}{3}\ (200\text{ ft}^2)\ (20\text{ ft})$$

$$= \frac{1}{3}\ (4000)\text{ ft}^3 \approx \mathbf{1333\ ft^3}.$$

Application

WARM-UP

7. A brick has dimensions 24 cm × 12 cm × 8 cm. How many bricks will be required to build a wall 24 m long, 8 m high and 60 cm thick?

Hint: Change all the measurements to the same unit.

Answers:

1. 945 cm^3
2. 64 in^3
3. 28.3 cm^3
4. 168 in^3
5. 180 cm^3
6. 14,400 ft^3
7. 50,000 bricks

EXAMPLE 7 A firm is shipping rectangular crates with dimensions 4 ft by 6 ft by 10 ft in a truck with dimensions 40 ft by 24 ft by 10 ft. How many of these crates can be loaded in this truck?

Solution

Step 1 Find the volume of each crate.

$V = (4 \text{ ft}) \cdot (6\text{ft}) \cdot (10 \text{ ft}) = 240 \text{ ft}^3.$

Step 2 Find the volume or capacity of the truck.

$V = (40 \text{ ft}) \cdot (10 \text{ ft}) \cdot (24 \text{ ft}) = 9600 \text{ ft}^3$

Step 3 The number of crates in the truck

$$= \frac{\text{capacity of the truck}}{\text{volume of each crate}} = \frac{9600 \cancel{\text{ft}^3}}{240 \cancel{\text{ft}^3}} = \textbf{40 crates}$$

EXERCISE 10.3

In exercises 1-4, name the figure and find its volume using the information given in the figure.

1.

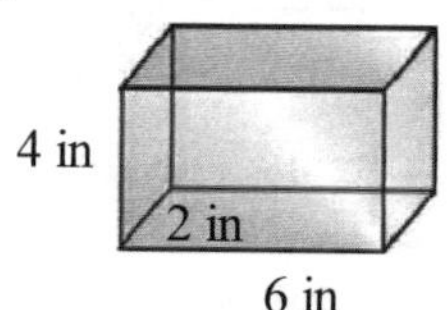

2.

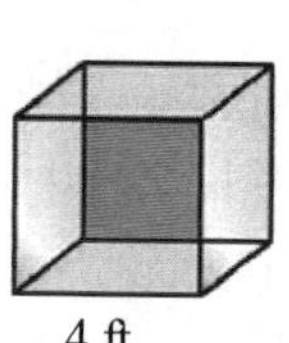

3.

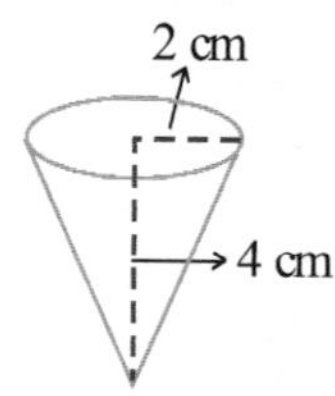

4.

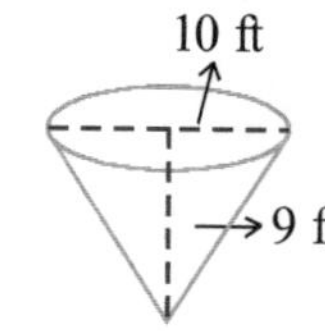

5. Find the volume of a cube whose side measure is:
   (a) 3.1 m **(b)** 1.75 cm
6. Find the volume of the rectangular solid with length 3 in, width 5 in, height 5 in.
7. Find the volume of the rectangular solid with length 8 in, width 11 in, and height 5 in.
8. A container is 2 ft by 1.5 ft by 5 ft. How many cubic feet of sand can be put in this container?
9. Find the volume of a cone with a circular base of radius $4\frac{3}{4}$ inches and height 6 inches. Use $\pi = \frac{22}{7}$.
10. Find the volume of a cylinder of radius 3 m and height 4 m.
11. Find the volume of a cylinder of radius 5 cm and height 4 cm.
12. Find the volume of a sphere of diameter 8 cm.
13. Find the volume of a sphere of radius 6 inches.
14. Find the volume of a pyramid with a base of area 24 in^2 and a height of 8 in.
15. What is the volume of a pyramid if its rectangular base is 23 ft by 18 ft and its height is 35 ft?
16. Find the volume of a pyramid with a square base with sides measuring 10 cm and a height of 12 cm.

Motions in Geometry

This chapter is divided into three sections:

11.1 *Constructions ;*

11.2 *Congruence Mappings ; and*

11.3 *Similarity Mappings.*

11.1 Constructions

A. Lines and Angles Construction

Perpendicular lines

- Earlier we have learnt about lines.
- In this section, we will learn about perpendicular lines.
- When we draw two lines, there are two possibilities :

1. Lines do not intersect each other.

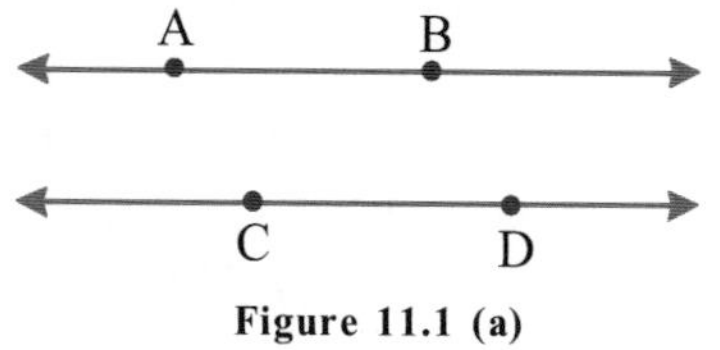

Figure 11.1 (a)

2. Lines intersect each other.

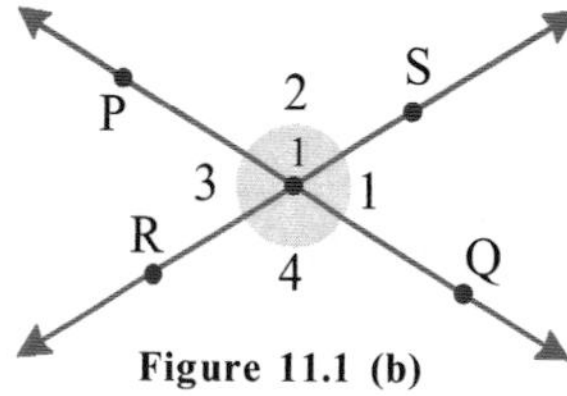

Figure 11.1 (b)

- When two lines intersect each other, four angles are formed.
- If one of these angles is a right angle, the remaining three angles are also right angles and the lines are said to intersect at a right angle.
- These lines intersecting at a right angle are called perpendicular lines.
- In the adjacent figure, DE is perpendicular to FG and FG is perpendicular to DE.
- Symbolically, it is written as DE $\perp$ FG, read as line DE is perpendicular to line FG; likewise FG $\perp$ DE.

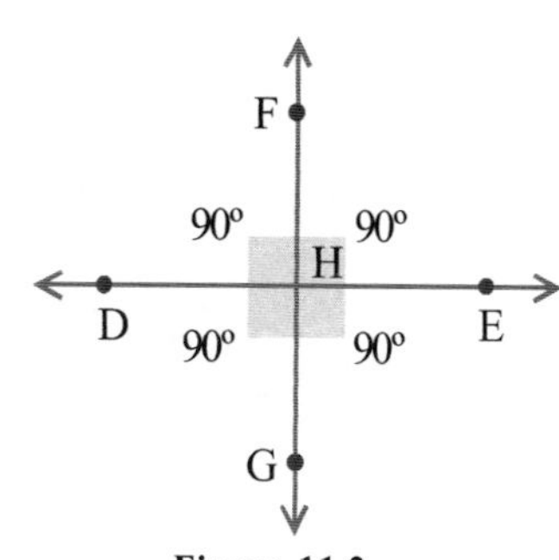

Figure 11.2

Some Examples :

- In the adjoining figure, Line l is perpendicular to line m.

  Symbolically, it can be written as: $l \perp m$ or $m \perp l$

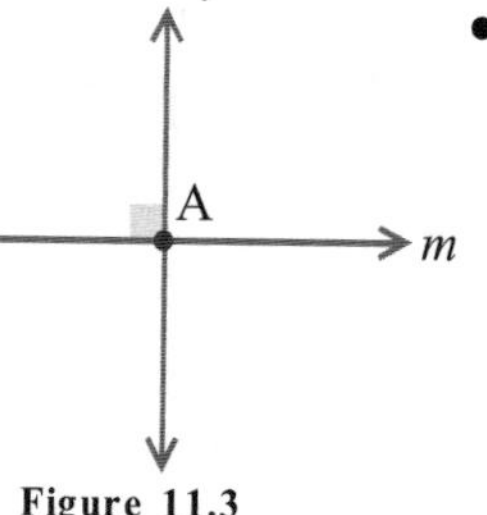

Figure 11.3

- In the adjoining figure, Line l_1 is perpendicular to lines l_2 and l_3.

  Symbolically, : $l_1 \perp l_2$ and $l_1 \perp l_3$

  or $l_2 \perp l_1$ and $l_3 \perp l_1$

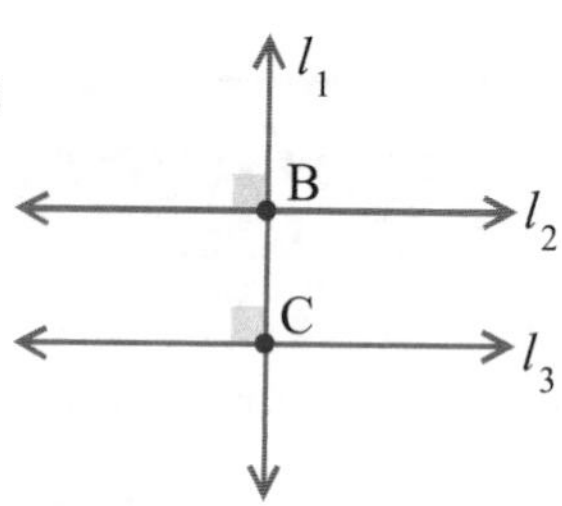

Figure 11.4

- This figure shows that : Line m_1 and line m_2 are perpendicular to line m_3.

  Symbolically, : $m_1 \perp m_3$ and $m_2 \perp m_3$

  or $m_3 \perp m_1$ and $m_3 \perp m_2$

Figure 11.5

➜ Constructing Perpendicular to a Line through a Point on it

Construct a line perpendicular to a given line through a point on the given line.

Using Ruler and Compasses :

Given : Line l and point P on this line.

To construct : Perpendicular PQ to the line l.

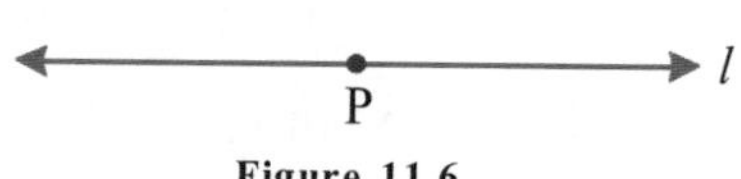

Figure 11.6

***Step* 1:** With given point P as centre and a convenient radius, draw an arc intersecting the line l at two points A and B.

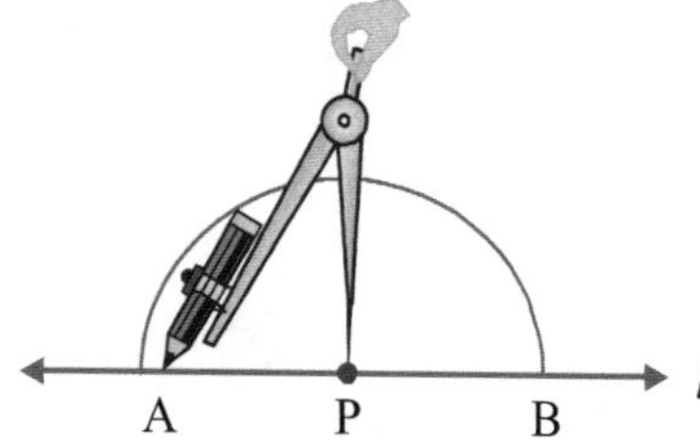

Figure 11.7

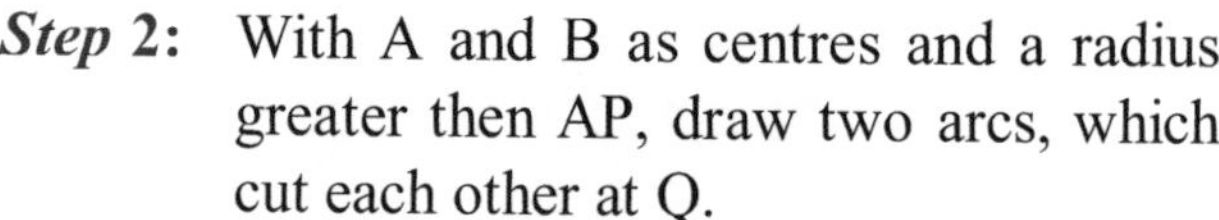

***Step* 2:** With A and B as centres and a radius greater then AP, draw two arcs, which cut each other at Q.

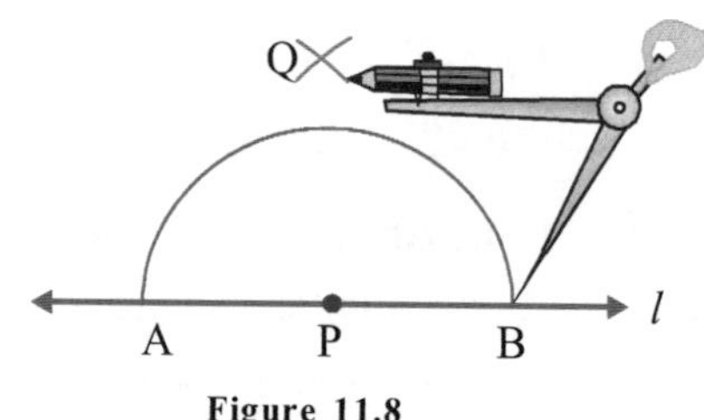

Figure 11.8

***Step* 3:** Join PQ.

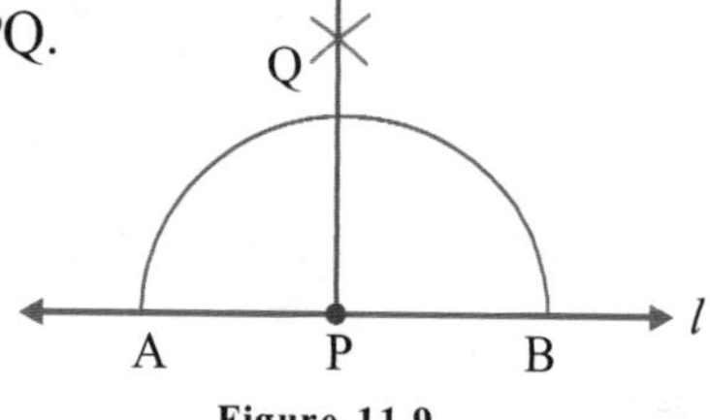

Figure 11.9

Then, $PQ \perp l$.

Using Ruler and Set-Square :

Given : A line XY and point A on it.

To construct : Perpendicular AB to the line XY.

Step 1: Put the right angle vertex of a set square at point A on XY in such a way that another vertex of the set square fits on part of XY towards Y (or towards X).

Step 2: On the vertical side of set square, select a point B and then remove the set square.

Step 3: Using a ruler, draw AB passing through points A and B.

Then, $AB \perp XY$.

AB is the required line perpendicular to line XY at A.

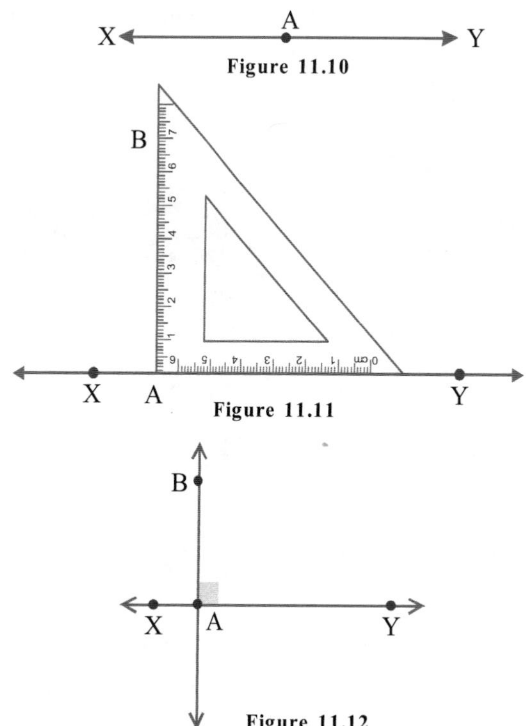

Figure 11.10

Figure 11.11

Figure 11.12

➜ Constructing Perpendicular to a Line through a Point not on it

Construct a line perpendicular to a given line through a point not on the given line.

Using Ruler and Compasses :

Given: Line l and point P not on line l.

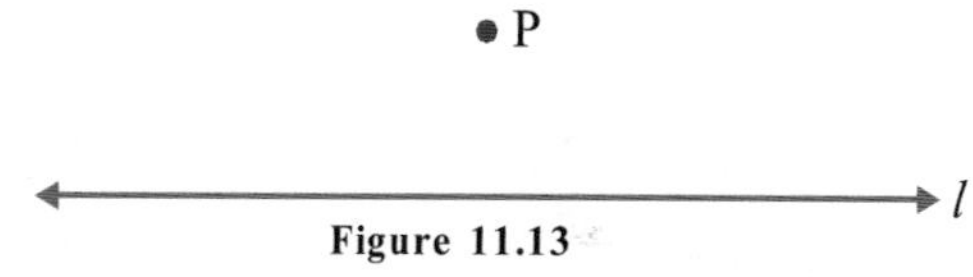

Figure 11.13

To construct : Line PQ perpendicular to the line l.

Step 1: With P as centre, draw an arc intersecting line l at D and E.

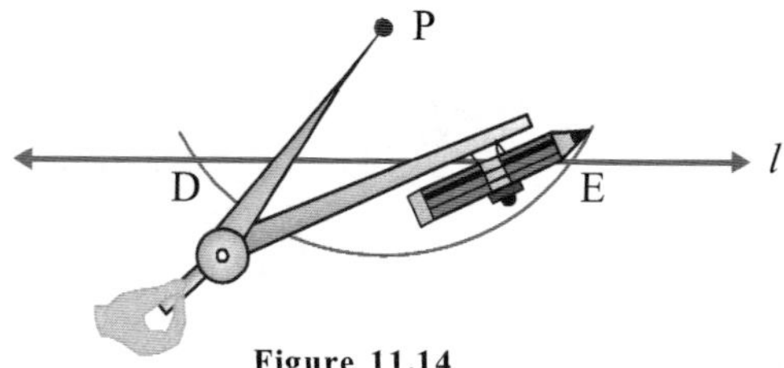

Figure 11.14

Step 2: With E as centre and more than $\frac{1}{2}$ DE as radius, draw an arc below line l.

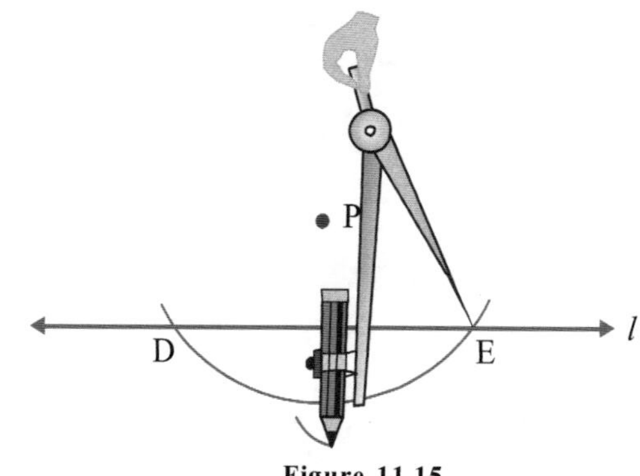

Figure 11.15

***Step* 3:** With D as centre and the same radius as in step 2, draw an arc intersecting the previous arc at a point Q.

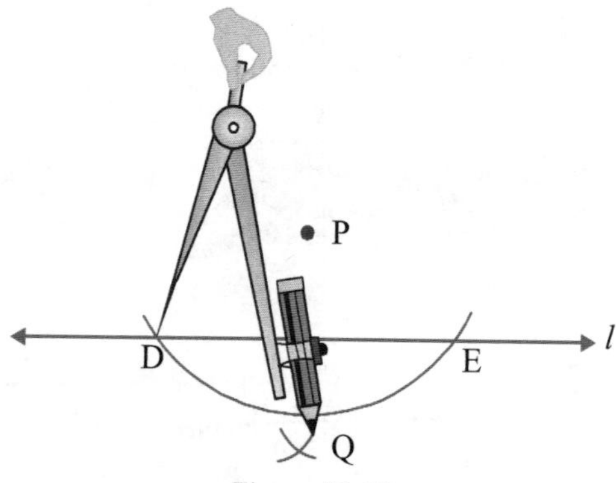

Figure 11.16

***Step* 4:** Join P and Q to draw line PQ.

Then, line PQ is the required line perpendicular to line *l* from P.

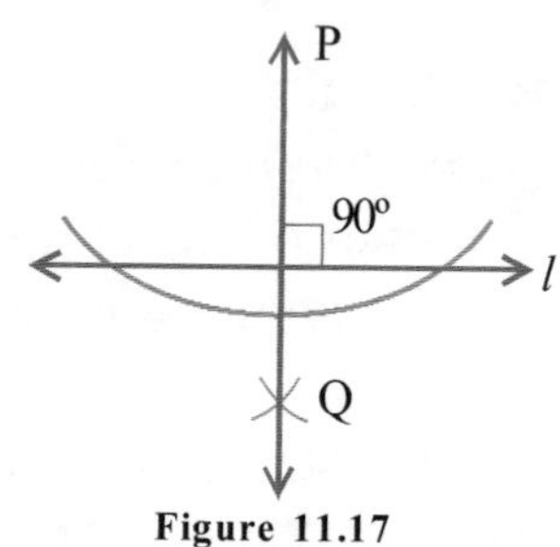

Figure 11.17

Using Set-Square :

Given: PQ and point C outside PQ.

To construct : Perpendicular CD to line PQ.

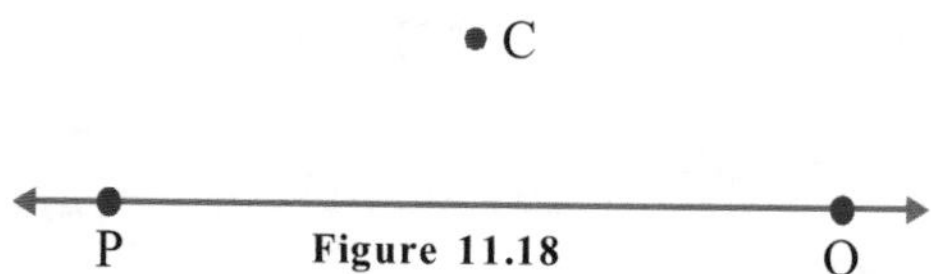

Figure 11.18

***Step* 1:** Place a set square on PQ in such a way that its one side forming a right angle falls on PQ and other side passes through the point C, outside PQ.

***Step* 2:** At the right angle vertex of the set square, mark the point D, and then remove the set square.

***Step* 3:** Using a ruler, draw line CD passing through points C and D.

Then, $CD \perp PQ$.

Thus, CD is the required line.

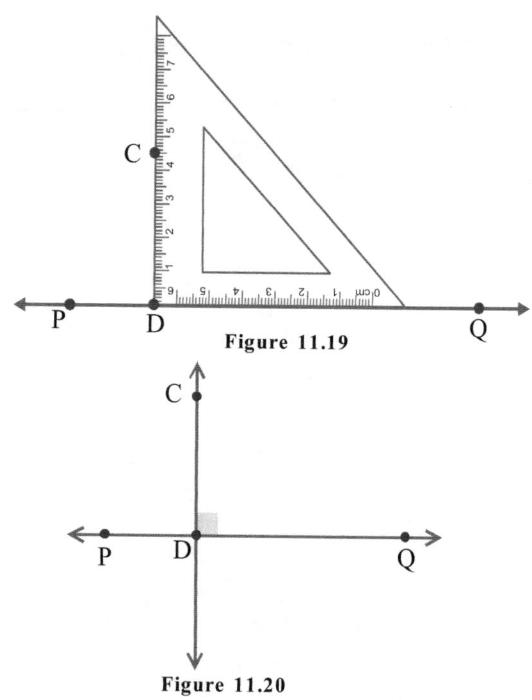

Figure 11.19

Figure 11.20

➜ Constructing Perpendicular Bisector of a Line Segment

Construct the perpendicular bisector of a given line segment.

Given: Line segment AB.

To construct : The perpendicular bisector CD of the line segment AB.

Figure 11.21

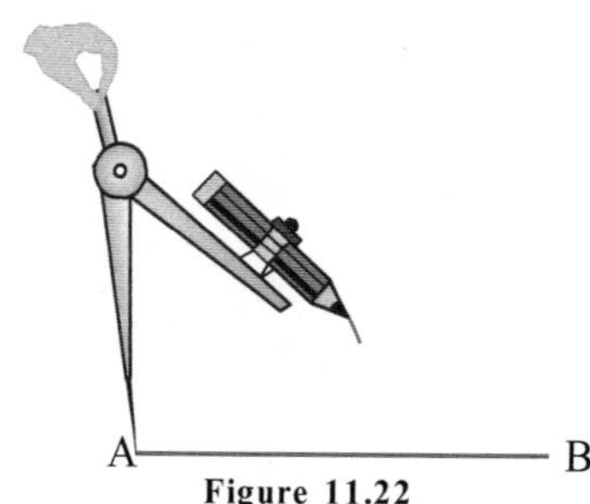

Figure 11.22

Step 1: With A as centre and more than $\frac{1}{2}$ AB as radius, draw arcs above and below line segment AB.

Step 2: With B as centre and the same radius as in step 1, draw arcs that intersect the previous arcs at points C and D.

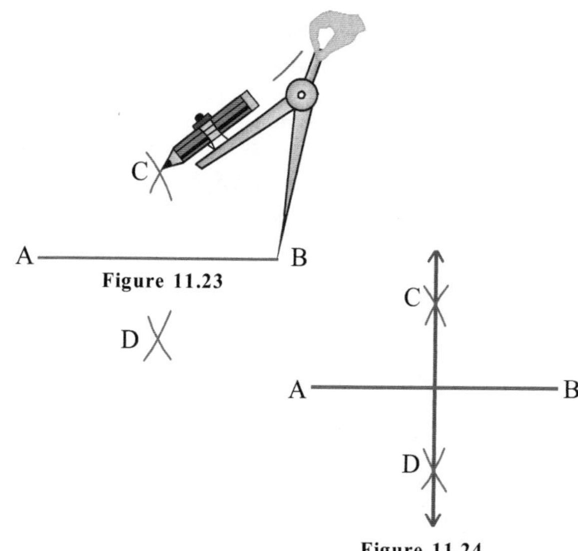

Figure 11.23

Step 3: Draw line CD.

Then, line CD is the required perpendicular bisector of the line segment AB.

Figure 11.24

(B.) CONSTRUCTION OF TRIANGLES

➜ SSS Construction

To construct a triangle when its three sides are given.

Given: Three sides of a triangle ABC such that AB = 4 cm, BC = 5 cm, and CA = 2.5 cm.

To construct : ΔABC.

Steps of Construction :

Step 1: Draw a rough sketch with measures marked on it (Figure 11.25). (This will give you an idea as to how to proceed further.)

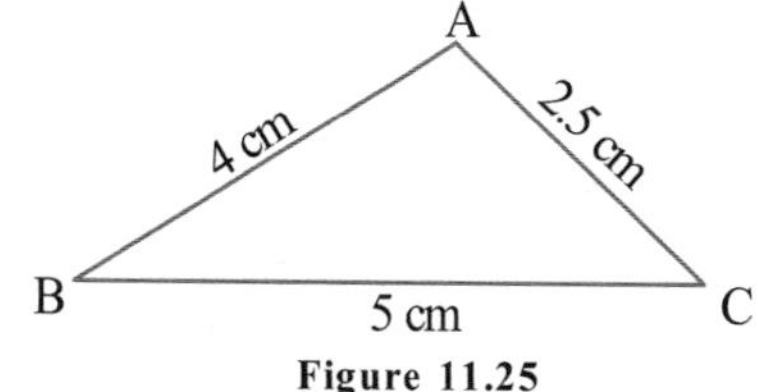

Figure 11.25

***Step* 2:** Construct a line segment BC of length 5 cm (Figure 11.26).

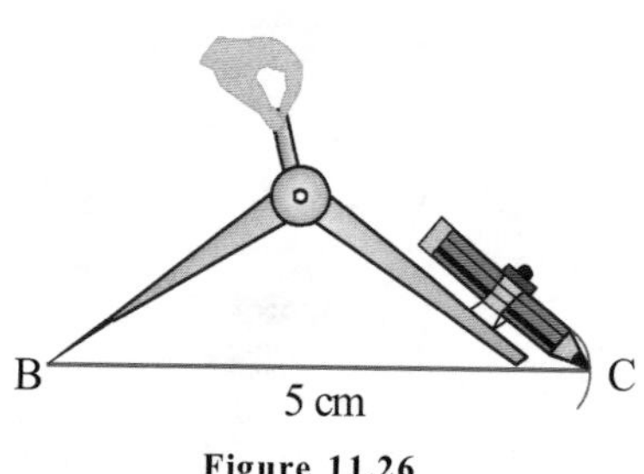

Figure 11.26

***Step* 3:** With B as centre and radius 4 cm (= AB), draw an arc on one side of BC (Figure 11.27).

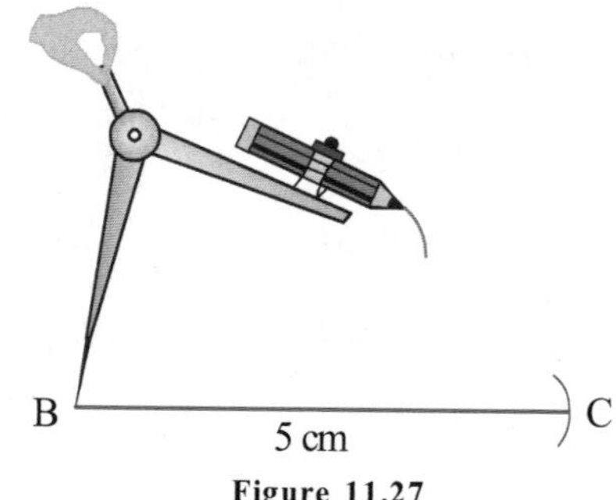

Figure 11.27

***Step* 4:** With C as centre and radius 2.5 cm (= AC), draw another arc intersecting the first arc at A (Figure 11.28).

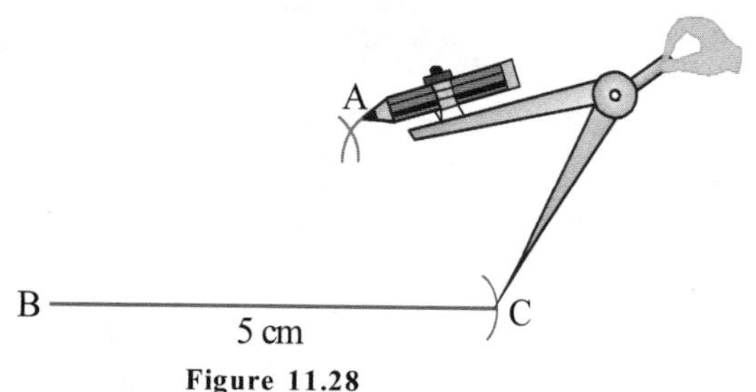

Figure 11.28

***Step* 5:** Join point A to B and point A to C (Figure 11.29).

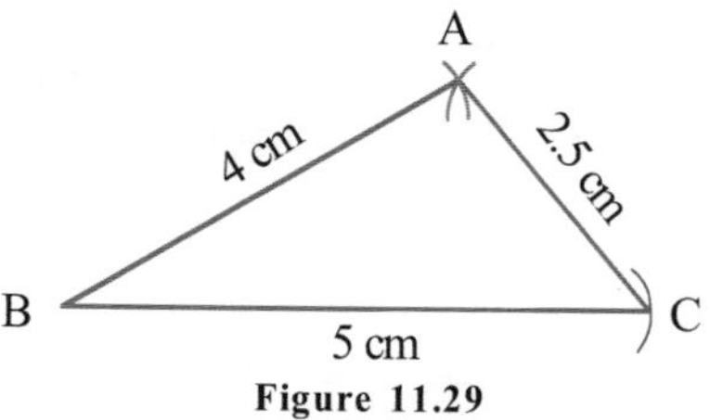

Figure 11.29

Then, ΔABC is the required triangle.

➜ SAS Construction

To construct a triangle when two of its sides and the included angle are given.

Given: Two sides and the included angle of a ΔABC such that AB = 3.5 cm, BC = 5 cm and the included angle ABC = 60°.

To construct : ΔABC.

***Steps of Construction* :**

***Step* 1:** First, draw a rough sketch of the triangle with measures marked on it. (Figure 11.30)

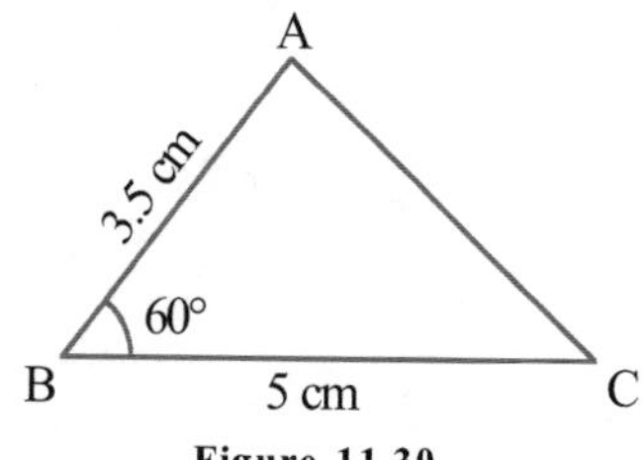

Figure 11.30

***Step* 2:** Draw ray and mark a line segment BC of length 5 cm (Figure 11.31).

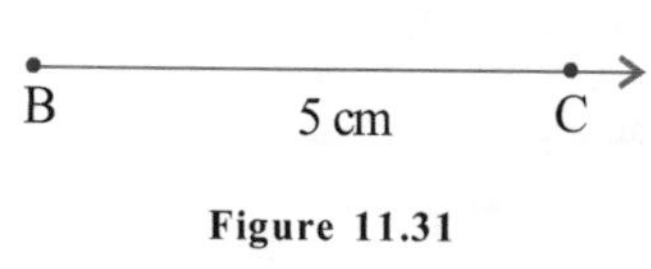

Figure 11.31

Step 3: At B, draw an angle XBC of measure 60° (= ∠ABC) (Figure 11.32).

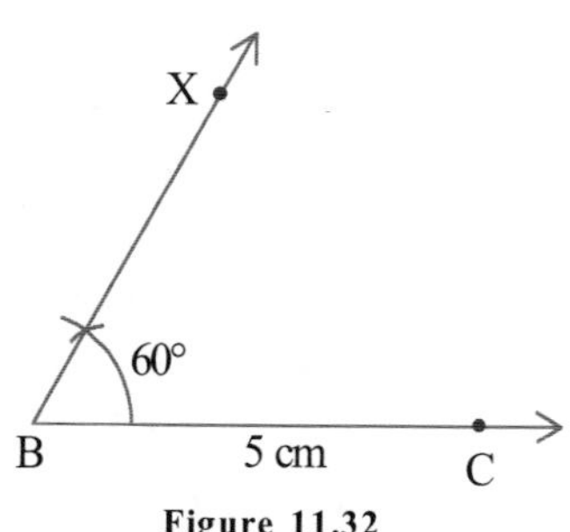

Figure 11.32

Step 4: With B as centre, draw an arc of radius 3.5 cm (= AB) intersecting the ray BX at the point A (Figure (11.33).

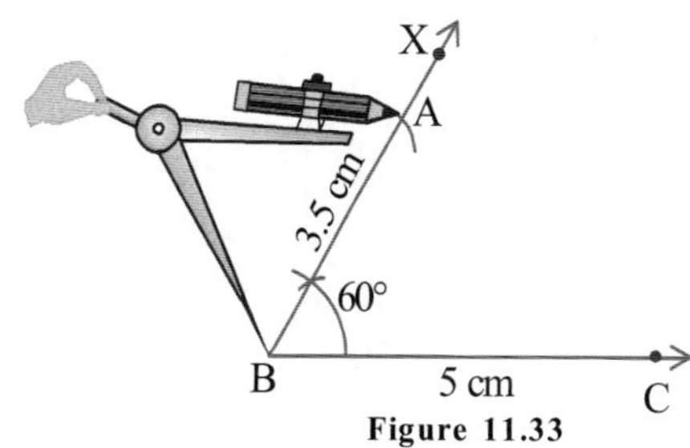

Figure 11.33

Step 5: Join AC (Figure 11.34).

Then, ΔABC is the required triangle.

X
A
3.5 cm
60°
B
5 cm
C

Figure 11.34

➡ ASA Construction

To construct a triangle when two of its angles and the included side are given.

Given: Two angles and the included side of a triangle ABC such that ∠A = 40°, ∠B = 70° and AB = 5 cm.

To construct : ΔABC.

Steps of Construction :

Step 1: First draw a rough sketch of ΔABC with measures marked on it (Figure 11.35).

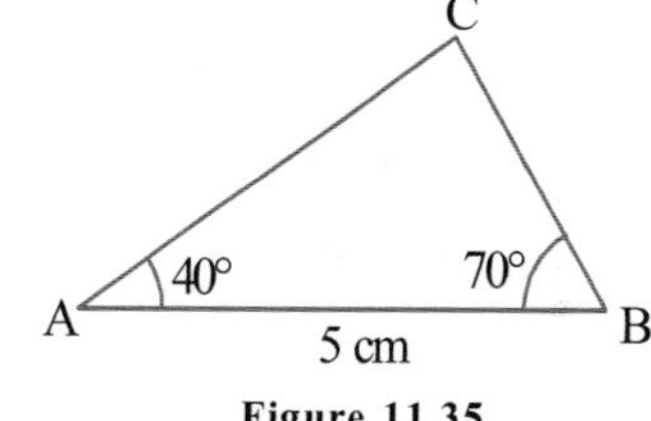

Figure 11.35

Step 2: Draw a line segment AB of length 5 cm (Figure 11.36).

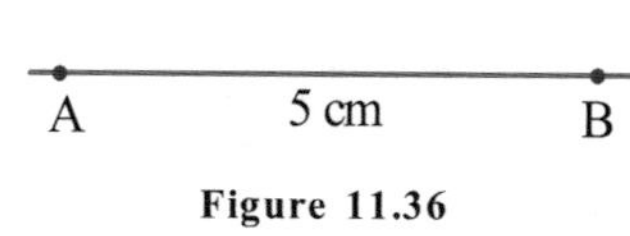

Figure 11.36

Step 3: At A, draw ∠XAB = 40°, using a protractor (Figure 11.37).

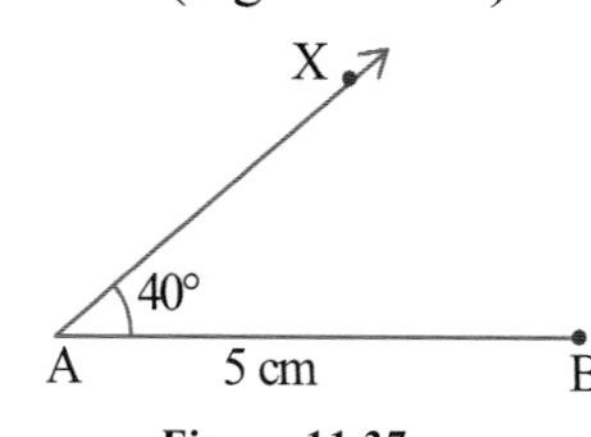

Figure 11.37

Step 4: At B, draw ∠YBA = 70°, using a protractor (Figure 11.38).

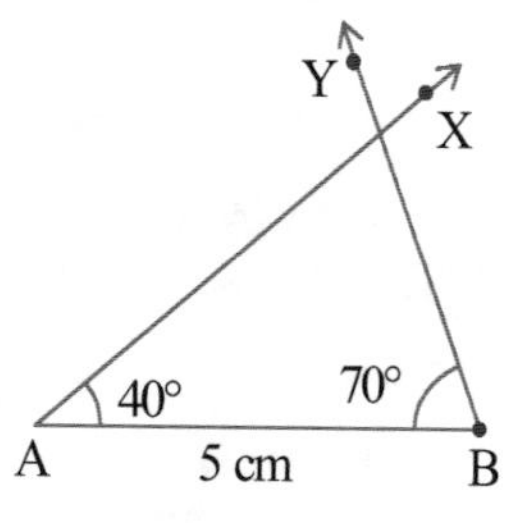

Figure 11.38

Step 5: Let the ray AX and BY intersect at C (Figure 11.39).

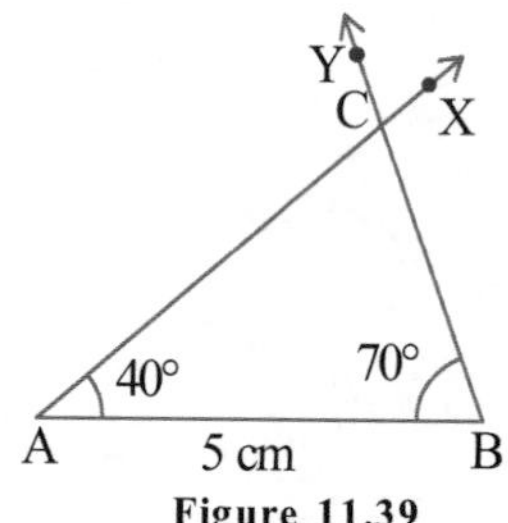

Figure 11.39

Then, ΔABC is the required triangle.

➔ RHS Construction

To construct a right triangle when its hypotenuse and one side are given.

Given: Hypotenuse AC = 5.5 cm and one side AB = 4 cm of a right triangle ABC.

To construct : Right ΔABC.

Steps of Construction :

Step 1: First draw a rough sketch of ΔABC with measures marked on it (Figure 11.40).

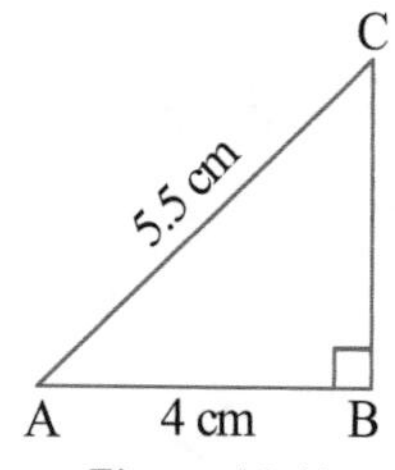

Figure 11.40

Step 2: Draw a line segment AB of length 4 cm.

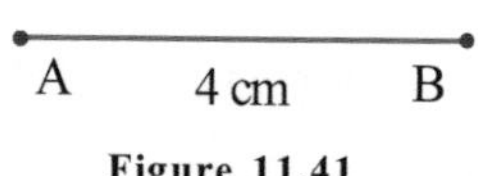

Figure 11.41

Step 3: At B, draw ∠DBA of measure 90° (Figure 11.42).

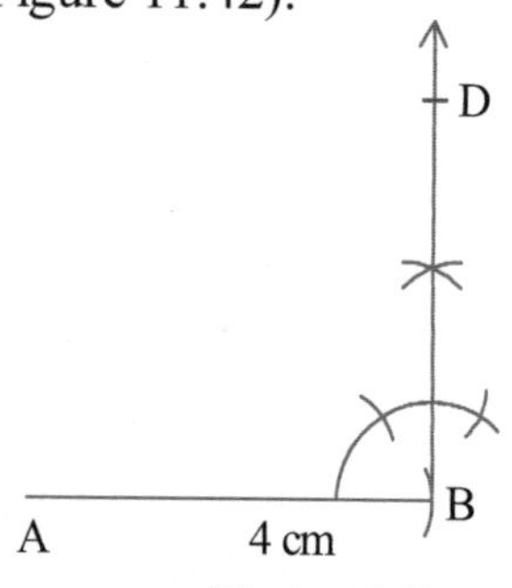

Figure 11.42

Step 4: With A as centre and radius 5.5 cm (= hypotenuse AC), draw an arc to intersect ray BD at C (Figure 11.43).

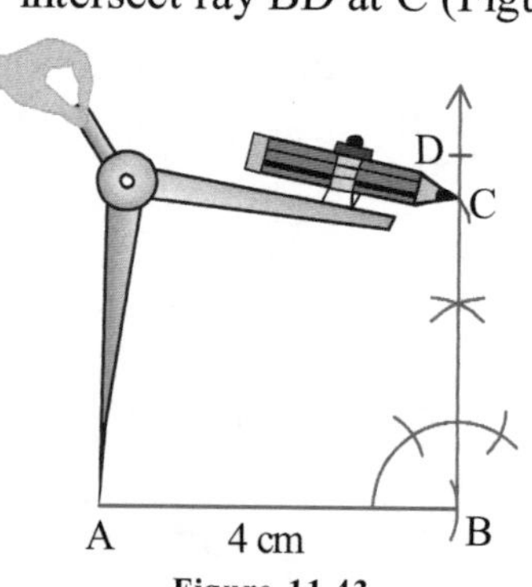

Figure 11.43

Step 5: Join points A and C to get AC (Figure 11.44).

Then, Δ ABC is the required right triangle.

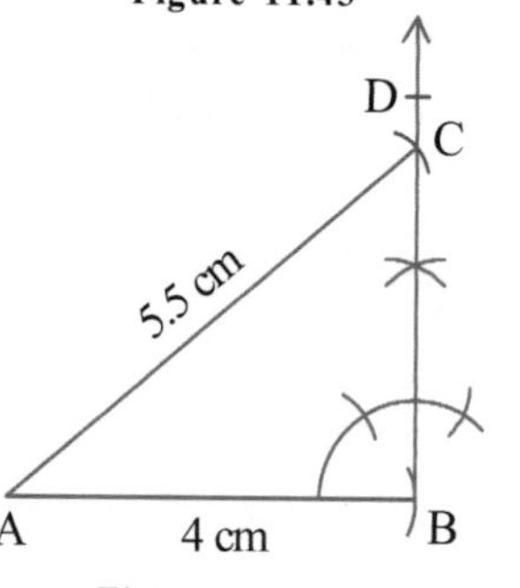

Figure 11.44

➡ Construction of triangle when altitude is given

Construct a ΔPQR.

Given: PQ, RQ and altitude.

Rough Sketch :

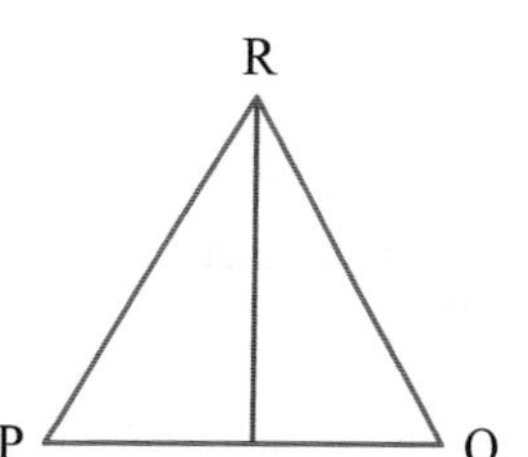

Steps of Construction :

***Step* 1:** Draw a line PQ.

***Step* 2:** Take a point S on PQ.

***Step* 3:** Draw RS ⊥ PQ.

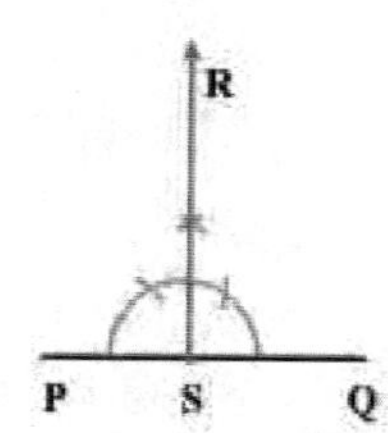

***Step* 4:** With S as centre and length of altitude as radius draw an arc, cutting RS at A.

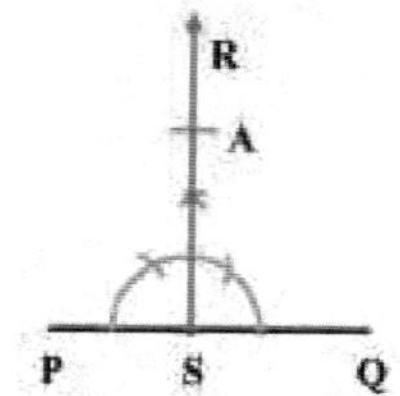

***Step* 5:** With A as centre and radii AB and AC, draw arcs, cutting PQ at B and C respectively.

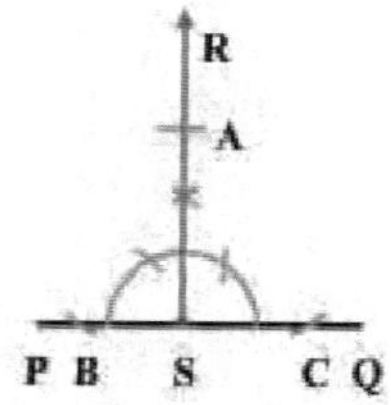

***Step* 6:** Join AB and AC.

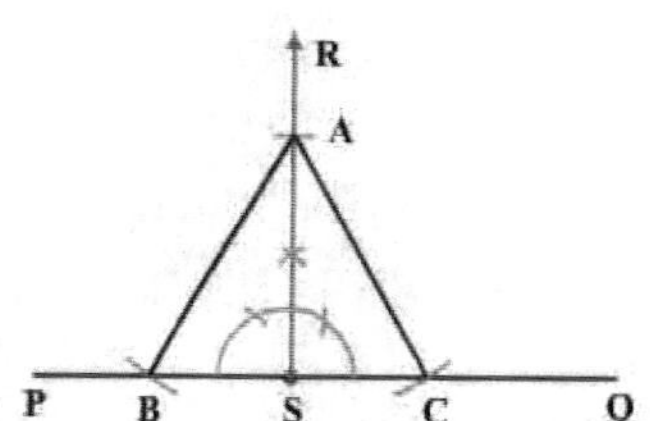

➡ Construction of Isosceles triangle

Construct an isosceles triangle ABC in which base BC and altitude from A on BC is given.

Given: Base BC and altitude from A on BC.

Rough Sketch :

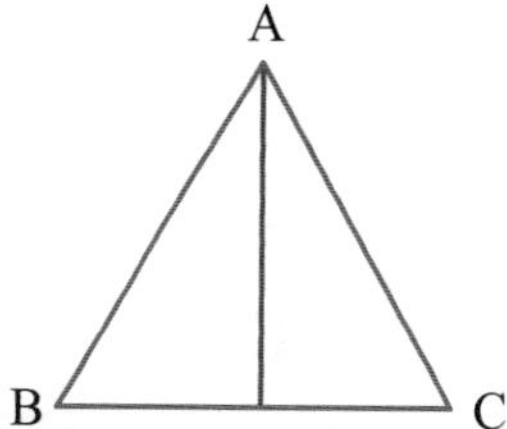

Steps of Construction :

Step 1: Draw BC of given length.

Step 2: Draw the perpendicular bisector of BC and name it PQ.

Step 3: With P as centre and given altitude as radius, draw an arc, cutting PQ at A.

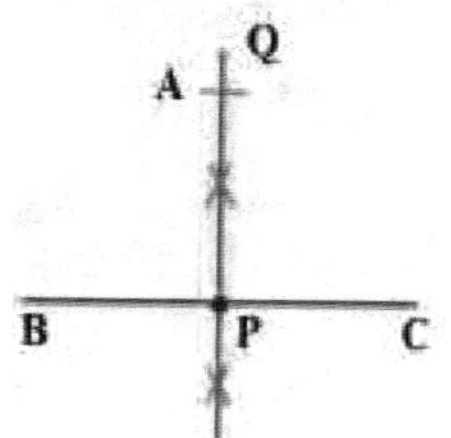

Step 4: Join AB and AC.

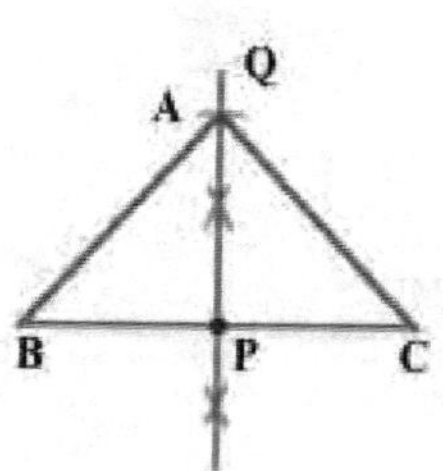

➜ Construction of triangle 1

Step 1: Draw the base BC and at the point B make an angle, say XBC equal to the given angle.

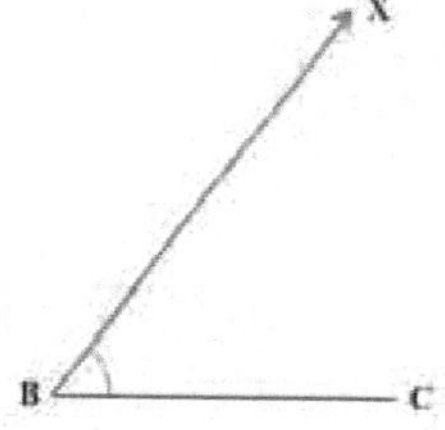

Step 2: From the ray BX, cut off line segment BD equal to AB + AC.

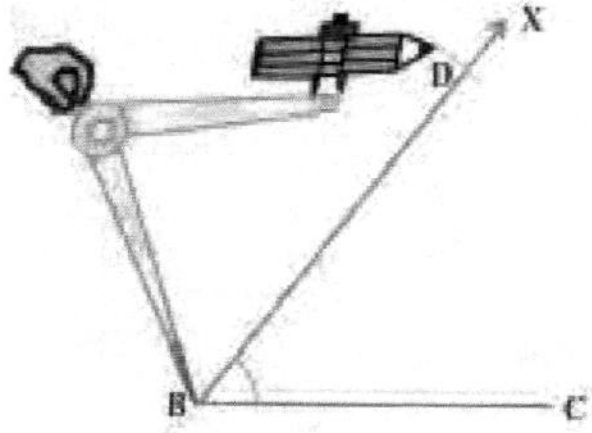

Step 3: Join DC.

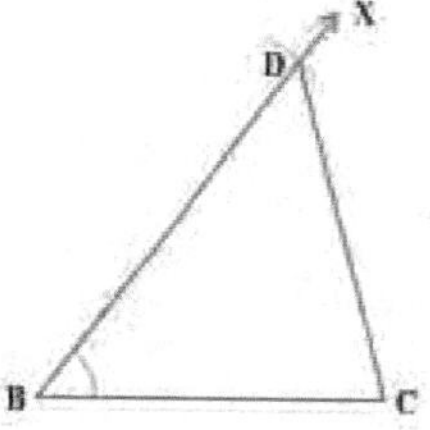

Step 4: Draw the perpendicular bisector PQ and CD to intersect BD at A.

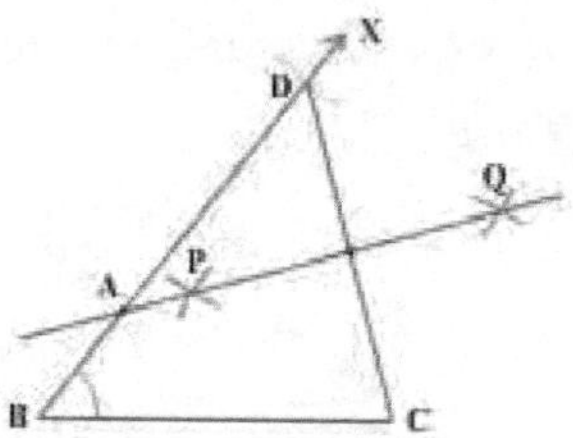

Step 5: Join AC to obtain the required triangle ABC.

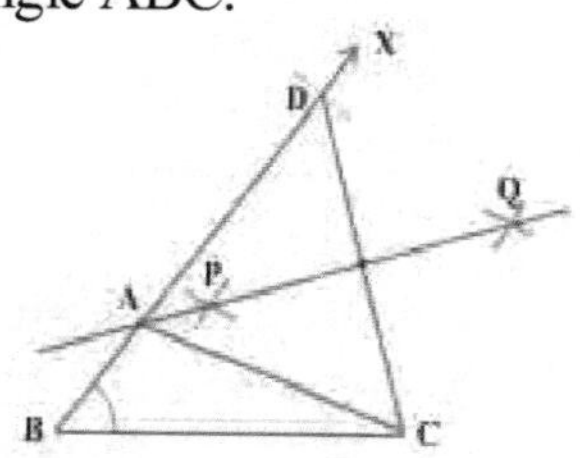

➜ Construction of triangle 2

To construct a triangle given its base, a base angle and the difference of the other two sides.

Given: The base BC, a base angle, say $\angle B$ and the difference of the other two sides

AB – AC or AC – AB.

Let AB > AC that is AB – AC is given.

Steps of Construction :

***Step* 1:** Draw the base BC and at the point B make an angle, say XBC equal to the given angle.

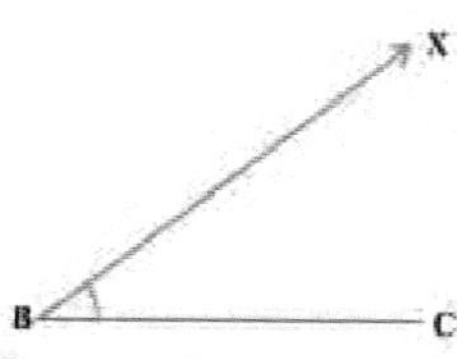

***Step* 2:** Cut the line segment BD equal to AB – AC from the ray BX.

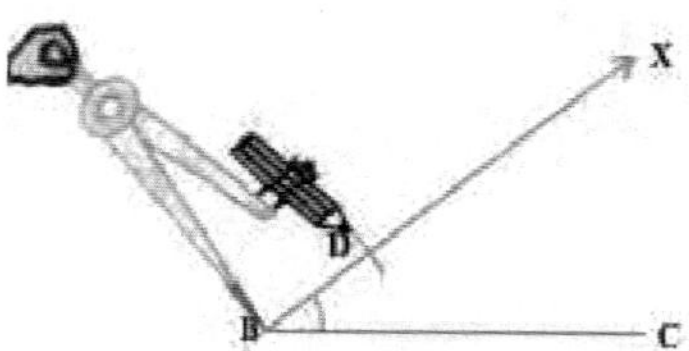

***Step* 3:** Join DC.

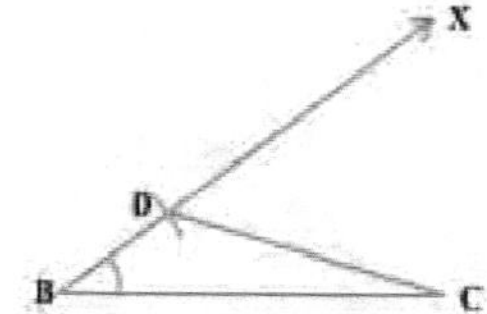

***Step* 4:** Draw the perpendicular bisector PQ of DC. Let it intersect BX at the point A.

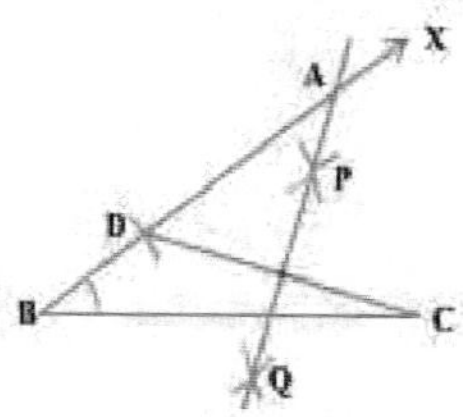

***Step* 5:** Join AC. Then ABC is the required triangle.

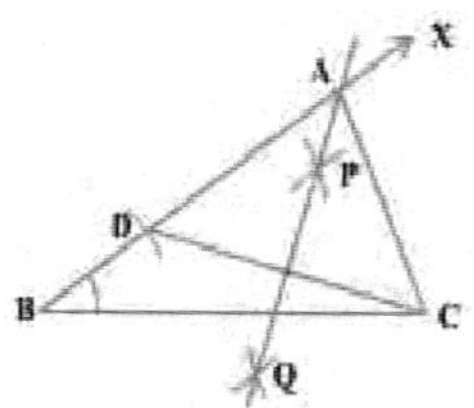

➜ Construction of triangle 3

To construct a triangle, given its perimeter and both the base angles.

Given: Base angles $\angle B$ and $\angle C$ of a ΔABC and the sum of its sides

AB + BC + CA

Steps of Construction :

***Step* 1:** Draw the line segment

XY = AB + BC + CA.

***Step* 2:** At X draw $\angle YXL = \angle B$ and at Y draw $\angle XYM = \angle C$

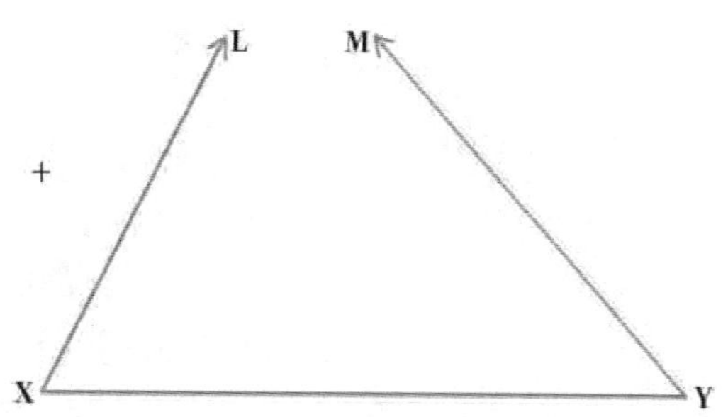

***Step* 3:** Draw the bisector XP of $\angle YXL$ and the bisector YQ of $\angle XYM$. Let XP and YQ meet at A.

***Step* 4:** Draw perpendicular bisector of XA meeting XY at B.

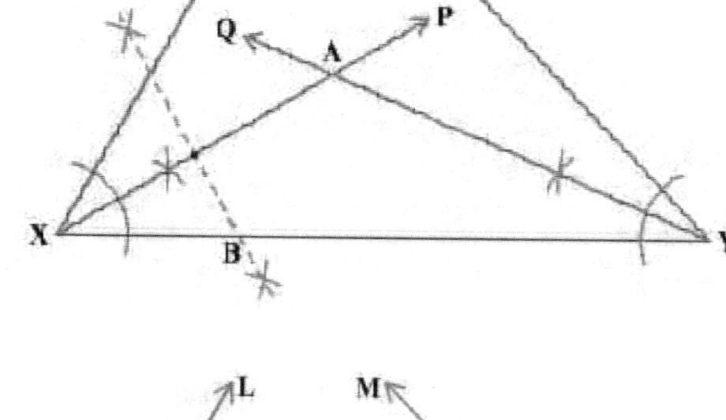

***Step* 5:** Draw perpendicular bisector of AY meeting XY at C.

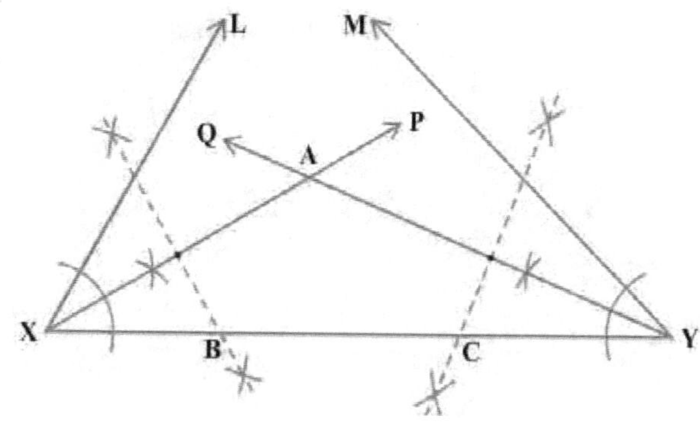

***Step* 6:** Join AB and AC. ΔABC is the required triangle.

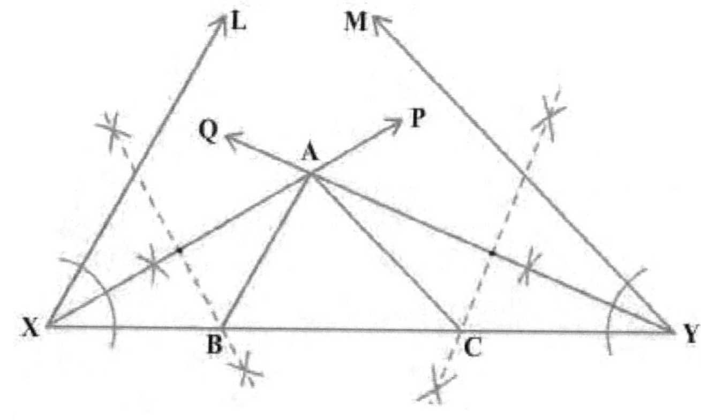

➜ **Construction of triangle: Base and one base angle given**

Construct: An isosceles triangle when BC = 5 cm and $\angle B = 45°$.

We know that the base angles of an isosceles triangle are equal.

(angles opposite to equal sides are equal)

Since base angles are equal, therefore, $\angle B = \angle C = 45°$.

Given: Side BC = 5 cm, $\angle B = 45°$.

To Construct : An isosceles triangle when BC = 5 cm and $\angle B = 45°$.

Steps of Construction :

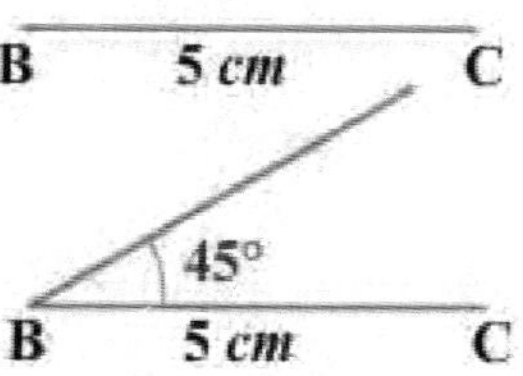

Step 1: Draw line segment BC = 5 cm.

Step 2: With B as centre, draw $\angle CBX = 45°$.

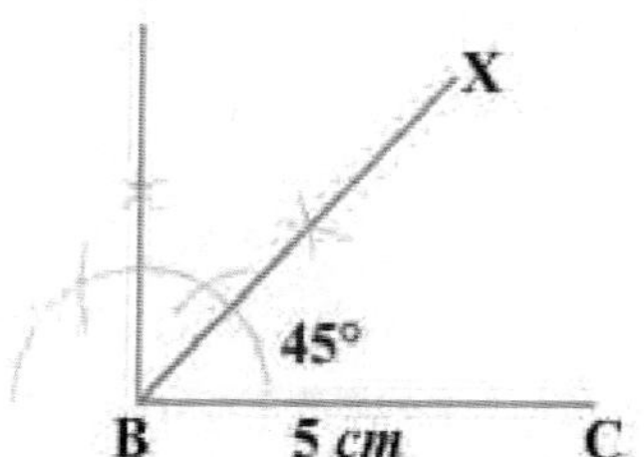

Step 3: With C as centre, draw $\angle BCY = 45°$.

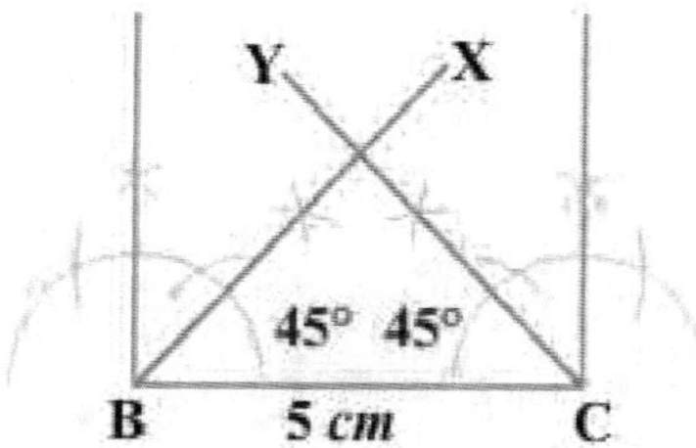

Step 4: BX and CY intersect at A. ΔABC is the required triangle.

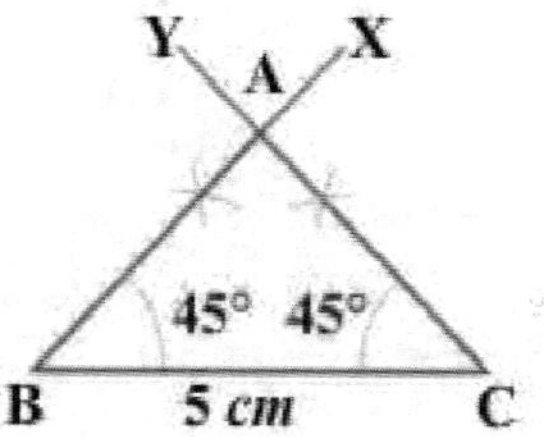

➜ **Construction of triangle: One of equal side and vertical angle given**

Construct: An isosceles ΔABC having one of its equal sides AB = 5.2 cm and vertical angle 75°.

An isosceles triangle has two equal sides. It is given that one of its equal sides AB = 5.2 cm.

$\therefore$ AB = BC (if we consider $\angle B$ as vertical angle)

and AB = AC (if we consider $\angle A$ as vertical angle)

For A as vertical angle, AB = 5.2, AC = 5.2 cm and $\angle A = 75°$.

Given: Side AB = 5.2 cm, AC = 5.2 cm, $\angle A = 75°$.

To Construct : An isosceles ΔABC having one of its equal sides AB = 5.2 cm and vertical angle 75°.

Steps of Construction :

Step 1: Draw line segment AX and cut off this at B such that AB = 5.2 cm.

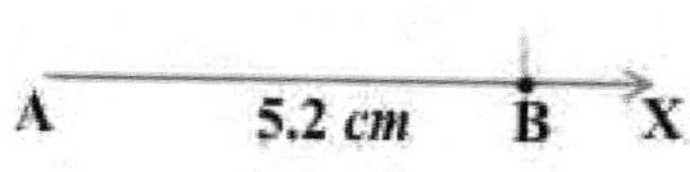

Step 2: With A as centre, draw $\angle BAY = 75°$.

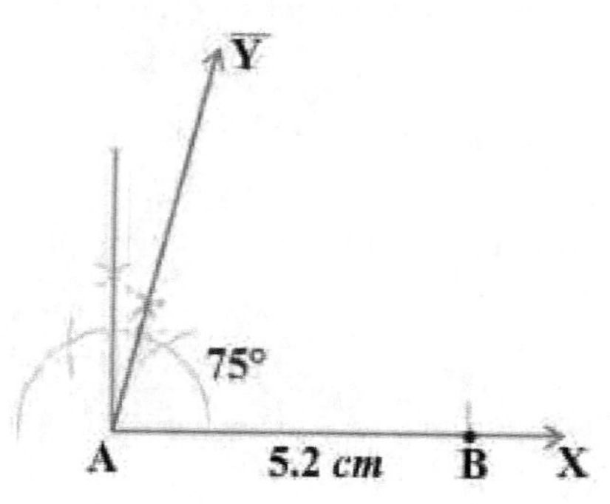

Step 3: With A as centre and radius 5.2 cm, draw an arc cutting AY at C.

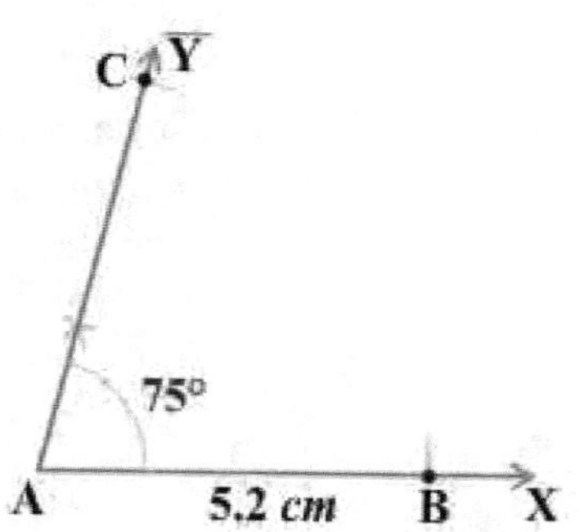

Step 4: Join BC. ΔABC is the required triangle.

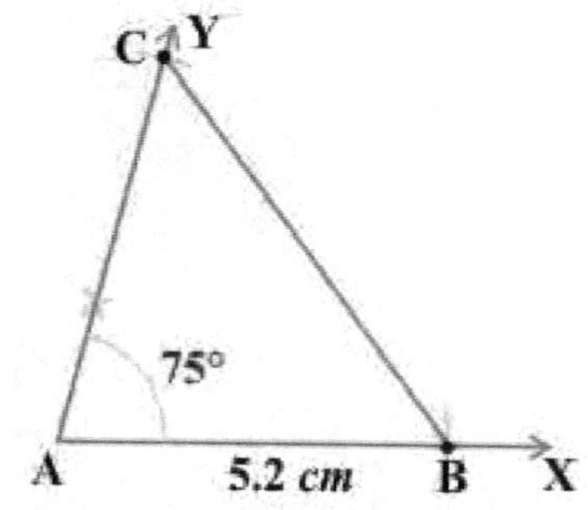

➜ **Construction of triangle: One of equal side and vertical angle given**

Construct: An equilateral ΔABC with side 5 cm.

All sides of an equilateral triangle are equal.

To Construct : An equilateral ΔABC with side 5 cm.

Steps of Construction :

Step 1: Draw BC = 5 cm.

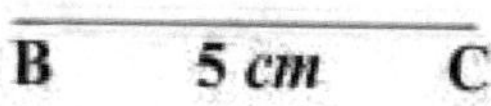

Step 2: With B as centre and radius 5 cm, draw an arc.

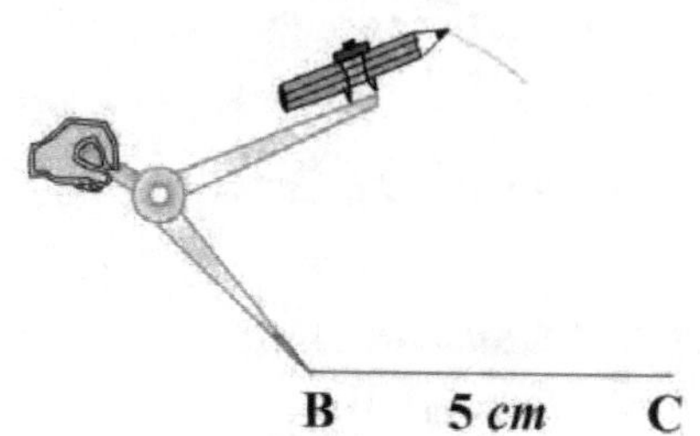

Step 3: With C as centre and radius draw another arc cutting previous arc at A.

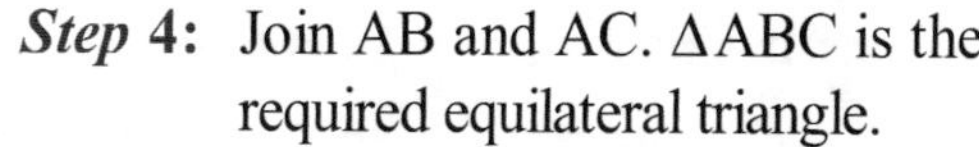

Step 4: Join AB and AC. ΔABC is the required equilateral triangle.

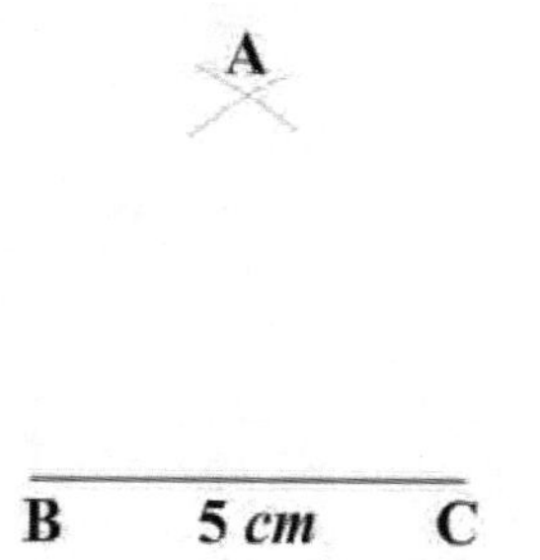

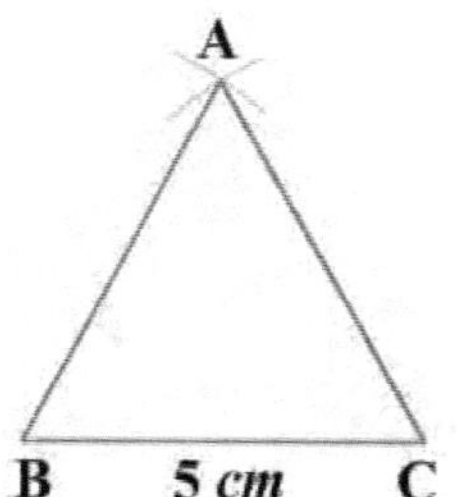

➜ Construction of Right angled Δ when sides are given

Construct: A right triangle when its sides are given.

To Construct : A right ΔABC where AB = 4cm, BC = 5 cm and ∠B = 90°.

Steps of Construction :

Step 1: Construct a line segment BC = 5 cm.

B 5 cm C

Step 2: Draw ∠CBX of measure 90°.

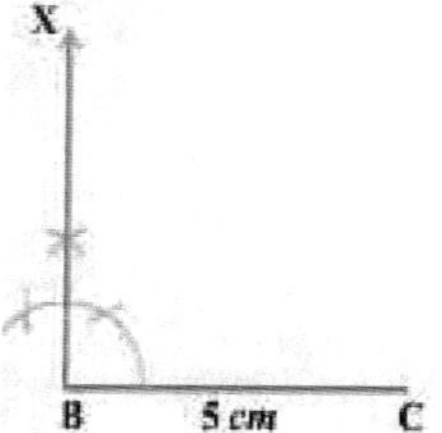

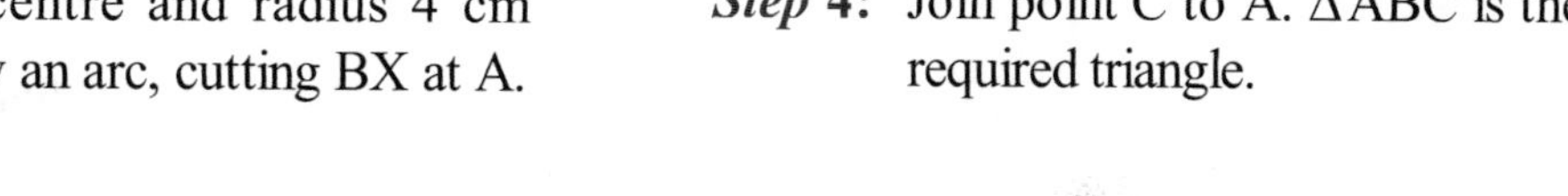

Step 3: With B as centre and radius 4 cm (= AB), draw an arc, cutting BX at A.

Step 4: Join point C to A. ΔABC is the required triangle.

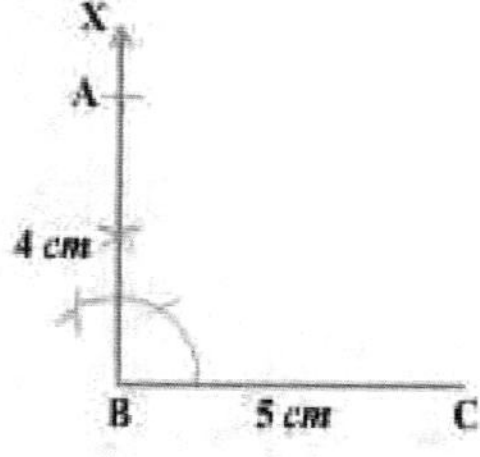

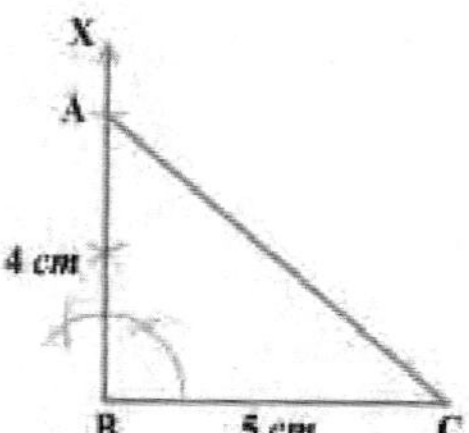

➜ One side and hypotenuse is given

Construct: A right triangle when its hypotenuse and one side are given.

To Construct : Line segment AB = 3 cm, AC = 5 cm and ∠B = 90°.

Steps of Construction :

***Step* 1:** Construct a line segment AB = 3 cm.

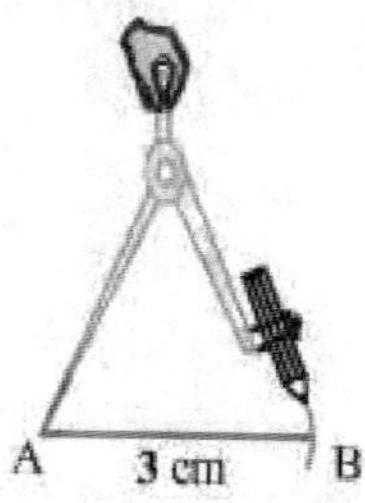

***Step* 2:** Draw ∠DBA of measure 90°.

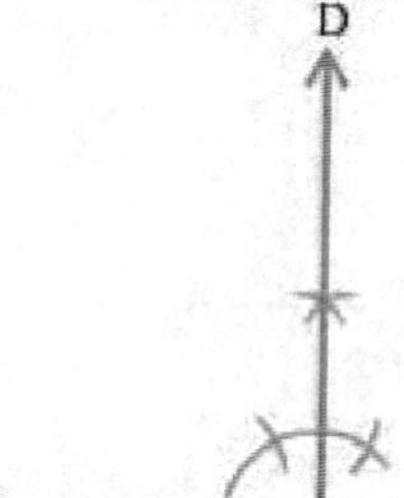

***Step* 3:** With A as the centre and radius 5 cm (= AC) *i.e.* hypotenuse draw an arc to intersect BD at C.

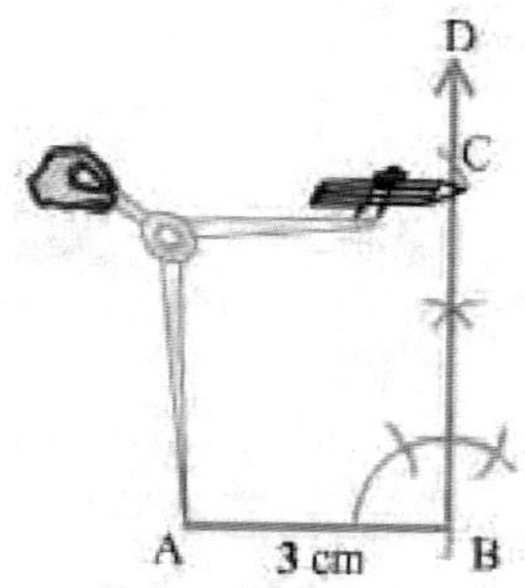

***Step* 4:** Join point A to C.

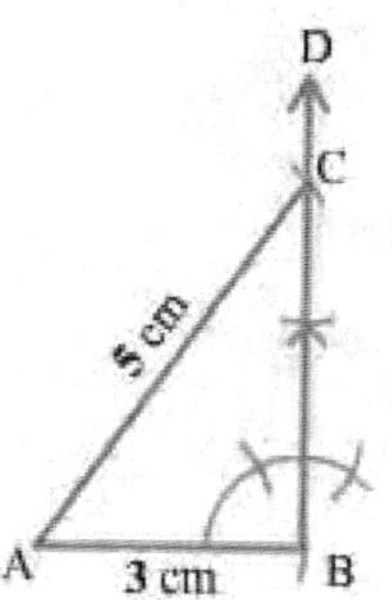

C. QUADRILATERALS

➔ Quadrilaterals

Let A, B, C and D be four points in a plane such that no three of them are collinear and the line segments AB, BC, CD and DA do not intersect except at their end points. Then the closed figure formed by these four line segments is called a quadrilateral and is read as quadrilateral ABCD.

A quadrilateral ABCD has

(i) four sides: AB, BC, CD and DA

(ii) four angles: ∠A, ∠B, ∠C and ∠D

(iii) two diagonals: AC and BD

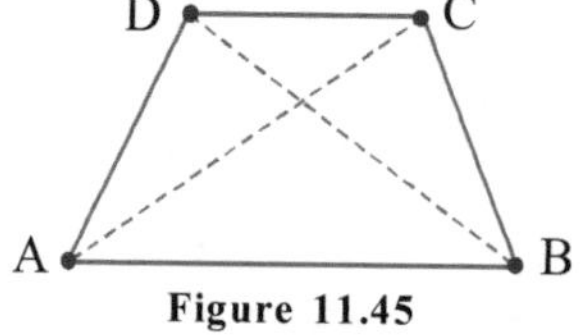

Figure 11.45

➔ Construction of Quadrilaterals

A quadrilateral has ten parts in all : four sides, four angles and two diagonals.

For constructing a quadrilateral, we need data about five specified parts of it.

We divide the required quadrilateral into two suitable triangles, which can be easily constructed. These two triangles together will form a quadrilateral.

➜ Construction

We consider quadrilateral ABCD as a figure made of two triangles :

(a) ΔABC and ΔADC when diagonal AC as common side is given.

(b) ΔABD and ΔBCD when diagonal BD as common side is given.

We first draw a rough sketch of the quadrilateral and then divide it into two suitable triangles which can conveniently be constructed.

➜ Construction of a quadrilateral when four sides and one diagonal are given

Illustration 1:

(a) To construct a quadrilateral ABCD in which AB = 3.5 cm, BC = 5.4 cm, CD = 4.8 cm, AD = 5 cm and AC = 7 cm.

Rough sketch

From a rough sketch , we observe that it is convenient to draw two triangles ABC and ACD.

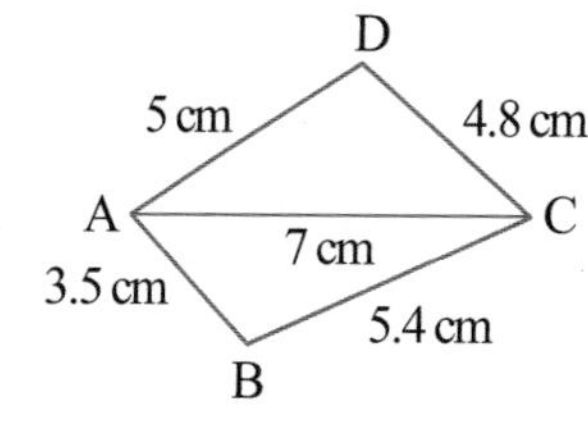

Figure 11.46

***Step* 1:** Draw AC = 7 cm.

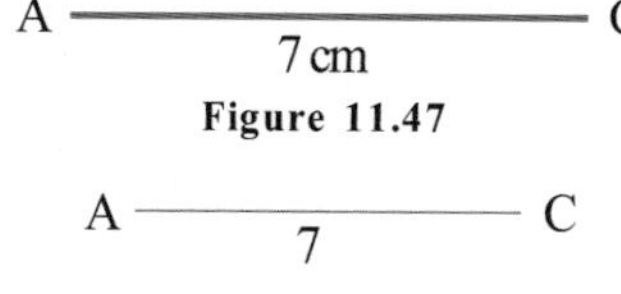

Figure 11.47

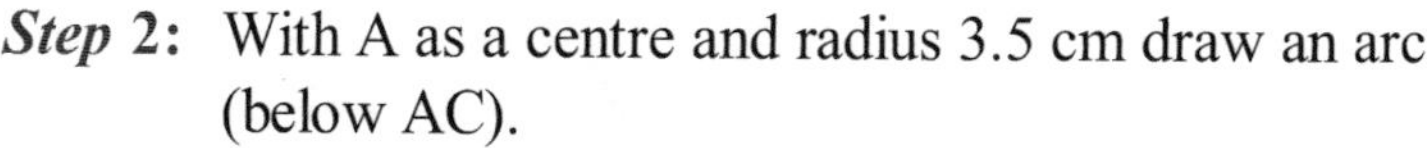

***Step* 2:** With A as a centre and radius 3.5 cm draw an arc (below AC).

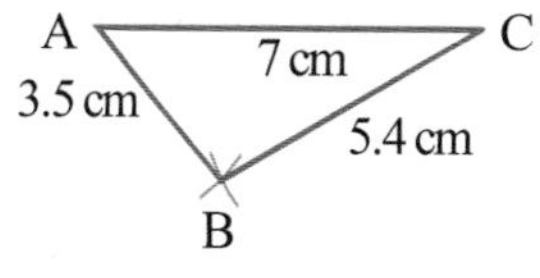

Figure 11.48

***Step* 3:** With C as a centre and radius 5.4 cm draw another arc cutting previous one at B, join AB and BC.

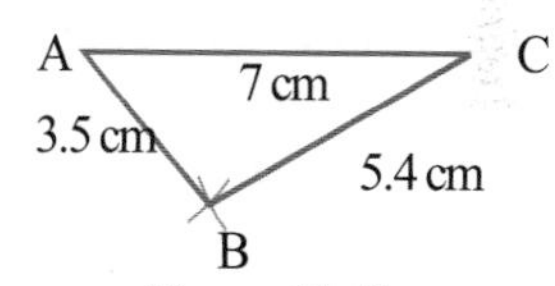

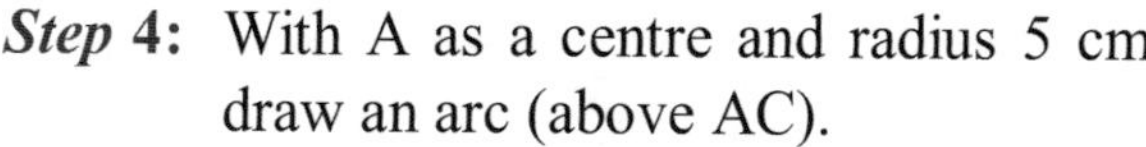

***Step* 4:** With A as a centre and radius 5 cm draw an arc (above AC).

Figure 11.49

***Step* 5:** With C as a centre and radius 4.8 cm draw another arc cutting previous one at D, join AD and CD.

***Step* 6:** ABCD is the required quadrilateral.

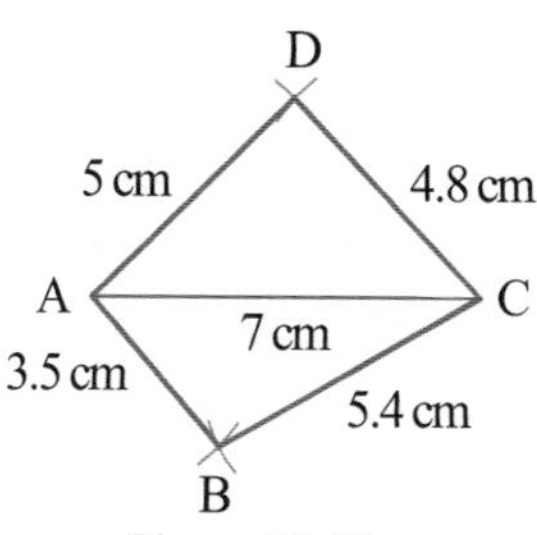

Figure 11.50

➜ Construction of a quadrilateral when three sides and two diagonals are given

Illustration 1:

Construct a quadrilateral ABCD in which BC = 4 cm, CA = 5.6 cm, AD = 4.5 cm, CD = 5 cm and BD = 6.5 cm.

Rough sketch

From the rough sketch, it is clear that the required quadrilateral is made up of two easily constructible triangles DCA and DCB, with side DC common.

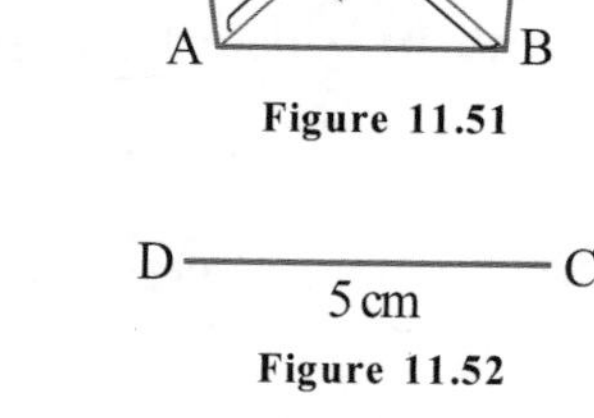

Figure 11.51

Step **1:** Draw DC = 5 cm.

D C
5 cm

Figure 11.52

Step **2:** With D as centre and radius 4.5 cm draw an arc.

D C
5 cm

Figure 11.53

Step **3:** With C as centre and radius 5.6 cm draw another arc to intersect previous arc at A. Join AD and AC.

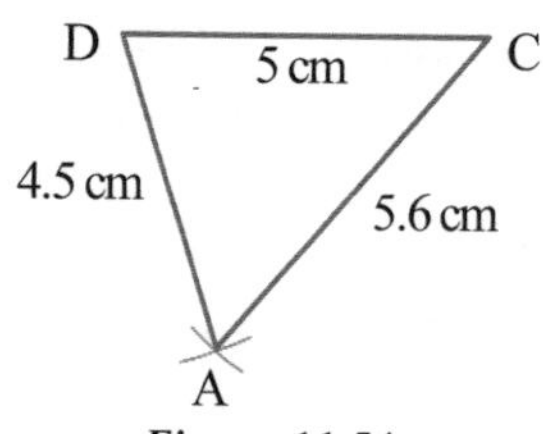

Figure 11.54

Step **4:** With D as centre and radius equal to 6.5 cm draw an arc.

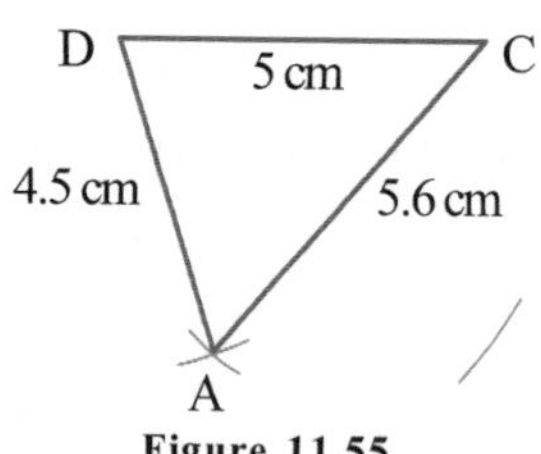

Figure 11.55

Step **5:** With C as centre and radius equal to 4 cm draw another arc to intersect the previously drawn arc at B. Join BC, BD and AB.

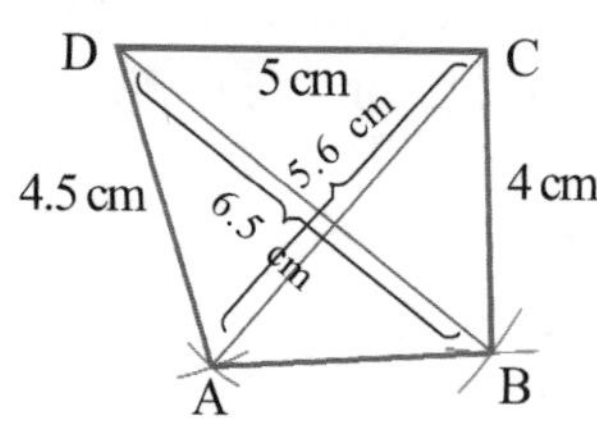

Figure 11.56

Step **6:** ABCD is the required quadrilateral.

➜ Construction of a quadrilateral when three angles and two included sides are given

Illustration 1:

Construct a quadrilateral ABCD in which AB = 4.3 cm, BC = 5 cm, ∠A = 75°, ∠B = 100° and ∠C = 70°.

Firstly, we draw a rough sketch.

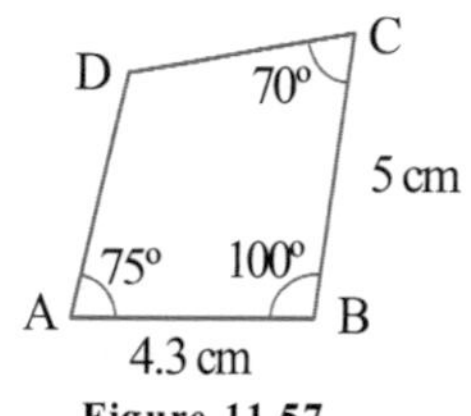

Figure 11.57

Steps of construction :

Step 1: Draw AB = 4.3 cm.

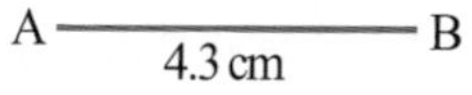

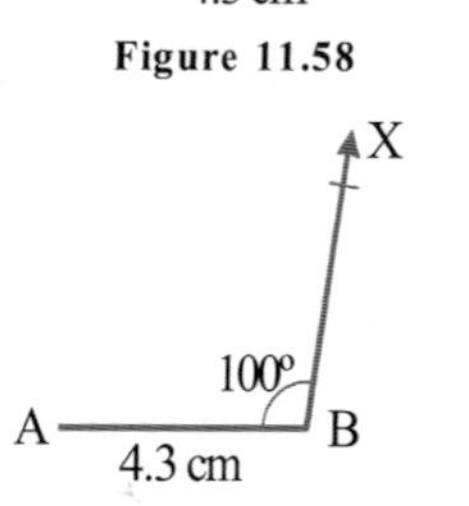

Figure 11.58

Step 2: Draw ∠ABX = 100°.

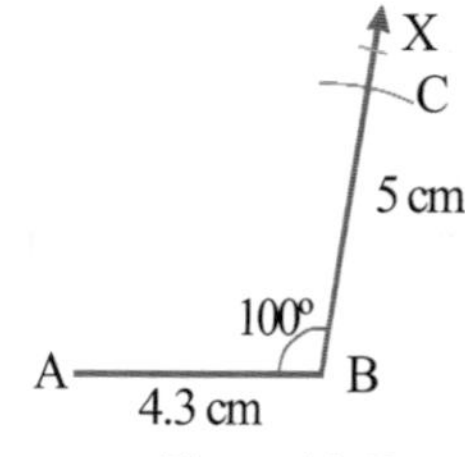

Figure 11.59

Step 3: With B as centre and radius 5 cm, draw an arc to cut BX at C.

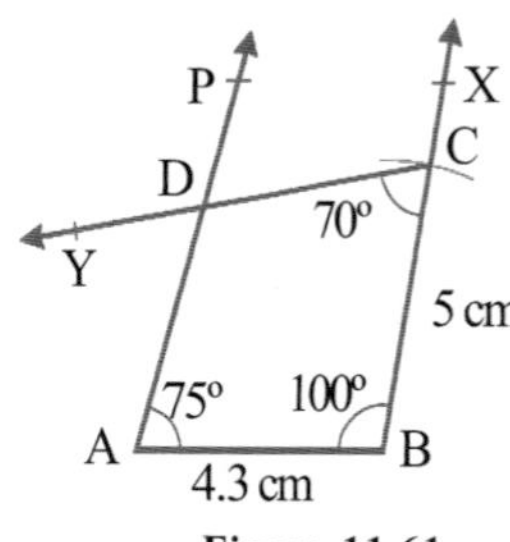

Figure 11.60

Step 4: Draw ∠BCY = 70° and ∠BAP = 75°.

Step 5: Let CY and AP intersect at D.

Step 6: ABCD is the required quadrilateral.

Figure 11.61

➜ Construction of a quadrilateral when three sides and their included angles are given

Construct: Construct a quadrilateral ABCD in which AB = 4.2 cm, BC = 5 cm, CD = 5.3 cm, ∠B = 120°, ∠C = 75°.

Rough sketch

On drawing rough sketch we observe that we can draw two triangles ABC and BCD as in each case two sides and the included angle are given. The side BC is common to both.

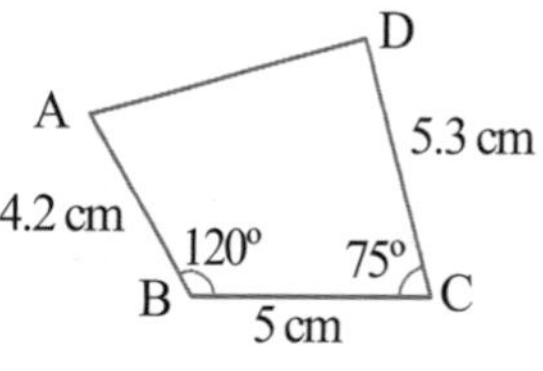

Figure 11.62

***Step* 1:** Draw BC = 5 cm.

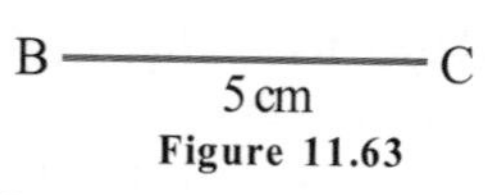

Figure 11.63

***Step* 2:** Draw ∠CBX = 120°.

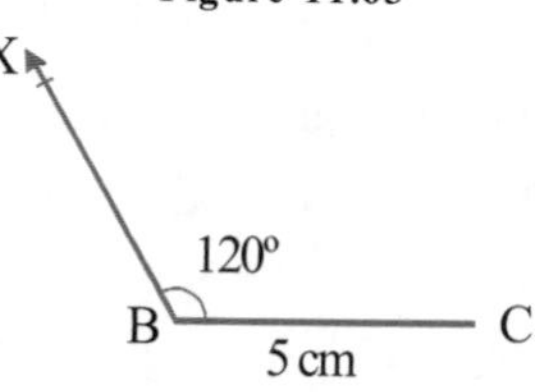

Figure 11.64

***Step* 3:** With B as centre and radius 4.2 cm, cut off BA = 4.2 cm along BX.

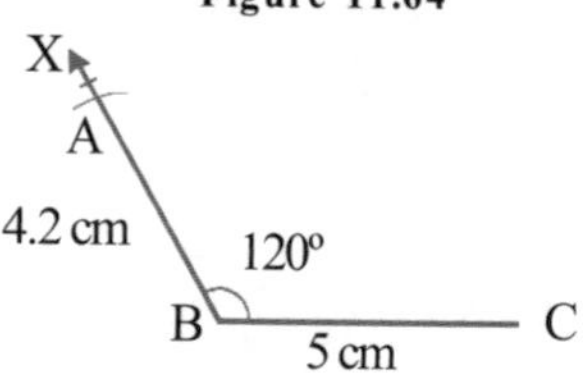

Figure 11.65

***Step* 4:** Draw ∠BCY = 75°.

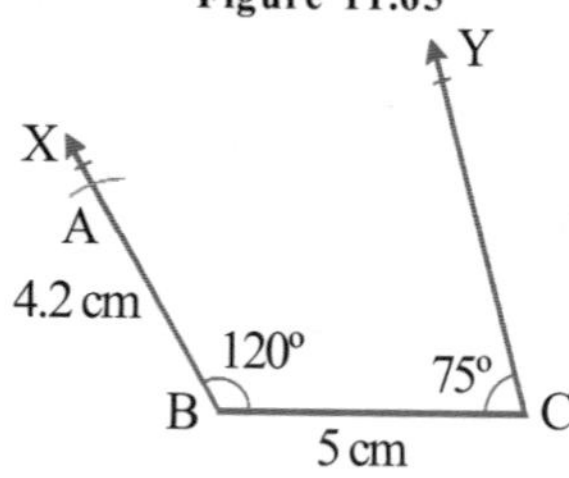

Figure 11.66

***Step* 5:** With C as centre and radius 5.3 cm, draw an arc to cut off CY at D.

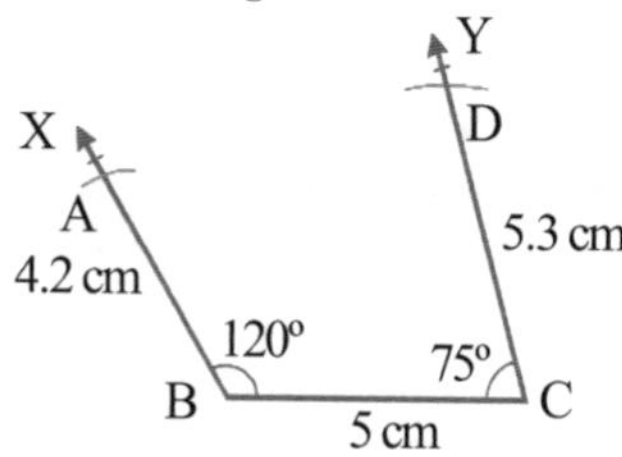

Figure 11.67

***Step* 6:** Join DA.

***Step* 7:** ABCD is the required quadrilateral.

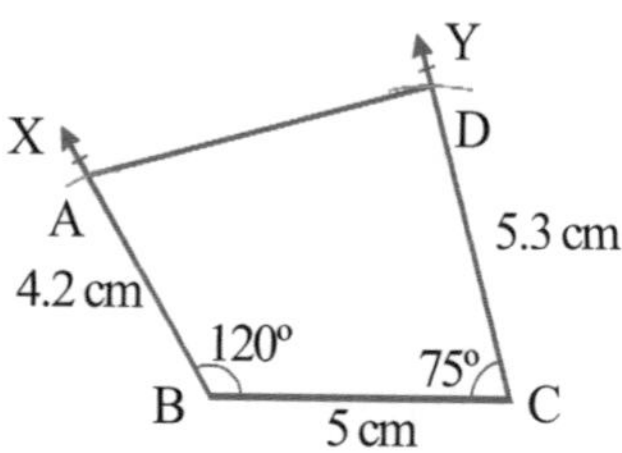

Figure 11.68

➔ Construction of a quadrilateral when its four sides and one angle are given

Construct: Construct a quadrilateral ABCD in which AB = 4.5 cm, BC = 3.8 cm, CD = 5 cm, AD = 6 cm and ∠B = 90°.

Rough sketch

From a rough sketch, it is clear that in ΔABC, two sides and the included angle are given. So, we first construct ΔABC. AC is known from ΔABC and AD and CD of ΔACD are given.

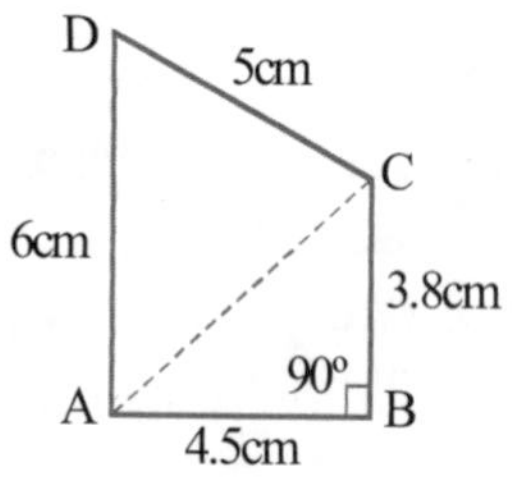

Figure 11.69

Steps of construction :

***Step* 1:** Draw AB = 4.5 cm.

A 4.5cm B

Figure 11.70

***Step* 2:** Draw $\angle$ ABX = 90°.

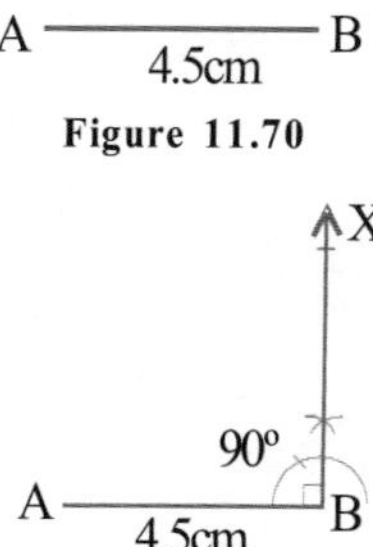

Figure 11.71

***Step* 3:** With B as centre and radius 3.8 cm cut off BC along BX.

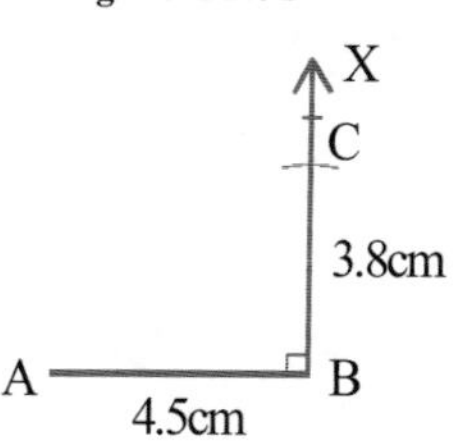

Figure 11.72

***Step* 4:** Join AC as a dotted line.

***Step* 5:** With A as centre and radius 6 cm draw an arc on the side opposite to B.

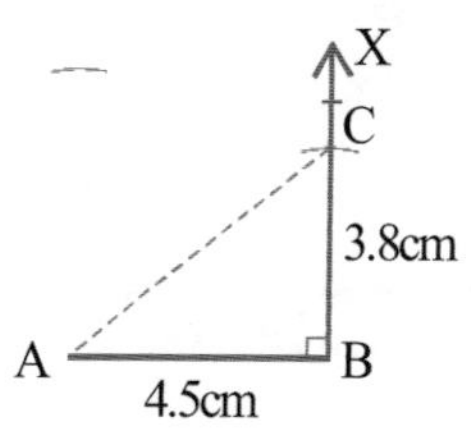

Figure 11.73

***Step* 6:** With C as centre and radius 5 cm, draw an arc intersecting the previous arc at D. Join CD and AD.

***Step* 7:** ABCD is the required quadrilateral.

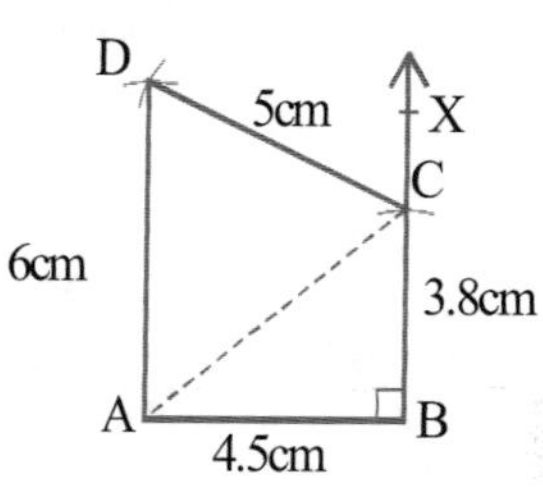

Figure 11.74

➜ Construction of a Parallelograms

Construct: Construct a parallelogram PQRS in which PQ = 5.6 cm, QR = 4.2 cm, $\angle$Q = 120°.

We know that opposite sides of a parallelogram are equal.

To Construct : A parallelogram PQRS in which PQ = 5.6 cm, QR = 4.2 cm, $\angle$Q = 120°.

Steps of construction :

Step **1:** Draw line segment PQ = 5.6 cm.

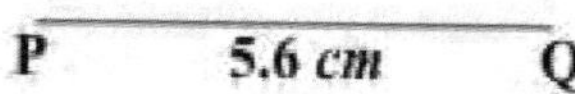

Step **2:** Draw ∠ PQX = 120°.

Step **3:** With Q as centre and radius 4.2 cm, draw an arc cutting QX at R.

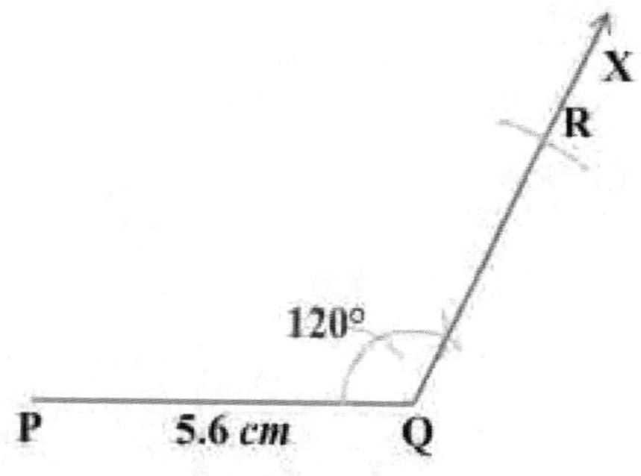

Step **4:** With P as centre and radius 4.2 cm, draw an arc. With R as centre and radius 5.6 cm, draw another arc cutting the previous arc at S.

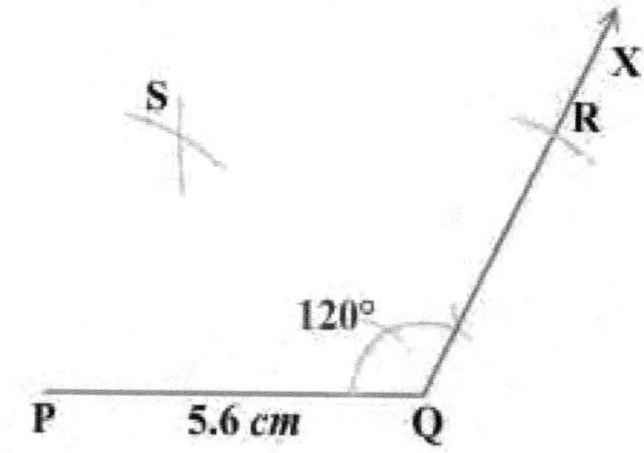

Step **5:** Join PS and SR. PQRS is the required parallelogram.

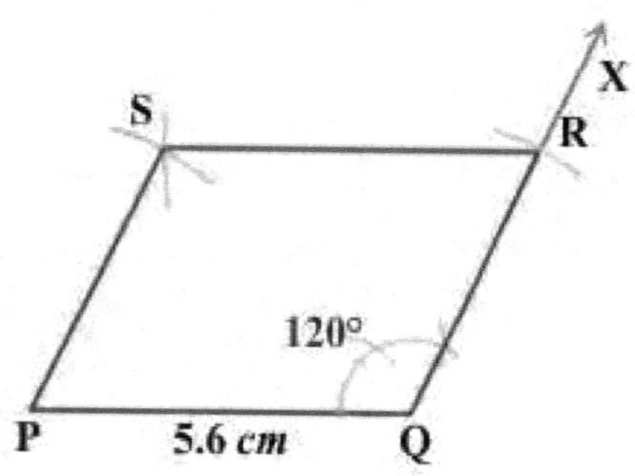

➜ **Two adjacent sides and one diagonal are given**

Construct: A parallelogram ABCD in which AB = 4.8 cm, BC = 3.5 cm and diagonal AC = 5.4 cm.

We know that oppposite sides of a parallelogram are equal.

To Construct : A parallelogram ABCD in which AB = 4.8 cm, BC = 3.5 cm and diagonal AC = 5.4 cm.

Steps of construction :

***Step* 1:** Draw line segment AB = 4.8 cm.

A 4.8 *cm* B

***Step* 2:** With B as centre and radius equal to BC = 3.5 cm, draw an arc.

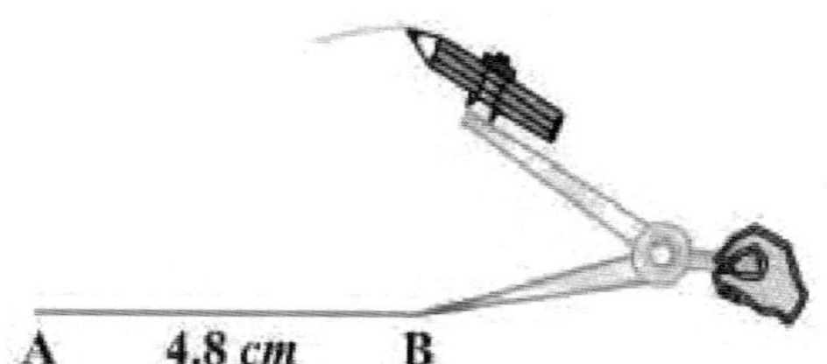

***Step* 3:** With A as centre and radius equal to diagonal AC = 5.4 cm, draw another arc, cutting previous arc at C.

C

A 4.8 *cm* B

***Step* 4:** With A as centre and radius 3.5 cm, draw an arc. With R as centre and radius 4.8 cm, draw another arc cutting the previous arc at D.

D C

A 4.8 *cm* B

***Step* 5:** Join AD, BC and CD. ABCD is the required parallelogram.

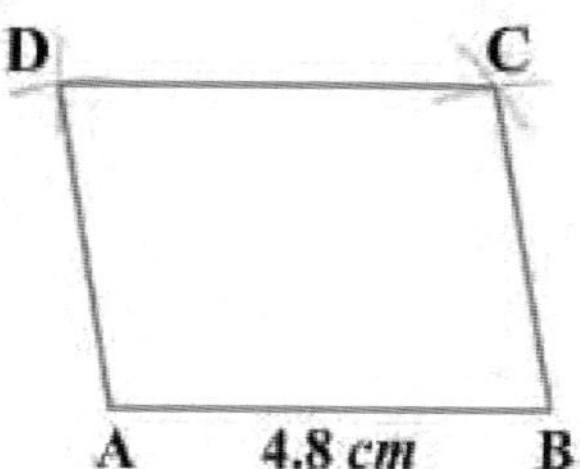

➜ One side and both diagonals are given

Construct: A parallelogram ABCD in which AB = 4.8 cm, BC = 4.2 cm and BD = 5.8 cm.

We know that oppposite sides of a parallelogram are equal.

Steps of construction :

***Step* 1:** Draw line segment AB = 4.8 cm.

A 4.8 *cm* B

***Step* 2:** With A as centre and radius = $\frac{1}{2}$ AC, draw an arc.

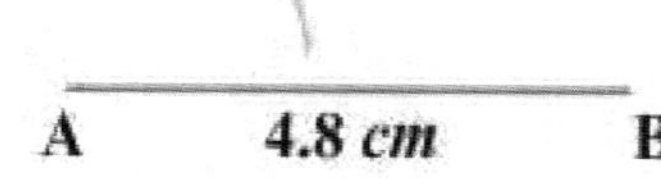

Step 3: With B as centre and radius = $\frac{1}{2}$ BD, draw another arc cutting previous arc at O.

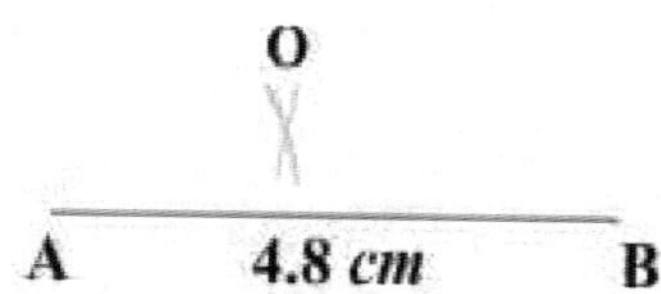

Step 4: Join AO and produce it to C so that AO = OC.

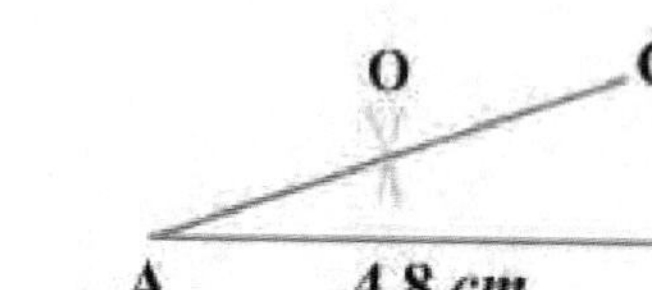
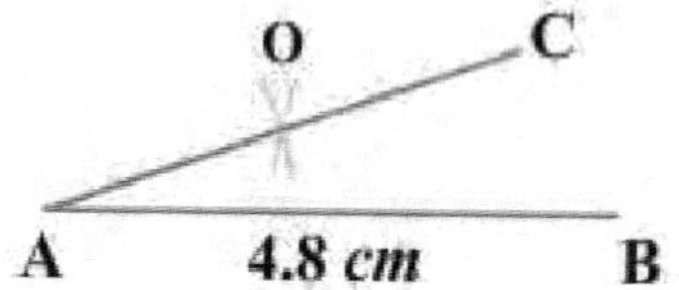

Step 5: Join BO and produce it to D, so that BO = OD.

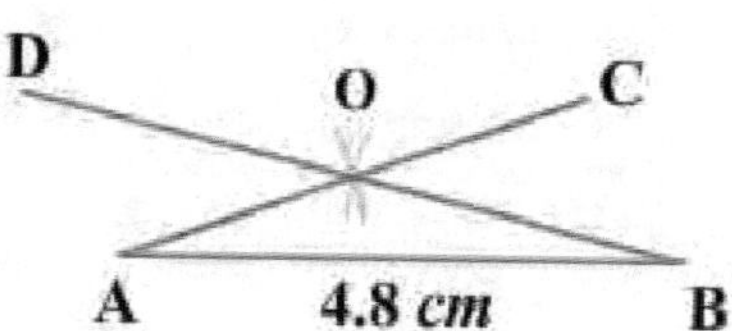

Step 6: Join AD, BC and CD. ABCD is the required parallelogram.

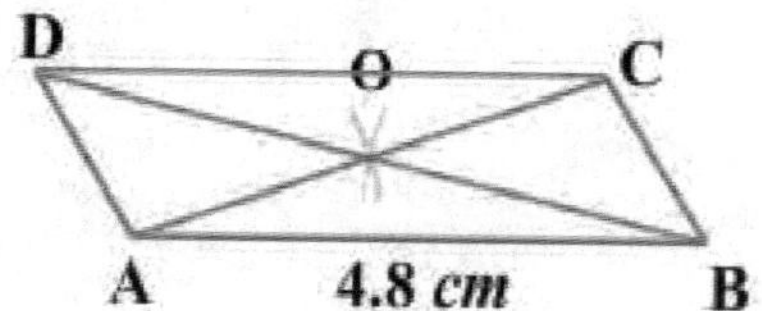

➜ Construction of Rhombus: One side and one angle are given

Construct: A rhombus ABCD such that AB = 6 cm, $\angle A = 60°$.

Steps of construction :

Step 1: Draw line segment AB = 6 cm.

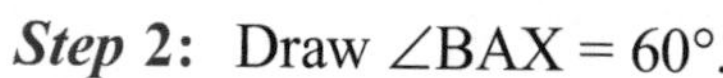

Step 2: Draw $\angle BAX = 60°$.

Step 3: Cut off AD = 6 cm from AX.

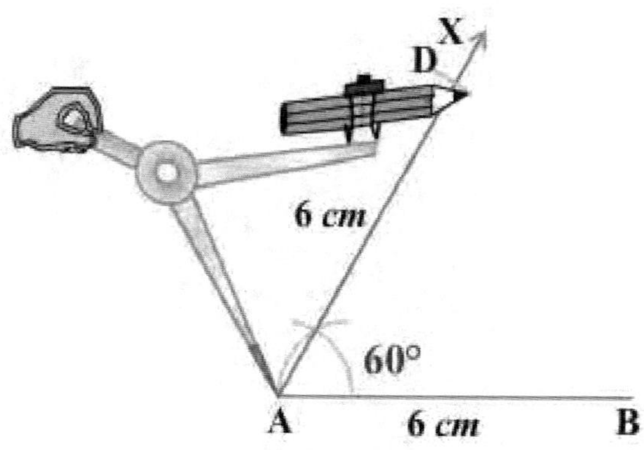

Step 4: With B as centre and radius 6 cm, draw an arc. With D as centre and same radius, draw another arc cutting the previous arc at C.

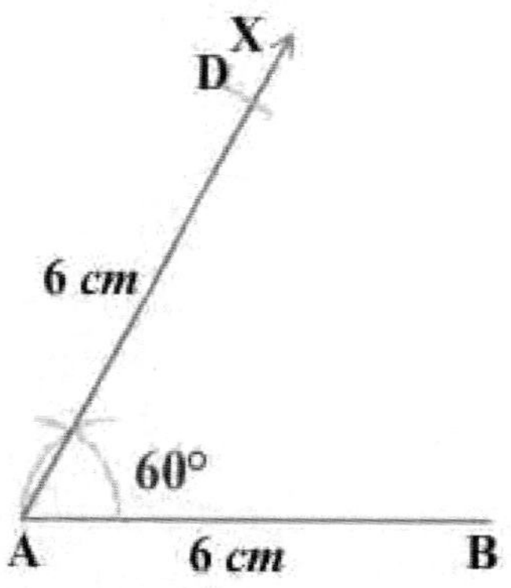

Step 5: Join BC and CD. ABCD is the required rhombus.

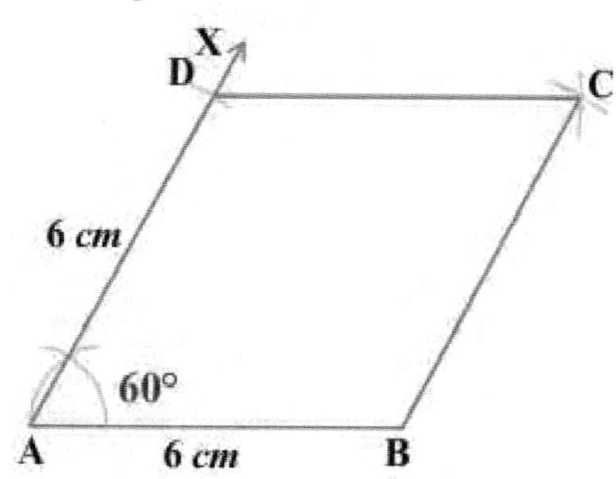

➜ One side and one diagonal are given

Construct: A rhombus ABCD in which AB = 4.2 cm and diagonal AC = 6 cm.

To Construct : A rhombus ABCD with diagonal AC = 6 cm and side AB = 4.2 cm.

Steps of construction :

Step 1: Draw diagonal AC = 6 cm.

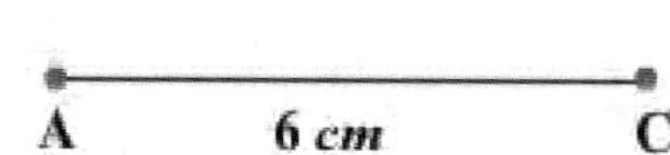

Step 2: With centres A and C and radius 4.2 cm, draw arcs on both sides of AC cutting each other at B and D.

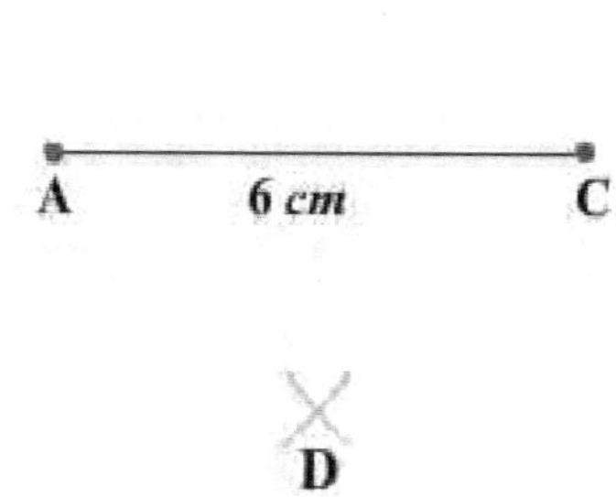

Step 3: Join AB, BC, CD and DA. ABCD is the required rhombus.

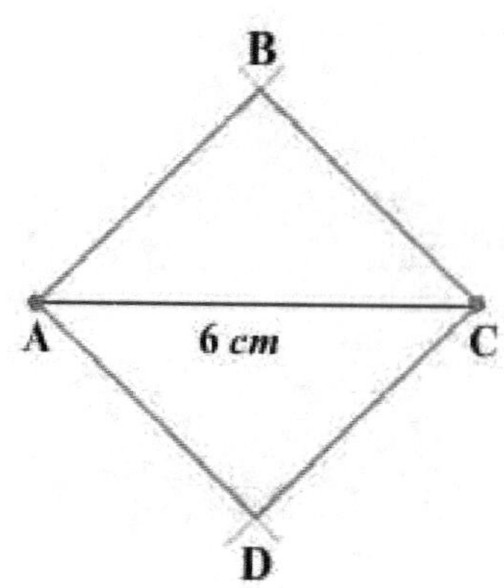

➜ Both diagonals are given

Construct: A rhombus ABCD in which BD = 5.8 cm and diagonal AC = 6.2 cm.

We know that the diagonals of a rhombus bisect each other at right angles.

Steps of construction :

Step 1: Draw line segment AC = 6.2 cm.

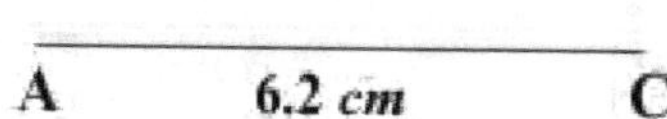

Step 2: Draw the perpendicular bisector PQ of AC bisecting it at O.

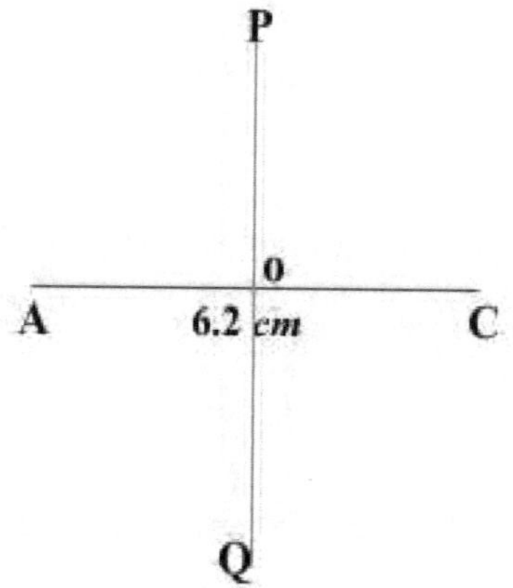

Step 3: Cut off OB = OD $= \frac{1}{2}(5.8) = 2.9$ cm from OP and OQ respectively.

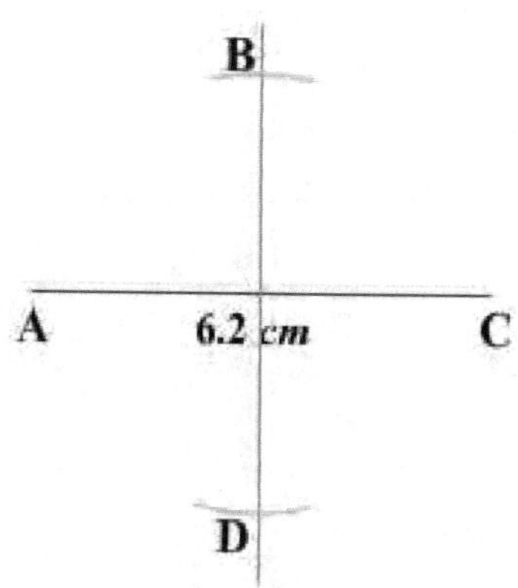

Step 4: Join AB, BC, CD and DA. ABCD is the required rhombus.

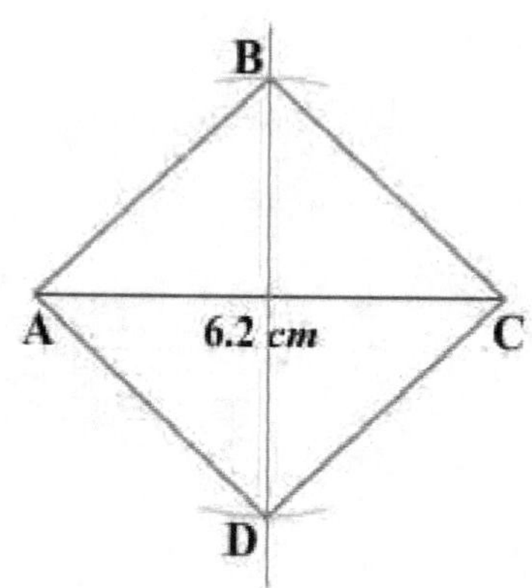

(D.) CONSTRUCTING ANGLES: 60°, 30°, 120°, 90°, 45°

➜ Constructing a 60° angle

***Step* 1:** Draw a line l and mark a point O on it.

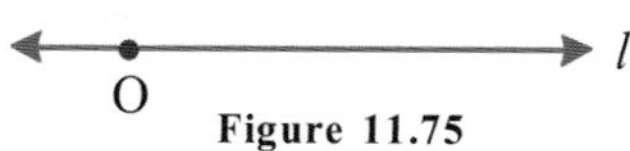

Figure 11.75

***Step* 2:** Place the pointer of the compasses at O and draw an arc of convenient radius which cuts the line l at a point say A.

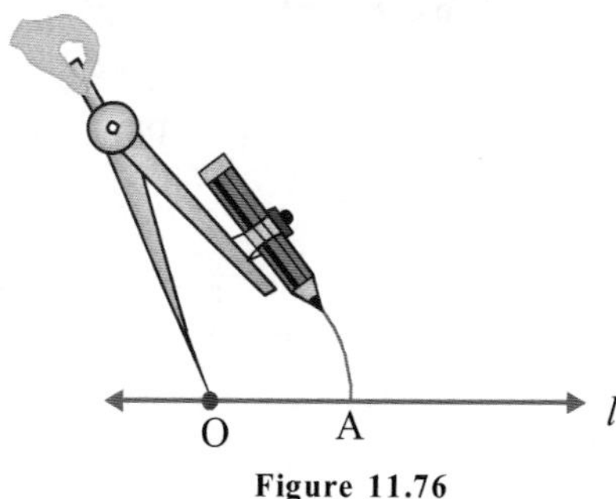

Figure 11.76

***Step* 3:** With the pointer at A (as centre), now draw an arc that passes through O.

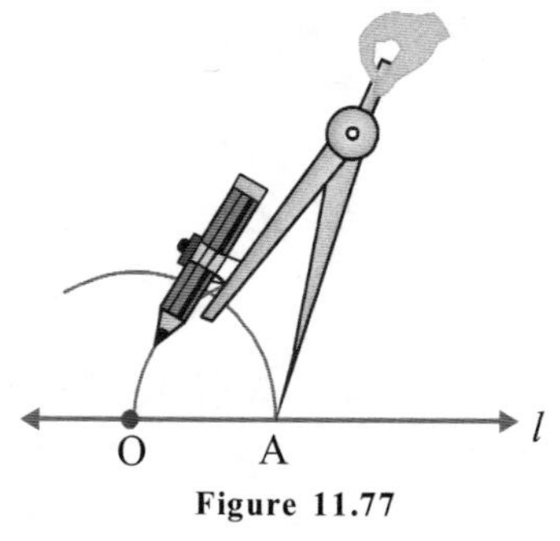

Figure 11.77

***Step* 4:** Let the two arcs of steps 2 and 3 intersect each other at B. Join OB.

We get ∠BOA whose measure is 60°.

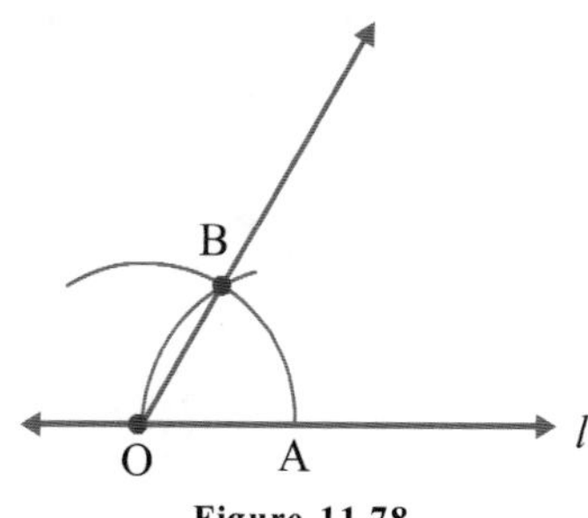

Figure 11.78

➜ Constructing a 30° angle

We know that an angle of 30° is half of an angle of 60°. So, we will first construct an angle of 60° and then bisect it to obtain an angle of 30°.

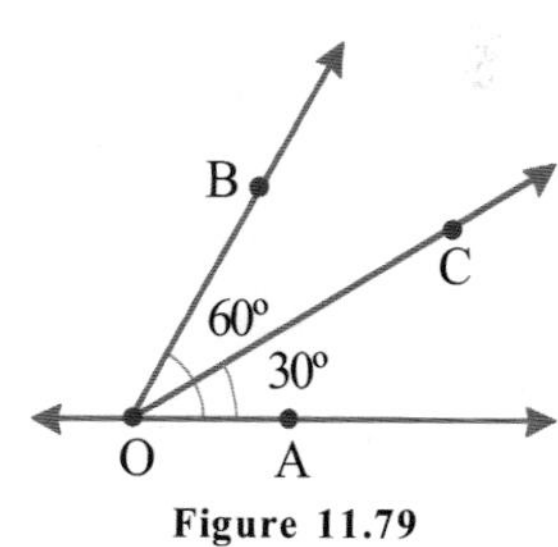

Figure 11.79

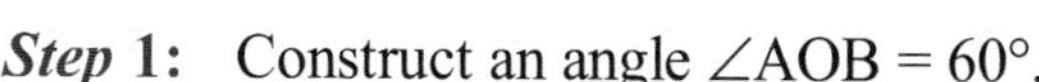

***Step* 1:** Construct an angle ∠AOB = 60°.

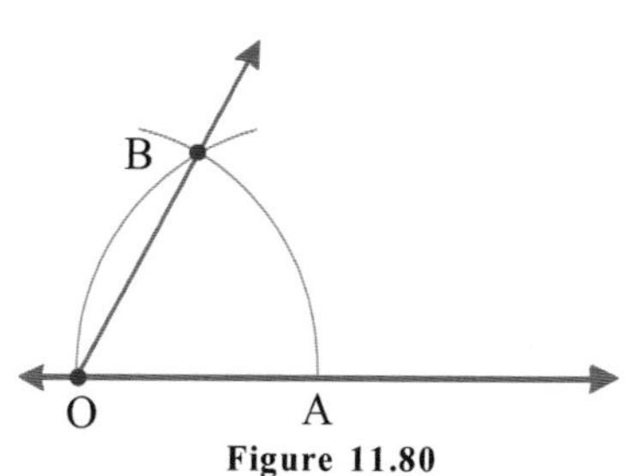

Figure 11.80

***Step* 2:** Draw the bisector OC of $\angle AOB$.

Then, $\angle AOC = 30°$.

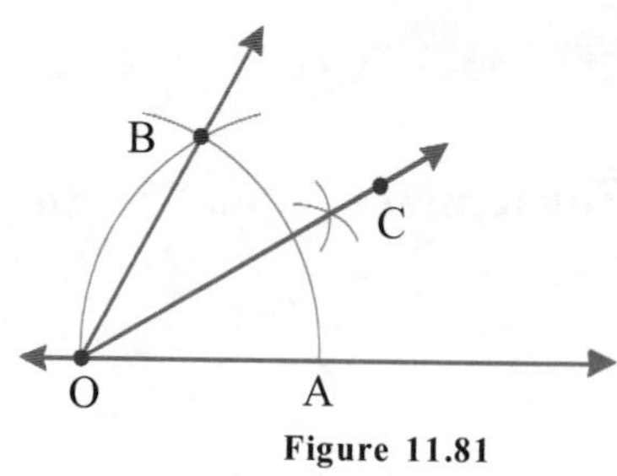

Figure 11.81

➜ Constructing a 120° angle

***Step* 1:** Draw any line PQ and take a point O on it.

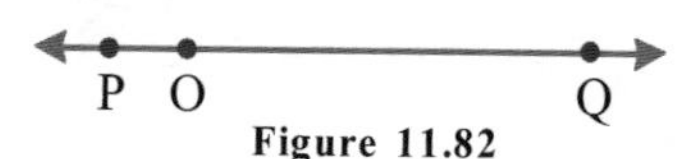

Figure 11.82

***Step* 2:** Place the pointer of the compasses at O and draw an arc of convenient radius which cuts the line at A.

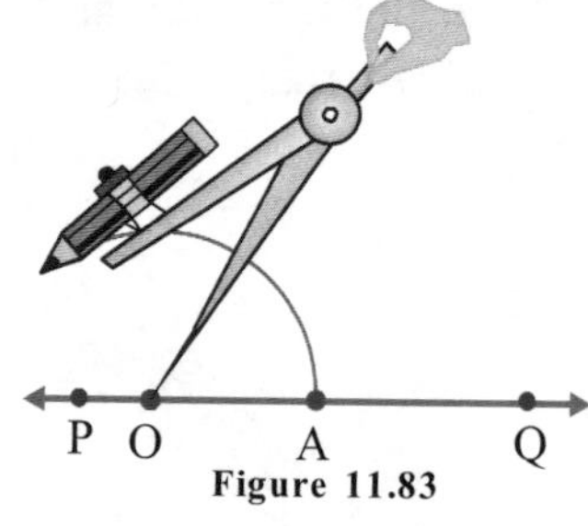

Figure 11.83

***Step* 3:** Without disturbing the radius on the compasses, draw an arc with A as centre which cuts the first arc at B.

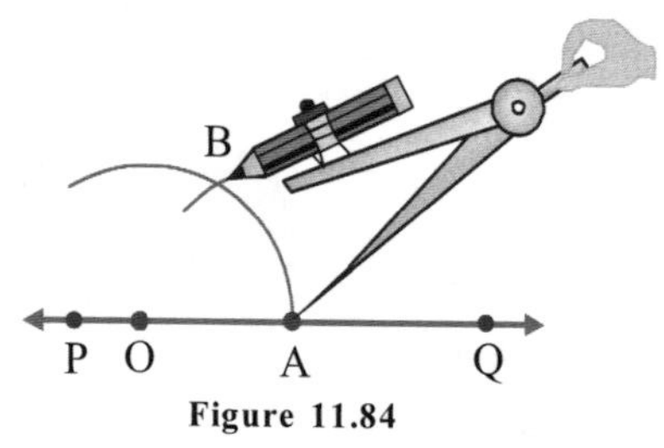

Figure 11.84

***Step* 4:** Again without disturbing the radius on the compasses and with B as centre, draw an arc which cuts the first arc at C.

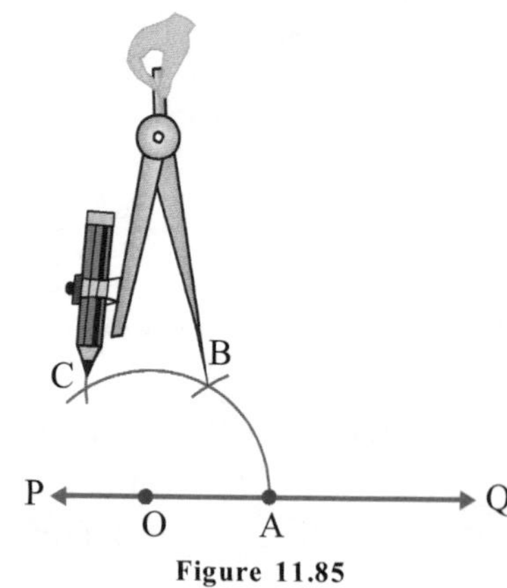

Figure 11.85

***Step* 5:** Join OC to form ray OC.

Then, $\angle COA$ is the required angle of 120°.

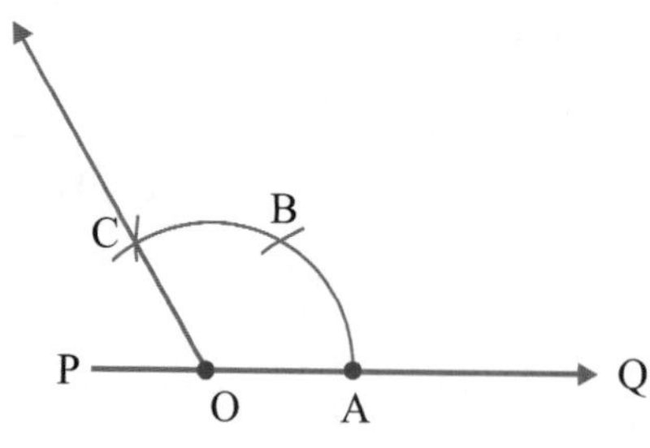

Figure 11.86

➜ Constructing a 90° angle

Step 1: Draw a ray OP.

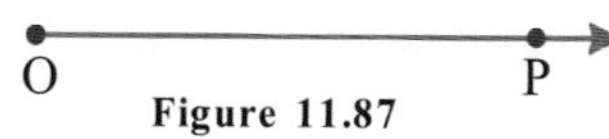

Figure 11.87

Step 2: With O as centre and a convenient radius, draw an arc, intersecting OP at A.

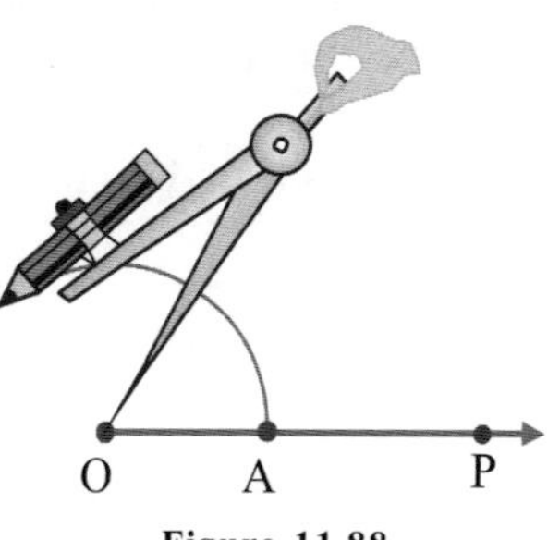

Figure 11.88

Step 3: With A as centre and the same radius, draw an arc which cuts the previous arc at B.

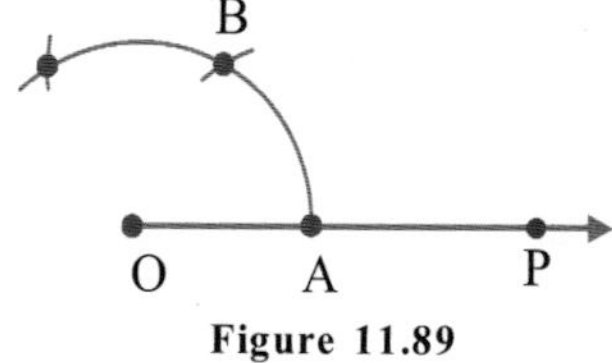

Figure 11.89

Step 4: With B as centre and the same radius, draw an arc cutting the first arc at C.

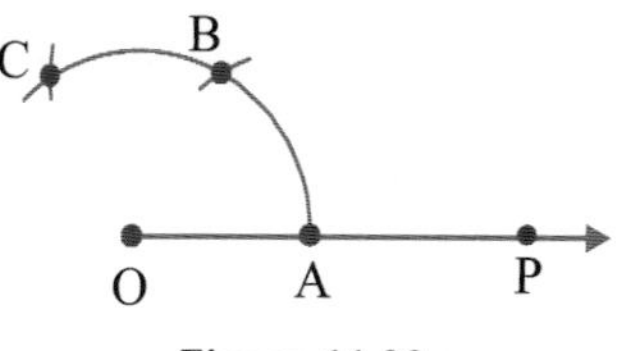

Figure 11.90

Step 5: With B as centre and convenient radius (more than $\frac{1}{2}$ BC), draw an arc.

Step 6: With C as centre and the same radius as in step 5, draw another arc cutting the arc drawn in the step 5 at D.

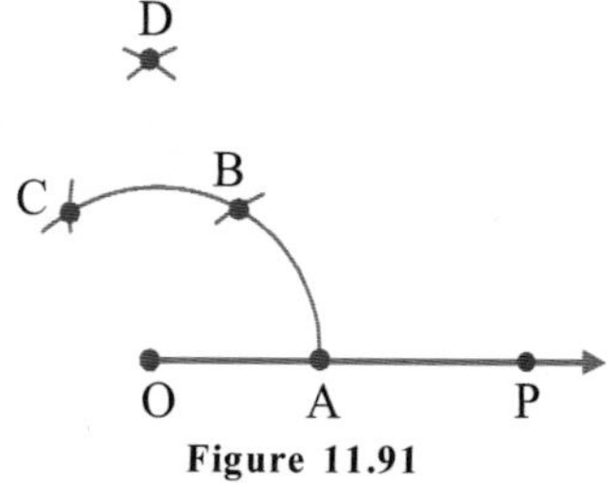

Figure 11.91

Step 7: Join OD to form ray OD. Then, $\angle POD = 90°$.

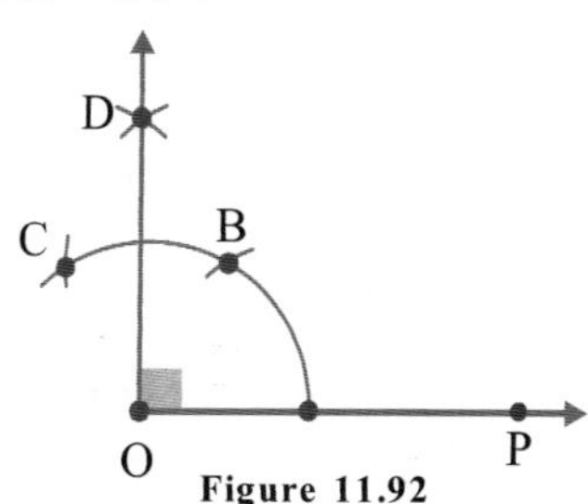

Figure 11.92

➜ Constructing a 45° angle

We know that an angle of 45° is half of an angle of 90°. So, we will first construct an angle of 90° and then bisect it to obtain an angle of 45°.

Step 1: Construct an angle $\angle AOB = 90°$.

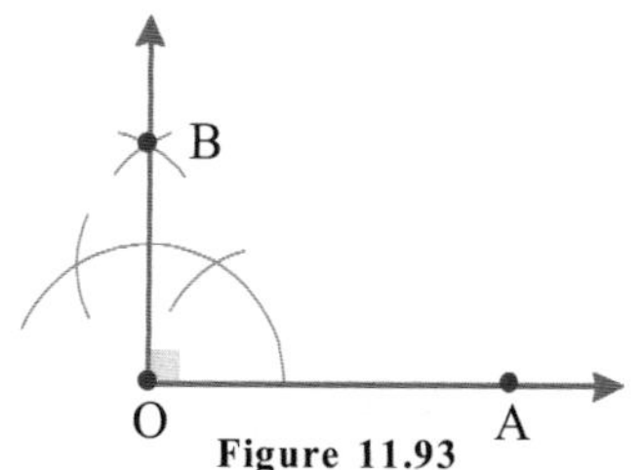

Figure 11.93

Step 2: Draw the bisector OC of $\angle AOB$.

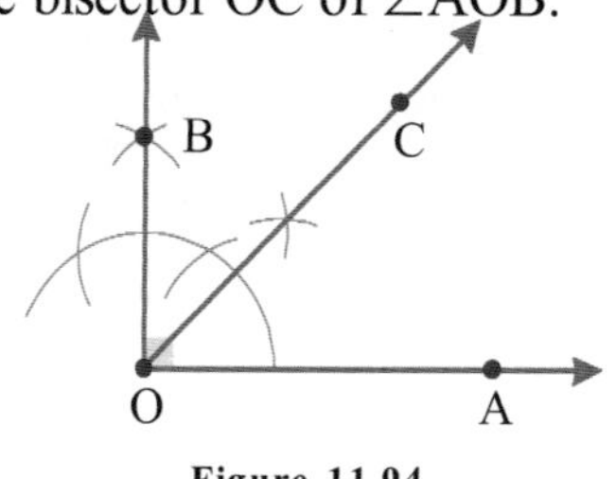

Figure 11.94

Then, $\angle AOC = 45°$.

➜ Construct an angle of measure 135°

To Construct : An angle of 135°.

We know that 135° = 90° + 45°.

We first construct an angle of 90° and then bisect its supplementary angle to obtain an angle of 135°

***Step* 1:** Draw a line AB and mark a point O on AB.

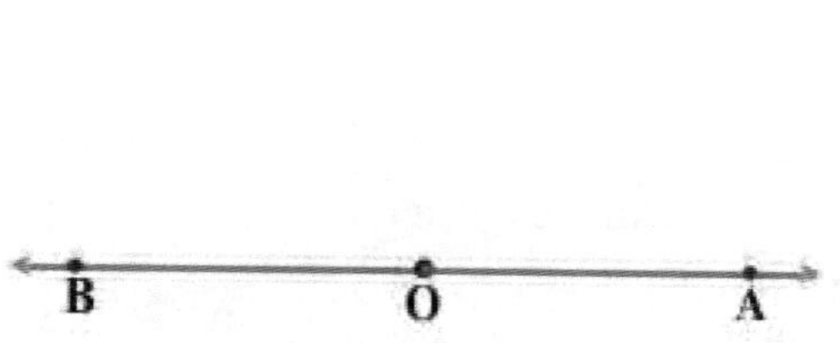

***Step* 2:** Construct an angle ∠AOC = 90°.

***Step* 3:** Draw a bisector OD of ∠BOC.

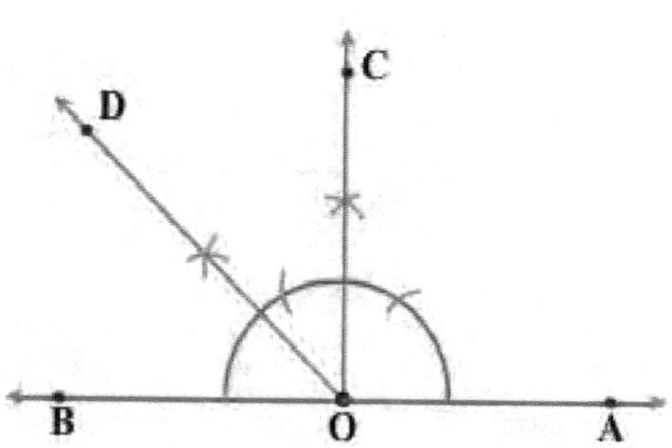

***Step* 4:** ∠DOA = ∠DOC + ∠AOC
= 45° + 90°

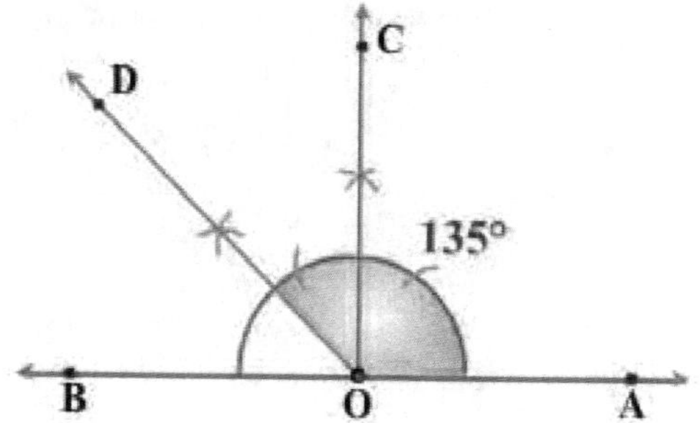

11.2 Congruence Mappings

Introduction

Congruence of Objects

In our day to day life, we come across many objects with **same shape** and **same size**. For example,

(i) Two stamps of the same denomination. **(ii)** Shaving blades of the same company

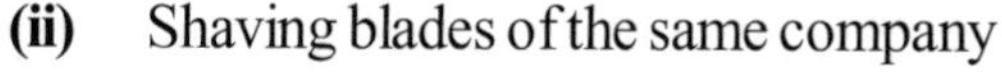

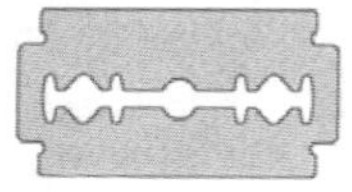

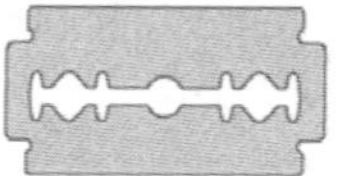

(iii) Two bangles of the same size. **(iv)** Two ATM cards issued by the same bank.

(v) Toys made of the same mould. **(vi)** Keys of same lock

etc.

Two objects of same shape and of same size are said to be *congruent*. Thus, two stamps of same denomination are congruent, two toys made of the same mould are congruent and so on. A figure and its carbon copy are surely of the same shape and of same size and hence congruent. The relation of two objects being congruent is called **congruence**.

Although congruence is a general idea applicable to even three dimensional shapes, in this chapter, we shall be dealing with plane figures only.

Congruence of Plane Figures

Look at the two figures given in Figure 11.95. Are they congruent? To check whether they are congruent, we take a trace copy of one of them and place it over the other. If the figures cover each other exactly, then surely they are of the same shape and of the same size and hence are congruent to each other. The other way is to cut out any one of them and place it over the other to check if they cover each other exactly or not.

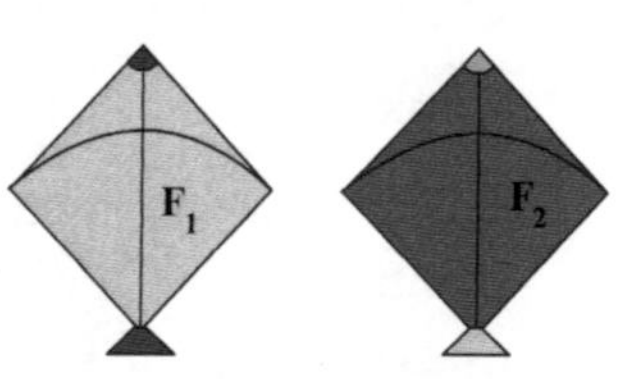

Figure 11.95

This method of comparing two figures is called the **method of superposition**. Now we can say that **two plane figures are congruent if each when superposed on the other, covers it exactly**. The symbol '≅' is used to indicate 'is congruent to'. If figure F_1 is congruent to figure F_2, we write $F_1 \cong F_2$. It may be noted that if $F_1 \cong F_2$, then $F_2 \cong F_1$.

Congruence of Line Segments:

Observe the two line segments in Figure 11.96. Are these line segments congruent? Again we use the method of tracing and superposing. If they cover exactly, we say the two line segments are congruent. Also, in this case, you can verify by measurement that the two line segments are of the same length. Thus, we say

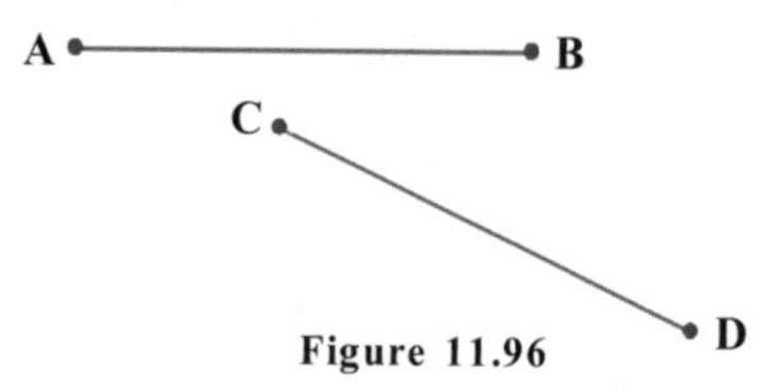

Figure 11.96

> Two line segments are congruent, if they have the same (equal) length.

Converse of this statement is also true. That is **if two line segments are congruent, then they have the same length**.

The two statements :

'line segment AB ≅ line segment CD' and 'AB = CD' are equivalent.

Illustration 1: To check whether the line segments PQ and RS in Figure 11.97 are congruent, apply the method of superposition. You will find that line segment PQ is **not** congruent to line segment RS. Also note that they are not of the same length.

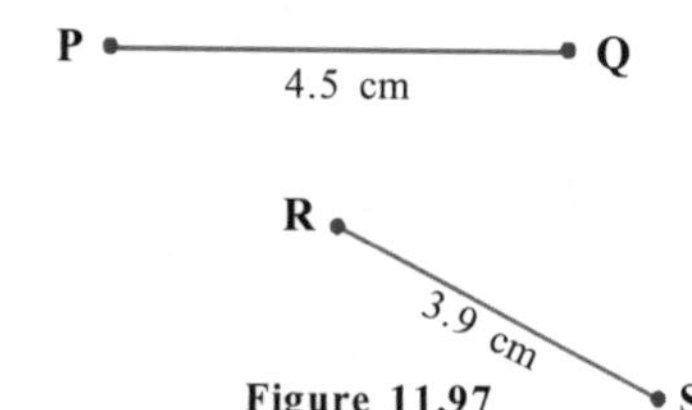

Figure 11.97

Congruence of Angles:

Look at the angle BAC and angle EDF in Figure 11.98.

Are they congruent ? Let us use the method trancing and superposing.

For this, place first D on A and ray DE along ray AB. You will see that ray DF falls along ray AC. Thus, ∠EDF covers ∠BAC exactly and we say that ∠BAC and ∠EDF are congruent, *i.e.*, ∠BAC ≅ ∠EDF

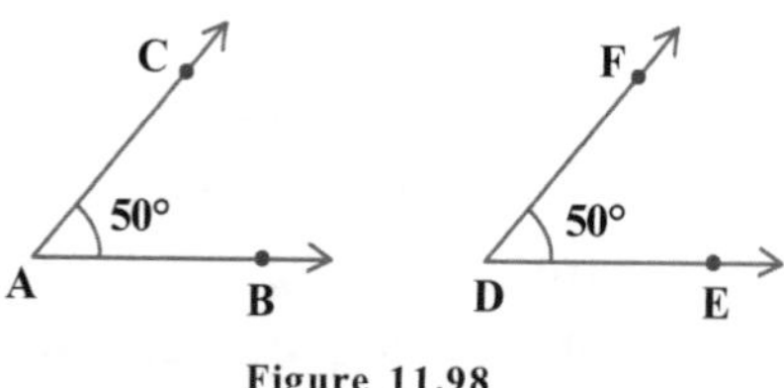

Figure 11.98

Note that the measures of these two angles are the same. We can say that

> If two angles have the same measure, they are congruent.

Converse of this statement is also true. That is, **if two angles are congruent, they have the same measure**.

Look at the angles BAC and XYZ in Figure 11.99.

Again apply the method of superposing to see if ∠BAC is congruent to ∠XYZ. This time, you will find that ∠XYZ does not cover ∠BAC exactly. So, they are not congruent.

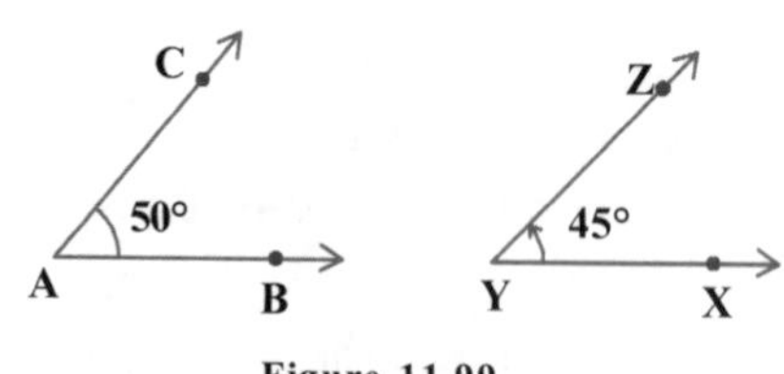

Figure 11.99

Congruence of Two Squares and Congruence of Two Rectangles:

Look at the squares in Figure 11.100. Are they congruent? Again apply the method of superposing. If PQ = AB, then square PQRS will cover the square ABCD exactly, otherwise not. Thus, we can say that

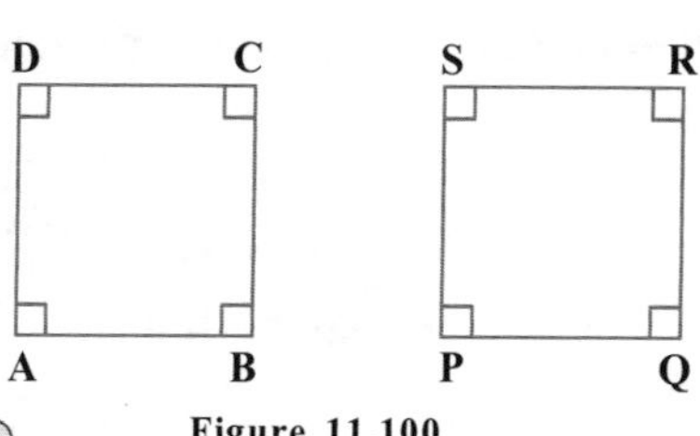

Figure 11.100

> Two squares are congruent if their sides are of the same length.

Look at the rectangles in Figure 11.101. Are they congruent? Again apply the method of superposing.

If AB = PQ and BC = QR. *i.e.*, if they have the same length and breadth, rectangle PQRS will cover rectangle ABCD exactly, otherwise not.

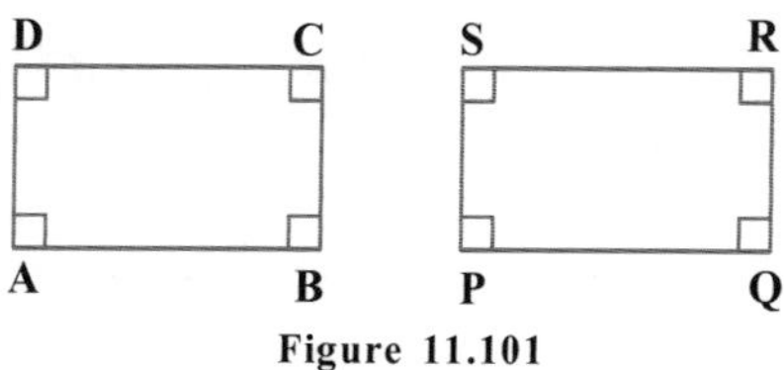

Figure 11.101

Thus, we can say that

> Two rectangles are congruent, if they have the same length and same breadth.

Congruence of Two Circles:

Look at the circles with centre O_1 and O_2 in Figure 11.102. Are they congruent? Apply the method of superposing. Surely, if they have the same (equal) radius, they cover each other exactly, otherwise not. Thus, we can say that

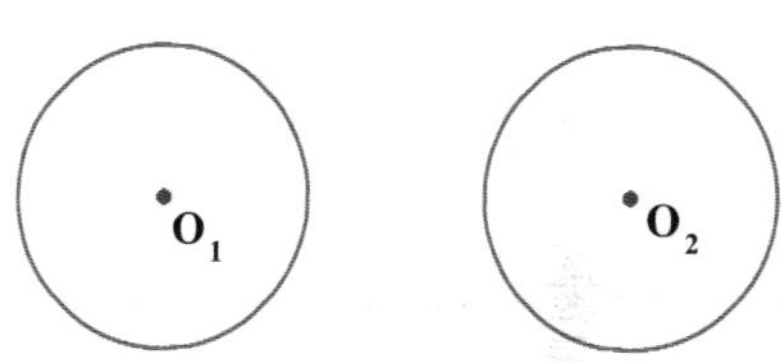

Figure 11.102

> Two circles are congruent, if they have the same (equal) radius.

Let us consider some examples to illustrate the concepts discussed above.

EXAMPLE 1 In the figure, which line segment is congruent to :

(i) PQ?

(ii) AB?

(iii) RS?

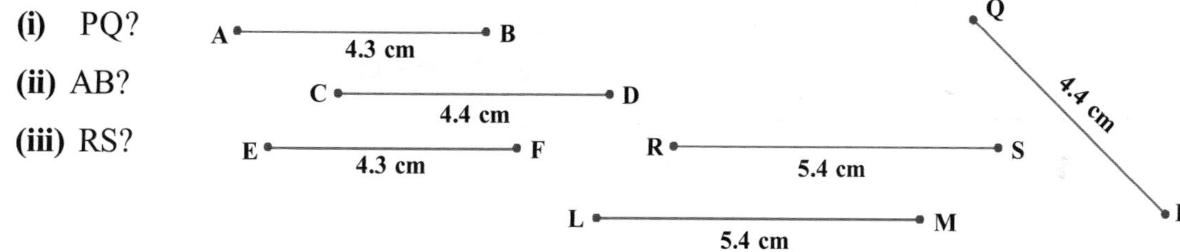

Solution: **(i)** Line segment CD is congruent to PQ as they have the same length 4.4 cm.

(ii) Line segment EF is congruent to AB as EF = AB = 4.3 cm.

(iii) Line segment LM is congruent to RS as LM = RS = 5.4 cm

EXAMPLE 2 The two line segments AB and CD are congruent. If AB = 3.9 cm, then what is the length of CD?

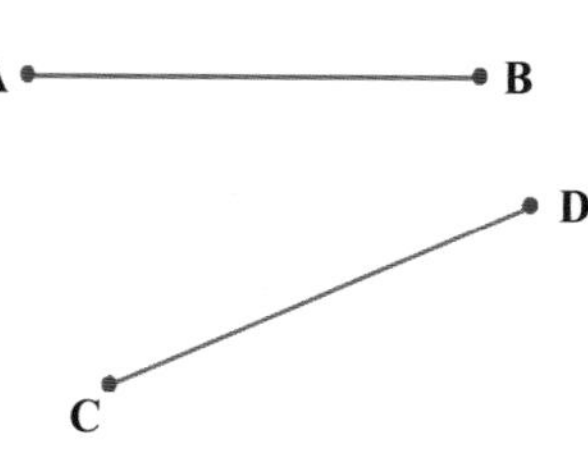

Solution:

As AB ≅ CD (Given)

so AB = CD

i.e., CD = 3.9 cm (AB = 3.9 given)

EXAMPLE 3 In the figure, which angle is congruent to $\angle AOC$?

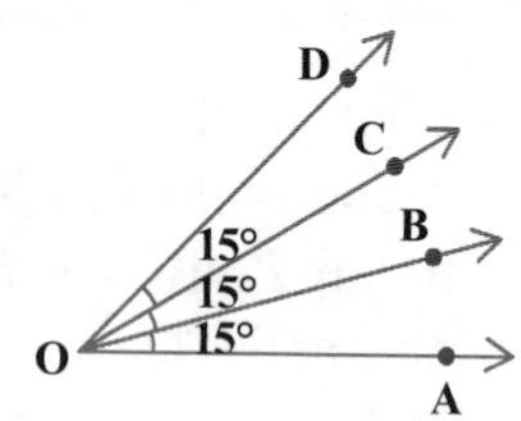

Solution: Measure of $\angle AOC = 15° + 15° = 30°$

Measure of $\angle BOD = 15° + 15° = 30°$

So, $\angle BOD \cong \angle AOC$

EXAMPLE 4 In the figure, $\angle AOC \cong \angle PYR$. Is $\angle BOC$ congruent to $\angle QYR$?

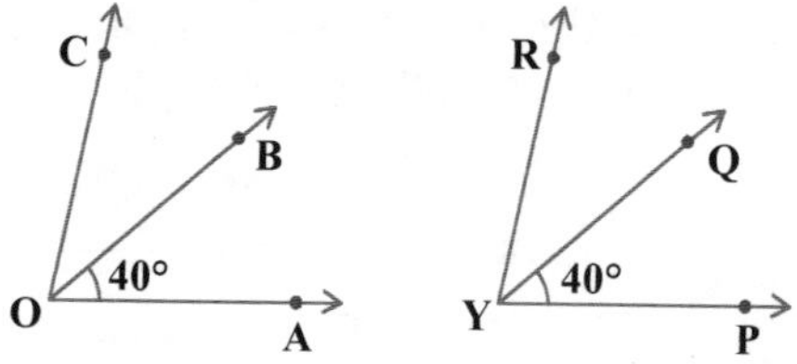

Solution:

$$
\begin{aligned}
\text{Since} \quad \angle AOC &\cong \angle PYR \\
\text{So,} \quad \angle AOC &= \angle PYR \\
\angle AOC - \angle AOB &= \angle PYR - \angle PYQ \\
\angle BOC &= \angle QYR \\
\text{So,} \quad \angle BOC &\cong \angle QYR
\end{aligned}
$$

B. Congruence of Triangles

In the previous section, you have learnt about congruence of some plane figures like line segments, angles, squares *etc.* A triangle is also a plane figure. What about congruence of two triangles? In this section, we shall learn about congruence of triangles.

Consider the triangles ABC and DEF (Figure 11.103).

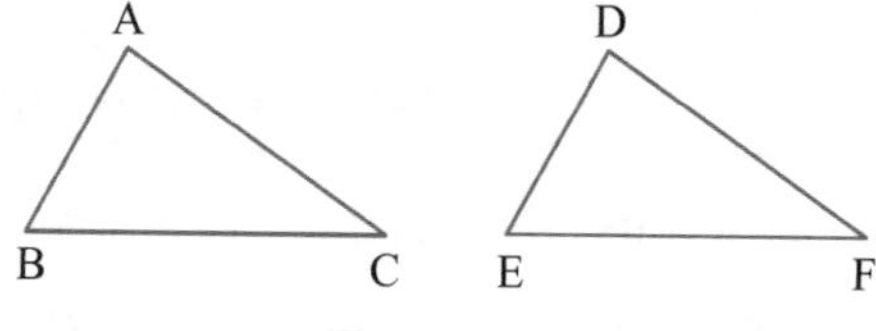

Figure 11.103

In order to see whether the triangles are congruent, we apply the same procedure which we followed for checking congruence of two line segments or two angles *etc.* That is, we apply the method of superposition.

We cut out ΔDEF or make a trace copy of it, superpose it on ΔABC. If they cover each other exactly, **the two triangles are congruent**, otherwise not.

In what follows, we shall label the trace copy of ΔDEF as ΔDEF itself.

When the two triangles cover each other exactly, the vertices D, E and F of triangle DEF will respectively coincide with the vertices A, B and C of other triangle ABC.

Thus, there will be *matching* between the vertices of the triangles.

There are more than one matching possible, but the triangles may be congruent in **one matching** only.

We may match the vertices in the following way :

A B C D E F $\rightarrow$ $A \leftrightarrow D$, $B \leftrightarrow E$, $C \leftrightarrow F$ or more briefly as $ABC \leftrightarrow DEF$

There are six possible matchings :

$ABC \leftrightarrow DEF$, $ABC \leftrightarrow EFD$, $ABC \leftrightarrow FDE$

$ABC \leftrightarrow DFE$, $ABC \leftrightarrow FED$, $ABC \leftrightarrow EDF$.

If ΔABC is congruent to ΔDEF, one of these six possible matchings will lead to superposition with exact covering and hence we will have three equalities of corresponding sides and three equalities of corresponding angles.

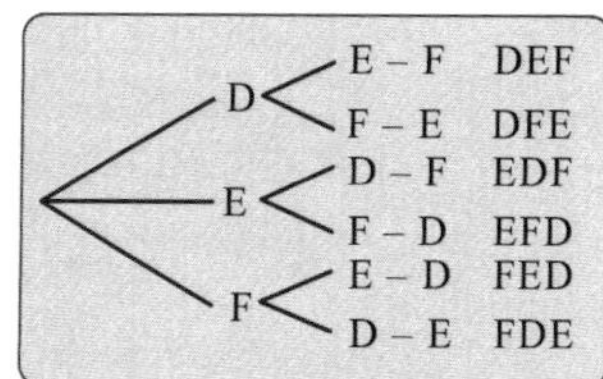

Congruence of Two Triangles

Two triangles ABC and DEF are congruent if there is a correspondence between the their vertices ($A \leftrightarrow D$, $B \leftrightarrow E$, $C \leftrightarrow F$) such that $\angle A = \angle D$, $\angle B = \angle E$, $\angle C = \angle F$ and AB = DE, AC = DF, BC = EF.

Symbolically, we write $\Delta ABC \cong \Delta DEF$.

Also, if $\Delta ABC \cong \Delta DEF$, then

$$\left.\begin{array}{l} AB = DE,\ AC = DF,\ BC = EF \\ \angle A = \angle D,\ \angle B = \angle E,\ \angle C = \angle F \end{array}\right\}$$ {Corresponding part of congruent triangles} (CPCT)

$\Delta ABC \cong \Delta DEF$

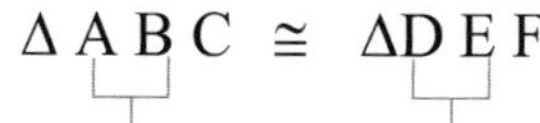

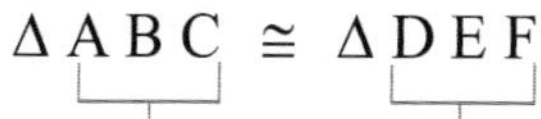

Remark: Usually, the corresponding parts of congruent triangles are shown by marking them alike as in the figure given below :

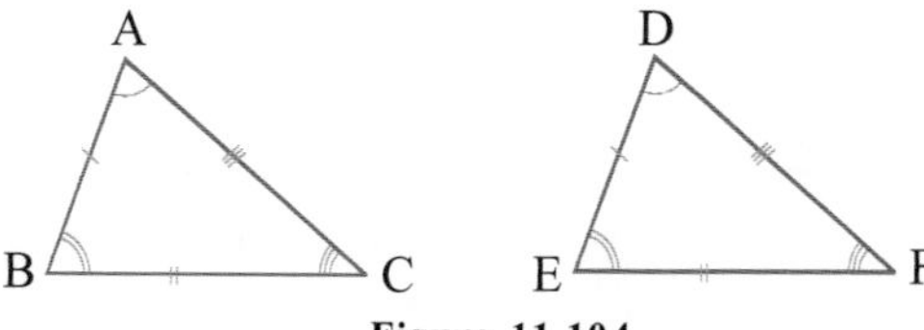

Figure 11.104

C. Criteria For Congruence of Triangles

We have seen that for two triangles to be congruent, it is necessary that all three corresponding sides and all three corresponding angles be equal. Now the question is **"Do we really need all the six conditions for the congruence of two triangles?"** No ! In case of two triangles if three (properly chosen) conditions out of six conditions are satisfied, the other three are automatically satisfied. There are four such cases.

Side - Side - Side (SSS) Congruence Criterion:

Activity : Draw a ΔABC, with AB = 3 cm, BC = 4.5 cm and CA = 6 cm. Draw another triangle DEF with DE = 3 cm, EF = 4.5 cm and DF = 6 cm. (Figure 11.105) Thus, we have AB = DE, BC = EF and AC = DF. Make a trace copy of ΔABC, and superpose it over ΔDEF.

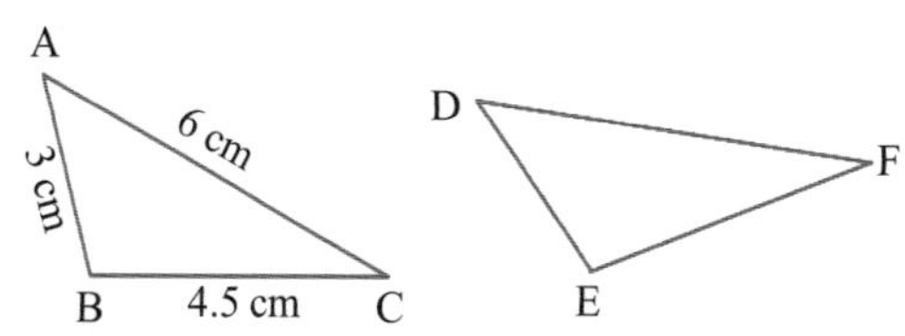

Figure 11.105

You will observe that with A on D, B on E and C on F, the two triangles cover each other exactly.

In other words, under the matching $ABC \leftrightarrow DEF$, the triangles cover each other exactly. Therefore, we have $\Delta ABC \cong \Delta DEF$.

Thus, we can say that

> Two triangles are congruent, if the three sides of one triangle are equal to the three sides of the other triangle.

This is called **Side - Side - Side (SSS) congruence criterion (or condition).**

Illustration 1: Consider the triangles :

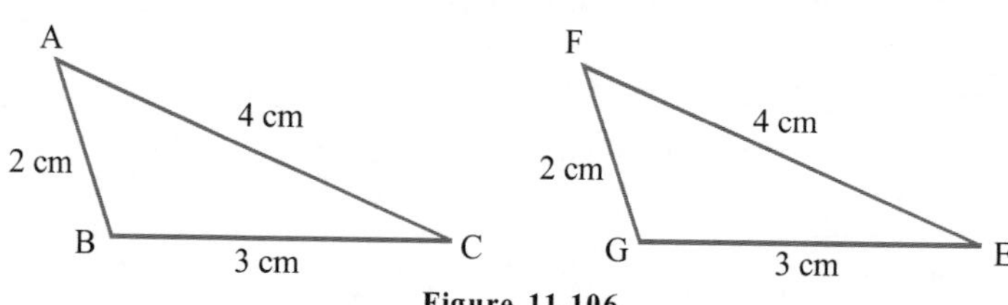

Figure 11.106

We have : AB = FG (= 2 cm), AC = FE (= 4 cm) and BC = GE (= 3 cm)

This shows that the three sides of the triangle ABC are respectively equal to the three sides of the triangle FGE.

From the above three relations, we have $A \leftrightarrow F$, $B \leftrightarrow G$ and $C \leftrightarrow E$ as explained below :

AB = FG

AC = FE

↓ ↓ $A \leftrightarrow F$

A common F common

Similarly, $B \leftrightarrow G$ and $C \leftrightarrow E$

Therefore, by SSS congruence condition, the two triangles are congruent under the correspondence (matching) $A \leftrightarrow F$, $B \leftrightarrow G$ and $C \leftrightarrow E$.

i.e., **$\Delta ABC \cong \Delta FGE$**. Is $\Delta CAB \cong \Delta EFG$?

Illustration 2: In the given figure, AB = AD and BC = DC. Let us try to find the third pair of corresponding parts that makes $\Delta ABC \cong \Delta ADC$ by SSS congruence criterion.

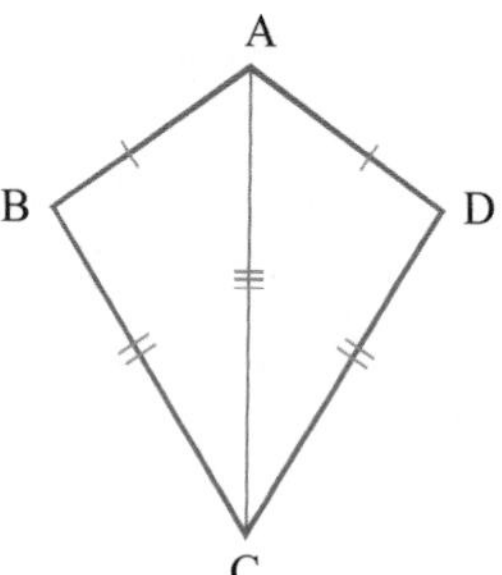

Figure 11.107

For ***SSS congruence*** condition , the third pair of corresponding parts are the remaining sides of two given triangles.

Now AC is common to both ΔABC and ΔADC. Therefore, the third pair of corresponding parts are AC and AC.

i.e. **AC = AC**

Note The correspondence is $A \leftrightarrow A$, $B \leftrightarrow D$ and $C \leftrightarrow C$.

Side - Angle - Side (SAS) Congruence Criterion:

Activity : Look at ΔABC and ΔDEF in Figure 11.108. To check congruence of these triangle, repeat the same activity as for SSS criterion.

You will find that under the matching $ABC \leftrightarrow DEF$ the two triangles cover each other exactly. Therefore, $\Delta ABC \cong \Delta DEF$. Thus, we can say that

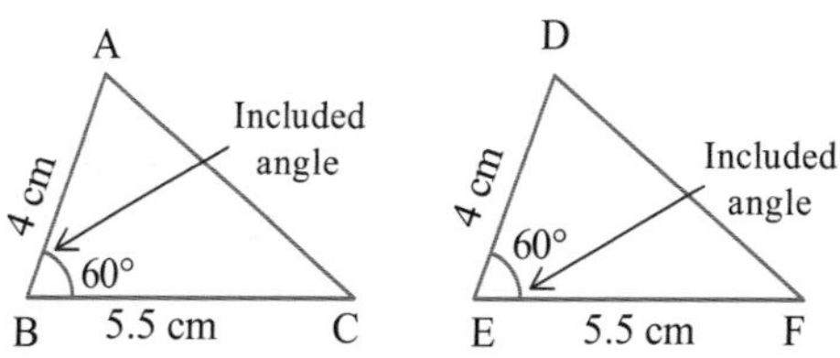

Figure 11.108

> Two triangles are congruent if *two sides* and the *included angle* of one triangle are equal to *two sides* and the *included angle* of the other triangle.

This is known as **Side-Angle-Side(SAS) congruence criterion**.

The angle in SAS congruence criterion should be *included* between the two given sides.

Illustration 3: Consider the triangles PQR and XYZ (See Figure 11.109)

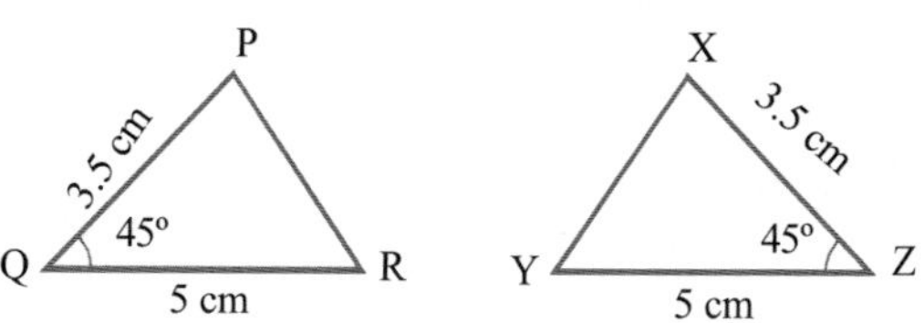

Figure 11.109

Here, $PQ = XZ = 3.5$ cm (given)

$QR = ZY = 5$ cm (given)

and included $\angle Q$ = included $\angle Z = 45^\circ$ (given)

Also, $P \leftrightarrow X$, $Q \leftrightarrow Z$ and $R \leftrightarrow Y$

So, by SAS congruence criterion (rule), the two triangles are congruent

i.e., $\mathbf{\Delta PQR \cong \Delta XZY}$

Illustration 4: Write the congruence criterion used in the following figures

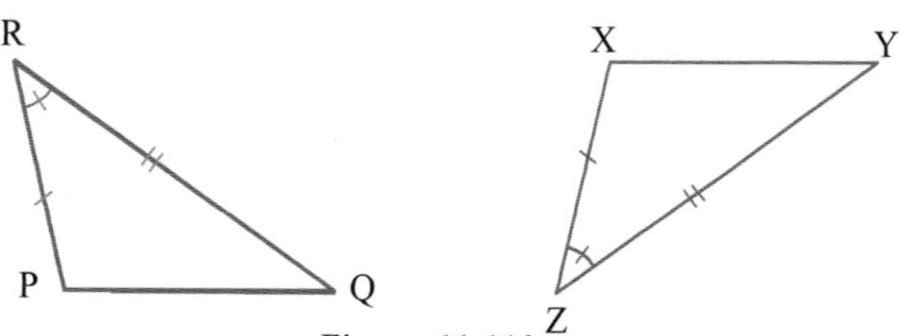

Figure 11.110

Given, $RP = ZX$ (Side (S))

$RQ = ZY$ (Side (S))

$\angle PRQ = \angle XZY$ (Angle (A))

So, $\Delta PQR \cong \Delta XYZ$

The congruence criterion is **SAS**.

Angle - Side - Angle (ASA) Congruence Criterion:

Activity : Look at ΔABC and ΔDEF in Figure 11.111. To check their congruence repeat the same activity as for SSS criterion. You will find that under the matching $ABC \leftrightarrow DEF$, the triangles cover each other exactly. So, $\Delta ABC \cong \Delta DEF$.

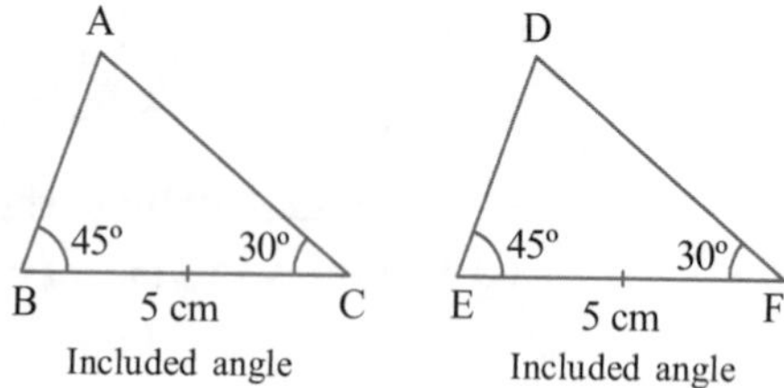

Figure 11.111

Thus, we can say that

> Two triangles are congruent if two angles and the *included* side of one triangle are equal to two angles and the included side of the other triangle.

This is known as **Angle - Side - Angle (ASA) congruence criterion**.

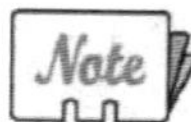

By angle sum property of a triangle, given two angles of a triangle, the third can be determined. Thus, whenever any two angles and one side of a triangle are respectively equal to two angles and the **corresponding** side of the other triangle we can change this to the type - "*two angles and the included side*" and apply the ASA congruence criterion.

Illustration 5: Consider ΔABC and ΔDEF (Figure 11.112)

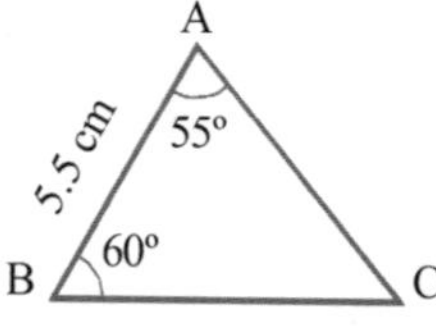

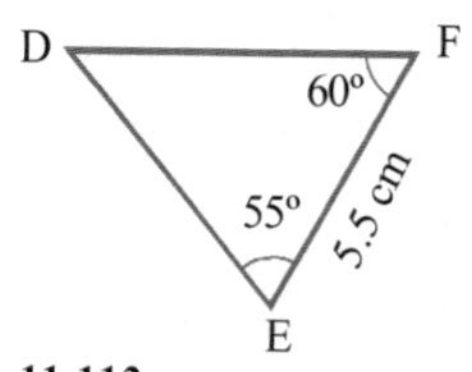

Figure 11.112

We have, $\angle A = \angle E = 55^\circ$

$\angle B = \angle F = 60^\circ$ and $AB = EF$. (Here, correspondence is $A \leftrightarrow E$, $B \leftrightarrow F$, $C \leftrightarrow D$)

So, $\Delta ABC \cong \Delta EFD$ (by ASA)

Right angle - Hypotenuse - Side (RHS) Congruence Criterion:

Activity : Look at ΔABC and ΔDEF in Figure 11.113.

To check their congruence, repeat the same activity as for SSS criterion.

You will find that under the matching $ABC \leftrightarrow DEF$ the two right triangles cover each other exactly. Thus, $\Delta ABC \cong \Delta DEF$.

Figure 11.113

So, we can say that

> Two right triangles are congruent if the hypotenuse and one side of one triangle are equal to the hypotenuse and one side of the other triangle.

This is known as **Right angle - Hypotenuse - Side (RHS) congruence criterion**.

Illustration 6: Consider ΔABC and ΔDEF (See figure 11.114)

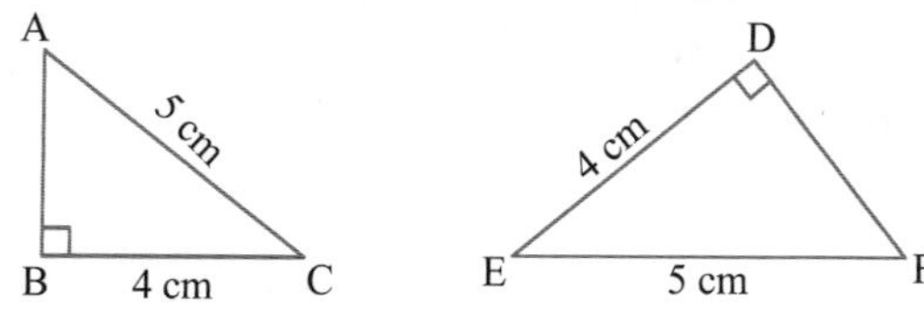

Figure 11.114

Here, ∠B = ∠D (= 90°)

Hypotenuse , AC = hypotenuse FE (= 5 cm)

Side BC = side DE (= 4 cm)

So, by RHS congruence criterion the two triangles are congruent.

Also, B ↔ D, A ↔ F and C ↔ E

Therefore, **ΔABC ≅ ΔFDE**

Now we consider some examples to illustrate the use of above criteria of congruence of triangles.

EXAMPLE 5 Without drawing the triangles, state the correspondence between the sides of congruent triangles represented as ΔABC ≅ ΔQRP.

Solution : From Δ A B C ≅ Δ Q R P [Given]

We have, A ↔ Q, B ↔ R and C ↔ P

Therefore, AB = **QR**, BC = **RP** and AC = **QP**

EXAMPLE 6 Without drawing the triangles, state the correspondence between the angles of the following pairs of congruent triangles : ΔABC ≅ ΔQRP.

Solution : From Δ A B C ≅ Δ Q R P [Given]

we have, A ↔ Q, B ↔ R and C ↔ P

Therefore, ∠A = **∠Q**, ∠B = **∠R** and ∠C = **∠P**

EXAMPLE 7 Which angle is included between the sides DE and EF of ΔDEF?

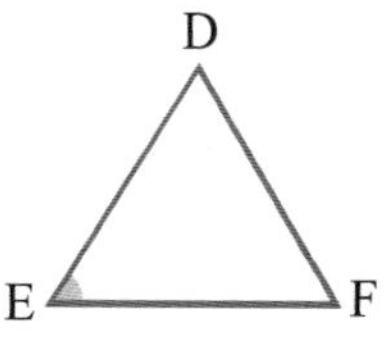

Solution : The angle included between the sides DE and EF is **∠E.**

EXAMPLE 8 In the figure, examine the equality of parts of two triangles. If the triangles are congruent, write them in symbolic form.

Solution : From the figure, we find :

AB = EF, BC = DE and ∠B = ∠E

Since ∠B is the angle included between AB and BC.

and ∠E is the angle included between EF and DE, therefore we can apply the SAS congruence rule.

Also, we note that A ↔ F, B ↔ E and C ↔ D

ΔABC ≅ ΔFED

EXAMPLE 9 From the given figure, identify the congruence rule and write the given pair of congruent triangles in symbolic form.

Solution : AC = RP = 2.5 cm, $\angle C = \angle P = 35°$, CB = PQ = 3 cm

So, $A \leftrightarrow R$, $C \leftrightarrow P$ and $B \leftrightarrow Q$

Therefore, by SAS congruence rule, **$\Delta ACB \cong \Delta RPQ$**

EXAMPLE 10 In the given figure, AB = AC and AD is bisector of $\angle BAC$. State whether $\Delta BAD \cong \Delta CAD$ or not and identify the congruence criterion.

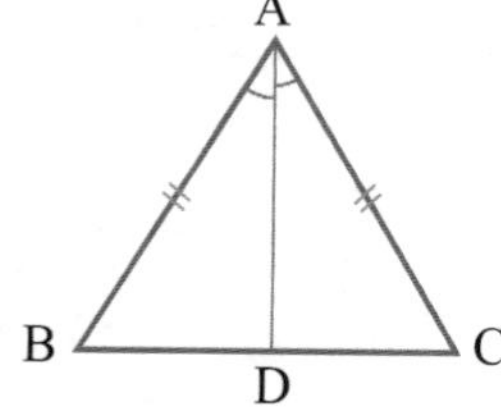

Solution :

$AB = AC$ (given)

$AD = AD$ (Common side)

$\angle BAD = \angle CAD$ (included angle)

Hence, by SAS congruence rule **$\Delta BAD \cong \Delta CAD$**

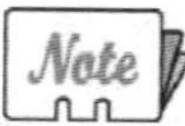

As $\Delta BAD \cong \Delta CAD$,

So, $\angle B = \angle C$ (CPCT)

In an isosceles ΔABC, if AB = AC, then $\angle B = \angle C$

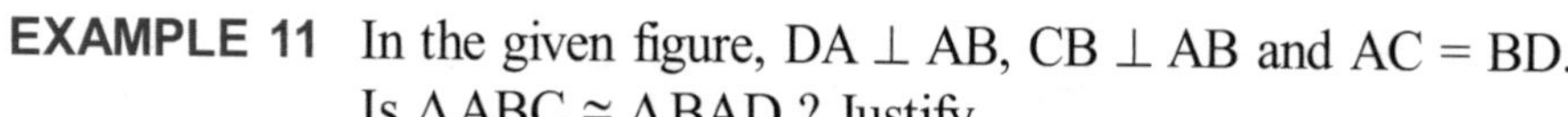

EXAMPLE 11 In the given figure, $DA \perp AB$, $CB \perp AB$ and AC = BD. Is $\Delta ABC \cong \Delta BAD$? Justify

Solution : We know that $DA \perp AB$ Therefore, $\angle BAD = 90°$

Also, $CB \perp AB$ Therefore, $\angle ABC = 90°$

In ΔABC and ΔBAD,

$\angle ABC = \angle BAD$ (Each equals 90°)

$AC = BD$ (Hypotenuse are equal)

$AB = BA$ (Common side to both triangles)

Therefore, by RHS congruence rule,

$\Delta ABC \cong \Delta BAD$

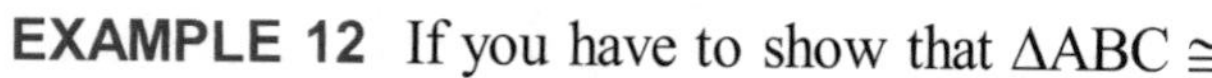

EXAMPLE 12 If you have to show that $\Delta ABC \cong \Delta XYZ$ using SSS criterion, then write the corresponding sides of the triangles.

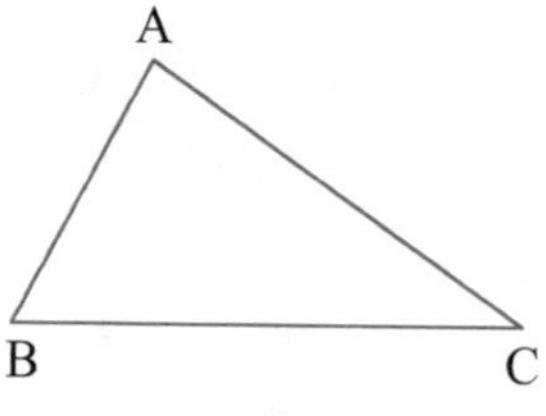

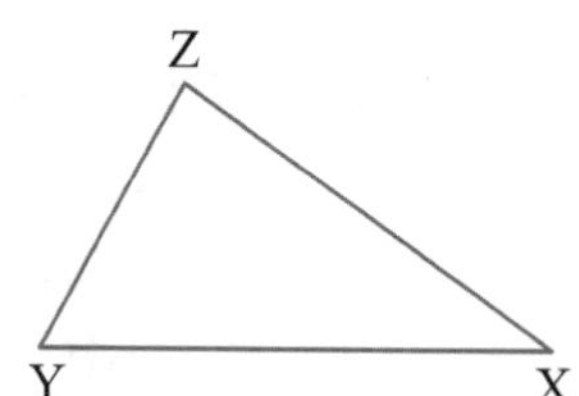

Solution : For $\Delta ABC \cong \Delta XYZ$ to be true, under SSS criterion, we must have

AB = **XY**, BC = **YZ**, CA = **ZX**

EXAMPLE 13 In ΔXYZ and ΔRPQ, $XY = 3$ cm, $YZ = 5$ cm, $XZ = 4$ cm, $PQ = 5$ cm, $QR = 4$ cm, and $PR = 3$ cm. Are the two given triangles congruent? If yes, write the congruence criterion used by you.

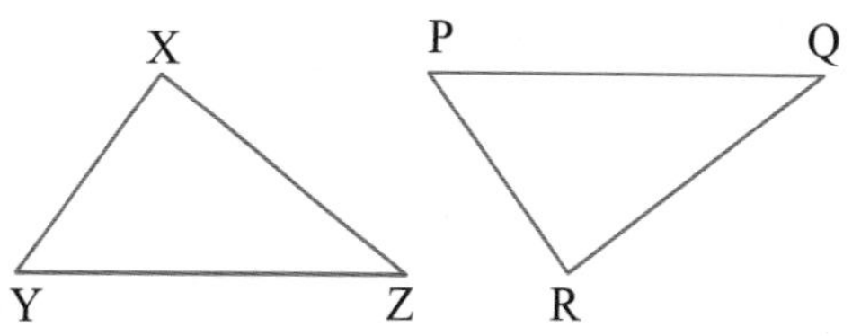

Solution : From the given data we have

$XY = RP = 3$ cm.

$YZ = PQ = 5$ cm.

$XZ = RQ = 4$ cm.

> In XY = RP and YZ = PQ
> Y is common on LHS and P is common on RHS.
> So, $Y \leftrightarrow P$. If $Y \leftrightarrow P$ then XY = RP and so on.

i.e. the three sides of one triangle are equal to the three sides of the other triangle.

Therefore, by SSS congruence criterion, the two triangles are congruent.

EXAMPLE 14 Which congruence criterion is used in the following?

Given : $DB = EB$

$AD = BC$

$\angle A = \angle C = 90^\circ$

Therefore, $\Delta ABD \cong \Delta CEB$

Solution : In ΔABD and ΔCEB,

$DB = EB$

i.e., hypotenuse DB = hypotenuse BE

$AD = CB$

i.e., side AD = side CB

and $\angle A = \angle C = 90^\circ$

Therefore, $\Delta ABD \cong \Delta CEB$ by **RHS congruence criterion.**

EXAMPLE 15 Observe the triangles in the figure. Are they congruent? If yes, write congruence relation in symbolic form.

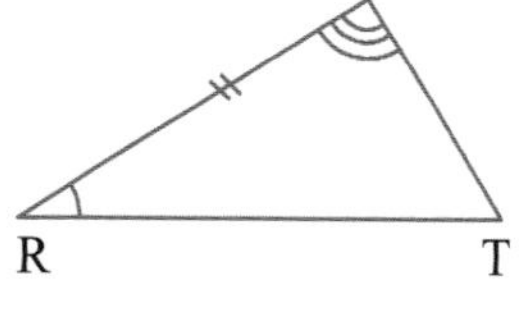

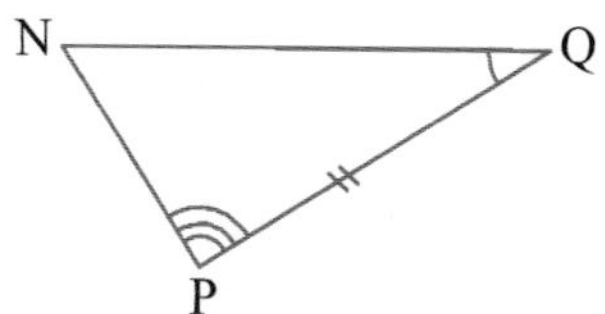

Solution : We see that $AR = PQ$, $\angle A = \angle P$ and $\angle R = \angle Q$

Therefore, $\Delta RAT \cong$ **ΔQPN** (by ASA)

Exercise 11.2

In questions 1-5, in the given figure, which line segment is congruent to :

1. PQ ?
2. AB ?
3. RS ?
4. XY ?
5. UV ?

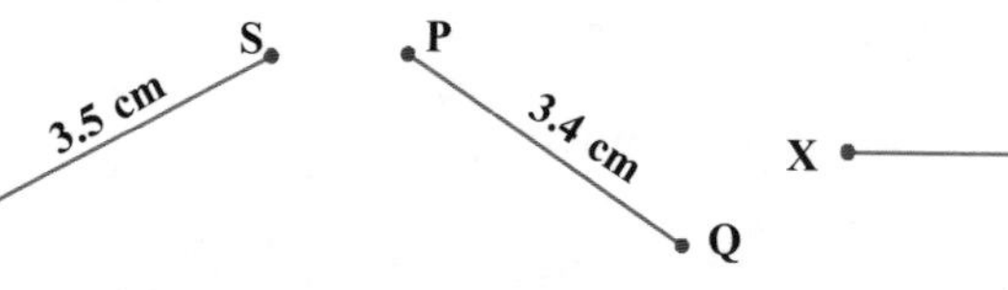

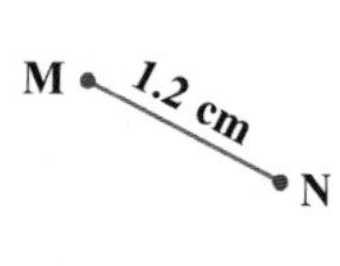

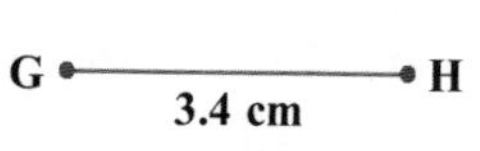

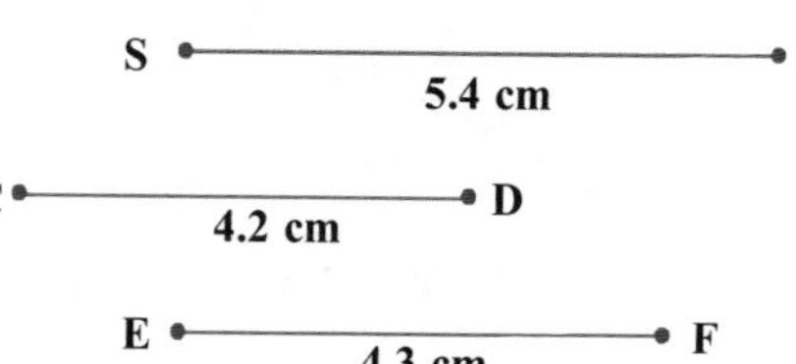

In questions 6-8, if line segment XY ≅ ZN, PQ ≅ RS, AB ≅ CD, find :

6. RS if PQ = 4.2 cm
7. AB if CD = 3.6 cm
8. XY if ZN = 6.3 cm

In questions 9-13, in the given figure :

9. Which angle is congruent to ∠AOE?
10. Which angle is congruent to ∠BOD?
11. Which angle (s) is (are) congruent to ∠AOB?

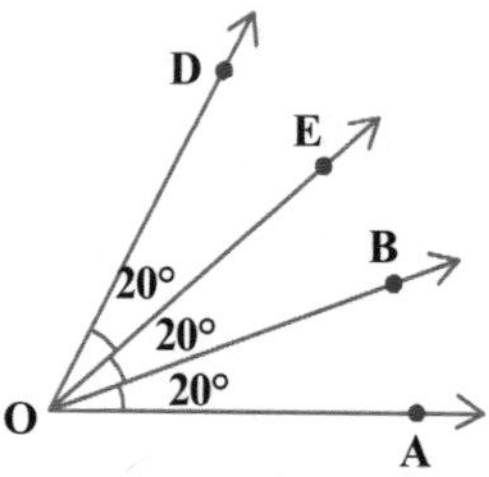

12. Which angle (s) is (are) congruent to ∠BOE?
13. Which angle (s) is (are) congruent to ∠DOE?
14. In the given figure, ∠AOC ≅ ∠XOY. Then which angle is congruent to ∠AOB?
15. In the given figure, if ∠AOC ≅ ∠COE, then what is the relation between a, b, c and d?

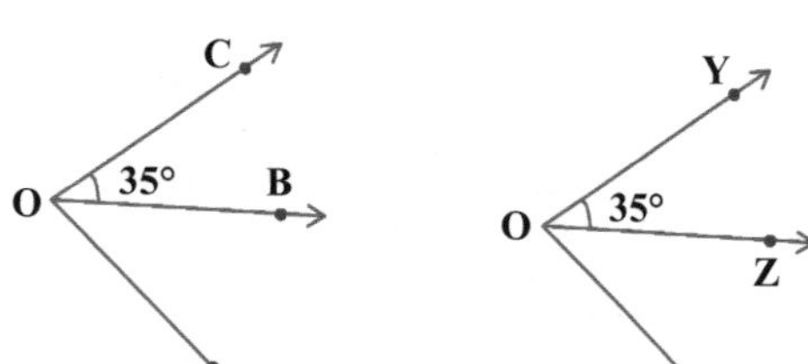

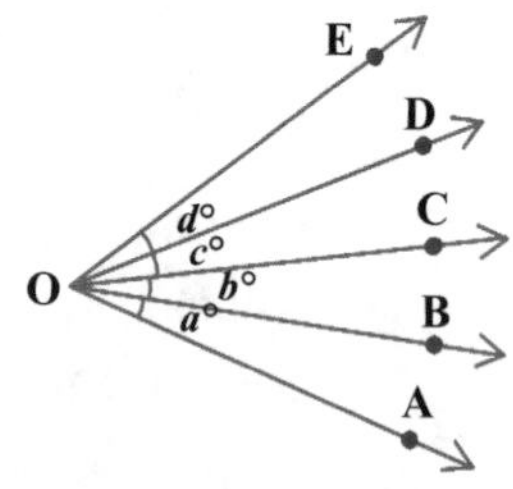

16. Without drawing the triangles, state the correspondence between the sides of following congruent triangles :

    (a) ΔPQR ≅ ΔBAC (b) ΔPQR ≅ ΔCBA (c) ΔABC ≅ ΔMNP
    (d) ΔPQR ≅ ΔMNP (e) ΔABC ≅ ΔPRQ

17. Without drawing the triangles, state the correspondence between the angles of the following pairs of congruent triangles :

    (a) ΔPQR ≅ ΔCBA (b) ΔPRQ ≅ ΔACB (c) ΔQPR ≅ ΔABC
    (d) ΔCBA ≅ ΔRQP (e) ΔBAC ≅ ΔPRQ

In questions 18-23, identify the included angle between the sides of the given triangle.

18. ED and DF

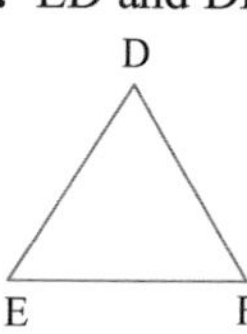

19. DF and FE

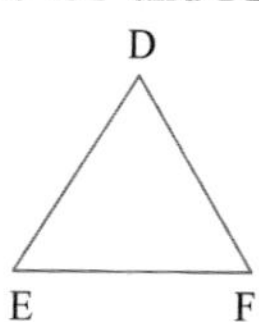

20. CA and AB

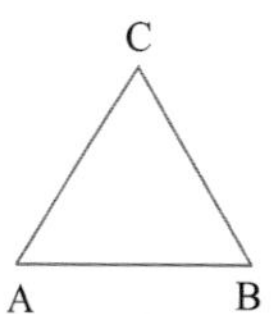

21. AB and BC

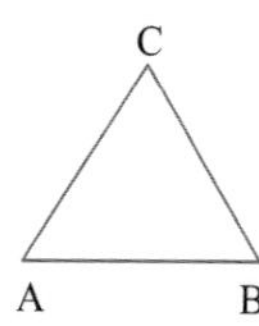

22. BC and CA

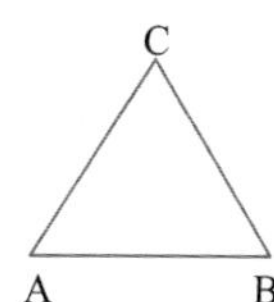

23. MN and MO

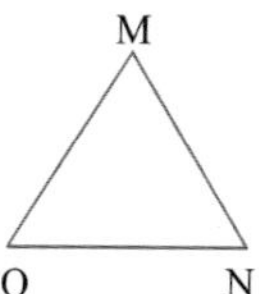

In questions 24-28, examine the equality of some parts of two triangles, shown in the figure. If they are congruent, write them in symbolic form.

24.

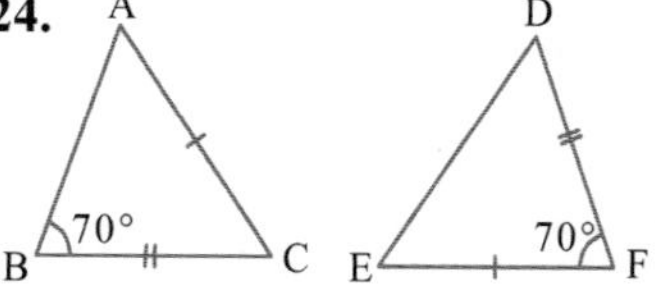

25.

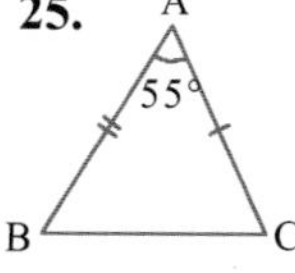

26.

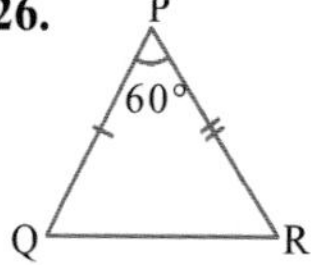

27. QR = 4 cm, PR = 3 cm, $\angle R = 45°$

28. PQ = 5 cm, PR = 4 cm, $\angle P = 60°$

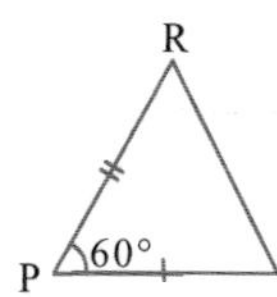

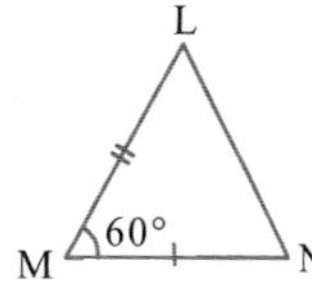

In questions 29-30, from the given figure, write the given pair of congruent triangles in symbolic form and identify the congruence rule.

29.

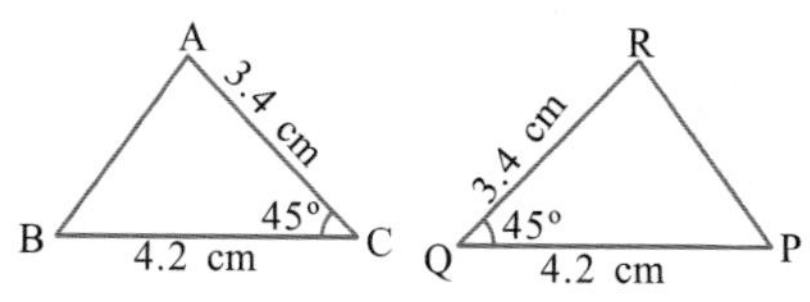

30.

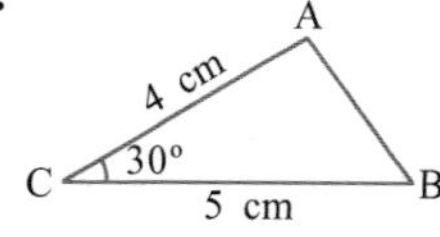

P
5 cm
30°
Q
4 cm
R

In questions 31-33, in the given figure, identify the congruency criterion and write the two triangles in symbolic form :

31.

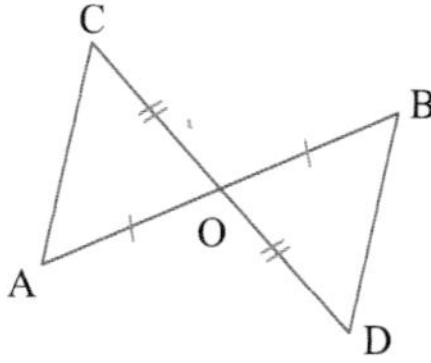

32.

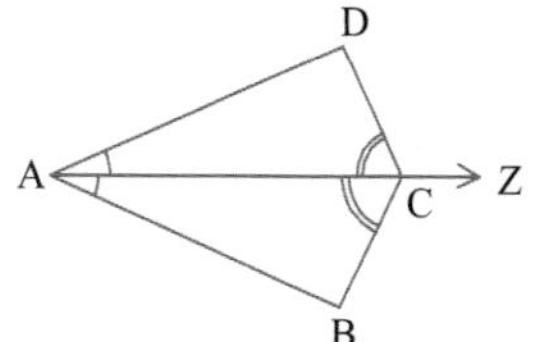

33.

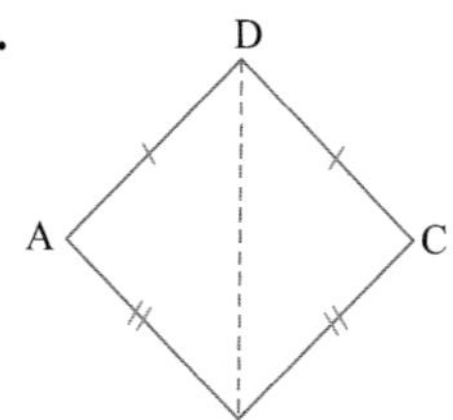

In questions 34-36, in the given figure, using RHS congruence rule. Write the two triangles in symbolic form :

34.

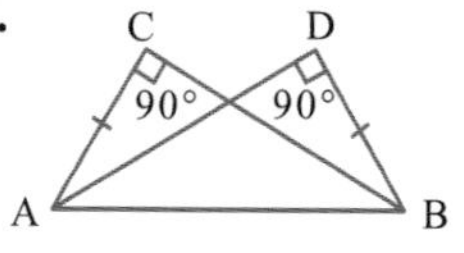

35.

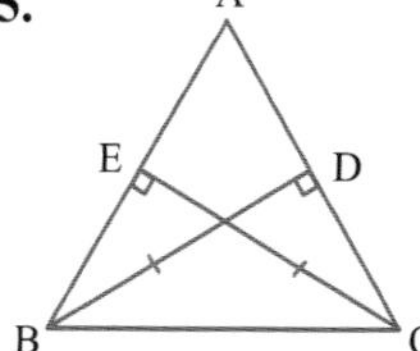

36.

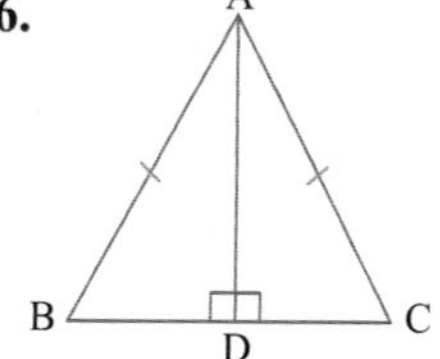

In questions 37-39, using SSS criterion then, find the corresponding sides of the given sides. If you have to show that :

37. ΔPQR ≅ ΔSTU

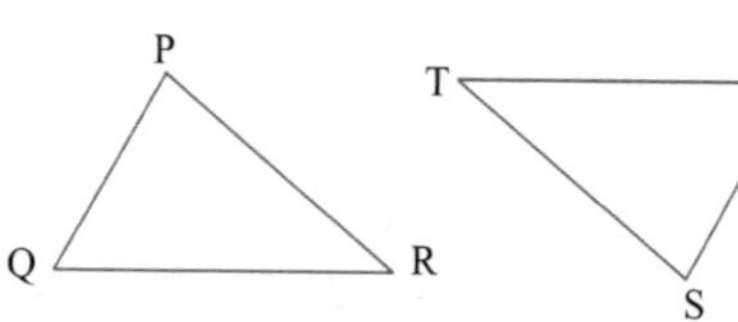

38. ΔBAT ≅ ΔCUP

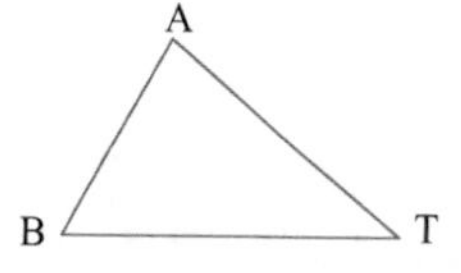

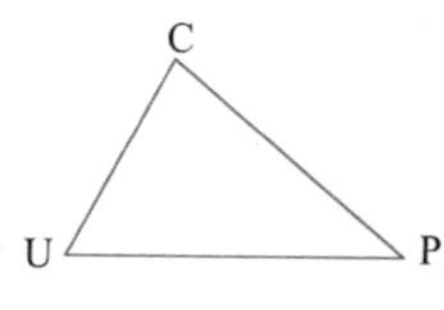

39. ΔLMN ≅ ΔPQR

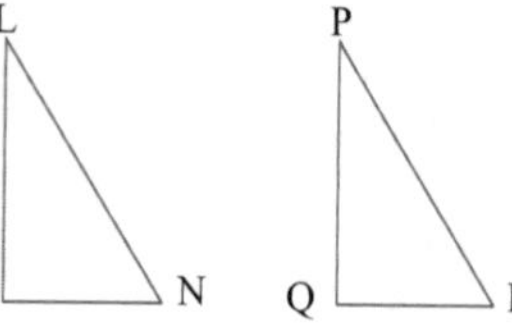

In questions 40-43, are the following two triangles congruent? If yes, write the congruence criterion used by you to answer the question :

40. In ΔABC and ΔRPQ, AB = 3.5 cm, BC = 7 cm, AC = 5 cm, PQ = 7 cm, QR = 5 cm, and PR = 3.5 cm.

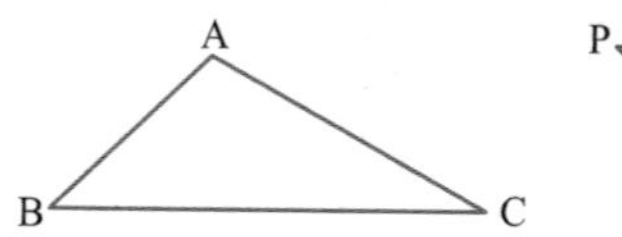

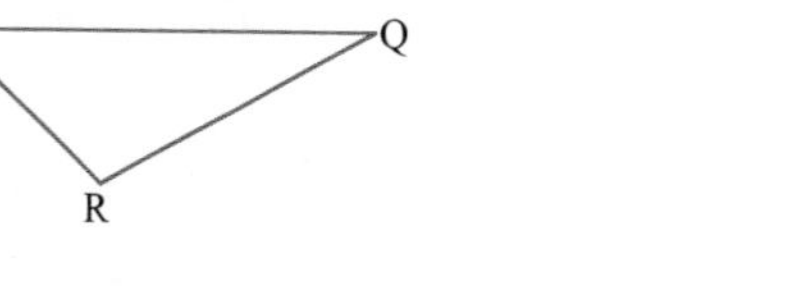

41. In ΔABC and ΔFED, AB = 7 cm, BC = 5 cm, ∠B = 50º, DE = 5 cm, EF = 7 cm, and ∠E = 50º.

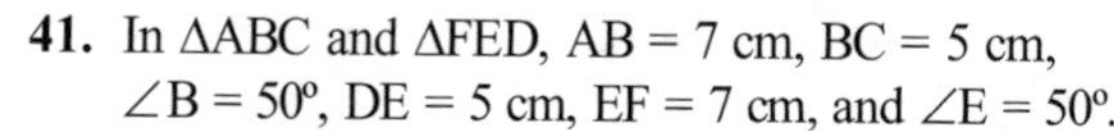

42. In ΔABC and ΔLNM, AB = 10 cm, BC = 7 cm, AC = 5 cm, LM = 5 cm, NM = 7 cm, and LN = 10 cm.

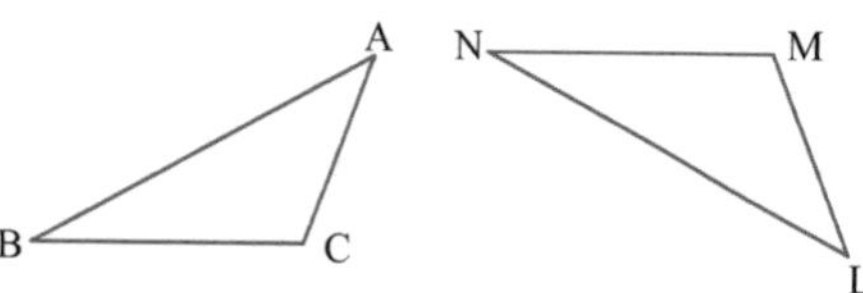

43. In ΔXYZ and ΔRPQ, XY = 6 cm, XZ = 5 cm, ∠X = 50º, PR = 6 cm, PQ = 5 cm, and ∠P = 50º.

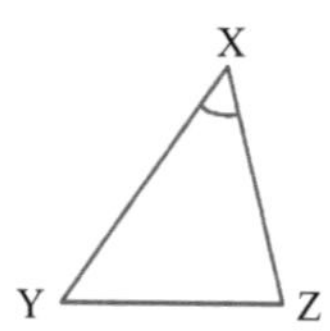

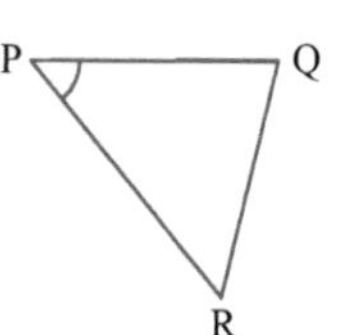

In questions 44-47, which congruence criterion is used in the following, if

44.

∠BAC = ∠EDF

∠CBA = ∠DEF

BA = ED

Therefore, ΔABC ≅ ΔDEF

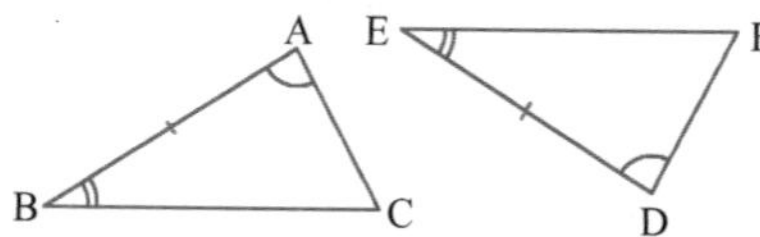

45.

AC = DF

AB = DE

BC = EF

Therefore, ΔABC ≅ ΔDEF

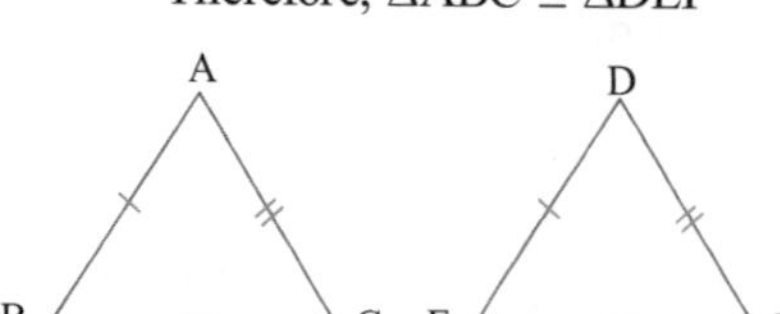

46.

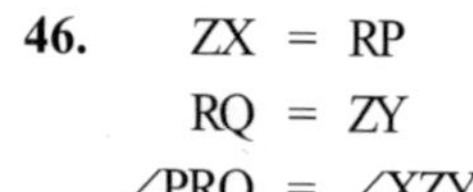

ZX = RP

RQ = ZY

∠PRQ = ∠XZY

Therefore, ΔPQR ≅ ΔXYZ

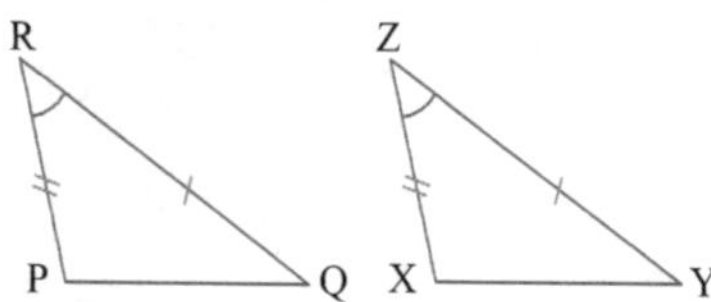

47.

∠MLN = ∠FGH

∠NML = ∠GFH

ML = FG

Therefore, ΔLMN ≅ ΔGFH

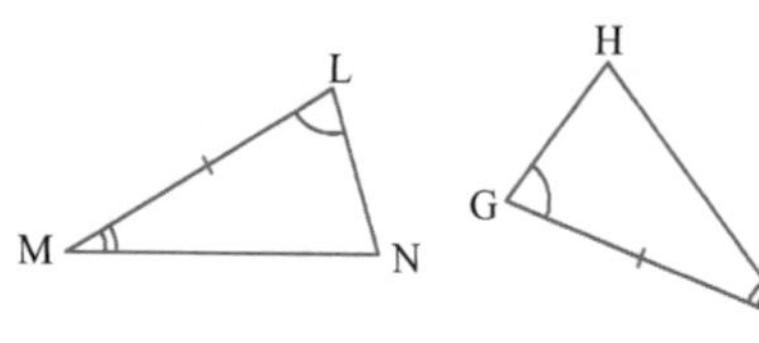

48. Observe the triangles in the figure. Are they congruent ? If yes, write congruence relation in symbolic form.

(a)

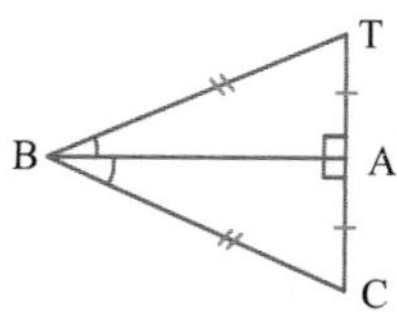

(b)

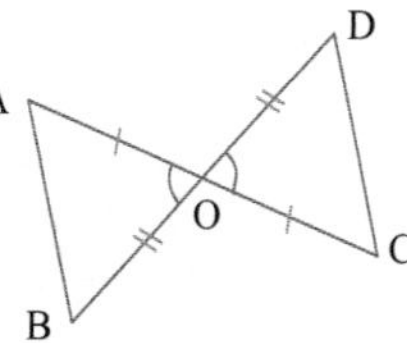

(c)

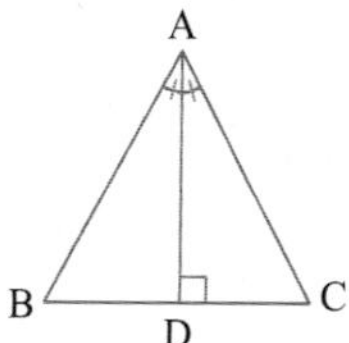

(d)

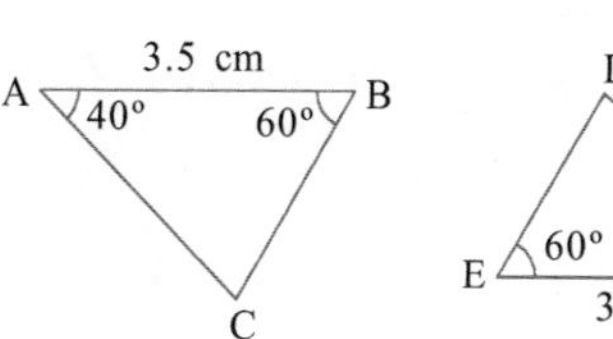

In questions 49-50, in the given figure, AB = DC and AD = BC. Find the third pair of corresponding parts that makes the following triangles congruent by SSS congruence condition.

49. $\Delta ABD \cong \Delta CDB$

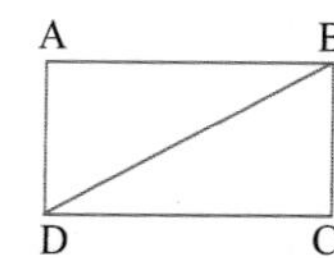

50. $\Delta ABC \cong \Delta CDA$

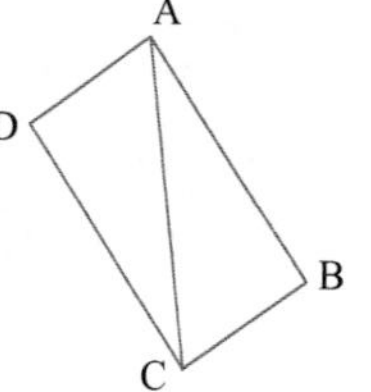

51. State whether the given triangles are congruent by SSS congruence condition ? If congruent, write the congruence of triangles in symbolic form.

(a)

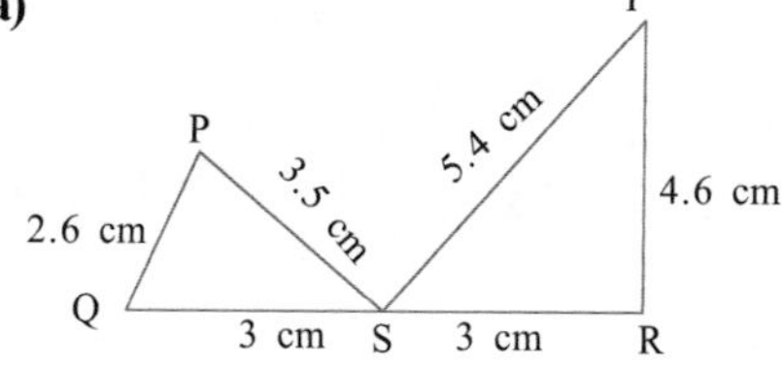

(b)

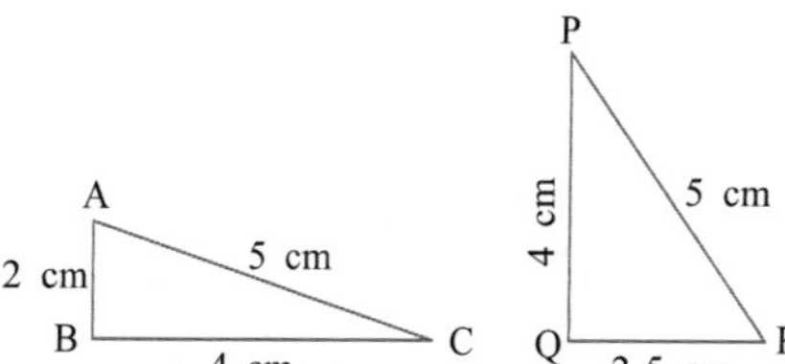

(c)

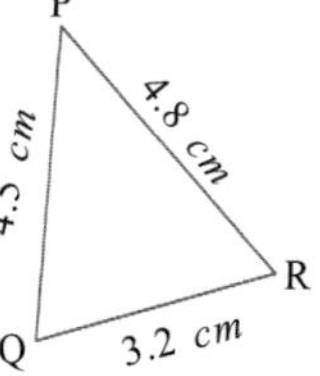

(d)

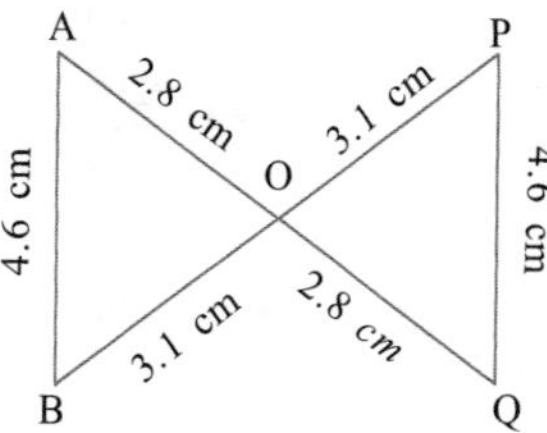

52. In given figures, state which pair of triangles are congruent by SAS congruence condition. In case of congruent triangles, write the congruence of the triangles in symbolic form.

(a)

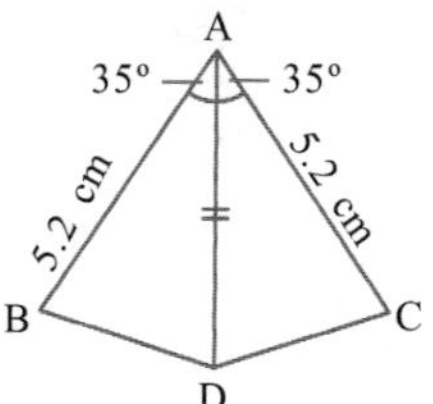

(b)

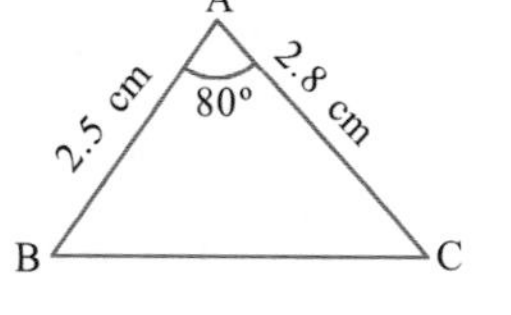

(c) 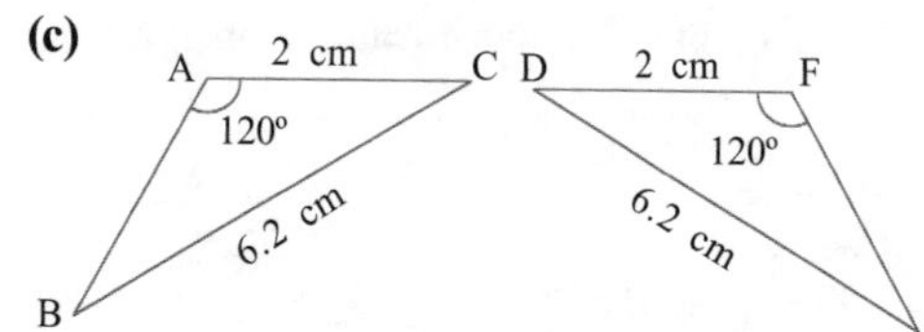

(d) 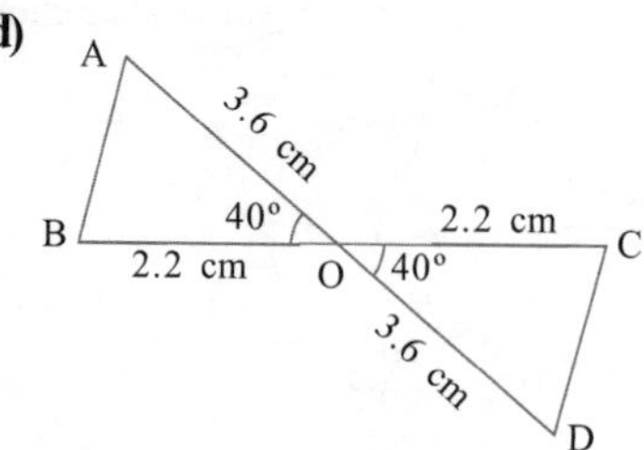

53. Write the congruence criterion used in the following figures :

(a) 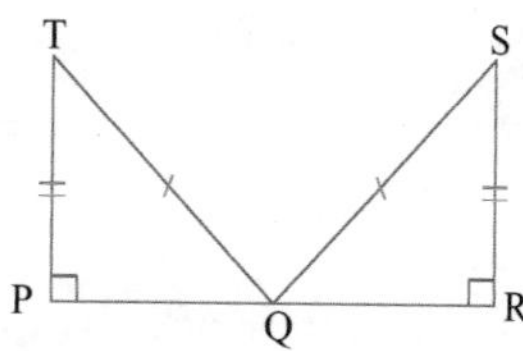

(b) 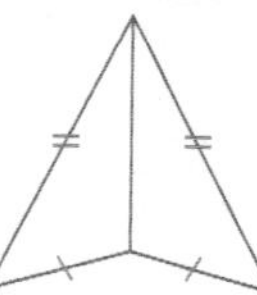

(c) 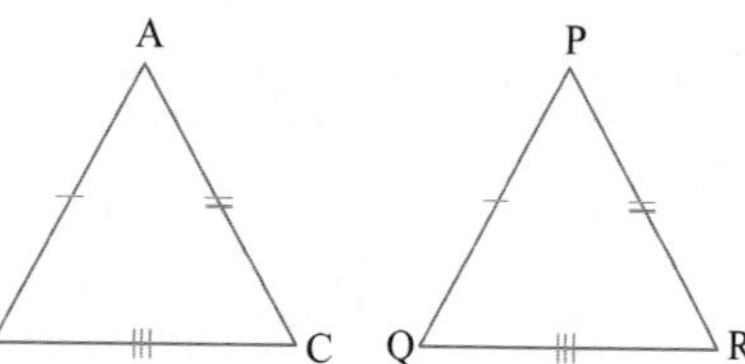

(d) 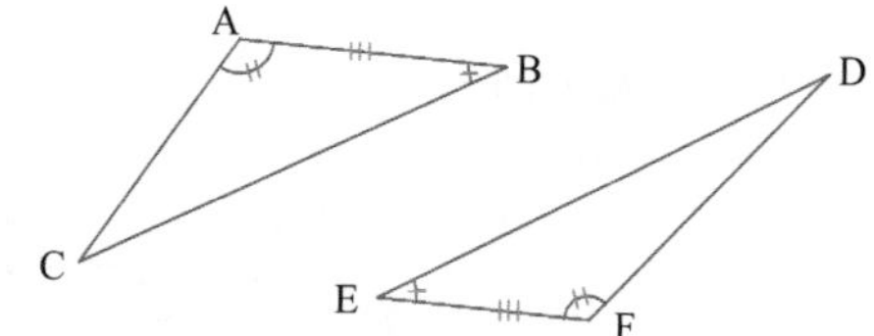

In exercises 54-57, find the third pair of corresponding parts which makes. the following triangles congruent by ASA criterion of congruence, if

54. 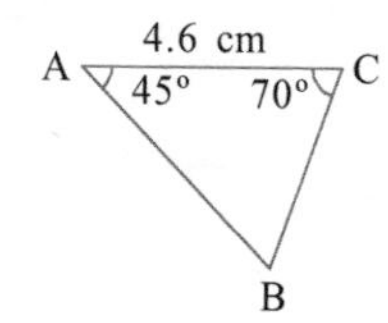

55. 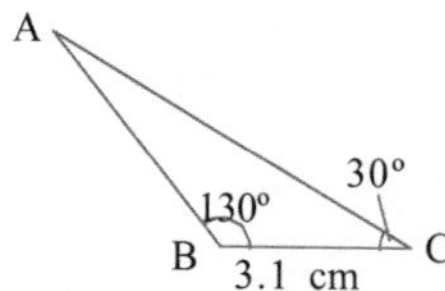

56. 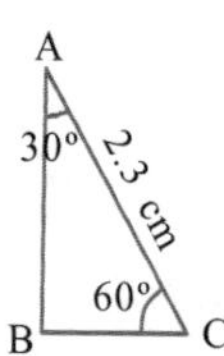

57. 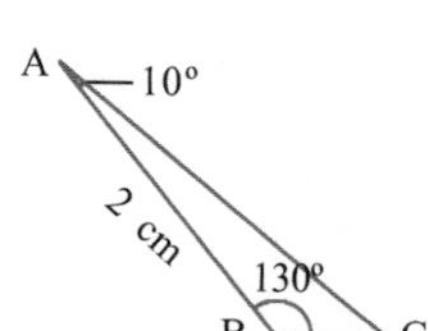

58. In given figures, which pair of triangles are congruent by ASA congruence condition? If congruent, write the congruence of the two triangles in symbolic form.

(a) 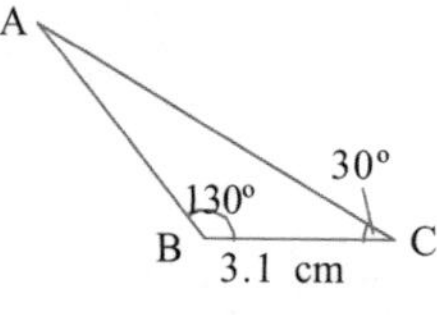

(b) 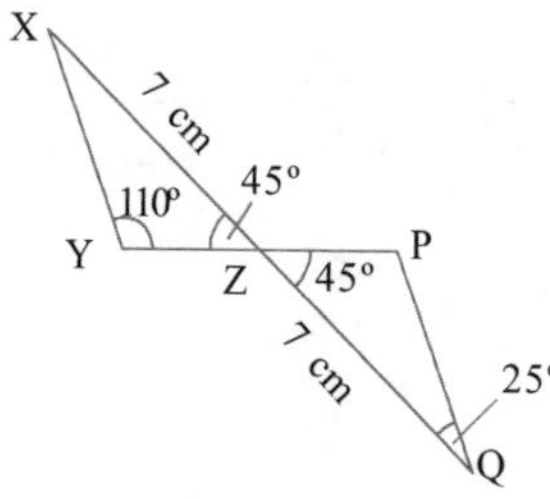

(c) 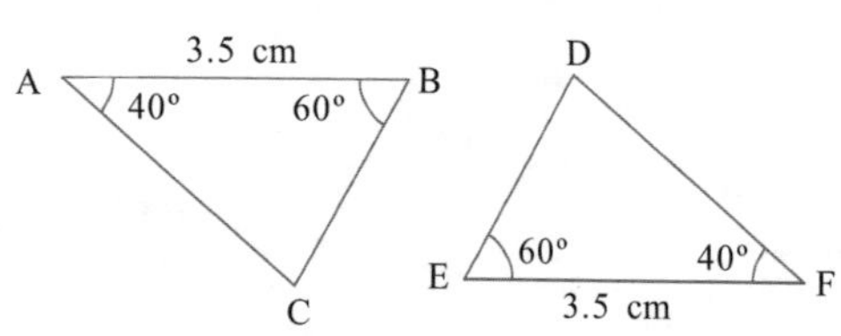

(d) 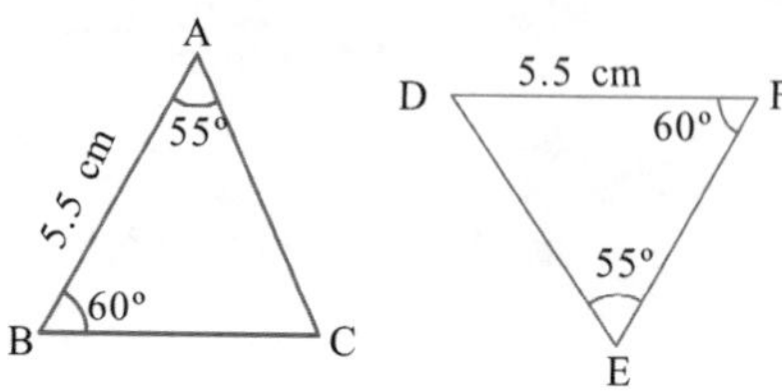

59. In the given figure, state whether the pair of triangles are congruent by RHS congruence condition. If congruent, write the congruence of triangles in symbolic form.

(a)

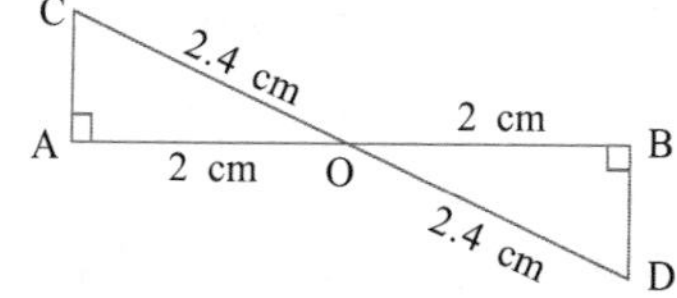

(b)

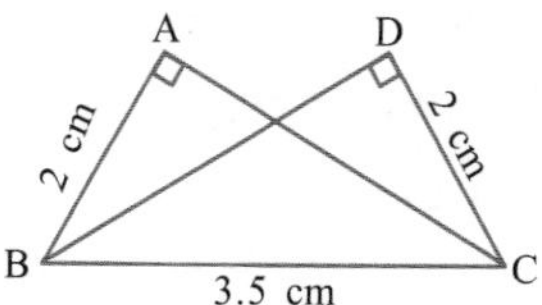

(c)

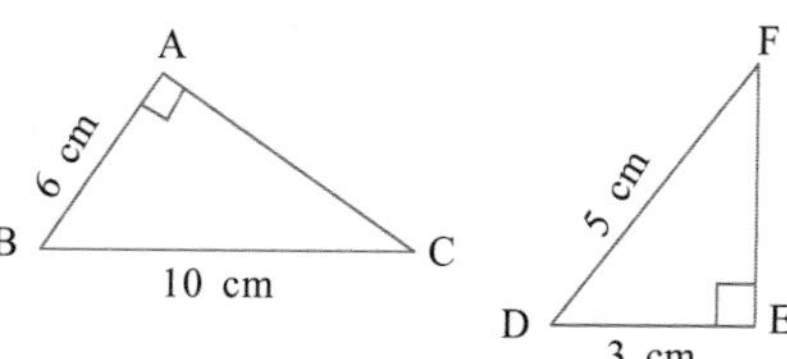

(d)

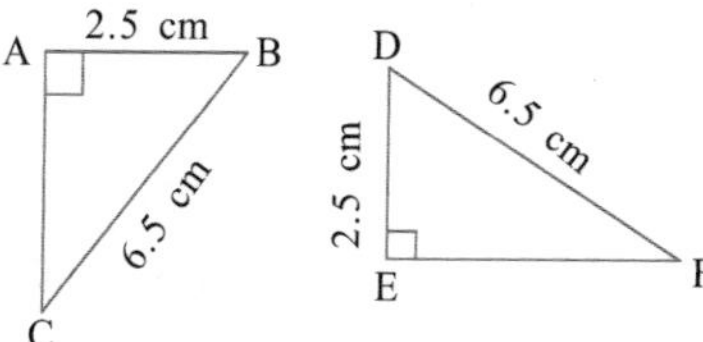

60. In the figure, AD bisects $\angle A$ and $AD \perp BC$.

(i) Is $\Delta ADB \cong \Delta ADC$ by ASA congruence criterion ?

(ii) Also, state the three facts, you have used to answer (i).

(iii) Is BD = DC. Give reason.

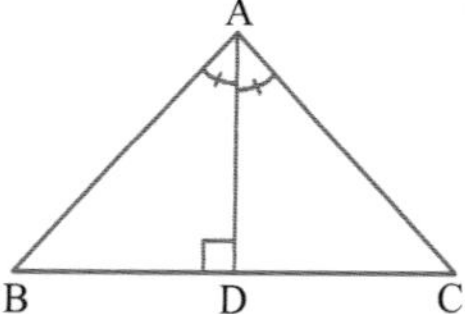

11.3 SIMILARITY MAPPINGS

A. CONCEPT OF SIMILARITY

Looking around, you will not always find objects of the same shape and same size. You can see a new leaf on a tree, smaller in size, but looking almost like a well developed bigger leaf on the same tree. You can see fishes of different sizes but of the same shape in a pond. Geometrical figures like circles of different radii, squares of different sides, line segments of different lengths and equilateral triangles of different sides are some examples of figures having the same shape but *not of same size* (See Figure 11.115).

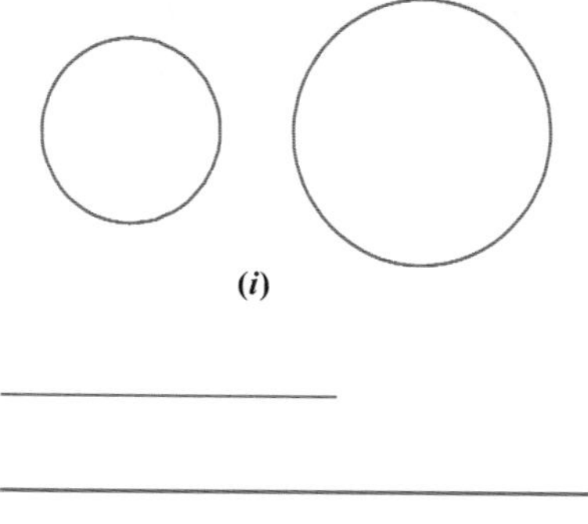

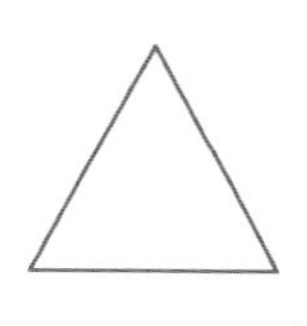

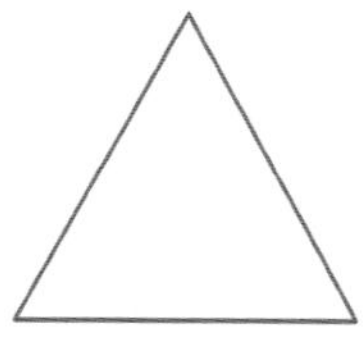

Figure 11.115

All such figures (objects) are called "**similar**". Thus, photographs of the same person or the same object or the same figure in different sizes printed from the same negative are all similar.

Thus, we say that **figures or objects which are of the same shape but not necessarily of the same size are called similar figures/objects.**

Recall that we have studied about the figures which have the same shape and also have the same size. We called them **congruent figures**. The property those figures had was that if one is superposed on the other, it will *exactly* cover the other. Similar figures, not necessarily being of the same size, cannot be superposed on each other even though they have the same shape. Thus, we can say that :

Two congruent geometrical figures are similar but the converse, *i.e.*, similar geometrical figures are congruent, need not be true.

In addition, as in the case of congruent figures, we can also find a one-to-one correspondence between the corresponding parts of two similar figures.

Reflection

Illustration 1 A cube and its reflection in a mirror are *similar*.

Figure 11.116

Illustration 2 The Tennis ball and its reflection through the prism are *similar*.

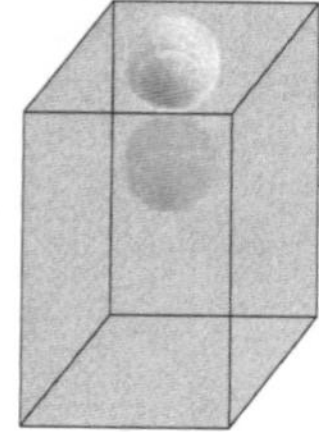

Figure 11.117

Enlarging Images

Illustration 3 Three balls are not of the same size but they are similar (Figure 11.118).

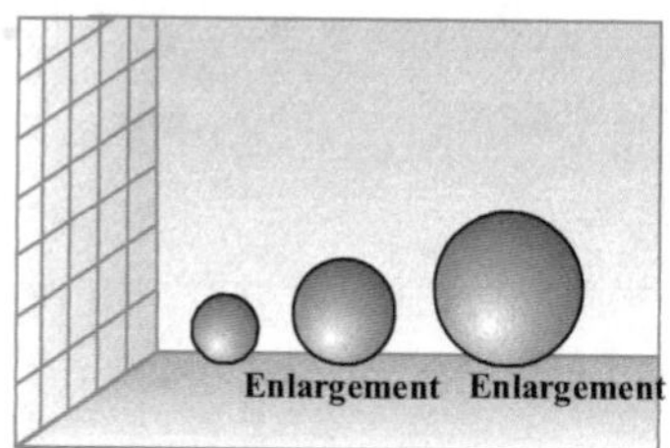

Figure 11.118

Similar Polygons

Two polygons, having the same number of sides are **similar**, if their corresponding *angles are equal* (*i.e.*, they are equiangular) and their corresponding *sides are in the same ratio (or proportion).*

Illustration 4 The quadrilateral ABCD is *similar* to quadrilateral EFGH, as

$\angle A = \angle E$, $\angle B = \angle F$, $\angle C = \angle G$, $\angle D = \angle H$ and

$$\frac{AB}{EF} = \frac{BC}{FG} = \frac{CD}{GH} = \frac{DA}{HE}. \left(= \frac{1}{2}\right)$$

Quadrilateral ABCD is *similar* to quadrilateral EFGH is written as ABCD ~ EFGH. (Symbol '~' stands for 'is similar to')

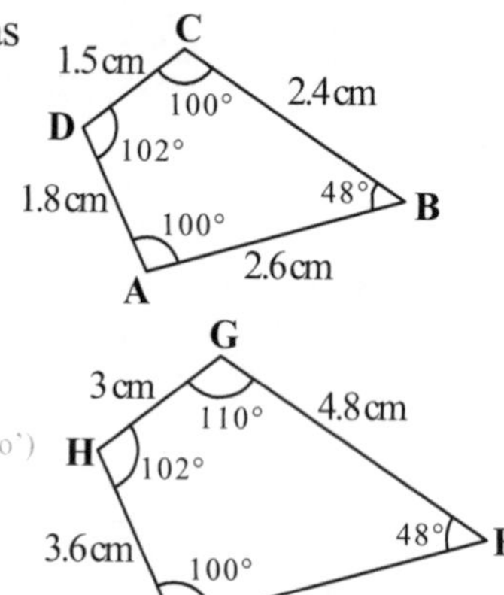

Figure 11.119

Illustration 5 In rectangles, IJKL and MNOP, angles are equal but sides are not proportional.

So, the rectangles are **not** similar.

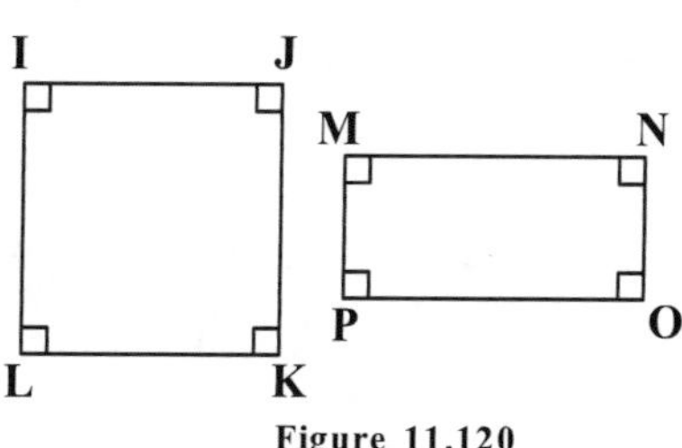

Figure 11.120

Illustration 6 In the given figures, QRST and WXYZ, corresponding sides are proportional

i.e., $\frac{QR}{WX} = \frac{RS}{XY} = \frac{ST}{YZ} = \frac{TQ}{ZW}$,

but corresponding angles are not equal.

So, the two figures are **not** similar.

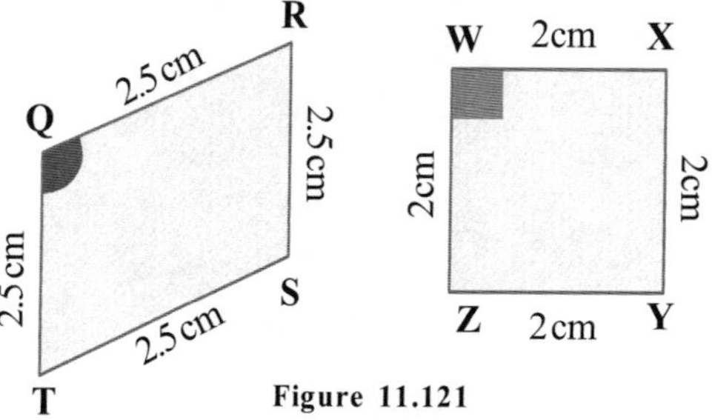

Figure 11.121

Illustration 7 All rectangles are similar.

Illustration 8 All equilateral triangles are similar.

➜ Segments divided Proportionally

Two segments AB and CD are divided proportionally at points X and Y, if $\frac{AX}{CY} = \frac{XB}{YD}$

In the following figure, the segments AB and CD are divided proportionally at points X and Y because

A —4— X —7— B C —6— Y —10.5— D

Figure 11.122

- $\frac{AX}{CY} = \frac{XB}{YD}$ since $\frac{4}{6} = \frac{7}{10.5}$, *i.e.*, $4 \times 10.5 = 7 \times 6$, *i.e.*, $42 = 42$ is a true statement

or ***equivalently***.

- $\frac{AX}{XB} = \frac{CY}{YD}$ or $\frac{4}{7} = \frac{6}{10.5}$, or $4 \times 10.5 = 6 \times 7$, or $42 = 42$ is a true statement.

➜ Similarity of Triangles

You may recall that triangle is also a polygon. Thus, we can state the same conditions for the similarity of two triangles also, *i.e.*, **two triangles are similar, if their corresponding angles are equal and their corresponding sides are in the same ratio (or proportion)**

i.e., two triangles ABC and DEF are similar (*i.e.*, $\Delta ABC \sim \Delta DEF$), if

$\angle A = \angle D$, $\angle B = \angle E$ and $\angle C = \angle F$

and $\frac{AB}{DE} = \frac{BC}{EF} = \frac{AC}{DF}$.

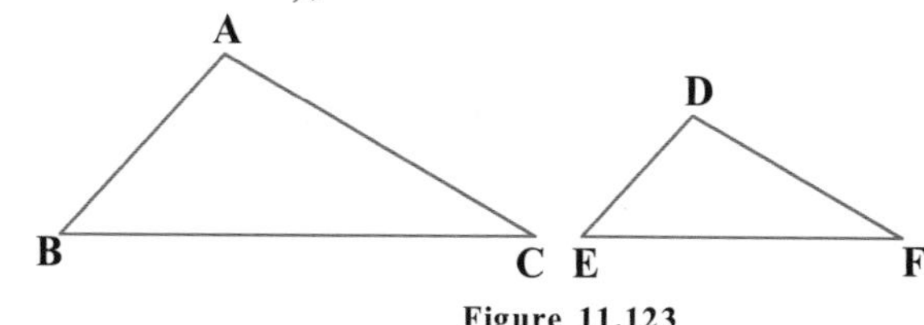

Figure 11.123

Here, A corresponds to D, B corresponds to E and C corresponds F. We can also write $\Delta BCA \sim \Delta EFD$, but it is **not** correct to write $\Delta ABC \sim \Delta EDF$ or $\Delta ABC \sim \Delta FED$.

EXAMPLE 1 Fill in the blank from the given list of words.

All circles are .... ? (Congruent, Similar)

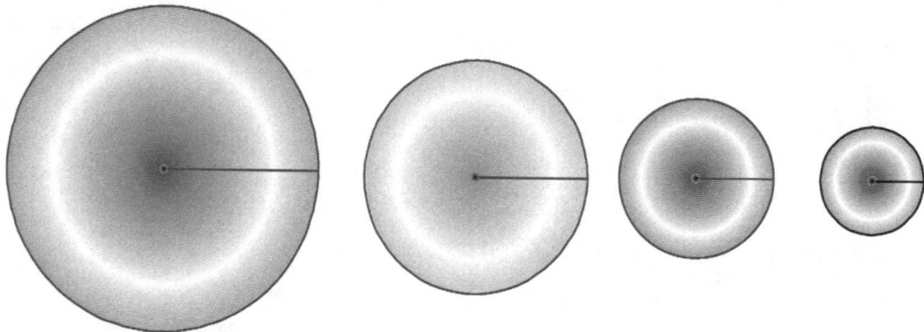

Solution : All the circles shown above do not have the same radii,
So, they are not *congruent* to each other.
All the circles have the same shape.

Figures having same shape but not necessarily the same size are said to be similar.
Therefore, all circles are *similar.*

EXAMPLE 2 In the given figure, $\Delta APQ \sim \Delta ABC$. Find the measure of $\angle Q$.

Solution : We know that in a triangle, the sum of all the three angles is 180°.
Therefore, in ΔABC,

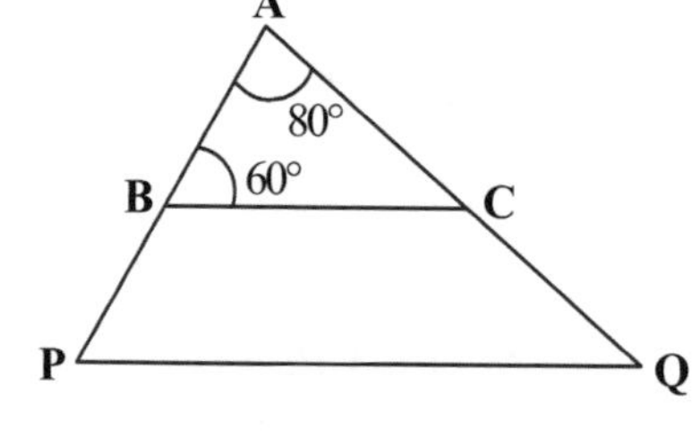

$$\angle A + \angle B + \angle C = 180^\circ$$

$$\angle C = 180^\circ - (\angle A + \angle B)$$

$$= 180^\circ - (80^\circ + 60^\circ)$$

$$= 180^\circ - 140^\circ = 40^\circ$$

Since $\Delta APQ \sim \Delta ABC$. Therefore, $\angle Q = \angle C$ or $\angle Q = 40^\circ$

EXAMPLE 3 If $\Delta ABC \sim \Delta PQR$, find the value of x.

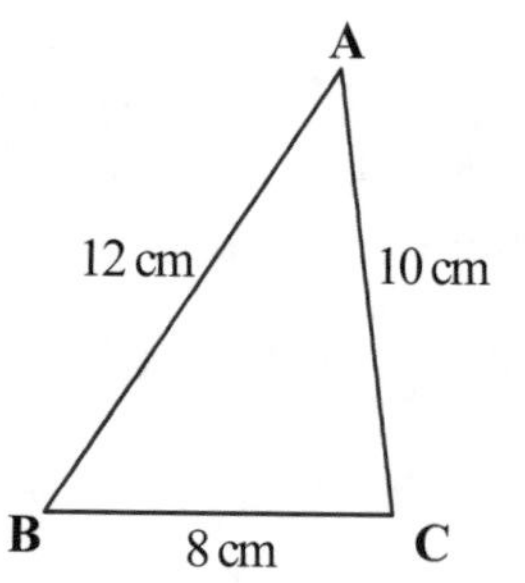

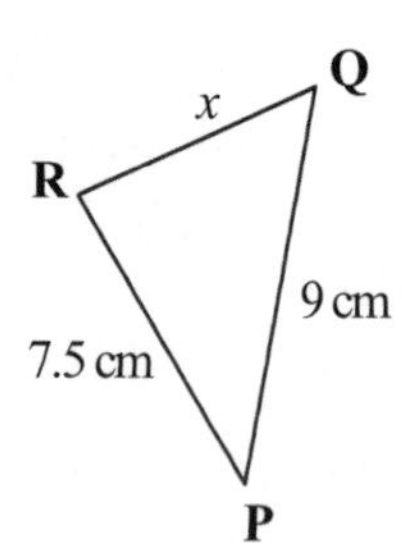

Solution : Since $\Delta ABC \sim \Delta PQR$,

Therefore, $\dfrac{AB}{PQ} = \dfrac{BC}{QR}$

i.e $\dfrac{12}{9} \times \dfrac{8}{x}$

or $x = \dfrac{8 \times 9}{12}$ or $x = 6$ cm

EXAMPLE 4 If quadrilateral ABCD is similar to quadrilateral PQRS, then find the value of x.

Solution : Since ABCD is similar to PQRS,

Therefore, the ratio of corresponding sides will be equal.

$$\frac{AB}{PQ} = \frac{AD}{PS}$$

or $\frac{15}{x} = \frac{20}{8}$

or $8 \times 15 = 20 \times x$

or $x = \frac{15 \times 8}{20}$ or $x = 6$ cm

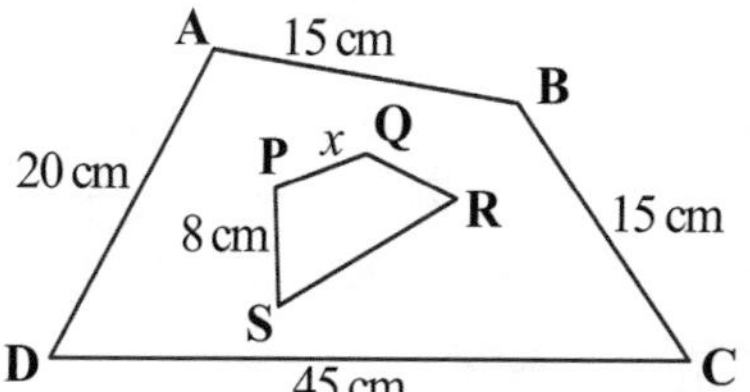

Exercise 11.3

1. Fill in the blank from the given list of words:
   (a) All .... triangles are similar. (isosceles, equilateral)
   (b) If two polygons of the same number of sides are similar, then, their corresponding angles are .... (equal, different), and their corresponding sides are .... (equal, proportional).
   (c) All squares are .... (congruent, similar)

In exercises 2-3, in the given figure, ΔAPQ ~ ΔABC. Find the measure of ∠Q.

2. ∠Q

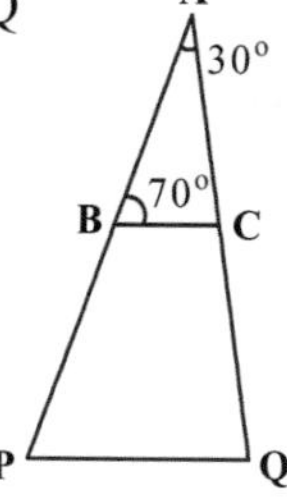

3. ∠P

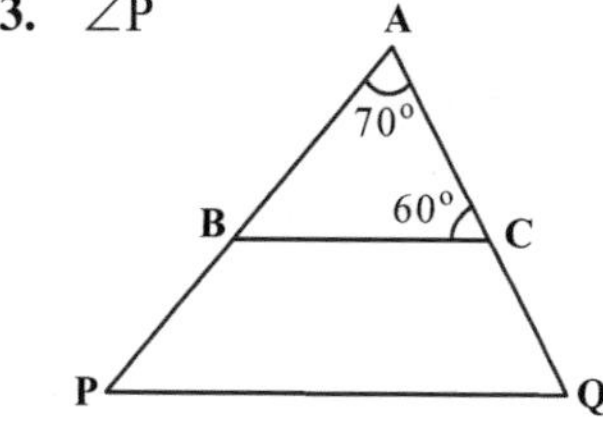

In exercises 4-7, if ΔABC ~ ΔPQR, find the value of x.

4.

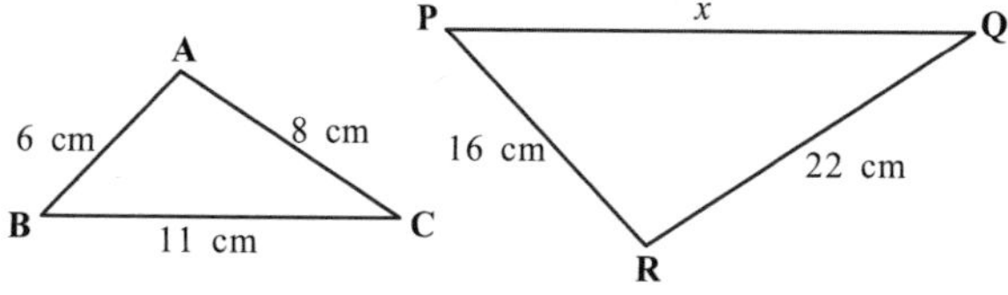

5.

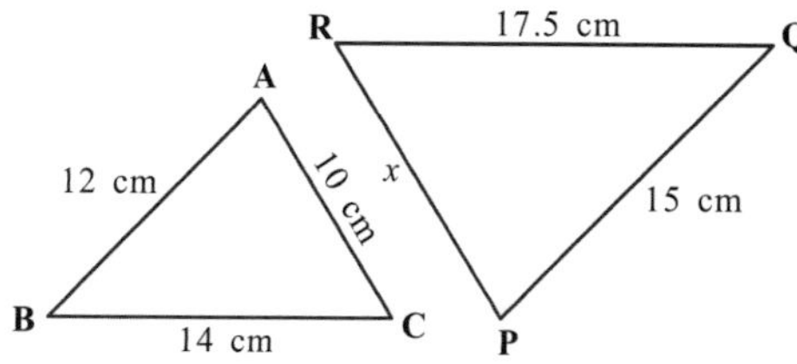

6.

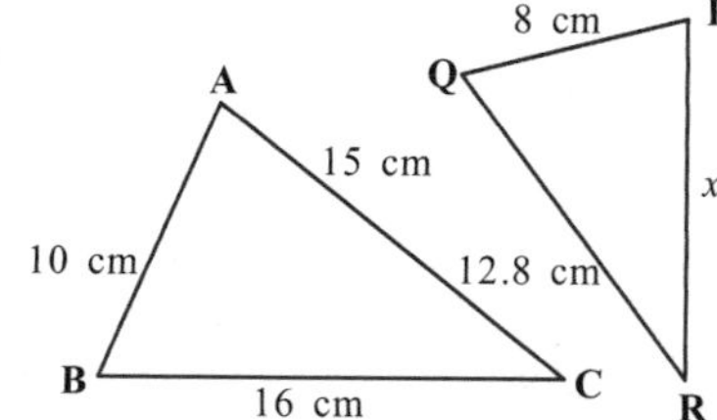

7.

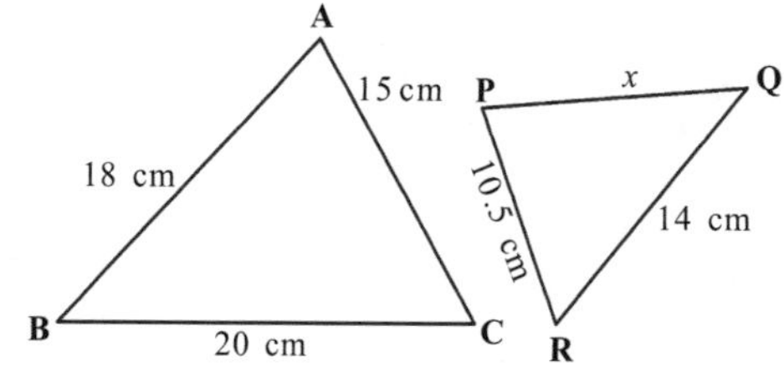

In exercises 8-11, if quadrilateral ABCD is similar to quadrilateral PQRS, find the value of x.

8.

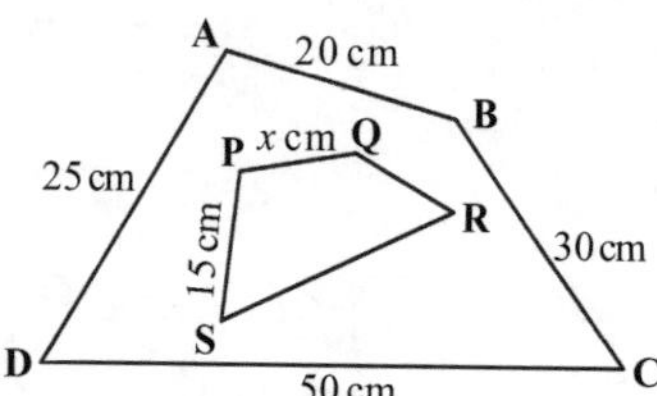

9.

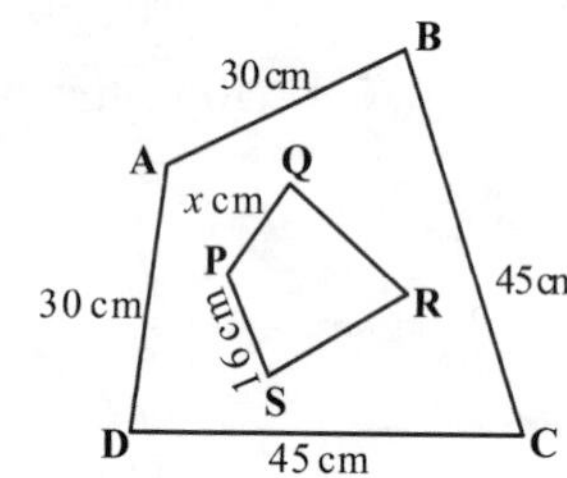

10.

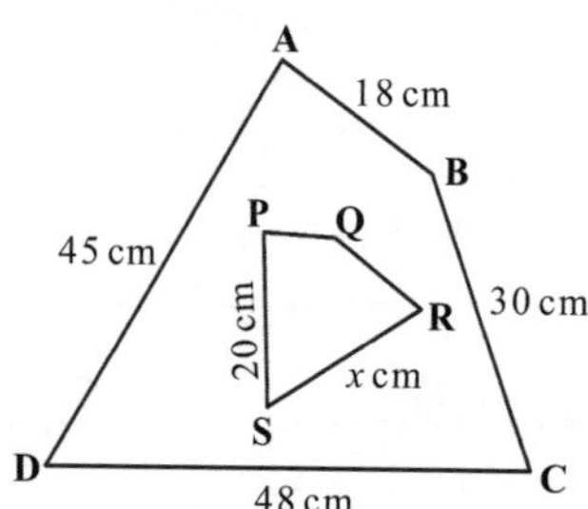

11.

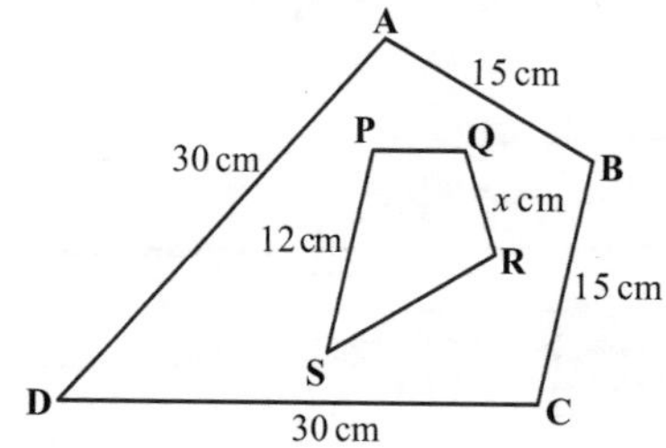

12. State whether the following quadrilaterals are similar or not.

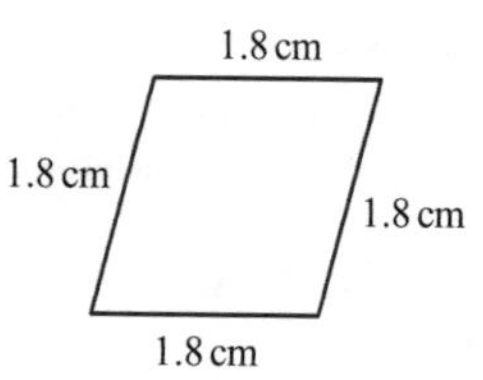

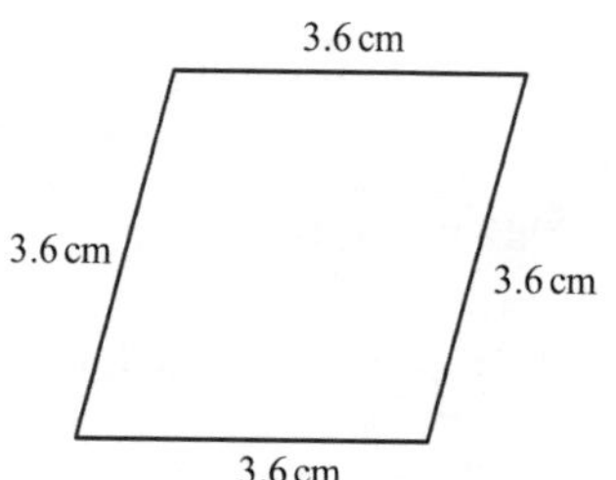

Chapter 1

Section 1.1

1. -15 3. 6 5. -7 7. 4 9. -1 11. 1 13. -1 15. x^2, 2
17. xy , 2 19. x^2y^2,1 21. y^2zx, -3 23. No variable part, -7 25. x^2, 1 27. x^2y, -4 29. Unlike terms
31. Like tems 33. Like terms 35. Unlike terms 37. Like terms 39. Unlike terms 41. $-3m$ 43. $11s - 18$
45. $8t^2 + 28$ 47. $17 - 6x$ 49. $y^2 + 3y + 13x$ 51. $y - 8x$ 53. $20x + y$ 55. $2z^3 - 11z^2 + 5z + 39$
57. $-18p - 8pq - 10q$ 59. $x + \frac{y}{3} + 4$ 61. $12a + 45$ 63. $3x + 114$ 65. $\frac{3}{2}x + \frac{7}{2}$ 67. $2x$
69. x^2 71. $2x + 14.8$ 73. $x + 8x$; $9x$ 75. $x + 2(x + 1)$; $3x + 2$ 77. $2x - 10$ 79. $\frac{2x+6}{x}$
81. $x^3 - 10x$ 83. $x + 4 - 2x$; $4 - x$ 85. $(8 - 3x)(x - 4)$

Chapter 2

Section 2.1

1. {2, 4, 6, 8, 10} 3. {0, 1, 2, 3, 4} 5. {1, 2, 3, 4, 5, 6, 7} 7. {3, 5, 7} 9. {2, 4, 6, 8}
11. {Alabama, Alaska, Arizona, Arkansas} 13. {1, 2, 5, 10} 15. {4, 8, 12, 16,...} 17. { }, the empty set.
19. {− 1, 1} 21. {x | x is a prime number less than 8} 23. {s | s is a state in USA whose name starts with W}
25. {x | x is square of natural number greater than one} 27. {d | d is an alternate day of the week starting from Sunday}
29. {m | m is a month with 31 days} 31. (a) True (b) False (c) False (d) False
33. (a) False (b) True (c) False 35. (a) True (b) False (c) False
37. {1, 3, 5, 7, 9, 11, 13, 21} 39. {3, 5, 7, 11} 41. {3, 5, 7, 11, 13} 43. {2, 4, 6, 8, 11, 14, 22}
45. {2, 4, 8} 47. {e, n} 49. {a, d, e, i, m, n , p, r, s, t, y} 51. {a, t, n}
53. {a, c, e, g, i, l, n, o, r, t, u, y} 55. {x : x is a multiple of 24} 57. {x : x is a multiple of 12}
59. $[-3, 8]$ 61. $(-5, 3)$ 63. $[-6, 9]$ 65. $[0, 5)$ 67. $[-3, 5]$ 69. $[4, 11]$
71. $(3, 6)$ 73. $[4, 5]$ 75. $(-\infty, \infty)$

Section 2.2

1. (a) Abscissa = 0, Ordinate = 2 (b) Abscissa = −3, Ordinate = 0 (c) Abscissa = −8, Ordinate = 5
(d) Abscissa = 4, Ordinate = − 4 (e) Abscissa = −7, Ordinate = −1 (f) Abscissa = 9, Ordinate = −2
(g) Abscissa = 1, Ordinate = −1 (h) Abscissa = −8, Ordinate = − 4 (i) Abscissa = −4, Ordinate = 3

2. (a) (4, 5) (b) (−5, −6) (c) (−3, 5)
(d) (5, −5) (e) (5, 4) (f) (4, 0)

3. (a) (6, 1) (b) (−5, −6) (c) (1, 5)
(d) (−3, 4) (e) (1, −2) (f) (−2, −3)
(g) (6, −3) (h) (−3, 2) (i) (3, −6)

4. (a) Abscissa = 4, Ordinate = 5 (b) Abscissa = −5, Ordinate = −6 (c) Abscissa = −3, Ordinate = 5
(d) Abscissa = 5, Ordinate = −5 (e) Abscissa = 5, Ordinate = 4 (f) Abscissa = 0, Ordinate = 3

5. (a) IV Quadrant (b) III Quadrant (c) II Quadrant
(d) I Quadrant (e) II Quadrant (f) IV Quadrant
(g) III Quadrant

6. (0, 5) 7. (–3, 0) 8. (0, –2) 9. (0, 0) 10. Zero 11. Zero

12. (a) A(1, 3), B(1, 1), and C(4, 1) (b) A(3, 5), B(1, 1), and C(5, 3)
(c) A(2, 4), B(2, 2), and C(5, 2) (d) A(3, 4), B(2, 1), and C(5, 1)

13. Coordinates = (5, 7), I Quadrant 14. Coordinates = (–3, –2), III Quadrant
15. Coordinates = (–3, 4), II Quadrant 16. Coordinates = (4, –3), IV Quadrant
17. 5 units 18. 5 units 19. 4 units 20. 2 units
21. (a) Abscissa = 2, Ordinate = 3, Coordinates = (2, 3) (b) Abscissa = 4, Ordinate = –5, Coordinates = (4, –5)
(c) Abscissa = –3, Ordinate = 4, Coordinates = (–3, 4) (d) Abscissa = –5, Ordinate = –3, Coordinates = (–5, –3)

22. No 23. Yes 24. Yes 25. No 26. No 27. No 28. No
29. Yes 30. Yes 31. No 32. Yes 33. No 34. Yes 34. Yes
35. Yes ; No 36. Yes ; No 37. Yes 38. No 39. Yes 40. 5 41. 8
42. –2 43. –2 44. 3 45. 4

46.

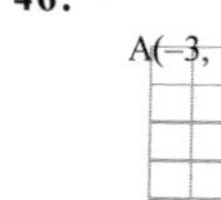

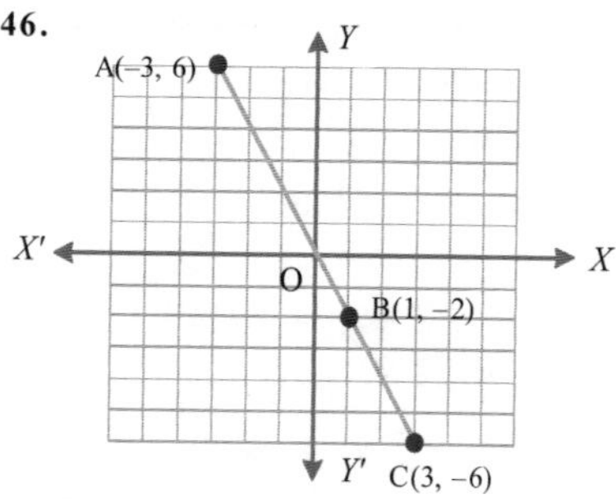

47.

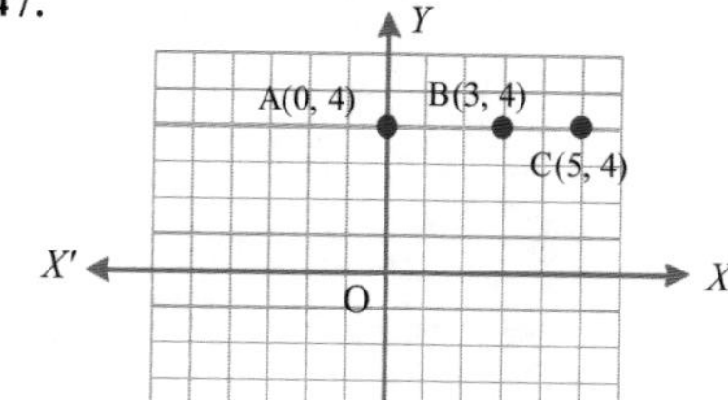

48.

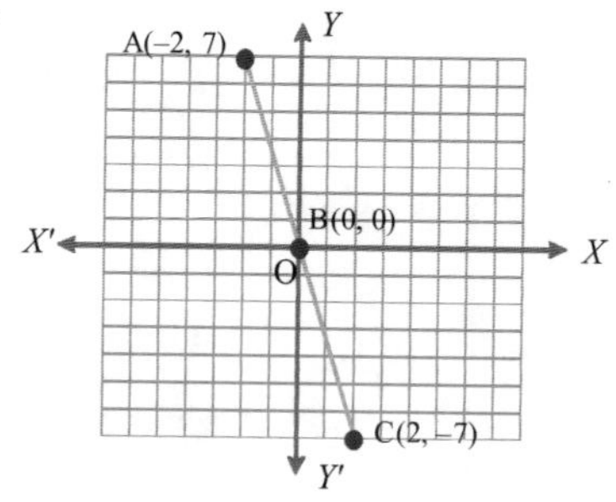

49.

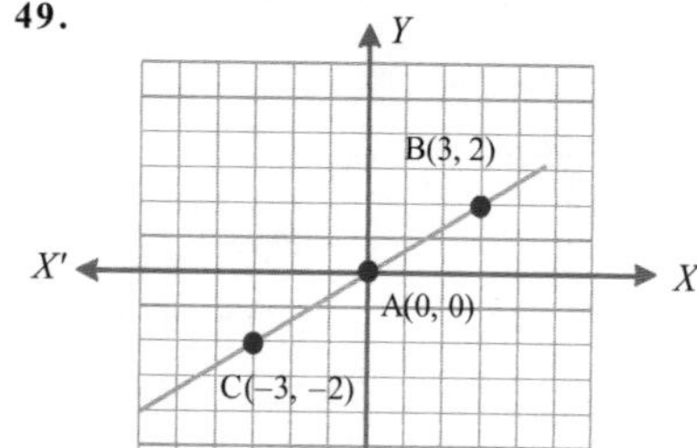

50.

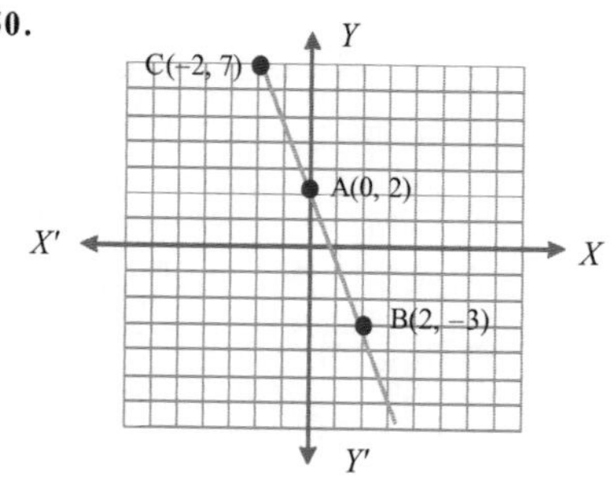

51. Consistent 52. Consistent 53. Inconsistent 54. Consistent 55. A(0, 0) ; B(6, 0) ; C(2, 2)
56. A(0, 0) ; B(0, –2) ; C(–6, –6) 57. A(–2, 0) ; B(6, 0) ; C(2, 4) 58. A(0, 6) ; B(0, –2) ; C(4, 2)
59. inconsistent 60. unique solution 61. inconsistent 62. unique solution

Section 2.3

1. $S(r) = 4\pi r^2$ 3. $V(r) = \frac{4}{3}\pi r^3$ 5. $A(a) = a^2$ 7. $V(x) = x^3$ 9. $p(x) = 3x$ 11. $C(F) = \frac{5}{9}(F - 32)$
13. It represents a function. 15. It represents a function. 17. It represents a function. 19. It represents a function
21. It defines a function. 23. It defines a function. 25. It does not define a function. 27. It defines a function.
29. It defines a function. 31. Yes 33. No 35. Yes 37. Yes 39. No 41. Yes
43. Yes 45. Yes 47. Yes 49. Absolute value 51. Rational 53. Radical
55. Absolute value 57. Piecewise 59. Polynomial 61. Piecewise 63. Piecewise
65. Absolute value 67. Rational 69. $4(3x - 1)$ 71. $5(x - 2)(x + 2)$

73. $(3x - 2)(x - 1)$ 75. $f(x) = 2 + x^2$ 77. $h(x) = \begin{cases} x-5 & \text{if } x \geq 5 \\ -(x-5) & \text{if } x < 5 \end{cases}$ 79. $H(x) = \begin{cases} -2x+7 & \text{if } x \leq 3 \\ 1 & \text{if } 3 < x < 4 \\ 2x-7 & \text{if } x \geq 4 \end{cases}$

81. $f(x) = \sqrt{x+9}$ 83. $\frac{x+2}{x+1}, x \neq 2$ 85. $\frac{x-5}{(x+3)(x+2)}, x \neq 0$ 87. $\frac{x+1}{x^2+x+1}, x \neq 1$

89. $\dfrac{3x}{|x|(x+1)^{\frac{1}{2}}}$ **91.** $(x+3)^{\frac{2}{5}}$ **93.** **(a)** 8 **(b)** 29 **(c)** -6 **(d)** $7a+15$

95. **(a)** 10 **(b)** 10 **(c)** 10 **(d)** 10

97. **(a)** 7 **(b)** -11 **(c)** -1 **(d)** $-2a^2-4a+5$ **99.** **(a)** 0 **(b)** 72 **(c)** 22 **(d)** $7a^2+17a+10$

101. **(a)** $\sqrt{15}$ **(b)** $2\sqrt{3}$ **(c)** $\sqrt{17}$ **(d)** $\sqrt{14-a}$ **103.** **(a)** $-\dfrac{5}{2}$ **(b)** -5 **(c)** 5 **(d)** undefined

105. **(a)** 0 **(b)** $\dfrac{1}{2}$ **(c)** $\dfrac{3}{4}$ **(d)** $\dfrac{2}{3}$ **107.** **(a)** $\dfrac{1}{5}$ **(b)** $-\dfrac{1}{4}$ **(c)** $\dfrac{-5}{2}$ **(d)** -1

109. **(a)** $\dfrac{3}{25}$ **(b)** $\dfrac{1}{12}$ **(c)** 0 **(d)** $\dfrac{1}{21}$ **111.** **(a)** $\dfrac{1}{2}$ **(b)** $\dfrac{1}{3}$ **(c)** $\dfrac{1}{5}$ **(d)** indeterminate

113. **(a)** 5 **(b)** 7 **(c)** 4 **(d)** $5+h$ **115.** **(a)** 2 **(b)** 4 **(c)** 1 **(d)** $2+h$

117. **(a)** 1 **(b)** 1 **(c)** 1 **(d)** 1 **119.** **(a)** indeterminate **(b)** 1 **(c)** -1 **(d)** 1

121. **(a)** 1 **(b)** 2 **(c)** -3 **(d)** $-h$ **123.** **(a)** -3 **(b)** 5 **(c)** 25 **(d)** $(2+h)^2$

125. **(a)** -1 **(b)** 0 **(c)** 25 **(d)** $(2+h)^2$ **127.** **(a)** -2 **(b)** -2 **(c)** 2 **(d)** 2

129. **(a)** \$2,250 **(b)** \$11,042.50 **(c)** \$31,039.50 **(d)** \$99,439.50

131. Cost = \$40,000 ; Revenue = \$120,000 ; Profit = \$80,000 **133.** $300x-\dfrac{x^2}{40}$; Revenue = \$116,000 ; Cost per DVD = \$290

135. $Y(x) = (x+24)(600-12x)$; Total yield = 15,660

137. The farmer should sell after **2 weeks** for the highest price per bushel.

Section 2.4

1. Conjecture **2.** True or false **3.** Inductive reasoning and deductive reasoning **4.** Inductive reasoning
5. Deductive reasoning **6.** (B) **7.** (B) **8.** (C) **9.** (A) **10.** (A)
11. (B) **12.** (A) **13.** (C) **14.** (C) **15.** (A) **16.** (B) **17.** (B)
18. (C) **19.** (B) **20.** (a) **21.** (d) **22.** (a) **23.** (a) **24.** (b)

25. Assertion **26.** Statement or proposition **27.** Opinion **28.** Logical connectives **29.** Compound statement
30. Conjunction **31.** Disjunction **32.** Not P **33.** The Law of the Excluded Middle
34. Implication or conditional statement **35.** Hypothesis ; conclusion **36.** Converse **37.** Inverse **38.** Contrapositive
39. Bi-conditional **40.** (C) **41.** (D) **42.** (E) **43.** (B) **44.** (D) **45.** (E) **46.** (A)
47. (C) **48.** (B) **49.** (D) **50.** (E) **51.** (A) **52.** (B) **53.** (C) **54.** (E)
55. (A) **56.** (B) **57.** (C) **58.** (E) **59.** (E) **60.** (F) **61.** (T) **62.** (T)
63. (T) **64.** (F) **65.** (T) **66.** (F) **67.** (E) **68.** (B) **69.** (A) **70.** (A)
71. (B) **72.** (C) **73.** (D) **74.** (E) **75.** (C)

76. **H:** The song is a hit. **C:** I will buy it
77. **H:** Dogs are happy. **C:** Dogs wag their tails
78. **H:** Helan is motivated **C:** She will study
79. **H:** Charles is a vegan **C:** He does not eat sushi
80. **H:** The figure is a triangle **C:** The figure is a convex
81. **H:** A person is a student **C:** The person takes geometry
82. **H:** Danny hears anyone sneeze **C:** Danny hears, "Bless you"
83. **H:** A set contains the prime numbers **C:** The set is an infinite set
84. (a) , (d) , (b) **85.** (c) , (d) , (b) **86.** (c) , (a) , (d)

87. Valid argument **88.** Law of Detachment **89.** Law of Syllogism **90.** The Law of Negative Inference.
91. Law of Disjunctive Syllogism **92.** Fallacy **93.** Fallacy of the Converse **94.** Fallacy of the Inverse **95.** (F)
96. (T) **97.** (F) **98.** (T) **99.** (F) **100.** (F) **101.** (T) **102.** (F) **103.** (a)
104. (b) **105.** (c) **106.** (d) **107.** (e) **108.** (a) **109.** (b) **110.** (c)

CHAPTER 3

Section 3.1

1. Ten **2.** Ten thousand **3.** Hundred **4.** Hundred Thousand **5.** Billion **6.** 7 **7.** 0 **8.** 5 **9.** 2
10. 2 **11.** 8 **12.** 6 **13.** 0 **14.** Five hundred thirty-eight **15.** Five hundred thirty
16. Five thousand, six hundred twenty-two **17.** Thirteen thousand, eighty-four **18.** Seven hundred three thousand one hundred nine
19. Six thousand, five hundred ninety-seven **20.** One million, two hundred thirty-five thousand, nine-hundred fifty six
21. Four billion, five hundred eighty million, two hundred fifty **22.** Thirty two million, three hundred two thousand, two
23. Three million, thirty thousand, three hundred **24.** Fifty one million, five hundred ten thousand, five hundred one
25. Three hundred billion, thirty million three thousand, three hundred **26.** 70,599 **27.** 215,000 **28.** 925 **29.** 7,255,032,070
30. 150,040,031 **31.** 807,230 **32.** 34,910 **33.** 6,000,002 **34. (a)** 8, 2, 6 **(b)** 0, 5, 4
35. 21,537 **36.** 8,056,290 **37.** 32,027,910 **38.** 115,300,400,065 **39.** Five hundred seventy-five dollars
40. Twelve thousand, seven hundred fifty dollars **41.** $10,658,500 **42.** $31,650,000
43. Fifty two million, four hundred twenty-five thousand square miles.
44. 20 **45.** 6000 **46.** 50,000 **47.** 400 **48.** 0 **49.** 5 **50.** 900 + 70 + 8 **51.** 400 + 30 + 3
52. 40,000 + 5,000 + 300 + 80 + 9 **53.** 50,000 + 0 + 300 + 20 + 7 **54.** 70,000 + 50 + 3 **55.** 90,000 + 6,000 + 7
56. 7,256 **57.** 70,529 **58.** 2,030,276 **59.** 8,052 **60.** 6,080,030 **61.** 25,624
62. 80 **63.** 700 **64.** 4,180 **65.** 1,751,000 **66.** 1,752,000 **67.** 5,840 **68.** 5,800
69. 52,430,000 **70.** 456,000,000 **71.** 82,600,000 **72.** 3,000 **73.** 1,620 **74.** 900,000
75. 72,000 **76.** 259,000 **77.** $1,400 **78.** $4,690,000 **79.** Jesse spent most ; Kevin spent least
80. Bidder B **81.** 793 ; 700 + 90 + 3

Section 3.2

1. 589 **2.** 549 **3.** 72 **4.** 757 **5.** 473 **6.** 1759 **7.** 1,854 **8.** 9,048
9. 9,736 **10.** 3,436, (Observation: when 0 is added to a number, the sum is the number itself.) **11.** 7,613
12. 7,082 **13.** 4,840 **14.** 95,780 **15.** 39,977 **17.** 3,050 **18.** 29,000 **19.** 24,700
20. 830 **21. (a)** 140 **(b)** 133 ; 130 **22. (a)** 800 **(b)** 887 ; 900 **23.** 112 **24.** 215
25. 1,162 **26.** 1,667 **27.** 368 **28.** 7,259 **29.** 6,319 **30.** 2,970 **31.** 2,731 **32.** 3,556
33. 8,128 **34.** 1,375 (***Observation:*** If 0 is subtracted from a number, the difference is the number itself) ;
35. 0 ; (***Observation:*** If a number is subtracted from itself, the difference is 0) **37.** 57,000 **38.** 40,000
39. 12,000 **40.** 3,200 **41.** 1,053 **42.** 7,898 **43. (a)** 500 **(b)** 418 ; 400
44. Sum in each case is 2,271 **45.** 192 ; No **46.** 12,960 in each case

Section 3.3

1. 205 **2.** 696 **3.** 0 **4.** 0 **5.** 4,236 **6.** 1200 **7.** 251 **8.** 35,000 **9.** 7,600
10. 0 **11.** 9,522 **12.** 7,285 **13.** 8,036 **14.** 1,025,156 **15.** 66,982 **16.** 63,745 **17.** 288,750 **18.** 1,691,068
19. 285,376 **20.** 411,700 **21.** 21,000 ; 23,358 **22.** 90,000 ; 95,496 **23.** 1,200,000; 1,494,513
24. 168,000 ; 186,304 **25.** 240,000 ; 244,316 **26.** 1,800 ; 1,691 **27.** 2,400,000 ; 2,313,367
28. 2,400,000 ; 2,344,518 **29.** 25,000,000 ; 25,502,148 **30.** 150,000,000 ; 158,702,248

Section 3.4

1. 421 2. 753 3. 788 4. 79 5. 1,052 6. 58 R 3 7. 358 R 6 8. 1,062 R 3
9. 179 R 1 10. 7,201 R 4 11. 34 R 15; 30 12. 77 R 11; 80 13. 157 R 1; 200 14. 104 ; 100 15. 48 ; 50
16. 2,032 R 32 ; 2000 17. 715 R 149 ; 700 18. 49,381 ; 50,000 19. 10 R 866 ; 10
20. 129 R 163 ; 100 21. 235 R 6 22. 23 R 56 23. 907 R 3 24. 9 R 73 25. 8,923 R 104
26. 1 27. 0 28. 0 29. No 30. No 31. Yes, The quotient is 0
32. 243 33. 64 34. 32 35. 1 36. 1 37. 3 38. 16 39. 14
40. 46 41. 34 42. 4 43. 39 44. 48 45. 1 46. 72 47. 56
48. 15 49. 3 50. 21 51. 18 52. 11 53. 0 54. 12 55. 13
56. 31 57. 7 58. 9 59. 4 60. 4 61. 0 62. 1 63. 0
64. 24 65. 10 66. 11 67. 63 68. 10 69. 45 70. 6 71. 21
72. 3 73. 109 74. 26 75. 5 76. 61 77. 528 78. 187

Chapter 4

Section 4.1

1. 1 · 10 ; 2 · 5 2. 1 · 12 ; 2 · 6 ; 3 · 4 3. 1· 14 ; 2 · 7 4. 1 · 20 ; 2 · 10 ; 4 · 5 5. 1 · 22 ; 2 · 11 6. 1 · 28 ; 2 · 14 ; 4 · 7
7. 1 · 41 8. 1 · 65 ; 5 · 13 9. 1 · 68 ; 2 · 34 ; 4 · 17 10. 1 · 100 ; 2 · 50; 4·25 ; 5·20 ; 10 · 10
11. 1 · 105 ; 3 · 35 ; 5 · 21 ; 7 · 15 12. 1· 116 ; 2 · 58 ; 4 · 29 13. 1 · 142 ; 2 · 71 14. 1 · 250 ; 2 · 125 ; 5 · 50 ; 10 · 25
15. 1· 1230 ; 2 · 615 ; 3 · 410 ; 5·246 ; 6·205 ; 10·123 ; 15 · 82 ; 30· 41 16. 1, 2, 3, 6, 9, 18 17. 1, 2, 3, 6 18. 1, 2, 4, 8
19. 1, 2, 3, 4, 6, 12 20. 1, 3, 5, 15 21. 1, 2, 11, 22 22. 1, 2, 3, 5, 6, 10, 15, 30 23. 1, 2, 4, 7, 8, 14, 28, 56
24. 1, 3, 5, 15, 25, 75 25. 1, 2, 4, 29, 58, 116 26. 1, 2, 3, 4, 6, 8, 9, 12,16, 18, 24, 32, 36, 48, 72, 96, 144, 288
27. 1, 3, 5, 7, 15, 21, 35, 105 28. 1, 239 29. 1, 3, 7, 11, 21, 33, 77, 231
30. 1, 3, 71, 213

Section 4.2

1. 3, 6, 9, 12, 15 2. 4, 8, 12, 16, 20 3. 5, 10, 15, 20, 25 4. 6, 12, 18, 24,30 5. 7, 14, 21, 28, 35
6. 10, 20, 30, 40, 50 7. 11, 22, 33, 44, 55 8. 12, 24, 36, 48, 60 9. 19, 38, 57, 76, 95 10. 23, 46, 69, 92, 115
11. 3, 5 12. 2, 3 13. 5 14. 2, 3, 5 15. 2, 3
16. 27, 30, 33, 36, 39, 42, 45, 48, 51, 54, 57, 60 17. 15, 20, 25, 30, 35, 40 18. 12, 18, 24, 30, 36, 42, 48 19. 4
20. 30 21. 45 22. 24 23. 60 24. 30 25. 72 26. 72 27. 80 28. 60
29. 165 30. 245 31. 78 32. 560 33. After 1 hour or at 5 a. m. 34. 500 gm
35. 720 cm 36. 216 lb. 37. 12 packages of Three Musketeers, 9 packages of Snickers and 8 packages of Nutrageous.

38. 9 39. 12 40. 6
41. 8 42. 10 43. 9 44. 18 45. 12

46.

Number of Programs	1	5	23	115
Length of each (in min)	115	23	5	1

47.

Number of Programs	1	2	4	19	38	76
Length of each (in min)	76	38	19	4	2	1

48. Answer will vary 49. The largest factor is 131, and the smallest is 3. 50. 1997 51. 30 in^2

CHAPTER 5

Section 5.1

1. 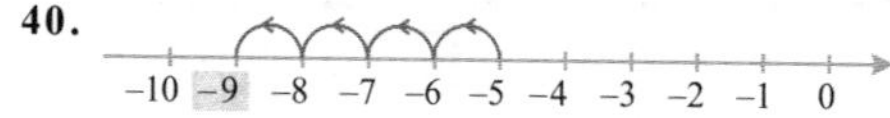

2. 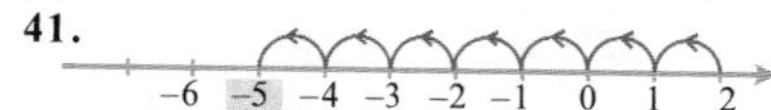

3. 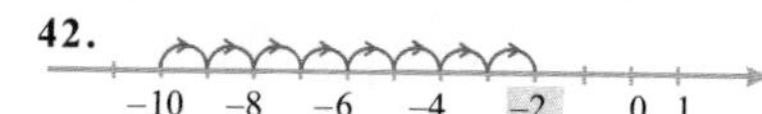

4. 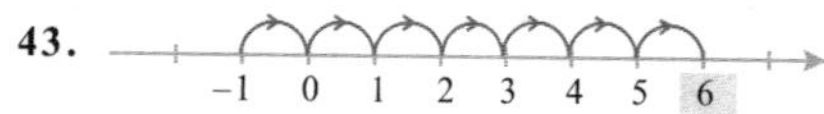

5. 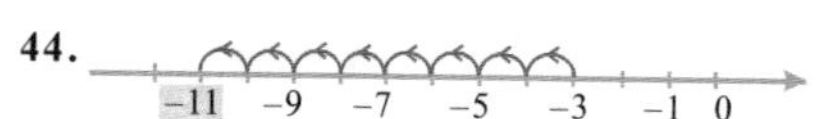

6. − 0.65 7. 4 8. 256

9. 175 10. − 11 11. − 5 12. − 12 13. 17 14. − 12.5 15. − 1027

16. A withdrawal of $1000 from the checking account 17. 560 yds below sea level 18. A gain of $35

19. 15° F above zero 20. 1360 A.D. 21. − 1700 yds 22. $2.50 23. − $350 24. − 35 lb 25. 17°C

26. 43 27. 6 28. 5 29. 85 30. 125 31. 45 32. 3 33. 0 34. 12.6 35. 17 36. −75

37. − 3°C 38. Monday + $375, Tuesday −$100 39. 2590 yds and − 3400 yds, or −2590 yds and 3400 yds ; 5990 yds

40. −10 −9 −8 −7 −6 −5 −4 −3 −2 −1 0 (answer: −9)

41. −6 −5 −4 −3 −2 −1 0 1 2 (answer: −5)

42. −10 −8 −6 −4 −2 0 1 (answer: −2)

43. −1 0 1 2 3 4 5 6 (answer: 6)

44. −11 −9 −7 −5 −3 −1 0 (answer: −11)

45. − 7 46. 11 47. − 21 48. − 12 49. − 7 50. − 6 51. − 4 52. − 2 53. − 1 54. 0

55. − 3 56. 1 57. − 5 58. − 90 59. 9 60. − 12 61. 1 62. − 2

Section 5.2

1. − 27 2. − 40 3. − 28 4. − 20 5. − 21 6. − 12 7. − 12 8. − 64 9. − 108

10. − 96 11. 72 12. 33 13. 420 14. 24 15. 100 16. 8 17. 3 18. 200

19. 0 20. 35 21. 180 22. − 10800 23. − 240 24. − 279 25. − 8 26. − 12,000 27. 108

28. 0 29. 10,800 30. − 168 31. − 5° C 32. − 20.5° C or 20.5° C below zero 33. 25.6°C

34. − $21.56 35. −1.75 lb ; −26.25 lb 36. − 5 37. − 13 38. − 13 39. 6 40. − 53 41. − 32

42. − 7 43. $\frac{1}{4}$ 44. $-\frac{8}{77}$ 45. − 9.8 46. 2 47. 0 48. $\frac{7}{4}$ 49. $\frac{3}{4}$ 50. − 1

51. 1 52. $x = -12$ 53. $y = -12$ 54. $x = 26$ 55. $x = -16$ 56. $t = \frac{18}{7}$ 57. $x = -30$ 58. $x = -\frac{1}{3}$

59. $x = -21$ 60. $x = 91$

Section 5.3

1. $\frac{3}{8}$ 2. $\frac{4}{5}$ 3. $\frac{3}{4}$ 4. $\frac{8}{8}$ 5. $\frac{2}{6}$ 6. $\frac{3}{2}$ 7. $\frac{7}{4}$ 8. $\frac{14}{9}$ 9. Proper: $\frac{7}{18}, \frac{4}{9}, \frac{2}{29}$ Improper: $\frac{13}{10}, \frac{5}{5}$

10. Proper: $\frac{21}{24}, \frac{7}{10}, \frac{13}{17}$; Improper: $\frac{20}{8}, \frac{16}{5}$ 11. Proper: All are proper fractions; Improper: None 12. $4\frac{3}{4}$ 13. $7\frac{1}{2}$

14. $3\frac{1}{8}$ 15. $9\frac{4}{5}$ 16. $13\frac{5}{10}$ 17. $3\frac{20}{21}$ 18. $19\frac{3}{8}$ 19. $150\frac{3}{8}$ 20. $37\frac{17}{101}$

21. $\frac{5}{3}$ 22. $\frac{23}{5}$ 23. $\frac{59}{8}$ 24. $\frac{93}{8}$ 25. $\frac{563}{3}$ 26. $\frac{677}{6}$ 27. $\frac{241}{3}$

28. $\frac{52}{45}$ 29. $\frac{311}{23}$

Section 5.4

1. $\frac{3}{5}$ **2.** $\frac{3}{5}$ **3.** $\frac{7}{10}$ **4.** $\frac{5}{12}$ **5.** $\frac{16}{25}$ **6.** $\frac{3}{8}$ **7.** $\frac{3}{4}$ **8.** $\frac{3}{5}$ **9.** $\frac{43}{59}$ **10.** $\frac{5}{6}$

11. $\frac{13}{45}$ **12.** $\frac{11}{12}$ **13.** $\frac{9}{15}, \frac{12}{20}, \frac{18}{30}$ **14.** $\frac{6}{21}, \frac{8}{28}, \frac{12}{42}$ **15.** $\frac{12}{15}, \frac{16}{20}, \frac{24}{30}$ **16.** $\frac{15}{27}, \frac{20}{36}, \frac{30}{54}$

17. $\frac{24}{33}, \frac{32}{44}, \frac{48}{66}$ **18.** $\frac{54}{39}, \frac{72}{52}, \frac{108}{78}$ **19.** 10 **20.** 4 **21.** 48 **22.** 35 **23.** 35 **24.** 66

25. 72 **26.** 80 **27.** 52 **28.** 60 **29.** 336 **30.** 135 **31.** $\frac{13}{10}$ **32.** $\frac{4}{5}$ **33.** $\frac{1}{3}$ **34.** $\frac{2}{5}$

35. $3\frac{2}{5}$ **36.** $2\frac{1}{3}$ **37.** $25\frac{1}{2}$ **38.** $\frac{17}{35}$ **39.** $12\frac{3}{8}$ **40.** $\frac{15}{20}$ **41.** True **42.** False **43.** True **44.** True

45. False **46.** False **47.** $>$ **48.** $<$ **49.** $<$ **50.** $=$ **51.** $>$ **52.** $=$ **53.** $=$ **54.** $>$

55. $<$ **56.** $<$ **57.** $\frac{11}{20}, \frac{2}{3}, \frac{13}{15}$ **58.** $\frac{2}{14}, \frac{3}{7}, \frac{5}{6}$ **59.** $\frac{6}{14}, \frac{13}{28}, \frac{17}{35}$ **60.** $15\frac{2}{5}, 15\frac{4}{7}, 15\frac{3}{4}$

61. $\frac{1}{4}, \frac{3}{8}, \frac{7}{16}, \frac{5}{8}$ **62.** $\frac{7}{8}, \frac{5}{6}, \frac{2}{3}$ **63.** $\frac{1}{3}, \frac{2}{9}, \frac{5}{27}$ **64.** $\frac{3}{4}, \frac{4}{7}, \frac{2}{5}$ **65.** $1\frac{1}{16}, \frac{7}{8}, \frac{3}{4}$ **66.** $\frac{2}{5}, \frac{7}{18}, \frac{11}{30}$

67. $\frac{11}{24}$ **68.** $\frac{1}{5}$ **69.** Smallest: $\frac{1}{2}$ ton; largest: $\frac{7}{8}$ **70.** On gas **71.** $7\frac{1}{8}$ lb, $7\frac{3}{16}$ lb, $7\frac{1}{4}$ lb **72.** $\frac{53}{77}, \frac{15}{22}$

Section 5.5

1. $\frac{1}{2}$ **2.** $\frac{2}{3}$ **3.** $\frac{1}{3}$ **4.** $\frac{15}{28}$ **5.** $\frac{1}{4}$ **6.** $\frac{2}{5}$ **7.** $\frac{3}{10}$ **8.** $\frac{1}{6}$ **9.** $\frac{4}{3}$

10. $\frac{16}{35}$ **11.** $\frac{8}{21}$ **12.** $\frac{4}{9}$ **13.** $\frac{1}{4}$ **14.** $\frac{32}{225}$ **15.** 11 **16.** $\frac{52}{45}$ **17.** 4 **18.** 10

19. $\frac{7}{10}$ **20.** $6\frac{3}{4}$ **21.** $1\frac{7}{27}$ **22.** $\frac{32}{45}$ **23.** $2\frac{38}{47}$ **24.** 0 **25.** 180 **26.** $17\frac{8}{9}$ **27.** $3\frac{2}{3}$

28. 8 **29.** 100 **30.** 180 **31.** 217 **32.** $\frac{13}{45}$ **33.** $\frac{19}{4}$ **34.** $\frac{13}{5}$ **35.** $\frac{100}{79}$ **36.** $\frac{5}{9}$

37. $\frac{3}{44}$ **38.** $\frac{2931}{1052}$ **39.** 1 **40.** $\frac{6}{7}$ **41.** $\frac{7}{3}$ **42.** $\frac{9}{5}$ **43.** $1\frac{1}{2}$ **44.** $\frac{2}{3}$ **45.** 1

46. $\frac{3}{5}$ **47.** $\frac{49}{90}$ **48.** $\frac{11}{10}$ **49.** $\frac{11}{6}$ **50.** $\frac{7}{9}$ **51.** $\frac{5}{4}$ **52.** $\frac{17}{15}$ **53.** $\frac{17}{114}$ **54.** $\frac{39}{245}$

55. $\frac{31}{110}$ **56.** $\frac{8}{21}$ **57.** $\frac{9}{49}$ **58.** $\frac{8}{15}$ **59.** $\frac{31}{24}$ **60.** $\frac{43}{48}$ **61.** $\frac{97}{60}$ **62.** $\frac{19}{24}$ **63.** $\frac{27}{16}$

64. 4 **65.** 4 **66.** $3\frac{3}{5}$ **67.** $4\frac{5}{6}$ **68.** $5\frac{7}{10}$ **69.** $4\frac{11}{15}$ **70.** $8\frac{3}{20}$ **71.** $11\frac{13}{15}$ **72.** $16\frac{1}{16}$

73. $22\frac{5}{6}$ **74.** $6\frac{11}{20}$ **75.** $8\frac{7}{50}$ **76.** $3\frac{3}{10}$ **77.** $9\frac{1}{4}$ **78.** $8\frac{7}{15}$ **79.** $\frac{1}{2}$ **80.** $\frac{3}{7}$ **81.** $\frac{4}{5}$

82. $\frac{1}{2}$ **83.** $\frac{3}{10}$ **84.** $\frac{7}{10}$ **85.** $\frac{5}{24}$ **86.** $\frac{8}{19}$ **87.** $\frac{1}{15}$ **88.** $\frac{6}{13}$ **89.** $\frac{1}{4}$ **90.** $\frac{5}{12}$

91. $\frac{1}{20}$ **92.** $\frac{11}{35}$ **93.** $\frac{11}{20}$ **94.** $\frac{1}{30}$ **95.** $\frac{1}{6}$ **96.** $\frac{164}{245}$ **97.** $\frac{23}{66}$ **98.** $\frac{19}{42}$ **99.** $4\frac{34}{45}$

100. $\frac{7}{10}$ **101.** 1 **102.** $1\frac{11}{15}$ **103.** $1\frac{13}{60}$ **104.** 2 **105.** 0 **106.** $4\frac{1}{12}$ **107.** $\frac{2}{3}$ **108.** $\frac{37}{48}$

109. $\frac{50}{81}$ **110.** $\frac{18}{25}$ **111.** 2 **112.** $\frac{2}{9}$ **113.** $2\frac{13}{36}$ **114.** $\frac{23}{60}$ **115.** $4\frac{1}{60}$ **116.** $\frac{1}{9}$

117. $\frac{26}{25}$ or $1\frac{1}{25}$ **118.** $\frac{4}{9}$ **119.** $\frac{7}{19}$ **120.** 1 **121.** $\frac{1}{2}$ **122.** $\frac{5}{9}$

Chapter 6

Section 6.1

1. Thousandths **2.** Tenths **3.** Hundredths **4.** Hundredths **5.** Ones **6.** Thousandths
7. Hundred-thousandths **8.** Thousandths **9.** Ten-Thousandths **10.** Tenths **11.** Thousandths **12.** Hundredths
13. Tenths **14.** Ten **15.** Ten **16.** Ten-Thousandths **17.** Tenths **18.** Ten-Thousandths
19. Hundredths **20.** Thousandths **21.** 8 **22.** 0 **23.** 2 **24.** 5 **25.** 0 **26.** 5 **27.** 0
28. 5 **29.** 2 **30.** 6 **31.** 3 **32.** 5 **33.** 6 **34.** 7 **35.** 4 **36.** 8

37. $50+4+\frac{2}{10}+\frac{7}{100}+\frac{1}{1000}$ **38.** $7+\frac{2}{10}+\frac{3}{100}+\frac{5}{1000}$ **39.** $40+7+\frac{2}{10}+\frac{2}{100}$ **40.** $\frac{9}{1000}$ **41.** $100+7+\frac{4}{10}+\frac{5}{1000}$

42. $\frac{2}{10}+\frac{3}{100}+\frac{5}{1000}+\frac{9}{10000}$ **43.** $20+7+\frac{3}{10}+\frac{2}{100}+\frac{6}{1000}$ **44.** $200+90+8+\frac{5}{100}$ **45.** $10+3+\frac{7}{10}+\frac{9}{100}+\frac{8}{1000}+\frac{4}{10000}$

46. $\frac{3}{10}+\frac{1}{1000}+\frac{4}{10,000}$ **47.** $9+\frac{3}{10}+\frac{2}{100}+\frac{5}{10000}+\frac{1}{100000}$ **48.** $50+\frac{2}{100}+\frac{3}{1000}+\frac{4}{10000}$

49. 5 tens + 1 one + 1 tenth + 3 hundredths + 9 thousandths **50.** 2 ones + 3 tenths + 9 hundredths + 5 thousandths
51. 1 ten + 6 ones + 9 tenths + 5 hundredths + 4 thousandths **52.** 4 ones + 9 thousandths + 3 ten-thousandths
53. 5 ones + 1 tenth + 4 hundredths + 3 thousandths **54.** 7 ones + 1 tenth + 5 thousandths + 4 ten-thousandths
55. 3 tens + 5 ones + 7 tenths + 8 hundredths + 2 thousandths **56.** 1 ten + 8 ones + 2 hundredths + 3 thousandths + 5 ten-thousandths
57. 1 hundred + 5 ones + 3 tenths + 6 hundredths **58.** 6 ones + 3 tenths + 7 hundredths + 5 thousandths
59. 239.034 **60.** 0.532 **61.** 9.009 **62.** 4.503 **63.** 25.0135 **64.** 0.0047 **65.** 92.4325
66. 0.491 **67.** 0.0006 **68.** 0.0048 **69.** 35.062 **70.** 0.0573
71. Four thousand five and eighty-three thousandths **72.** Two and six hundred forty-three thousandths
73. Twelve and sixty-four thousandths **74.** Eight and six hundred fifty thousandths
75. Seven and two thousand three hundred fifty-four ten-thousandth
76. Twenty-three and fifteen hundredths **77.** Sixteen and one hundred thirty-five thousandths
78. Four hundred thirty-five and seven tenths **79.** Five and seven ten-thousandths
80. Twenty eight and thirty-five hundredths **81.** Eight and nine thousandths **82.** Forty and one hundredths
83. One hundred three and seven thousandths **84.** Seven hundred fifty-eight and six tenths
85. Four hundred thirteen and three hundred five thousandths **86.** 217.03 **87.** 29.5 **88.** 1009.349 **89.** 5.25
90. 4532.092 **91.** 8.0008 **92.** 1,000,092.12 **93.** 8.8 **94.** Ninety-five and thirty-five hundredths dollars
95. Three hundred twenty-two and seventeen hundredths dollars **96.** \$564.28 **97.** 275.6 **98.** 63.45 **99.** 17.04
100. 570 **101.** 43.009 **102.** 1.0 **103.** 15.00 **104.** 2560 **105.** 0.060 **106.** 800
107. 30 ; 26 ; 26.1 ; 26.11 **108.** 400 ; 400 ; 399.6 ; 399.56 **109.** \$2073.50 **110.** \$53
111. The number is rounded to 5500.00; 5500.0; 5500; 5500 **112.** 0.155 percent **113.** 14.059 lb

Section 6.2

1. 49.7 **2.** 8.5 **3.** 7.3 **4.** 3.6 **5.** 32.5 **6.** 33.2 **7.** 45.18 **8.** 204.153
9. 0.999 **10.** 926.466 **11.** 33.0585 **12.** 42.1555 **13.** 114.264 **14.** 148.72 **15.** 510.23 lb **16.** 517.7355
17. 219.04 **18.** 28.4431 **19.** 49.215 **20.** 10.1 **21.** 6.202 **22.** 560.36 **23.** 70.105 **24.** 11.55
25. 119.98 **26.** 1.111 **27.** 17.576 **28.** 151.2571 **29.** 23.6 **30.** 0.1617 **31.** 47.358 **32.** 356.742
33. 0.165 **34.** 26.322 **35.** 554.15 **36.** 124.945 **37.** 1722.565 **38.** 81.235 **39.** 496.65 **41.** 173
42. \$150 **43.** 1886 **44.** 620 **45.** 23 lb **46.** 38 **47.** 86 **48.** 2434 **49.** 1,999,929
50. 301.644 **51.** 1.4093 **52.** \$34.45 **53.** Yes **54.** \$1608.63 **55.** 0.08 **56.** 0.008 **57.** 0.0015
58. 1.46 **59.** 0.06012 **60.** 0.0105 **61.** 46.2 **62.** 2.7 **63.** 0.3705 **64.** 2.266 **65.** 5.72
66. 0.1659 **67.** 10.032 **68.** 5.6 **69.** 24.5 **70.** 0.0065 **71.** 41.5 **72.** 1.6284 **73.** 0.00048
74. 4.9 **75.** 0.048 **76.** 0.0336 **77.** 0.0744 **78.** 0.588 **79.** 1.0875 **80.** 1.232 **81.** 0.00924
82. 6.1765 **83.** 15.0816 **84.** 24.9 **85.** 3.6 **86.** 48.24 **87.** 0.5688 **88.** 0.4060 **89.** 1.1132

90. 4.125 **91.** 0.42 **92.** 3.92 **93.** 0.000048 **94.** 0.000255 **95.** 209.76 **96.** 0.10488 **97.** 12.765
98. 716.25 **99.** 1279.53 **100.** 93.003 **101.** 10.591 **102.** 8.1002 **103.** 91.2 **104.** 30.502 **105.** 10.3653
106. 22.761 **108.** 1.7 **109.** 1.6 **110.** 14.5 **111.** 0.4 **112.** 2.15 **113.** 11.52 **114.** 4.7
115. 0.4525 **116.** 2.47 **117.** 4.256 **118.** 3.92 **119.** 0.145 **120.** 17.4 **121.** 1.8 **122.** 0.346
123. 0.0865 **124.** 0.127 **125.** 3.44 **126.** 13.04 **127.** 3.075 **128.** 0.58 **129.** 2.10 **130.** 2.68
131. 1.63 **132.** 0.32 **133.** 1.38 **134.** 0.03 **135.** 2.14 **136.** 3.76 **137.** 5.22 **138.** 0.08
139. 1.35 **140.** 4.27 **141.** 1.35 **142.** 0.12 **143.** 3.76 **144.** 2.43 **145.** 6.85 **146.** 12.50
147. 11.04 **148.** 113.2 **149.** 52.6 **150.** 452 **151.** 4970 **152.** 1584.8 **153.** 400 **154.** 900
155. 0.9 **156.** 0.375 **157.** 877 **158.** 236.65 **159.** 0.625 **160.** 120 **161.** 181.37 **162.** 0.0025
163. 73.34 **164.** 0.02 **165.** 12.37 **166.** 2132.86 **167.** 0.06 **168.** 47.853846 ≈ 47.85
169. 3708.2352 ≈ 3708.24 **170.** 7.231 ≈ 7.23 **171.** 3703.125 ≈ 3703.13 **172.** 11.482285 ≈ 11.48
174. 0.02 **175.** 3.39 **176.** 237.2 **177.** 7144 **178.** 2.6 **179.** 108 **180.** 1.7 **181.** 0.002
182. 781 **183.** 1520 **184.** 18 cents per ounce **185.** 8.8 mph **186.** 285; 0.75 yd **187.** 21.76 lb
188. 28.025 ohms **189.** 56 ; 58.9536 **191.** 700 ; 1,022.25 **193.** 6 ; 6.2144
195. 200 ; 209.167 **197.** 0.02 ; 0.0205 **199.** 2 ; 2.05 **201.** 0.0175 ; 0.0178
203. 0.06 ; 0.0486 **205.** −6 ; −4.86 **207.** −18 ; −17.4018 **209.** 250 ; 229.325
211. 25 ; 21.266 **213.** −200 ; −180.829 **215.** −200 ; −346.6946 **217.** 15 ; 16.0101
219. 1.6 ; 1.3568 **221.** 3 ; 2.967

Section 6.3

1. $12\frac{3}{40}$ **2.** $\frac{3}{20}$ **3.** $17\frac{7}{25}$ **4.** $\frac{1}{8}$ **5.** $\frac{1}{80}$ **6.** $1256\frac{3}{1000}$ **7.** $6\frac{92}{125}$ **8.** $7\frac{61}{200}$ **9.** $\frac{7}{1000}$ **10.** $542\frac{1}{1250}$

11. $67\frac{17}{500}$ **12.** $15\frac{27}{200}$ **13.** $\frac{19}{20}$ **14.** $417\frac{3}{20}$ **15.** $\frac{1}{250}$ **16.** $1040\frac{1}{250}$ **17.** 0.675 **18.** 2.2 **19.** 0.5 **20.** 8.5

21. 5.25 **22.** 6.4 **23.** 23.4 **24.** 0.07 **25.** 2.625 **26.** 0.625 **27.** 0.03125 **28.** 14.625 **29.** 1.08 **30.** 0.85

31. 0.28 **32.** 0.8 **33.** 0.8 **34.** 1.1 **35.** 5.4 **36.** 3.6 **37.** 61.5 **38.** 22.0 **39.** 22.4 **40.** 1.0

41. 0.7 **42.** 51.5 **43.** 2.1 **44.** 6.6 **45.** 2.3 **46.** 8.8 **47.** $0.5\overline{3}$, non-terminating

48. 0.6875, terminating **49.** 4.74 , terminating **50.** 0.3125, terminating **51.** $0.9\overline{3}$, non-terminating

52. 21.68, terminating **53.** $23.\overline{714285}$, non-terminating **54.** $2.91\overline{6}$, non-terminating **55.** 16.875, terminating

56. 117.25, terminating **57.** $10.208\overline{3}$, non-terminating **58.** $7.\overline{3}$, non-terminating **59.** 1.90625, terminating

60. $6.541\overline{6}$, non-terminating **61.** $3.7\overline{3}$, non-terminating **62.** 0.2 **63.** 2.2 **64.** 0.45 **65.** 3.1 **66.** 0.4

67. 13.4 **68.** 0.79 **69.** 0.91 **70.** 32.407 **71.** 4.85 **72.** 12.9 **73.** 3.21 **74.** 0.78 **75.** 8.5
76. 17.8 **77.** 0.380 **78.** 6.540 **79.** 0.686 **80.** 73.963 **81.** 2.579 **82.** 15.278 **83.** 4.375 glasses of milk; 2.2 cups sugar

84. 6.6 inches **85.** $5\frac{7}{8}$ % is better **86.** 0.5625 **87.** $2\frac{1}{10} = 2.1$ inches; $3\frac{2}{5} = 3.4$ inches; $4\frac{1}{12} \approx 4.1$ inches.

88. 21.513 > 21.509 **89.** 0.432 < 0.48
90. 139.25 > 132.95 **91.** 65.825 > 65.8247 **92.** 29.799 < 30.001 **93.** 3.489 < 3.524 **94.** 9.378 < 93.78
95. 84.35 > 84.3495 **96.** 17.3564 > 17.3556 **97.** True **98.** False **99.** False **100.** True **101.** 18.001, 12.6 , 8.9, 3.08
102. 100.1, 10.01, 10.001, 1.001 **103.** 0.4, 0.22, 0.033, 0.011 **104.** The numbers are already in descending order.
105. 12.6, 9.01, 8.76, 2.609, 2.34 **106.** 10.05, 1.53, 1.053, 1.05 **107.** 0.3139, 0.32, 0.321, 0.337
108. 0.975, 1.99, 2.65, 2.72, 2.75 **109.** 5.55, 5.85, 55.05, 55.55, 555.5 **110.** 6.049, 6.058, 6.06, 6.1, 6.12
111. 115.34, 134.015, 143.15, 143.51, 314.5 **112.** 7.009, 7.09, 7.099, 7.9, 9.79 **113.** 0.07, 4.33, 5.67, 7.77, 43.3
114. 10.95, 10.951, 13.925, 14.056, 14.35

Section 6.4

1. 3257 **2.** 175.8 **3.** 42.1 **4.** 53,400 **5.** 0.5 **6.** 752.35 **7.** 285,100 **8.** 2378.1 **9.** 0.0123
10. 5,200 **11.** 757.89 **12.** 7578.9 **13.** 75,789 **14.** 757,890 **15.** 3.12 **16.** 975,620 **17.** 27,540,000
18. 872,530 **19.** 7254.8 **20.** 4.2 **21.** 0.005 **22.** 0.07 **23.** 4.735 **24.** 0.027 **25.** 0.32256 **26.** 0.074
27. 19.8345 **28.** 6.54 **29.** 0.0000055 **30.** 0.3535 **31.** 35.69 **32.** 3.569 **33.** 0.3569 **34.** 0.03569
35. 0.000225 **36.** 0.18137 **37.** 0.0740625 **38.** 7.564 **39.** 0.0000625 **40.** 0.000427175
41. 4.501×10^3 **43.** 9.537×10^1 **45.** -8.47509×10^2 **47.** 4.0009×10^2 **49.** 3.4×10^{-2} **51.** 8.09×10^{-3}
53. 2.456×10^6 **55.** 4.3×10^{-5} **57.** -8.19×10^8 **59.** 5.29×10^3 **61.** 7.75×10^7 **63.** 3.7×10^{-6}
65. 6.78×10^{-7} **67.** 1.08×10^9 Km **69.** 7.15×10^{-4} oz

Section 6.5

1. $\frac{38}{27}$ **2.** $\frac{3}{2}$ **3.** $\frac{62}{43}$ **4.** $\frac{27}{13}$ **5.** $\frac{7}{15}$ **6.** $\frac{17}{12}$ **7.** $\frac{7}{20}$ **8.** $\frac{35}{4}$ **9.** $\frac{12}{5}$ **10.** $\frac{28}{17}$ **11.** $\frac{\text{16 feet}}{\text{3 seconds}}$
12. $\frac{3}{5}$ **13.** $\frac{\text{10 chairs}}{\text{13 people}}$ **14.** $\frac{3}{2}$ **15.** $\frac{8}{9}$ **16.** $\frac{\text{3 gallons}}{\text{16 dollars}}$ **17.** $\frac{3}{2}$ **18.** $\frac{1}{3}$ **19.** $\frac{\text{3 oak trees}}{\text{7 birch trees}}$ **20.** $\frac{\text{9 people}}{\text{1 Sq. mile}}$
21. 2.5 candy bars per child. **22.** 13 feet per second **23.** \$12.5 per book **24.** 3.5 miles per day **25.** 7.2 trees per cow
26. 1.6 gallons per mi **27.** 3.4 apples per man **28.** 5 books per student **29.** 2.4 children per family
30. 2.1 Russian book per German book **31.** 105.4 people per sq. miles **32.** 27 miles per gallon
33. 7.6 pages per min **34.** 6.5 feet per second **35.** \$2.3 per gallon **36.** \$13.50 per shirt **37.** 45.7 mi per hr
38. 4 books per studnet **39.** 3.1 children per family **40.** 97.6 people per square mile. **41.** $\frac{16}{31}$
42. 49 German books for every 27 Russian books **43.** 8 people per square mile **44.** The first car **45.** City B **46.** $\frac{7}{12}$

Section 6.6

1. 19% **2.** 33% **3.** $\frac{37}{100}$ **4.** $\frac{1}{4}$ **5.** $\frac{9}{25}$ **6.** $\frac{3}{20}$ **7.** $\frac{16}{25}$ **8.** $\frac{23}{400}$ **9.** $\frac{517}{1600}$ **10.** $\frac{843}{2000}$
11. $\frac{17}{375}$ **12.** $\frac{48}{175}$ **13.** $\frac{9}{40}$ **14.** $\frac{1}{80}$ **15.** 0.066 **16.** 2.715 **17.** 0.0001 **18.** 4 **19.** 0.4 **20.** 0.04
21. 0.004 **22.** 0.32 **23.** 5 **24.** 1.25 **25.** 0.0004 **26.** 0.000035 **27.** 0.07 **28.** 0.025
29. 0.12375 **30.** 0.02125 **31.** 0.0024 **32.** 0.01063 **33.** 0.0075 **34.** 0.48 **35.** $\frac{3}{20}$ **36.** $\frac{1}{5}$ **37.** $\frac{23}{200}$
38. $\frac{3}{28}$ **39.** 0.012 **40.** $\frac{11}{6}\%$ **41. a)** Citi Bank rates are higher **b)** Wachovia Bank is better for a loan. **42.** 0.068
43. 40% **44.** 152% **45.** 30% **46.** 65% **47.** 14% **48.** 43.75% **49.** 12.5% **50.** 175%
51. 85% **52.** 206.5% **53.** 5.75% **54.** 11.875% **55.** 42% **56.** 107.5% **57.** 82% **58.** 216.7%
59. 66.7% **60.** 181.8% **61.** 57.1% **62.** 121.4% **63.** 346.7% **64.** 144.4% **65.** 63.6% **66.** 0.1%
67. 53% **68.** 71.4% **69.** 6.7% **70.** 36.4% **71.** 76.9% **72.** 35% **73.** 20.6% **74.** 59.3%
75. 177.8% **76.** 72.7% **77.** 50.5% **78.** 25% **79.** 258% **80.** 44.4% **81.** 3500% **82.** 8%
83. 65.9% **84.** 0.15% **85.** 400% **86.** 2% **87.** 204.3% **88.** 100.7% **89.** 6.4% **90.** 9%
91. 1.6% **92.** 65% **93.** 205% **94.** 27.5% **95.** 6.3% **96.** 120%

	Fraction	Decimal	Percent
97.		0.9	90%
100.	$\frac{1}{2}$	0.5	
103.		$0.416\overline{6}$	$41\frac{2}{3}\%$
106.		2.5	250%
109.		≈ 0.429	≈ 42.9%

	Fraction	Decimal	Percent
98.	$\frac{2}{3}$	$0.66\overline{6}$	
101.		0.12	12%
104.	$\frac{1}{1}$ or 1	1.0	
107.	$\frac{19}{16}$	1.1875	
110.	$\frac{5}{8}$	0.625	

	Fraction	Decimal	Percent
99.	$\frac{7}{4}$		175%
102.	$\frac{1}{3}$		$33\frac{1}{3}\%$
105.	$\frac{263}{5000}$		5.26%
108.	$\frac{32}{11}$		≈ 290.9%

111. $56\frac{1}{4}\%$ **112.** 94.7% **113.** 66.7% **114.** $9\frac{1}{3}\%$ **115.** 4% **116.** Girls: 26%, Boys: 74% **117.** $13\frac{1}{3}\%$ **118.** 3%

Section 6.7

1. 37.5 **2.** 25 boys **3.** 112 horses **4.** 3 miles **5.** 5 **6.** \$34.88 **7.** \$75 **8.** 250

9. 546 **10.** 56 **11.** 36 **12.** 42 boxes **13.** 52.2 **14.** $2\frac{2}{3}$ **15.** 22.2 **16.** 156.25

17. 100 **18.** 700 **19.** \$250 **20.** $25\frac{3}{4}$ **21.** 750 chairs **22.** 550 **23.** 1000 **24.** 1000

25. 300 **26.** 40% **27.** 32 % **28.** 30% **29.** 7.5% **30.** 0.5% **31.** \$1062.50 **32.** 27%

33. 42% **34.** 61% **35.** 24 **36.** \$180.75 **37.** 20% **38.** 144.9% **39.** \$60 **40.** \$89,814

41. \$34.32 **42.** \$1600.05 **43.** 20% **44.** 3.5% **45.** \$12075 , \$10505.25 **46.** \$400 **47.** \$860

48. 33.33% **49.** \$216.75 **50.** \$220.50 **51.** 16% **52.** \$1,377 **53.** \$11,970

54. **(a)** \$140 **(b)** \$180 **(c)** \$2.36 **55.** \$1,798

Section 6.8

1. Rational number **3.** Not a Rational number **5.** Rational number **7.** Not a Rational number **9.** Rational number

11. Rational number **13.** $\frac{-4}{5}, \frac{4}{-5}$ **15.** $\frac{-15}{7}, -\frac{15}{7}$ **17.** $\frac{3}{8}$ **19.** $\frac{3}{4}$ **21.** $\frac{2}{6}$ **23.** $\frac{7}{10}$ **25.** $\frac{11}{5}$

27.
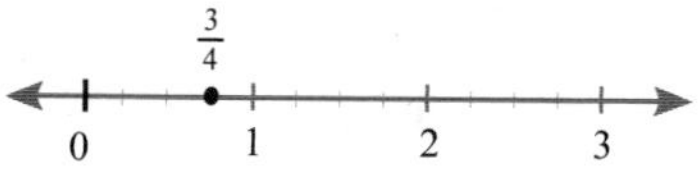

29.
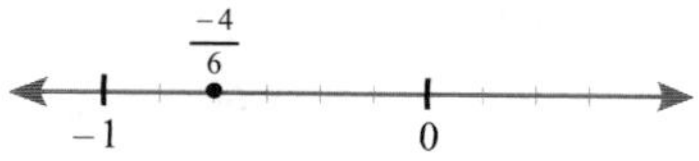

31.
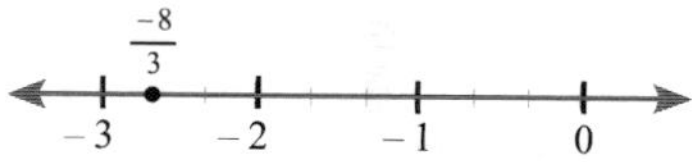

33.
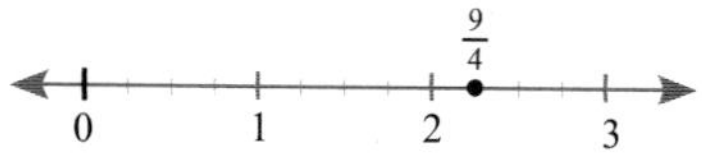

35.
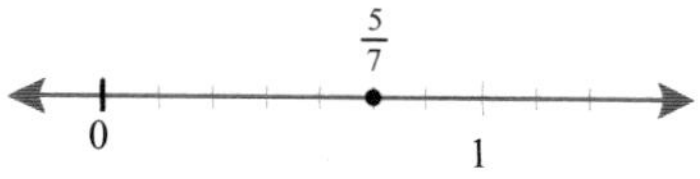

37.

39.
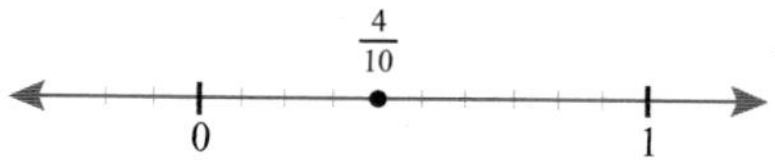

41.
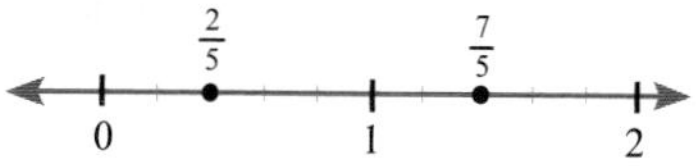

43.
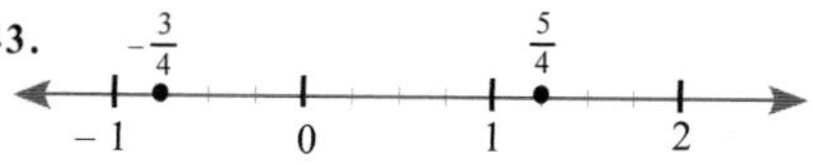

45.
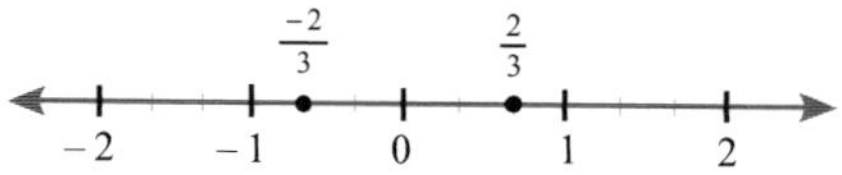

47.
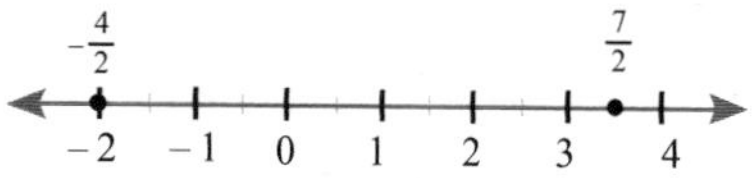

49.

51.
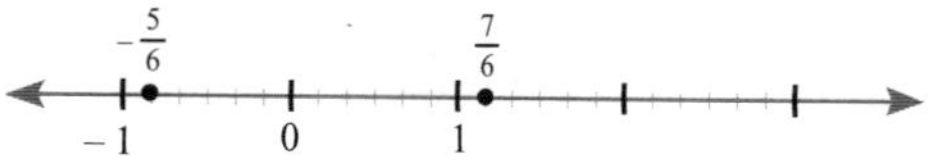

53.
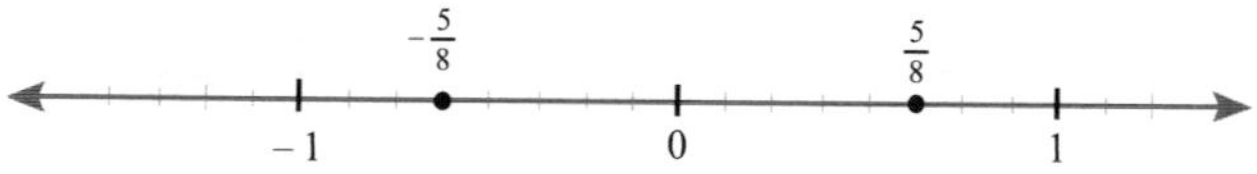

55. $1\frac{3}{8}$ in ; $3\frac{2}{5}$ cm **57.** $2\frac{1}{16}$ in ; $5\frac{1}{5}$ cm **59.** $1\frac{3}{16}$ in ; 3 cm **61.** $\frac{7}{3}$ **63.** 0 **65.** $\frac{7}{9}$ **67.** $\frac{9}{17}$ **69.** $\frac{19}{70}$

Section 6.9

1. 1 **3.** $-\frac{11}{12}$ **5.** $-\frac{13}{6}$ **7.** $\frac{43}{15}$ **9.** -6 **11.** -3 **13.** $-\frac{28}{15}$

15. $-\frac{13}{10}$ **17.** 6 **19.** $-\frac{3}{2}$ **21.** 14 **23.** 14 **25.** -2 **27.** -65

29. -18 **31.** $\frac{8}{5}$ **33.** $-\frac{45}{13}$ **35.** undefined **37.** 6 **39.** undefined **41.** 92

43. 4 **45.** 17 **47.** -31 **49.** 40 **51.** -102 **53.** -11 **55.** $\frac{26}{21}$

57. $\frac{29}{2}$ **59.** Undefined **61.** -17 **63.** $-\frac{276}{5}$ **65.** -1 **67.** 0 **69.** 7

71. 29 **73.** $\frac{13}{10}$ **87.** $-10°$ **89.** -32 ft **91.** 19°C **93.** 11,331 ft

CHAPTER 7

Section 7.1

1. \$18.1 million or \$18,100,000 **2.** 12% **3.** $\frac{15}{4}$ **4.** 26.7% **5.** B, B **6.** $\frac{11}{41}$

7. 22.73% **8.** $\frac{9}{2}$ **9.** 30.5% **10.** 370 **11.** Plant II **12.** C, because its transport cost is greatest.

13. 35.3% **14.** Yes since 1,020 quantities are required and 1,060 are available

15. Plant II, because its transport cost is lowest. **16.** \$2485 **17.** 23% **18.** 22%

19. $\frac{18}{37}$; 48.65% **20.** 2001 **21.** 1999, 2003 **22.** 30 in **23.** 36.7 in

24. 2004 **25.** 17.5 thousand **26.** 2003, 2004 **27.** 1998 **28.** 85 thousand **29.** 20 thousand

30. Line graph **31.** 400 **32.** 4 - 5 **33.** 300 **34.** 8 - 9 **35.** Pie-chart or circle graph **36.** 20%

37. 30% **38.** \$678,000 **39.** \$3,580,000

41. Mean = 67.67
Median = 65
Mode = None
Range = 40

43. Mean = 76.38
Median = 73.5
Mode = 72
Range = 15

45. Mean = 2.47
Median = 2.3
Mode = 2.3
Range = 1.8

47. Mean = 14.375 yr
Median = 14.5 yr
Mode = 15 yr
Range = 4 yr

49. Mean = \$25.33
Median = \$24
Mode = \$24
Range = \$16

51. Mean = 22.3
Median = 21
Mode = 23
Range = 19

53. Mean = 145.4 cm
Median = 145.5 cm
Mode = None
Range = 14 cm

55. Mean = 11.7
Median = 12
Mode = 12

Section 7.2

5. **(a)** N = 281, n = 23 **(b)** N = 214, n = 15 **(c)** N = 32, n = 4 **(d)** N = 512, n = 57 **(e)** N = 341, n = 19

7. **(a)** Quantitative **(b)** Qualitative **(c)** Quantitative **(d)** Qualitative **(e)** Quantitative

CHAPTER 8

Section 8.1

1. $\frac{2}{3}$ **2.** $\frac{1}{2}$ **3.** $\frac{1}{2}$ **4.** $\frac{1}{3}$ **5.** $\frac{1}{3}$ **6.** $\frac{1}{3}$ **7.** $\frac{1}{3}$ **8.** $\frac{3}{14}$

9. $\frac{1}{2}$ **10.** $\frac{2}{7}$ **11.** $\frac{1}{2}$ **12.** $\frac{4}{7}$ **13.** $\frac{9}{19}$ **14.** $\frac{2}{7}$ **15.** $\frac{2}{7}$ **16.** $\frac{1}{7}$

17. $\frac{1}{7}$ **18.** $\frac{1}{20}$ **19.** $\frac{5}{26}$ **20.** $\frac{5}{26}$ **21.** $\frac{2}{15}$ **22.** $\frac{1}{6}$ **23.** $\frac{1}{10}$ **24.** $\frac{1}{5}$

25. 1 **26.** $\frac{1}{2}$ **27.** $\frac{1}{2}$ **28.** $\frac{3}{4}$ **29.** $\frac{9}{19}$ **30.** 0.18 **31.** 0.07

32. **(i)** $\frac{6}{17}$ **(ii)** $\frac{16}{17}$ **33.** **(i)** $\frac{1}{18}$ **(ii)** $\frac{2}{3}$ **34.** $\frac{5}{13}$ **35.** $\frac{13}{18}$ **36.** $\frac{1}{2}$ **37.** $\frac{3}{13}$

38. $\frac{1}{2}$ **39.** $\frac{1}{13}$ **40.** $\frac{1}{13}$ **41.** $\frac{1}{13}$ **42.** $\frac{1}{13}$ **43.** $\frac{1}{13}$

44. **(i)** $\frac{13}{49}$ **(ii)** $\frac{3}{49}$ **(iii)** $\frac{10}{49}$ **45.** **(i)** $\frac{3}{49}$ **(ii)** $\frac{13}{49}$ **46.** **(i)** $\frac{4}{49}$ **(ii)** $\frac{1}{49}$

47. $\frac{5}{11}$ **48.** $\frac{5}{9}$ **49.** $\frac{121}{125}$ **50.** $\frac{97}{100}$ **51.** $\frac{24}{9}$

52. $\frac{5}{6}$ **53.** **(i)** $\frac{1}{4}$ **(ii)** $\frac{1}{2}$ **(iii)** $\frac{1}{4}$ **54.** $\frac{3}{4}$ **55.** $\frac{7}{8}$ **56.** $\frac{1}{2}$ **57.** $\frac{3}{8}$

58. $\frac{1}{2}$ **59.** $\frac{7}{8}$ **60.** $\frac{3}{8}$ **61.** $\frac{7}{8}$ **62.** $\frac{1}{2}$ **63.** $\frac{5}{36}$ **64.** $\frac{1}{6}$ **65.** $\frac{5}{36}$

66. $\frac{1}{12}$ **67.** $\frac{1}{9}$ **68.** $\frac{5}{12}$ **69.** $\frac{1}{2}$ **70.** $\frac{2}{9}$ **71.** **(i)** $\frac{11}{36}$ **(ii)** $\frac{25}{36}$

72. **(i)** $\frac{11}{36}$ **(ii)** $\frac{25}{36}$ **73.** **(i)** $\frac{11}{36}$ **(ii)** $\frac{25}{36}$ **74.** **(i)** $\frac{11}{36}$ **(ii)** $\frac{25}{36}$ **75.** 15 **76.** 24

77. $\frac{\pi}{15}$ **78.** $\frac{25\pi}{252}$ **79.** $\frac{3}{4}$ **80.** $\frac{1}{2}$ **81.** $\frac{8}{25}$ **82.** $\frac{4}{5}$ **83.** 8 **84.** 18

85. 6 **86.** 5 **87.** **(i)** $\frac{364}{365}$ **(ii)** $\frac{1}{365}$ **88.** $\frac{1}{4}$ **89.** $\frac{5}{9}$

90. **(i)** correct **(ii)** Not correct, outcomes are not equally likely. Reason is that 'one of each' can result in two ways HT, TH **(iii)** Not correct. The sums are not equally likely.

CHAPTER 9

Section 9.1

1. Closed curve **2.** Open curve **3.** Closed curve **4.** Closed curve **5.** Closed curve

6. Closed curve **7.** Closed curve **8.** Closed curve **9.** Open curve

10. Line segments: OA, OB, OC and BD ; Angles: ∠ AOB or ∠ BOA, ∠ AOC or ∠ COA, ∠ BOC or ∠ COB, ∠ OBD or ∠ DBO

11. Line segments: OA, OB, OC and AD ; Angles: ∠ AOB or ∠ BOA, ∠ AOC or ∠ COA, ∠ BOC or ∠ COB, ∠ OAD or ∠ DAO

12. Line segments: OA, OB, OC ; Angles: ∠ AOB or ∠ BOA, ∠ AOC or ∠ COA, ∠ BOC or ∠ COB

13. Line segments: OB, OC and CD ; Angles: ∠ BOC or ∠ COB, ∠ OCD or ∠ DCO

14. **(a)** Z **(b)** X and Y **(c)** A, B, C, P and Q **15.** **(a)** L and M **(b)** N and O **(c)** A, P, Q and R

16. **(a)** A and B **(b)** P and Z **(c)** X and Y **17.** **(a)** X and Y **(b)** P and Q **(c)** A and B

18. **(a)** X and Y **(b)** S and T **(c)** A, B and C **19.** **(a)** C **(b)** D **(c)** A and B

20. **(a)** Segment **(b)** Sector **(c)** Segment **(d)** Semi-circular region **21.** Diameter

22. Arc **23.** Chord **24.** Radii **25.** 6 **26.** 9 **27.** 7 **28.** 5 **29.** 8 **30.** 6

31. Vertex: O ; Arms: $\overrightarrow{OX}$ and $\overrightarrow{OB}$ **32.** Vertex: X ; Arms: XB and XA **33.** Vertex: A ; Arms: AY and AX

34. Diameter **35.** Diameter **36.** Circumference **37.** Segment **38.** Sector

Section 9.2

1. 2 **2.** 4 **3.** 9

4. **(a)** Faces = 4, Edges = 6, Vertices = 4 **(b)** Faces = 6, Edges = 12, Vertices = 8 **(c)** Faces = 5, Edges = 8, Vertices = 5

Section 9.3

1. Only *l* **2.** Both *l* and *m* **3.** Both *l* and *m* **4.** Neither *l* nor *m* **5.** Neither *l* nor *m*

6. Both *l* and *m* **7.** Only *m* **8.** Only *l* **9.** Both *l* and *m* **10.** Only *l*

11. 1 **12.** 2 **13.** No line of symmetry **14.** 1 **15.** 2

16. No line of symmetry

17.

18.

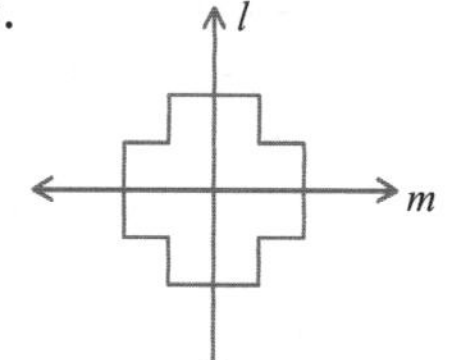

19.

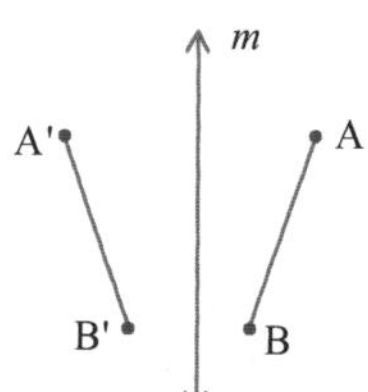

20.

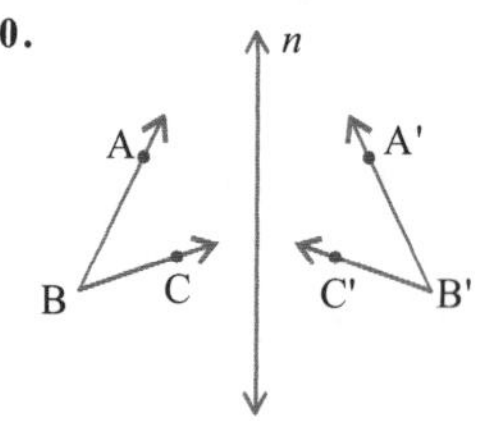

21. Four

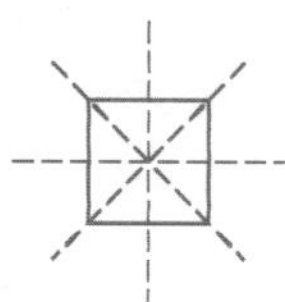

22. Five

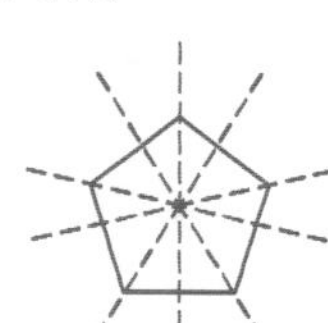

23. Six

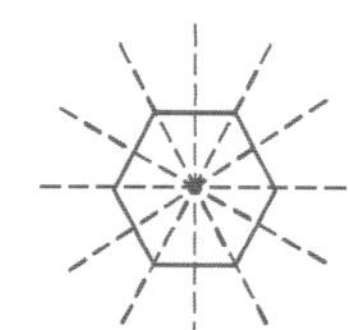

24. Seven

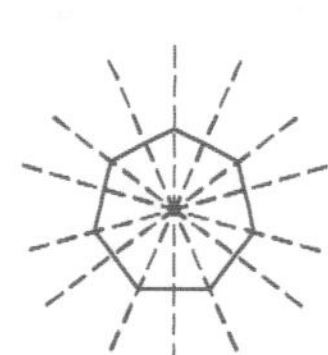

25. Eight

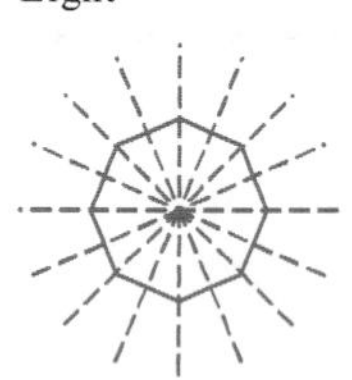

CHAPTER 10

Section 10.1

1. 216 ounces **2.** 160 meters **3.** 9 lb **4.** 6 g **5.** 210 cm **6.** 3.4 miles **7.** 2.5 gallons **8.** 1.35 oz **9.** 68 kg
10. 4.375 liters **11.** 22 g **12.** 35.8 cg **13.** 1.08 feet **14.** 5 ounces **15.** 93 m **16.** 6 quarts **17.** $26\frac{2}{3}$ kg
18. 214.5 mg **19.** 1.376 l **20.** 32 gallons **21.** 144 m **22.** 124 g **23.** 102 kl **24.** 48 cm **25.** 41 min
26. 27 lb **27.** 51.4 ml **28.** 8.06 ounces **29.** 72.8 yd **30.** 2.092 kg **31.** 44 ft 6 in **32.** 14 hr 45 min
33. 15 gal 1 qt **34.** 17 yd **35.** 55 lb 7 oz **36.** 5 kg 396 g **37.** 11 kl 6 hl **38.** 12 hr 53 min 49 sec
39. 7 ft 8 in **40.** 3 yd 1 ft 8 in **41.** 70.5 lb **42.** 6 yd 1 ft 6 in **43.** 25 ft. 4 in. **44.** 4.8845 g
45. 7 **46.** 48 **47.** 80 **48.** 9 **49.** 90 **50.** 7 **51.** 63,360 **52.** 4.5 **53.** 19,300 **54.** 158,400
55. 0.15 **56.** 21.6 **57.** 316.5 **58.** 22.5 **59.** 25 **60.** 72 **61.** 336 **62.** 10,080 **63.** 5.23
64. $27\frac{1}{3}$ **65.** 60 mi/hr **66.** 120 lb/ft **67.** $\frac{\$4.25}{\text{min}}$ **68.** 6 lb/ft **69.** 45 gal/hr **70.** 2016 in^2 **71.** 31.25 cents/in^2 **72.** 155.52 dollars/yd^2
73. 0.1125 tons/yd^2 **74.** 0.9 lb/ft^2 **75.** 6000 cm **76.** 0.0766 m **77.** 870 dm **78.** 2.7 dm **79.** 0.000003 km
80. .0015 km **81.** 4000 mm **82.** 0.000005 km **83.** kg, hg, dag, g, dg, cg, mg **84.** 12000 cg **85.** 800 cg **86.** 0.64 hg
87. 23240 dg **88.** 0.000005 kg **89.** 400 mg **90.** 0.0042 kg **91.** 0.0433 hg
92. kl, hl, dal, l, dl, cl, ml **93.** 2.04 hl **94.** 0.015 *l* **95.** 6000 cl **96.** 5700 ml **97.** 76.8 *l* **98.** 20000 dl
99. 0.0076 kl **100.** 49.6533 hl **101.** 43.85 g **102.** 144km/hr **103.** 17 m/ml
104. 24 g/m^2 **105.** Second pineapple **106.** Maria **107.** 16 **108.** 108 sq ft.
109. 87.63 m **110.** 2365.63 *l* **111.** 3.5047 miles **112.** 4.20 miles **113.** 1.713 m **114.** 235 lb **115.** 9.6012 m **116.** 209.92 ft
117. 5.07 km **118.** 1595.12 **119.** 658.37 cm/sec **120.** 313 cm/sec **121.** 48 km/hr **122.** 96.8 ft/sec **123.** 43.49 kg **124.** 8.2 lb
125. 289 km/hr **126.** 138,696.5 mi/hr **127.** 5.44 kg **128.** 2.76 × 1.97 × 1.77 inches **129.** 3 tsp **130.** 473 ml
131. 0.635 cm **132.** 38.21 in **133.** 0.130 cm **134.** 9×10^7 cycles/min
135. *b* **136.** *b* **137.** *a* **138.** *c* **139.** *c* **140.** *c* **141.** *c* **142.** *c* **143.** *d* **144.** *a* **145.** *b* **146.** *a* **147.** *b* **148.** *b*
149. *a* **150.** *d* **151.** *a* **152.** *a* **153.** *b* **154.** *c* **155.** *d* **156.** *b* **157.** *a* **158.** *d* **159.** *c*

Section 10.2

1. 10.9 m **2.** 75 m **3.** 76 ft **4.** 176 yd **5.** 11 cm **6.** 324 cm^2 **7.** 20.01 m^2 **8.** 133.062 m^2 **9.** 30 cm^2
10. 15.45 cm^2 **11.** 73.5 in^2 **12.** 36.04 ft^2 **13.** 8.05 ft^2 **14.** 18 m^2 **15.** 27 ft^2 **16.** 73.5 cm^2 **17.** 140.85 yd^2 **18.** 1100 cm^2
19. \$1,320 , \$2,193.75 **20.** 80 m by 59 m

Section 10.3

1. Rectangular solid, 48 in^3 **2.** Cube, 64 ft^3 **3.** Cone, 16.8 cm^3 **4.** Cone, 236 ft^3 **5.** **(a)** 29.79 ft^3 **(b)** 5.36 cm^3
6. 75 in^3 **7.** 440 in^3 **8.** 15 cube feet **9.** ≈ 142 in^3 **10.** ≈ 113 m^3
11. ≈ 314 cm^3 **12.** ≈ 268 cm^3 **13.** ≈ 905 in^3 **14.** 64 in^3 **15.** 4830 ft^3 **16.** 400 cm^3

CHAPTER 11

Section 11.2

1. PQ ≅ GH **2.** AB ≅ CD **3.** RS ≅ WX **4.** XY ≅ ST **5.** UV ≅ MN

6. RS = 4.2 cm **7.** AB = 3.6 cm **8.** XY = 6.3 cm **9.** ∠BOD **10.** ∠AOE

11. ∠BOE and ∠EOD **12.** ∠AOB and ∠EOD **13.** ∠BOE and ∠AOB **14.** ∠XOZ **15.** $a + b = c + d$

16. **(a)** PQ = BA, QR = AC and PR = BC **(b)** PQ = CB, QR = BA and PR = CA **(c)** AB = MN, BC = NP and AC = MP **(d)** PQ = MN, QR = NP and PR = MP **(e)** AB = PR, BC = RQ and AC = PQ **17.** **(a)** ∠P = ∠C, ∠Q = ∠B and ∠R = ∠A **(b)** ∠P = ∠A, ∠R = ∠C and ∠Q = ∠B **(c)** ∠Q = ∠A, ∠P = ∠B and ∠R = ∠C **(d)** ∠C = ∠R, ∠B = ∠Q and ∠A = ∠P **(e)** ∠B = ∠P, ∠A = ∠R and ∠C = ∠Q **18.** ∠D **19.** ∠F **20.** ∠A **21.** ∠B **22.** ∠C

23. ∠M **24.** Triangle not congruent **25.** ΔBAC ≅ ΔEDF **26.** ΔQPR ≅ ΔMLN **27.** ΔPRQ ≅ ΔLNM

28. ΔRPQ ≅ ΔLMN **29.** SAS, ΔACB ≅ ΔRQP **30.** SAS, ΔBCA ≅ ΔPQR **31.** ΔAOC ≅ ΔBOD, SAS

32. ΔBAC ≅ ΔDAC, ASA **33.** ΔABD ≅ ΔCBD, SSS **34.** Δ ABC ≅ ΔBAD **35.** ΔBDC ≅ ΔCEB **36.** ΔADB ≅ ΔADC

37. PQ = ST, QR = TU and PR = SU **38.** BA = CU, AT = UP and BT = CP **39.** LM = PQ, MN = QR and LN = PR

40. Yes, SSS **41.** Yes, SAS **42.** Yes, SSS **43.** Yes, SAS **44.** ASA **45.** SSS **46.** SAS **47.** ASA

48. **(a)** ΔBCA ≅ ΔBTA **(b)** ΔAOB ≅ ΔCOD **(c)** ΔABD ≅ ΔACD **(d)** ΔABC ≅ ΔFED

49. BD = DB **50.** AC = CA **51.** **(a)** Not Congruent **(b)** Not Congruent **(c)** ΔPQR ≅ ΔXZY **(d)** ΔABO ≅ ΔQPO

52. **(a)** ΔBAD ≅ ΔCAD **(b)** Not Congruent **(c)** Not Congruent **(d)** ΔAOB ≅ ΔDOC

53. **(a)** RHS **(b)** SSS **(c)** SSS **(d)** ASA **54.** AC = EF **55.** BC = FE

56. AC = ED **57.** AB = DF **58.** **(a)** ΔABC ≅ ΔPRQ **(b)** ΔXYZ ≅ ΔQPZ **(c)** ΔABC ≅ ΔFED **(d)** Not congruent

59. **(a)** ΔACO ≅ ΔBDO **(b)** ΔABC ≅ ΔDCB **(c)** Not Congruent **(d)** ΔABC ≅ ΔEDF

60. **(i)** Yes **(ii)** ∠BAD = ∠CAD, AD = AD, ∠BDA = ∠CDA **(iii)** Yes, corresponding parts of congruent triangles Δ ADB and Δ ADC

Section 11.3

1. **(a)** Equilateral **(b)** Equal, Proportional **(c)** Similar **2.** 80° **3.** 60° **4.** 12 cm **5.** 12.5 cm

6. 12 cm **7.** 12.6 cm **8.** 12 cm **9.** 16 cm **10.** 21.33 cm **11.** 6 cm **12.** Yes